# Plumbing Engineering Services
# Design Guide

# The Institute of Plumbing

Compiled and published by

**The Institute of Plumbing**

64 Station Lane, Hornchurch, Essex RM12 6NB.

Telephone: +44 (0)1708 472791
Fax: +44 (0)1708 448987

www.plumbers.org.uk
www.registeredplumber.com

**Project Co-ordinator**
Stan Tildsley

**Secretary & Project Manager**
Dale Courtman IEng FIOP RP
IoP Technical Manager

**Administration Support**
Emma Tolley
Lorraine Courtman
Janice Grande
Jenni Cannavan

**Technical Editors & Designers** - Tarot Millbury
**Printers** - Saunders & Williams Printers Ltd

ISBN 1 871956 40 4

Published 2002

© The Institute of Plumbing

**The Institute of Plumbing**
64 Station Lane, Hornchurch, Essex RM12 6NB.
Telephone: +44 (0)1708 472791
        Fax: +44 (0)1708 448987
www.plumbers.org.uk        www.registeredplumber.com

DTLR

TRANSPORT
LOCAL GOVERNMENT
REGIONS

# Foreword

**Dr Alan Whitehead MP**

*Minister for Building Regulations
Department for Transport,
Local Government
and the Regions
May 2002*

*Note: On 29 May 2002 the
Department of Transport, Local
Government and the Regions
(DTLR) was disbanded and
responsibility for Building
Regulations in England and Wales
was transferred to the Office of the
Deputy Prime Minister.*

It is my pleasure to provide the foreword for this edition of the Plumbing Engineering Services Design Guide. For many years now, the Institute of Plumbing has supported the construction industry on the wide range of issues that are concerned with plumbing engineering services and this design guide has been key to the success of that support.

As with other sectors of the construction industry, plumbing engineering services is an area that is rapidly developing with new, improved and innovative technologies and the role of the Institute of Plumbing in this is an important one. The Guide has needed to evolve with the advances in industry practice and techniques.

Since the guide was first launched in 1977 it has continued to be an indispensable reference source for designers, engineers and trades-persons and this is reflected by the constant demand for it, both from home and abroad.

This new edition will provide additional information and guidance on current technologies and practices and will, no doubt, continue to be a valuable source of information for those engaged in the design, approval, and installation of plumbing engineering services.

I commend it to the plumbing industry.

**Dr Alan Whitehead MP**

# Preface

This Design Guide 2002 replaces the previous edition published in 1988.

The object of the Guide is to advance knowledge of plumbing technology to those engaged in plumbing design and system installation.

The Guide has been considerably enhanced utilising an easier to read three-column format, bound within a silver cover to celebrate the 25th Anniversary since the original Data Book was published.

Technology in the plumbing industry has changed considerably in the 14 years since the guide was last published. This edition seeks to include as much information as possible, on new technologies. Indeed, the Guide reflects as many of the changes related to UK plumbing technology of which we are aware.

Throughout the publication, several British Standards have been replaced by European Harmonised Standards. Many BS/EN Standards have now been brought together within the standards, codes and miscellaneous data section.

The water services section has been greatly expanded to include many additional design considerations and to take account of the statutory requirements of the Water Supply (Water Fittings) Regulations 1999 in England and Wales and the Water Byelaws 2000 in Scotland.

The heating section has been completely re-written to concentrate on gas, as the most widely used heating medium. It also includes information on systems and heating appliances currently in use, including condensing boilers and wet under floor heating systems.

The sanitary plumbing and drainage section has changed significantly to reflect the requirements of BS EN 12056, which replaced BS 5572. This section has also been extended to include information on the technologies involved in vacuum drainage and syphonic rainwater disposal systems.

The piped gases section has undergone a major review and the section on steam now includes condensate recovery information.

Information on the design and installation of residential sprinkler systems is included for the first time, along with completely new sections on resource efficient design and swimming pools.

As co-ordinator of this Guide, I acknowledge the unstinting voluntary work of the many people associated with its production. I'm especially grateful to the Institute's full time head office technical team, consisting of Dale Courtman and Emma Tolley.

Finally, my thanks also go to the authors, manufacturers and professional organisations who have contributed to this publication. Their essential participation should be appreciated by all who adopt the Guide as a source of reference for the design of plumbing engineering services.

**Stan Tildsley Eng Tech HON FIOP MIP RP**
*Design Guide Project Co-ordinator*
*Past President*
*The Institute of Plumbing*
*June 2002*

# Acknowledgements

In today's fast moving world, talented volunteers are hard to come by.

The Institute is most fortunate in having benefitted from the expertise of a number of such people who have stepped forward to make contributions to the contents of this Design Guide. They have been ably led by Institute Past President, Stan Tildsley, an engineer of distinction in plumbing engineering services, who has acted as project co-ordinator. He has been helped by several IoP head office staff members, in particular, Dale Courtman and Emma Tolley who deserve special mention for their hard work and commitment to the project.

We greatly appreciate the assistance received from contributing organisations. These include Government Departments and Agencies; sister professional bodies, research establishments and commercial companies. We also thank printers, Saunders and Williams and technical editors, Tarot Milbury for their co-operation and professionalism.

During the lifetime of this Guide, it will become common place for the dissemination of up-to-date technical information to take place through fast broadband connections to the Internet accessible via either static computers or wireless handheld devices. As a result, this is probably the last time the Guide will be available as a complete work in bound, hard-cover printed format.

We pay tribute to all those who have contributed. They can be justifiably proud of their efforts.

**Andy Watts  MBE  EngTech  MIP  RP**
*Chief Executive and Secretary*
*On behalf of the Board of Trustees of The Institute of Plumbing*
*June 2002*

## Contributing Organisations

ARUP

British Standards Institution

Brook Water Management

Building Research Establishment Ltd

Copper Development Association

Department for Environment, Food & Rural Affairs

Department for Transport, Local Government and the Regions

Donald Smith, Seymour & Rooley

Energy Efficiency Best Practice Programme

Grundfos Pumps Ltd

Hepworth Plumbing Products

Her Majesty's Fire Service Inspectorate (DTLR)

Marley Plumbing and Drainage

Spirax – Sarco Ltd

The Council for Registered Gas Installers

The Institution of Electrical Engineers

Uponor Ltd

Vernagene

*Resource Efficient Design: Energy Efficiency (excluding section on Plate Heat Exchanger): this has been contributed by the government's Housing Energy Efficiency Best Practice Programme, and Crown Copyright is reserved.*

## Contributing Authors

G F Baker

L C Bassett  IEng, FIDiagE, MIP, MIHEEM, ACIBSE

M Bates  AIP, RP

G Bell  MCIM, Eng Tech, MIP, RP

E Blundell  AIP, ACIBSE

I O Boyd  IEng, FIOP, RP

P Cook  CEng, FIEE, MCIBSE

A J Goodger  BSc, MSc, CEng, MIM, MICorrST

J C Griggs  FIOP

R A Hanson-Graville  MA, FIOP

D Harper  Eng Tech, MIHEEM, FWMSoc, MIP, MIIE, MASEE

N Hay  BSc (Hons)

G Henderson  MSc, CEng, MIEE

N Howard  BEng (Hons), CEng, FIOP, MCIBSE, MCIWEM

D E Huckett

S Ingle  MSc, IEng, FIOP, ACIBSE, LCG, RP

J C Lane  AIP, RP

P Lang  FISPE

J K Love  CEng, FCIBSE, FIP, FIDHE, MInstR, FConsE

A J Malkin  Eng Tech, MIP, RP

G L Puzey  IEng, FIOP, RP, MRSH, MIHEEM

M C Shouler  BSc, MSc, COMP IP

S Tildsley  Eng Tech, HON FIOP, MIP, RP

C P Topp  IEng, FIOP, FIHEEM, MRSH, MAE, RP

M Vint

J S Walley  Eng Tech, LCGI, MIP, MWMSoc, RP

S A Walsh  CEng, FCIWEM, FIOP, MCIBSE, MIOSH, MAE, MEWI

P J White  Eng Tech, FIOP, RP

B F Whorlow  IEng, FIOP, RP

P M Williams

# Contents

# Hot and cold water supplies

# Sources of water

The source of water varies dependant on which area of the British Isles a supply is required. The types are:

1. Upland catchment (reservoir)

2. Ground water (borehole/artisan)

3. River extraction.

These sources provide water for supply purposes, each with a wide range of physical, and bacterial quality differences, i.e.

1. Hardness

2. Bacteria count

3. Minerals.

The quality of water supplied for distribution to, and for use by persons and properties is controlled by an Act of Parliament, the Water Supply (Water Quality) Regulations 1989, and subsequent amendments. The enforcement of the Act is undertaken by the Drinking Water Inspectorate (DWI), who regulate a wide range of key elements to attain and maintain the water supply quality. See Table 1.

The standards cover colour, alkalinity, taste, odour, undesirable and toxic substances, and micro-organisms to specified parameters. The standards are called 'Prescribed Concentrate values' (PCV's) to either maximum, minimum, average or percentage levels.

These standards are imposed on all water supply companies, with relaxation only considered under emergency situations, i.e. extreme drought or flooding, but under no circumstances if there is a risk to public health.

# Water supply companies

The water supply companies operate under the requirements of the Water Industry Act 1991, enforced by the Office of Water Services (OFWAT).

Water supply companies are responsible for the catchment or abstraction of raw water; it's conditioning, treatment and distribution to consumers within their region. The characteristics of the water supplied varies, region to region and within regions dependant upon the actual source, single or multiple, and the level of treatment provided in order to attain the prescribed quality at the point of connection to the customer's supply.

*Table 1* *Drinking water standards*

| | |
|---|---|
| Temperature | 25°C |
| PH | 5.5-9.5 |
| Colour | 20 Hazen units |
| Turbidity | 4 Formazin units |
| Qualitative odour | All odour invest |
| Qualitative taste | All taste investg |
| Dilution odour | Dilution No |
| Dilution taste | 3 at 25 |
| Conductivity | 1500us/cm 20°c |
| Total hardness | Applies only |
| Alkalinity | if softened |
| Free chlorine | Comparison |
| Total chlorine | against average |
| Faecal coliforms | 0/100 ml |
| Clostridia | 1/20 ml |
| Faecal streptococci | 0/100 ml |
| Total coliforms | 0/100 ml (95%) |
| Colony count, 2 day | Comparison |
| Colony count, 3 day | against average |
| Oxidisability | 5 mg/l |
| Ammonia | 0.5 mg/l |
| Nitrite | 0.1 mg/l |
| Nitrate | 50 mg/l |
| Chloride | 400 mg/l |
| Fluoride | 1500 ug/l |
| Phosphorus | 2200 ug/l |
| Sulphate | 250 mg/l |
| Magnesium | 50 mg/l |
| Iron | 200 ug/l |
| Manganese | 50 ug/l |
| Aluminium | 200 ug/l |
| Calcium | 250 mg/l |
| Potassium | 12 mg/l |
| Sodium | 150 mg/l |
| Copper | 3000 ug/l |
| Zinc | 5000 ug/l |
| Lead | 50 ug/l |
| Silver | 10 ug/l |
| Antimony | 10 ug/l |
| Arsenic | 50 ug/l |
| Barium | 1000 ug/l |
| Boron | 2000 ug/l |
| Cyanide | 50 ug/l |
| Cadmium | 5 ug/g |
| Chromium | 50 ug/l |
| Mercury | 1 ug/l |
| Nickel | 50 ug/l |
| Selenium | 10 ug/l |
| Total organic carbon | Comparisons |
| Trihalomethanes | 100 ug/l |
| Tetrachloromethane | 3 ug/l |
| Trichloroethene | 30 ug/l |
| Tetrachloroethene | 10 ug/l |
| Benzo 3,4 pyrene | 10 ng/l |
| Fluoranthene, benzo 3, 4, 11, 12, fluoranthene, benzo1, 12 perylene indeno (123cd) pyrene | Individual testing of these substances to provide total |
| Total PAH's | 0.2 ug/l |
| Anionic detergents | 200 ug/l |
| Pesticides & Comp'ds | 5 ug/l total |

From this connection, which generally incorporates a water company meter, the consumer is responsible for all aspects of the supply and distribution of water.

# Consumers' rights

Every consumer has the right to be supplied with water for domestic purposes from the water supply company's distribution network. New or modified existing connections can incur a charge by the water company for the following services

1. New or replacement supply

2. Meter installation

3. Supply network reinforcement

4. Infrastructure charge.

All these charges relate to the anticipated daily demand ($m^3$), peak flow rate (l/s), and number of draw-off fittings being served from the supply.

# Water regulations

Consumers water supply installations are required to comply to the Water Supply (Water Fitting) Regulations 1999, and The Water Supply (Water Fitting) (Amendments) Regulations 1999 (2) (the Water Byelaws 2000 (Scotland)). These regulations are enforced by the water company that supplies water to the consumer.

The regulations govern the whole of the consumer's installation from the connection to the water company's communication pipe and meter termination, to all the draw-off fittings, inclusive of any alterations.

The regulations require that no water fitting shall be installed, connected, arranged or used in such a manner, or by reason of being damaged, worn or otherwise faulty that it causes, or is likely to cause:

1. Waste

2. Misuse

3. Undue consumption

4. Contamination

5. Erroneous measurement.

The water supply companies are required to be notified of certain proposed installations, which may be subject to inspection and acceptance prior to receiving the water company's supply connection.

The regulations are a statutory instrument, which is supported by an interpretation of the regulations. The water supply companies have the authority to apply to the Regulator for relaxation of any part of the regulation considered inappropriate to a particular case.

## Water regulations guide

The Water Regulations Advisory Scheme (WRAS) publish a guide which provides formal guidance and recommendations on how the regulations should be applied to the actual water installations and include the Water Byelaws 2000 (Scotland).

## Water demand

The water demand for a building is dependant on a number of factors.

1. Type of building and it's function

2. Number of occupants, permanent or transitional

3. Requirement for fire protection systems.

4. Landscape and water features.

In dwellings the resident's water consumption is divided between the many appliances. A typical percentage break down provided by the Environment Agency is:

1. WC suite               32%

2. Washing machine      12%

3. Kitchen sink          15%

4. Bath                  15%

5. Basin                  9%

6. Shower                 5%

7. Outside supply         3%

8. Miscellaneous          9%

Overall consumption increases by around 10% during warmer months when out door usage increases to over 25%. In general, consumption per person decreases with an increase in dwelling size given the shared facilities.

For guidance on the total water demand for typical types of buildings refer to Table 2 for daily water demand. The figures stated have been assembled from a number of sources, including BS 6700, Chartered Institute of Building Services Engineers (CIBSE) and Environmental Agency studies and can be used as a basis for good practice.

## Water storage

The storing of water has a number of purposes,

1. Providing for an interruption of supply

2. Accommodation peak demand

3. Providing a pressure (head) for gravity supplies.

Design Codes recommend that storage is provided to cover the interruption of an incoming mains supply, in order to maintain a water supply to the building.

Water supply companies are empowered to insist on specific terms, including the volume or period of storage, within the term of their supply agreement with a consumer. However many water supply companies only recommend that storage be provided in accordance with the BS 6700, placing the responsibility and decision firmly on the consumers.

Table 2 provides guidance on typical water usage within buildings over a 24 hour period.

In designing storage capacities, account needs to be taken of the building and its location.

1. Period and hours of occupation

2. Pattern of water usage

3. Potential for an interruption of supply

4. Available mains pressure, and any inadequacies during the hours of building use

5. Health & Safety, prevention of bacteria, including legionella.

If a building is occupied 24 hours a day, then an interruption of supply will have a greater impact than that for say an office, which may only be occupied for eight to ten hours. Where a building is occupied by elderly or infirmed people then avoiding any disruption of the water supply is an important consideration as they would be unable to easily leave the building should water become unavailable.

Clients, such as the National Health Service, require their buildings to be provided with storage to safeguard against an interruption of the mains supply. Industrial clients may well require storage to ensure their business and/or production is not interrupted. If water ceases to be available within a building then the occupiers will eventually leave as toilet facilities will become unusable. It is likely that when an interruption of supply occurs then the water available would be conserved as much as possible, thereby extending the time of occupancy beyond that anticipated under normal usage rates.

*Table 2* Daily water demand

| Type of Building | Litres | Criteria/Unit |
|---|---|---|
| Dwellings | | |
| - 1 bedroom | 210 | Bedroom |
| - 2 bedroom | 130 | Bedroom |
| - 3+ bedrooms | 100 | Bedroom |
| - Student en-suite | 100 | Bedroom |
| - Student, communal | 90 | Bed space |
| - Nurses Home | 120 | Bed space |
| - Children's Home | 135 | Bed space |
| - Elderly sheltered | 120 | Bedroom |
| - Elderly Care Home | 135 | Bed space |
| - Prison | 150 | Inmate |
| Hotels | | |
| - Budget | 135 | Bedroom |
| - Travel Inn/Lodge | 150av | Bedroom |
| - 4/5 Star Luxury | 200 | Bedroom |
| Offices & general work places | | |
| - with canteen | 45 | Person (1) |
| - without canteen | 40 | Person (1) |
| Shops | | |
| with canteen | 45 | Person |
| - without canteen | 40 | Person |
| Factory | | |
| - with canteen | 45 | Person |
| - without canteen | 40 | Person |
| Schools | | |
| - Nursery | 15 | Pupil |
| - Primary | 15 | Pupil |
| - Secondary | 20 | Pupil |
| - 6th Form College | 20 | Pupil |
| - Boarding | 90 | Pupil |
| Hospitals | | |
| - District General | 600 | Bed |
| - Surgical ward | 250 | Bed |
| - Medical ward | 220 | Bed |
| - Paediatric ward | 300 | Bed |
| - Geriatric ward | 140 | Bed |
| Sports Changing | | |
| - Sports Hall | 35 | Person |
| - Swimming Pool | 20 | Person |
| - Field Sports | 35 | Person |
| - All weather pitch | 35 | Person |
| Places of Assembly (excl. staff) | | |
| - Art Gallery | 6 | Person |
| - Library | 6 | Person |
| - Museum | 6 | Person |
| - Theatre | 3 | Person |
| - Cinema | 3 | Person |
| - Bars | 4 | Person |
| - Night Club (3) | 4 | Person |
| - Restaurant | 7 | Cover |

*SUPPORTING INFORMATION*
*If the number of building occupants are not accurately known then as a guide the following criteria can be used.*
*Offices, one person per 14m$^2$ of the gross building floor area.*
*Sports hall, four persons per badminton court area per hour open, maximum.*
*Swimming pool, one person per cubical per hour open, with a factor of 0.6 for diversity.*
*Field sports changing, persons per teams per number of pitches, per day.*

*All Weather Field, persons per teams per hours used.*
*Museums, Art Galleries, Libraries, One person per 30m² of the gross building floor area.*
*Restaurants, One person per 1.0m² of the dining area.*
*Bars, One person per 0.8m² of the public bar/seating area..*

When the water supply companies, regulations, or client requirements do not specifically dictate the period to cover an interruption of a mains supply then Table 3 provides recommendations for reasonable periods of storage, expressed as a percentage of the daily water demand.

*Table 3  Period of storage*

| Type of Building | % of the daily demand |
|---|---|
| Hospitals | 50% |
| Nursing Homes | 50% |
| Dwellings | 0 - 50% |
| Hotels, Hostels | 50% |
| Offices | 0 - 50% |
| Shops | 0 - 25% |
| Library, Museum, Art Galleries | 0 - 25% |
| Cinema, Theatre | 0 - 25% |
| Bars, night-club | 0 - 25% |
| Sports Facilities | 0 - 25% |
| Schools, Colleges, Universities | 50% |
| Boarding Schools | 50% |

# Water distribution

The water distribution installation requires to be able to deliver the correct flow and volume of hot and cold water when and where it is needed. The mains pressure can provide the initial means of delivering water into the building. The water supply companies are required to deliver their water to the boundary with a minimum pressure of 1.0 bar. Often their delivery pressure can be higher, however at times of high demand, the pressure will be closer to the minimum provision.

## Type of system

The type and style of water distribution needed for a particular building will depend mainly on the building height and its use.

a.  The building height will determine whether pumping will be required to deliver water to the highest level

b.  The building use will determine the amount of storage that will be required.

The type of water system will need to be one or a combination of the following:

a.  Direct mains fed

b.  High level storage with gravity down feed

c.  Pumped from a break cistern or storage provision.

Potentially a one or two storey building in a locality where an interruption of water supply is very infrequent and causing little inconvenience, there is an option for the water supply to be direct from the mains without storage being provided. If the provision of storage is possible at high level then the system could be enhanced to provide storage coupled with it becoming a gravity down feed system. See Figure 1.

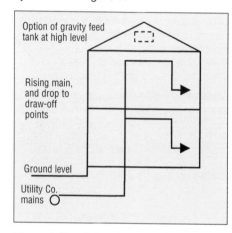

*Figure 1  Supply to a two storey building*

## Storage tanks

A building requiring a large water storage provision may not be able to accommodate it at high level, in which case a low level location will be needed, in conjunction with a pumped distribution system.

A combination of high and low storage can be considered if a gravity distribution is preferred for all or part of the building. This has an advantage of providing some storage in the event of an interruption of the water supply, or power supply to the pumps. A storage ratio of 2 : 1 low/high level is a typical arrangement.

Storage can comprise of two compartments or cisterns/tanks in order that maintenance can be carried out without interrupting distribution.

For small storage quantities one piece cisterns can be used, which generally are of a low height construction. For storage of 2500 litres or more, sectional panel tanks may be considered more appropriate with a centre divide.

Above 4000 litres storage twin cisterns/tanks may be considered appropriate. See Figure 2.

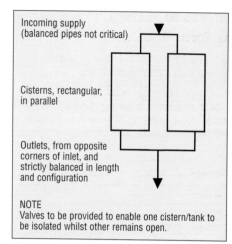

*Figure 2  Storage cistern/tank layout*

Sectional tanks commonly have flanges, being internal or external. External flanges permit tightening without needing to enter the tank, and on the base permit the tank to be self draining through a single drain point, without further draining of any entrapped water between flanges. Such a feature reduces maintenance and assists the prevention of water stagnation which can lead to harmful bacteria growth, including legionella.

In calculating the storage capacity a free board allowance is necessary to accommodate the float valve, over flow installations and any expansion from the hot water system. Depending on pipe sizes, commonly a 250 – 300 mm free board depth is required on ciserns/tanks having a capacity greater than 2500 litres. Raised ball (float) valve housings in conjunction with a weir overflow can provide an increased depth of water stored over the main area of the cistern/tank(s).

The location of the inlet and outlet connections is important. A cross flow through the cistern/tank needs to be achieved to assist the complete regular turn over of water throughout the storage period.

Sub divided, twin and multiple cisterns/tanks ideally should be installed in parallel to each other. The inlets require to be positioned at the same level to ensure they supply the cisterns/tanks in unison, and as far as possible the same flow rate to assist a balanced throughput. The outlet connections and manifold pipe work needs to be arranged with symmetrical and equal lengths, also to provide, as far as is possible a balanced flow from the tanks.

The use of a delayed action float valve may also be considered to ensure a greater turn over of water.

# Access to storage cisterns/tanks

Access for installation and maintenance is required. Table 4 is a guide.

For large buildings, accommodation for water storage has an significant impact. Table 5 provides an outline guide to the space that may be required.

*Table 4  Access to storage cisterns/tanks*

| Location | (mm) |
|---|---|
| Around | 750 |
| Between, tanks | 750 |
| Above, allowing beams to intrude | 1000 |
| Below, between supports | 600 |
| For outlet pipe work, incl. access | 1500 |
| Tank construction thickness | 100 |
| Insulation (may form part of tank) | 25 |
| Raised float valve housing | 300 |
| Entry to tank | 800 dia |

*Table 5  Water storage plant room area*

| Storage (Litres) | Tank Height | | |
| | 1.5 metre | 2 metre | 3 metre |
|---|---|---|---|
| 5,000 | 18 m² | 18 m² | – |
| 10,000 | 31m² | 23m² | – |
| 20,000 | 50m² | 40m² | |
| 40,000 | 72m² | 60m² | 50m³ |
| 60,000 | – | 80m² | 60m² |
| 100,000 | – | 10m² | 80m² |

# Gravity supplies

For gravity supplies to be effective, the storage requires to be at a sufficient height to deliver the water to the draw-off point at the required flow rate and pressure. The available head is the dimension between the bottom of the storage cistern/tank(s) and the highest draw-off point, or draw-off point with the greatest head/pressure loss. See Figure 3.

The advantages of gravity supplies are:

a. Availability of water in the event of water mains or power failure

*Figure 3  Gravity supplies available head*

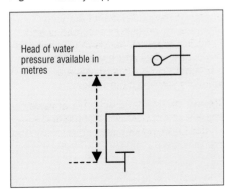

b. No pump running costs

c. Potentially less noise due to lower pipe flow velocities.

The disadvantages are:

a. Greater structural support

b. Larger pipe sizes due to limited available head, when compared to pumps

c. Lower delivery pressures.

# Pumped supplies

The delivery of water by pumping will provide flexibility in the positioning of the storage cisterns/tanks. The delivery flow rate and pressure demanded by the system are met entirely by selecting the correct duty for the pumps. The pump set is required to deliver a constantly varying flow rate as draw-off points are randomly used by the occupants. The use of multi-stage variable duty and/or inverters is an advantage. See Figure 4.

Generally a minimum of two pumps are used, each having 100% system duty and controlled to enable them to be a stand by to each other. To prevent high pressure overrun when demand is less than the design demand, a pressure limiting or variable control flow device needs to be fitted on the outlet from the pumps.

For high buildings a combination of pumped and gravity may be appropriate. The advantage of this is to provide a proportion of the daily water usage in a cisterns/tank(s) at roof level, which would provide a gravity down feed service, and continue to provide water in the event of a failure of the pump. See Figure 5. Such a system would comprise of:

a. An incoming main

b. Low level break or storage cistern/tank

c. Pump set

d. High level cistern/tank(s)

*Figure 4  Pumped supply layout*

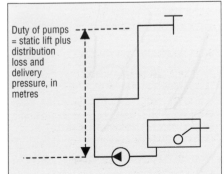

e. Cold water and hot water cold feed gravity distribution.

The low level pump set can be sized to provide a low volume, more frequent operation and high head to deliver the water to the tanks at roof level.

If a 'mains' water supply is required to be provided specifically for drinking water points or drink making equipment, then either of these can be supplied from the incoming main up to the number of floors that the available mains pressure will reach, and from the pumped rising main above that level; or entirely from the pumped rising main. See Figure 6.

Whilst all water supplied for domestic uses has to be suitable for drinking purposes, supplying drinking water points direct from incoming mains or pumped mains provides a cooler, more oxygenated supply for taste purposes.

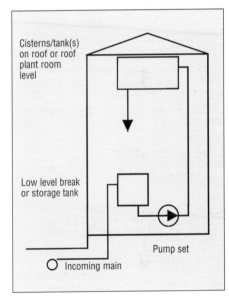

*Figure 5  Combined pump and gravity*

*Figure 6  'Mains' water for drinking*

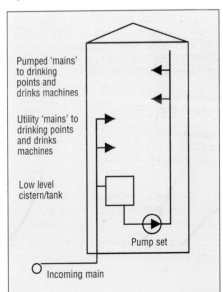

# Hot water production

Hot water can be generated by a differing number of methods, and the selection will depend mainly on the quantities of hot water required and the types of energy readily available.

The demand for hot water will vary considerably between types of buildings, governed by their occupants and the activities taking place. For example:

**Office buildings** will require small quantities frequently and regularly throughout the 'normal' working day, and availability at other times as and when occupant's 'overtime' working hours demand.

**A factory** with a production line will require sufficient hot water to meet the demand at breaks in the shift when the work force may all wish to wash hands etc.

**A sports pavilion** will need to be able to provide large quantities of hot water for team's showering needs over a short period of time following games, whenever they occur.

## Selection of hot water production

In the selection of the type of hot water production, the time available for re-heating is an important consideration.

If a high volume or rapid re-heat rate is required then it would be necessary to ensure that a sufficient energy capacity is available. If the energy capacity needed is not available then a greater volume of water storage would have to be provided to ensure hot water is available during the slower re-heat period.

Hot water production and storage temperatures are required to comply to the Health & Safety requirements for the minimisation of legionella bacteria. This demands a minimum storage temperature of 60°C to be attained, with a minimum secondary return (if provided) temperature of 50°C. See Figure 7.

Therefore in calculating the hot water demand for a building it is necessary to ensure that the output water temperature from the hot water production plant is never less than 60°C, and never less than 50°C throughout the distribution system.

The HSC 'Control of Legionella' Code L8 states that 50°C should be achieved within 60 seconds at all outlets.

*Table 6* Hot water demand

| Type of building | Daily (litres) | Stored (litres) | Unit |
|---|---|---|---|
| **Dwellings** | | | |
| - 1 bedroom | 115 | 115 | Bedroom |
| - 2 bedroom | 75 | 115 | Bedroom |
| - 3 + bedrooms | 55 | 115 | Bedroom |
| - Student en-suite | 70 | 20 | Bedroom |
| - Student, comm | 70 | 20 | Bedspce |
| - Nurses home | 70 | 20 | Bedspce |
| - Children's home | 70 | 25 | Bedspce |
| - Elderly sheltered | 70 | 25 | Bedroom |
| - Elderly care home | 90 | 25 | Bedspace |
| - Prison | | | Inmate |
| **Hotels** | | | |
| - Budget | 115 | 35 | Bedroom |
| - Travel Inn/Lodge | 115 | 35 | Bedroom |
| - 4/5 Star Luxury | 135 | 45 | Bedroom |
| **Offices & general work places** | | | |
| - with canteen | 15 | 5 | Person |
| - without canteen | 10 | 5 | Person |
| **Shops** | | | |
| - with canteen | 15 | 5 | Person |
| - without canteen | 10 | 5 | Person |
| **Factory** | | | |
| - with canteen | 15 | 5 | Person |
| - without canteen | 10 | 5 | Person |
| **Schools** | | | |
| - Nursery | 15 | 5 | Pupil |
| - Primary | 15 | 5 | Pupill |
| - Secondary | 15 | 5 | Pupil |
| - 6th form college | 15 | 5 | Pupil |
| - Boarding | 114 | 25 | Pupil |
| **Hospitals** | | | |
| - District General | 200 | 50 | Bed |
| - Surgical ward | 110 | 50 | Bed |
| - Medical ward | 110 | 50 | Bed |
| - Paediatric ward | 125 | 70 | Bed |
| - Geriatric ward | 70 | 40 | Bed |
| **Sports changing** | | | |
| - Sports Hall | 20 | 20 | Person |
| - Swimming Pool | 20 | 20 | Person |
| - Field Sports | 35 | 35 | Person |
| - All weather pitch | 35 | 35 | Person |
| **Places of assembly (excl. staff)** | | | |
| - Art Gallery | 2 | 1 | Person |
| - Library | 2 | 1 | Person |
| - Museum | 1 | 1 | Person |
| - Theatre | 1 | 1 | Person |
| - Cinema | 1 | 1 | Person |
| - Bars | 2 | 1 | Person |
| - Night Club | 1 | 1 | Person |
| - Restaurant | 6 | 6 | Cover |

*SUPPORTING INFORMATION*

The storage figures stated are based on a re-heat period of two hours, an inlet temperature of 10°C and a stored temperature of 65°C.

If the number of building occupants are not accurately known then as a guide the following criteria can be used.

Offices, One person per 14m² of the gross building floor area.

Sports hall, Four persons per badminton court area per hour open, maximum.

Swimming pool, One person per cubical per hour open, with a factor of 0.6 for diversity.

Field sports changing, persons per teams per number of pitches, per day.

All weather field, persons per teams per hours used.

Museums, art galleries, libraries, One person per 30m² of the gross building floor area.

Restaurants, One person per 1.0m² of the dining area.

Bars, One person per 0.8m² of the public bar/seating area.

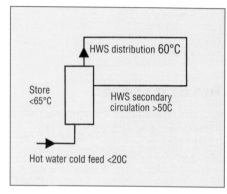

*Figure 7* Hot water temperature protocol

When a conventional bulk hot water vessel is used it is necessary to ensure that the contents of the whole vessel achieves the correct stored water temperature as stratification can occur. To overcome this situation the storage vessel should incorporate the following features:

a. Base inlet hot water cold feed supply

b. Top outlet hot water outlet flow

c. Convex ends to vessel

d. Provide a 'shunt' pump to move the hot water from the top of the vessel to the base to avoid stratification.

## Hot water demand

When assessing the hot water production requirements for a building it is necessary to determine the peak demand. The peak demand is the volume of hot water required during the building's period of greatest usage. This may be over an hour, or shorter period dependant on the occupants and activities taking place.

Having determined the peak demand the volume of hot water needing to be stored can be selected, the rate of recovery and the associated energy input needed can be established.

The buildings total daily hot water usage is relevant to the assessment of the peak demand. Once the daily usage is determined then the more critical peak demand can be assessed.

Traditionally hot water peak usage was based on a two hour storage re-heat period and this has generally proved to be a satisfactory benchmark for peak demands for that period.

Table 6 schedules a compilation of figures currently recommended by the water industry's design codes, with additional categories added as considered useful. The recommended storage volumes are based on a 65°C storage temperature and a two hour re-heat period, i.e. a bulk storage vessel. This data should be considered as representative of capacities, which have not given rise to complaints of inadequacy.

## Two hour re-heat

The two hour re-heat storage volume figures can provide a guide to the peak water volume used during a peak two hour usage period. The same hot water output could also be achieved by the use of low volume/rapid reheat 'semi-storage' types of hot water generators, if the energy input capacity is available.

The 'semi-storage' type of hot water heaters can meet shorter peak demand periods i.e. 1 hour, or less, although detailed secure information about peak period demands during periods of less that 1 hour are not sufficiently available, and therefore a design risk margin will be required.

The established two hour peak usage figures cannot simply be evenly sub-divided into shorter periods without the risk of seriously under estimating the actual hot water volume that will be required during that shorter period. The shorter the period, the greater the dis-proportion of the two hour peak storage figure will be required.

For example, the recommended two hour re-heat period storage volume for a budget hotel is 35 litres per bedroom. For a 50 bedroom hotel the stored volume would need to be 1750 litres, which when supplemented by the re-heated water during the envisaged peak two hour draw-off period, less the loss (25%) of hot water due to the mixing effect of the incoming cold water feed, is capable of providing a notional 2625 litres, should that demand occur. This is because 1750 litres of 65°C hot water is notionally available at the start of the notional peak draw-off period, and whilst the stored hot water is being drawn off it is also being re-heated at a rate of 1750 litres per two hours, less the loss through the mixing of incoming cold water and the stored hot water (25%).

Therefore it can be seen that the stored water is there to provide for a peak 1750 litre draw-off occurring over any period from, say ten minutes upwards.

For consideration purposes 1750 litres equates to 35 baths, each using 50 litres of 60°C stored hot water. Dependant on the bath usage ratio of either 1200, 2400, or 4800 seconds frequency of use (see simultaneous demand data) the hot water stored could be used up after a 63 minute period. Alternatively 1750 litres could provide for 73 persons having a shower, each lasting 5 minutes using 24 litres of 60°C of stored hot water (mixed with cold). Dependant on the shower usage rate of 900, 1800, or 2700 seconds frequency of use, the hot water stored could be used up after a 45 minute period. These two examples are based on a peak statistical usage which would likely not reoccur during the remaining time of the two hour re-heat period.

A 'semi-storage' hot water generator requiring to meet the same demand for baths would need to be capable of providing, approximately a 3.3 litre per second flow rate of 65°C continuous hot water output, assuming an initial stored volume capacity of 500 litres.

These potential peak demands could be considered as being extreme examples. However they clearly demonstrate the demands capable of being put on hot water generation, when taking account of the maximum simultaneous usage that is imposed on draw-off fittings by the building occupants, and accordingly has to be considered for design purposes.

Whatever the building, the likely pattern of hot water usage should be assessed and considered. The hot water usage will be directly related to the building function, its occupancy and the type of

activity that is likely to take place. In determining the pattern of usage, it is important to differentiate between a maximum daily demand and an average daily demand, so that the implications of the system not meeting the buildings hot water requirements can be recognised, and the maximum requirements designed for where necessary.

Measured quantities of hot water consumption should not stand alone as a sizing guide. The rate at which these amounts are drawn off must also be considered. To project the demand pattern over the operating period of the building, an hour by hour analysis of likely hot water usage should be made, taking into account the number of occupants, the type and level of activity and any other factors that may affect hot water demand. The projected pattern of demand should be recorded in the form of a histogram profile.

Typical examples of daily demand in various types of buildings are illustrated in Figures 8 and 9.

By establishing a hot water demand histogram a representative peak demand volume can be established. Typically the peak hour is between 15-20% of the day's total usage.

When selecting a 'semi-storage' hot water production unit(s) it needs to be recognised that the small stored volume is there to meet the short period peak draw-offs that occur in any water supply system. The shortest of these peak draw-offs is the 'maximum' simultaneous demand litre per second flow rate figure calculated from the sum of the draw off 'demand' or 'loading' units used for pipe sizing. However, periods of time that these flow rates occur are very short, and are based on the period of individual draw- off, i.e. length of time to fill a basin,

**Figure 8** *Typical demand pattern histogram*

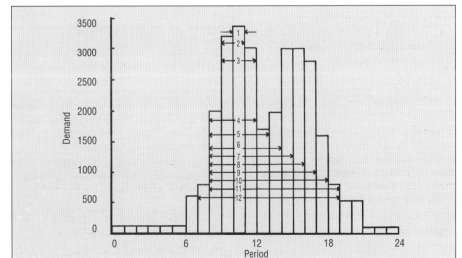

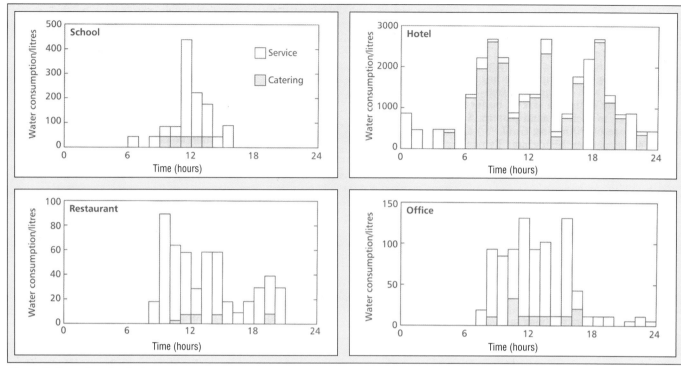

**Figure 9** *Examples of daily demand patterns for commercial premises*

*Reproduced from CIBSE Guide G: Public Health Engineering, by permission of the Chartered Institution of Building Services Engineers.*

sink, or bath, have a shower, and the number of times the draw-off is used during the peak demand period, i.e. every 5, 10, or 20 minutes, or more. The 'maximum simultaneous demand' must not be applied to periods greater than the period and frequency of 'maximum simultaneous demand.

# Hot water generators

The production of hot water can be achieved by a varied number of energy sources.

1. Electric, generally with direct immersed elements

2. Gas, either direct, or indirect by a dedicated circulator

3. Low Temperature Hot Water (LTHW) boiler plant, dedicated or more likely forming part of the space heating plant

4. Steam, when available from a central plant facility.

Energy forms, which provide a direct means of heating hot water, i.e. electric and gas in particular, are the most effective in terms of efficiency because of least loss of heat during the heat transfer process. Sharing hot water generation with space heating plant can decrease the energy efficiency through the

additional transfer process and less efficient operation when space heating is not needed.

Solar heating, when available and viable is an excellent supplementary heat source and effective in reducing annual energy tariffs.

Commonly used forms of hot water heating are:

Dwellings and small buildings: Electric, or gas combination (HWS & Heating) boilers.

Offices: Electric, local or 'point of use' water heaters.

Larger premises and sports facilities: Gas direct fired water heaters.

## Local or central plant

The adoption of local or central plant is generally dependant on the type of building, where hot water is needed and the volume required. For toilet wash basin 'hand rinse' purposes only, where relatively little hot water is required then a local heater positioned adjacent to the draw-off fittings would be appropriate. This may be considered particularly suitable for office and school toilets. The advantages of this type of installation can be low installation, energy consumption, and maintenance costs, plus alleviating the need for secondary circulation pipework and pump to maintain distribution temperatures.

## Vented or unvented generators

A vented hot water generator is supplied by a gravity hot water down feed and expansion pipe and having an open vent pipe over the feed cistern/tank to provide for pressure relief, in addition to

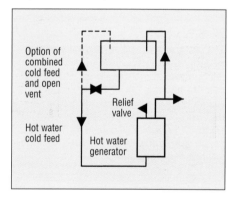

**Figure 10** *Vented hot water generator*

**Figure 11** *Unvented hot water generator*

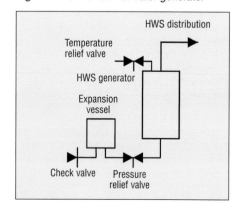

expansion. These units generally are storage type units rather that semi-storage units. As an open vessel the maximum pressure is the static head from the cold water feed cistern/tank. Individual vessels should be provided with their own open vent. A pressure and/or temperature relief valve can be considered in place of a separate open vent subject to the vent being combined with the cold feed/expansion pipe, and there being no means of closing off the vent.

Unvented hot water generators are generally supplied from Utility Company's mains, or pumped distribution systems. Provision for expansion and pressure/temperature relief is provided by mechanical fittings to provide a safe system. Unvented units are commonly semi-storage types. The pressures that they are subjected to are the operational head of the 'mains' or 'pumped ' system inclusive of any 'closed head' situation. For unvented units with a capacity of 112 litres or less, the Building Regulations require that the unit is provided complete with all it's safety fittings. For larger unvented units the 'Designer' is required to specify the safety fittings in accordance with the Water Regulations.

## Multiple hot water generators

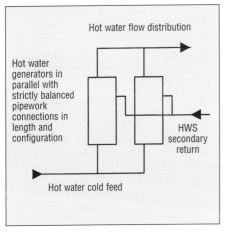

Hot water flow distribution

Hot water generators in parallel with strictly balanced pipework connections in length and configuration

HWS secondary return

Hot water cold feed

*Figure 12  Multiple hot water heaters*

Where multiple hot water generators become necessary for capacity/output, and/or standby/back up purposes care must be taken to ensure that the interconnecting pipework configuration provides a balanced use and flow through the two of more hot water generators.

## Secondary circulation and trace heating

Secondary circulation or trace heating needs to be provided when the length of hot water pipework and the volume of water the pipework contains, becomes such that it would take an unreasonable length of time to draw off the cool water. The Water Regulations Guide recommends that un-circulated hot water distribution pipes should be kept as short as possible and if uninsulated not exceed the maximum length stated.

*Table 7  Water Regulations Guide*

| Max. lengths of uninsulated pipes | | |
|---|---|---|
| Pipe OD | Length | (Seconds) |
| < 12 mm | 20 m | (11) |
| < 22 mm | 12m | (25) |
| < 28 mm | 8m | (26) |
| > 28 mm | 3m | (>15) |

The 'seconds' column illustrates the approximate length of time it would take to draw of the cool water based on the draw off rate of a wash basin tap with an 0.15 l/s flow rate. The Health & Safety Legionella Code L8 states a maximum draw off period for hot water to reach its correct temperature shall be 60 seconds.

Insulating the pipes does not stop the hot water cooling, it only slows down the cooling rate. Once the temperature has dropped below 50°C, then the Health & Safety's '60 seconds' maximum length of time criteria applies. The insulating of pipes is desirable as it delays the cooling rate of the hot water enabling it to be 'useful' for longer, and by that means saves energy and the associated costs.

Once it becomes necessary to provide secondary circulation or trace heating, then it should be extended to serve the whole of the hot water distribution system making un-circulated or trace heated sections of pipework as short as practicably possible, and not the maximum lengths stated in the table.

## Local heaters

These generally comprise of small self contained electrically heated hot water units individually placed near to the position that hot water is required, and serve either a single draw off or a number of draw off's which are adjacent to each other. Gas heaters are available, but not commonly used due to the need to make provision for flues.The purpose of such units provide hot water in a simple manner, in particular where the draw off is remote and only low volumes of hot water is required, such as for hand rinsing. Office toilet accommodation and single showers are

particularly suited for these type of units.

A number of different types of local heaters are available. Most commonally are 'unvented units' supplied directly from the incoming mains or from the main cold water distribution system within the building. Usually a minimum inlet pressure is required, often being 1.0 bar or above, subject to the manufactures instructions.

The Water Regulations govern the requirements for unvented water heaters. Heaters with a capacity of less than 15 litres are classed as being instantaneous and need no temperature or pressure relief valves, or expansion valves or vessels. Units above 15 litres capacity require such devices.

# Control of legionella

The means of controlling legionella bacteria is determined by the Health & Safety Approved Code of Guidance L8.

*Figure 13  Design temperature and associated risks (CIBSE TM13)*

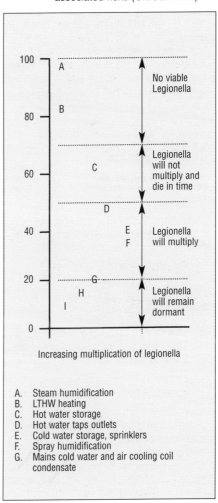

Increasing multiplication of legionella

A. Steam humidification
B. LTHW heating
C. Hot water storage
D. Hot water taps outlets
E. Cold water storage, sprinklers
F. Spray humidification
G. Mains cold water and air cooling coil condensate

The Code identifies specific practical guidance on how this is to be achieved in water supply systems. The key aims being:

1. Maintain cold water below 25°C

2. Maintain stored hot water between 60-65°C

3. Maintain hot water distribution above 50°C, and preferably at 55°C

4. Insulate all cold and hot water storage vessels and distribution pipework

5. Minimise the length of un-circulated and none trace heated hot water pipes

6. Avoid supplies to little or unused draw-off fittings

7. Maintain balanced use and flows through multiple cold water cisterns/tanks and hot water vessels. See Figure 13.

NOTE:
*For further details please see 'legionella section', contained within this guide.*

**Graph 1** *Temperature and duration of exposure, sufficient to cause burns in thin areas of skin*

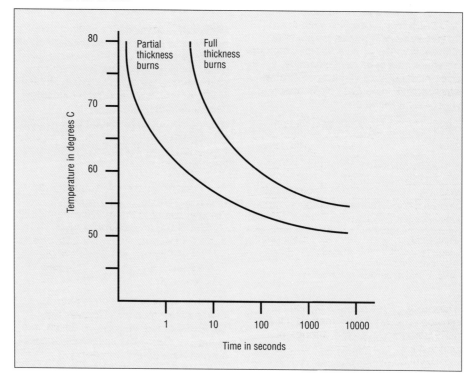

# Safe water temperatures

Safe water temperatures need to be considered for hot water supplies to appliances used by the elderly, infirmed and young. The Legoinalle requirements for 60-65°C stored hot water and a minimum 55-55°C distributed hot water means that consideration is needed to provide temperature control at the draw-off fittings use by persons at risk of being scalded.

The Medical Research Council, Industrial Injuries and Burns Unit produced data which illustrates the time and temperature relationship which result in partial and full thickness burns. See Graph 1.

**Table 8** *NHS estates health guidance for Safe hot water temperatures*

| Appliance | Application | Max Temp |
|-----------|-------------|----------|
| Bidet | All | 38°C |
| Shower | All | 41°C |
| Wash basin | Hand rinse only under running water, i.e. toilets | 41°C |
| Wash basin | For an integral part of ablution, i.e. bathroom | 43°C |
| Bath | All | 44°C |
| Bath | Where difficult to attain an adequate bathing temperature | 46°C |

Design Codes for Health buildings require that all draw-off points that can be used by patients have the temperature of the hot water limited to a safe temperature.

The Health Codes also extends to elderly care homes and sheltered dwellings, which are under the responsibility or licence of the Local Authority. Other buildings that require consideration are nurseries, schools, and anywhere where there is a 'duty of care' by the building owner's landlord, and/or management.

The temperature control is achieved by the deployment of single control mixer taps or valves. The type of valves can vary dependant on their application.

The types of mixing valve, as defined by the Health Guidance Note, are:

Type 1 – a mechanical mixing valve, or tap including those complying with BS 1415 part 1, or BS5779 incorporating a maximum temperature control stop device.

**Table 9** *Recommended application for mixing valves*

| Application | Type |
|-------------|------|
| Bidet | Type 3 |
| Shower | Type 3 |
| Wash basin, hand rinse, for persons not being at risk | Type 1 |
| Wash basins for persons at risk, i.e. elderly, infirmed, young, etc | Type 3 |
| Bath | Type 3 |

Type 2 – a thermostatic mixing valve, complying with BS 1415 part 2.

Type 3 – a thermostatic mixing valve with enhanced thermal performance compiling with the NHS Estates Model Engineering Specification DO8.

# Water conservation

The efficient management of water usage and supplies is necessary to comply with National and International environmental conservation 'best practice' aims and is covered in detail within the Resource Efficient Design section. The Water Regulations incorporate this requirements under their prevention of 'waste, misuse, and undue consumption, and also the specification for reduced capacity of WC flushing cisterns and limit to automatic urinal flushing cisterns.

The key water conservation areas within a water supply installation are

1. Low volume flush WC's

2. Urinal Controls

3. Draw-off tap controls

4. Clothes and dish washing machines

5. Leak detection

6. Limited need for garden and landscape watering

7. Rainwater reuse

8. Grey water recycling.

The DTER (now DEFRA) Water Conservation in Business document (2000) provides proposals and examples for water savings. An example the document proposes is the potential water savings that could possibly be made in an office building.

*Table 10  Office water consumption*

| Activity | % water used | Anticipated % saving |
|---|---|---|
| WC flushing | 43% | 30% - 60% |
| Washing | 27% | 50% - 60% |
| Urinal flushing | 20% | 50% - 80% |
| Miscellaneous | 10% | 20% |

*Significant additional water reductions can be made by incorporating leak detection systems, grey water recycling, rain water collection and water efficient garden and landscape.*

The Building Research Establishment provide an assessment method called 'BREEM' which provides a range of performance criteria to assess water economy in buildings. For an office building the BREEM design and procurement performance scoring gives a 'pass' for 200 points, and an 'excellent' for 490 points. Table 11 shows the importance of water conservation design and management, which overall represents 62 points out of the total BREEM score.

*Table 11  BREEM 98 for offices water assessment prediction check list*

| Item | Score |
|---|---|
| Where predicted water consumption is 10-20m$^3$ per person per year | 6 |
| Where predicted water consumption is 5-9m$^3$ per person per year | 12 |
| Where predicted water consumption is <5m$^3$ per person per year | 18 |
| Where a water meter is installed to all supplies in the building | 6 |
| Where a leak detection system is installed covering all mains supplies | 6 |
| Where proximity detection shut off is provided to water supplies in WC areas | 6 |
| Where there are established and operational maintenance procedures covering all water system, taps, sanitary fittings and major water consuming plant | 6 |
| Where water consumption monitoring is carried out at least every quarter using historical data | 6 |
| Where storm water run off is controlled at source | 14 |

*The other assessment criteria for the building are Building performance, Design procurement assessments, and management and operational assessments.*

# Water regulations

The Water Regulations Guide is published by the Water Regulation Advisory Scheme (WRAS), incorporating the Department of the Environment, Transport, and the Regions (DETR, now DEFRA) Guidance and Water Industry recommendations.

The Guide interperates the Regulations and identifies how water supply systems shall be installed to comply with the Statutory Regulations.

The prevention of contamination is the overall main aim of the Water Regulations, and the identification of risks is one of the main changes between the previous Water Bylaws and the Water Regulations. The risks are categorised into five Fluid Category definitions. Refer to Table 13.

The risk of contamination is made present through back pressure and/or back syphonage, termed as Backflow being the source of risk into the water distribution system.

To Protect against Backflow there are a range of mechanical and non-mechanical devices. Reference to the Water Regulations is required for the selection of the appropriate device to match the fluid category risk.

Air gaps are the most effective means of protecting against backflow and the resulting risk of contamination, and a correctly provided air gap protects against all fluid categories from 1 up to 5. All other means of protection, will protect between Fluid Categories 1-4.

## Notification

The Water Regulations requires that notice shall be given to the water undertaker (company) of work intending to be carried out, which shall not begin without the consent, and shall comply with any conditions set by the water undertaker (company).

Notice of the work shall include details of:

1. Who requires the work

2. Who is to carry the work out

3. Location of premises

4. A description of the work

5. Name of the approved contractor, if an approved contractor is to carry out the works.

*Table 12  Notifiable installations*

| Ref | Installation |
|---|---|
| 1 | The erection of a building or other structure, not being a pond or swimming pool |
| 2 | The extension or alteration of a water system on any premises other than a house |
| 3 | A material change of use of any premises |
| 4 | The installation of: |
| (a) | A bath having a capacity, as measured to the centre line of overflow, of more than 230 litres |
| (b) | A bidet with an ascending spray or flexible hose |
| (c) | A single shower unit (which may consist of one or more shower heads within a single unit) not being a drench shower installed for reasons of safety or health, connected directly or indirectly to a supply pipe which is of a type specified by the regulator |
| (d) | A pump or booster drawing more than 12 litres per minute, connected directly or indirectly to a supply pipe |
| (e) | A unit which incorporates reverse osmoses |
| (f) | A water treatment unit which produces a waste water discharge, or which requires the use of water for regeneration or cleaning |
| (g) | A reduced pressure zone valve assembly or other mechanical device for protection against a fluid which is in fluid category 4 or 5 |
| (h) | A garden watering system unless designed to be operated by hand, or |
| (i) | Any water system laid outside a building and either less than 750mm or more than 1350mm below ground level |
| 5 | The construction of a pond or a swimming pool with a capacity of more than 10,000 litres which is designed to be replenished by automatic means and is to be filled with water supplied by a water undertaker. |

*Crown copyright 1999 with the permission of the Controller of Her Majesty's Stationery Office.*

## Backflow prevention

It is necessary to protect against the likelihood of the backflow of contaminated water back into the water supply installation, The contaminated water is any water that has been delivered to the draw off point and has left the water supply system. The degree of contamination is as defined by the Water Regulations Guide, categorised as Fluids 1 to 5. Refer to Table 13.

*Table 13  Water regulation fluid categories and examples*

| | |
|---|---|
| **Fluid Category 1**: Wholesome water supplied by a water undertaker and complying with the requirements of regulations made under section 67 of the Water Industries Act 1991. (The incoming water supply). | Water supplied directly from a water undertaker's main. |
| **Fluid Category 2:** Water in fluid category 1 whose aesthetic quality is impaired owing to:<br>a.   A change in its temperature, or<br>b.   the presence of substances or organisms causing a change in its taste, odour or appearance, including water in a hot water distribution system. | Mixing of hot and cold water supplies.<br>Domestic softening plant.<br>Drink vending machines having no ingredients injected into the distribution pipe.<br>Fire sprinkler systems without anti-freeze.<br>Ice making machines.<br>Water cooled air conditioning units (without additives). |
| **Fluid Category 3:** Fluid which represents a slight health hazard because of the concentration of substances of low toxicity, including any fluid which contains:<br>a.   Ethylene glycol, copper sulphate solution or similar chemical additives; or<br>b.   sodium hypochlorite (chloros and common disinfections). | Water in primary circuits and heating systems in a house.<br>Domestic wash basins, baths and showers.<br>Domestic clothes and dishwashing machines.<br>Home dialysing machines.<br>Drink vending machines having ingredients injected.<br>Commercial softening plant.<br>Domestic hand held hoses.<br>Hand held fertilizer sprays.<br>Irrigation systems. |
| **Fluid Category 4:** Fluid which represents a significant health hazard because of the concentration of toxic substances, including any fluid which contains:<br>a.   Chemicals, carcinogenic substances or pesticides (including insecticides and herbicides), or<br>b.   environmental organisms of potential health significance. | **General:** Primary circuits and central heating systems in other than a house. Fire sprinkler systems using anti-freeze solutions.<br>**House and gardens:** Mini-irrigation systems without fertilizer or insecticide application such as pop-up sprinklers or permeable hoses.<br>**Food processing:** Food preparation, dairies, bottle washing apparatus.<br>**Catering:** Commercial dishwashing machines, bottle washing apparatus, refrigeration equipment.<br>**Industrial and commercial installation:** Dyeing equipment. Industrial disinfecting equipment. Printing and photographic equipment. Car washing degreasing plant. Commercial clothes washing plants. Brewery and distillation plant. Water treatment plant or softeners using other than salt. Pressurised fire fighting systems. |
| **Fluid Category 5:** Fluid represents a serious health hazard because of the concentration of pathogenic organisms, radioactive or very toxic substances, including any fluid which contains:<br>a.   Faecal matter or other human waste;<br>b.   butchery or other animal waste; or<br>c.   pathogens from any other source. | **General:** Industrial cisterns, Non-domestic hose union taps. Sinks, urinals, WC pans and bidets. Permeable pipes in other than domestic gardens laid below or at ground level with or without chemical additives. Grey water recycling systems.<br>**Medical:** Any medical or dental equipment with submerged inlets. Laboratories. Bed pan washers. Mortuary and embalming equipment. Hospital dialyses machines. Commercial clothes washing plant in health care premises. Non-domestic sinks, baths, washbasins and other appliances.<br>**Food processing:** Butchery and meat trades slaughterhouse equipment. Vegetable washing.<br>**Catering:** Dishwashing machines in health care premises. Vegetable washing.<br>**Industrial and commercial installations:** Industrial and chemical plant, etc. Mobile plant, tankers and gully emptiers. Laboratories. Sewage treatment and sewer cleansing. Drain cleaning plant. Water storage for agricultural purposes. Water storage for fire fighting purposes.<br>**Commercial agricultural:** Commercial irrigation outlets below ground or at ground level and/or permeable pipes with or without chemical additives. Insecticides or fertiliser applications. Commercial hydroponic systems. |

COMMENTS:
1. *The list of examples of applications shown above for each fluid category is not exhaustive, others will present themselves and require to be matched to a Fluid Category, possibly by seeking guidance from the Water Regulations Advisory Scheme.*
2. *The Categories distinguish between domestic use, m eaing dwellings; and non-domestic uses, meaing commercial buildings.*
3. *The Fluid Categories define that the water within sinks, baths, basins and showers in domestic premises is a lesser Fluid Category risk, than the water within sinks, baths, basins and showers in medical premises, ie hospitals.*

# Distribution pipe sizing

The sizing of a water distribution pipe system is achieved by establishing the anticipated flow rates, in litres per second (l/s) taking account of the diversity of use of all the various types and numbers of appliances, and equipment requiring a water supply connection.

In practical terms all the water draw-off points are not in use at the same time. The actual number in use, in relation to the total number capable of being used varies dependant on the occupational use in the various types of building.

## Probability theory

The use of probability theory in assessing simultaneous demand is only fully applicable where large numbers of appliances are involved, as probability theory, as the name implies, is based on the likelihood of situations occurring and therefore its predictions may on occasions be at variance with the actual demand.

The criteria for this occurrence is deemed to be reasonable if it is taken as 1%. This has been established to be reliable in that it has not led to an under assessment of simultaneous demand calculation.

The probability of a particular number of draw off's occurring at any one time is determined by dividing the time for the appliance to be filled, by the time between successive usage of the appliance to arrive at the probability factor.

$$P = \frac{t - \text{time in seconds of appliance filling}}{T - \text{time in seconds between successive usage of the appliance}}$$

*Graph 2 Probability graph*

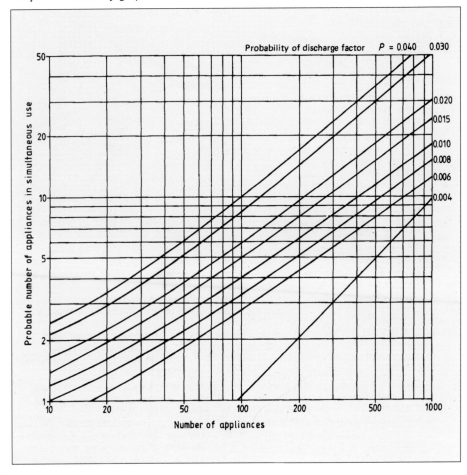

An example of this application which utilises the probability graph is if 100 appliances each take 30 seconds to be filled, and are used at 1200 seconds (20 minutes) frequency intervals, then:

$$P = \frac{t}{T} = \frac{300}{1200} = 0.025 \text{ probability}$$

Using the Probability graph, and the probability factor in this example, then out of the 100 appliances being supplied, only 7 would be in use at any one time.

## Simultaneous demand

The number of draw-off points that may be used at any one time can be estimated by the application of probability theory.

The factors, which have to be taken into account, are:

a. Capacity of appliance in litres

b. Draw-off flow rate in litres per second

c. Draw-off period in seconds, i.e. time taken to fill appliance

d. Use frequency in seconds, i.e. time between each use of the appliance.

All of these factors can vary.

The capacity of wash basins, sinks and other appliances all vary in capacity. Draw-off tap sizes and flow rates differ between appliances. The frequency of

*Table 14 Simultaneous demand – base data*

| Type of appliance | Capacity (litres) | Flow rate (litres/sec) | Demand (seconds) | Frequency (seconds) | Usage ratio | Prop of base appl. ratio | Prop of base appl. flow rate | Demand figure | Demand unit |
|---|---|---|---|---|---|---|---|---|---|
| Basin , 15mm sep. taps | 5 | 0.15 | 33 | 1200 | 0.282 | 1.00 | 1.00 | 1.000 | 1 |
| | 5 | 0.15 | 33 | 600 | 0.055 | 2.00 | 1.00 | 2.000 | 2 |
| | 5 | 0.15 | 33 | 300 | 0.110 | 4.00 | 1.00 | 4.000 | 4 |
| Basin, 2 × 8mm mix tap | 5 | 0.08 | 33 | 1200 | 0.028 | 1.00 | 0.53 | 0.533 | 1 |
| | 5 | 0.08 | 33 | 600 | 0.055 | 2.00 | 0.53 | 1.067 | 1 |
| | 5 | 0.08 | 33 | 300 | 0.110 | 4.00 | 0.53 | 2.133 | 3 |
| Sink, 15mm sep./mix tap | 12 | 0.2 | 60 | 1200 | 0.050 | 1.82 | 1.33 | 2.424 | 2 |
| | 12 | 0.2 | 60 | 600 | 0.100 | 3.64 | 1.33 | 4.848 | 5 |
| | 12 | 0.2 | 60 | 300 | 0.200 | 7.27 | 1.33 | 9.697 | 10 |
| Sink, 20mm sep./mix tap | 18 | 0.3 | 60 | 600 | 0.100 | 3.64 | 2.00 | 7.273 | 7 |
| Bath, 15mm sep./mix tap | 80 | 0.3 | 266 | 4800 | 0.055 | 2.02 | 2.00 | 4.030 | 4 |
| | 80 | 0.3 | 266 | 2400 | 0.111 | 4.03 | 2.00 | 8.061 | 8 |
| | 80 | 0.3 | 266 | 1200 | 0.222 | 8.06 | 2.00 | 16.121 | 16 |
| Bath, 20mm sep./mix tap | 80 | 0.5 | 266 | 3000 | 0.089 | 3.22 | 3.33 | 10.747 | 11 |
| WC Suite, 6 litre cistern | 4.5 | 0.1 | 60 | 1200 | 0.050 | 1.82 | 0.67 | 1.212 | 1 |
| | 4.5 | 0.1 | 60 | 600 | 0.100 | 3.64 | 0.67 | 2.424 | 2 |
| | 4.5 | 0.1 | 60 | 300 | 0.200 | 7.27 | 0.67 | 4.848 | 5 |
| Shower, 15mm head | 6 | 0.08 | 300 | 2700 | 0.111 | 4.04 | 0.53 | 2.155 | 2 |
| | 6 | 0.08 | 300 | 1800 | 0.167 | 6.06 | 0.53 | 3.232 | 3 |
| | 6 | 0.08 | 300 | 900 | 0.333 | 12.12 | 0.53 | 6.465 | 6 |
| Urinal, single bowl/stall | 0 | 0.003 | 1500 | 1500 | 1.000 | 36.36 | 0.02 | 0.727 | 1 |
| Bidet, 15mm mix tap | 0 | 0.08 | 33 | 1200 | 0.028 | 1.00 | 0.53 | 0.533 | 1 |
| | 0 | 0.08 | 33 | 600 | 0.055 | 2.00 | 0.53 | 1.067 | 1 |
| Hand spray, 15mm | 0 | 0.08 | 75 | 1200 | 0.067 | 2.27 | 0.53 | 1.212 | 1 |
| Bucket sink, 15mm taps | 0 | 0.15 | 60 | 3600 | 0.017 | 0.61 | 1.00 | 0.606 | 1 |
| Slop hopper, cistern only | 7.5 | 0.1 | 75 | 600 | 0.125 | 4.55 | 0.67 | 3.030 | 3 |
| Slop hopper, cistern/taps | 7.5 | 0.2 | 60 | 600 | 0.100 | 3.64 | 1.33 | 4.848 | 5 |
| Clothes washing m/c, dom. | 5 | 0.2 | 25 | 600 | 0.042 | 1.52 | 1.33 | 2.020 | 2 |

the use of the appliances are different in varying locations, both within a building, and within different buildings.

# Frequency of use

This is the time between each use of the appliance. Refer to Tables 14 and 15.

Low use is deemed to have 1200 seconds (20 minutes) between each use, and is appropriate for dwellings, and in other buildings where appliances are dedicated for use by a single person, or a small group of people, as a private facility.

Medium use is deemed to have 600 seconds (10 minutes) between use, being appliances that are available to be used by a larger group of people, as and when they require on a random basis with no set time constraint, typically associated with 'public use' toilets.

High use is deemed to have 300 seconds (5 Minutes) between each use for appliances to be used by large numbers of persons over a short period, as would be the case within buildings such as theatres, concert halls and fixed period sports events.

# Loading units

To account for these variations, a 'loading unit' system has been devised which takes account of the appliance type, it's capacity, flow rate, period of use, and frequency of use characteristics, to establish a calculation method which satisfactorily reflects a 'maximum simultaneous design flow rate,' in litres for any part of a pipework distribution system.

This method of calculation should be

*Table 15* Loading units

| Type of appliance | Frequency of use | | |
|---|---|---|---|
| | Low | Med | High |
| Basin, 15mm sep. taps | 1 | 2 | 4 |
| Basin, 2 × 8mm mix. tap | 1 | 1 | 2 |
| Sink, 15mm sep/mix tap | 2 | 5 | 10 |
| Sink, 20mm sep/mix tap | - | 7 | - |
| Bath,15mm sep/mix/tap | 4 | 8 | 16 |
| Bath, 20mm sep/mix tap | - | 11 | - |
| WC Suite, 6.litre cistern | 1 | 2 | 5 |
| Shower, 15mm head | 2 | 3 | 6 |
| Urinal, single bowl/stall | - | 1 | - |
| Bidet, 15mm mix tap | 1 | 1 | - |
| Hand Spray, 15mm | - | 1 | - |
| Bucket sink, 15mm taps | - | 1 | - |
| Slop Hopper, cistern only | - | 3 | - |
| Slop Hopper, cistern/taps | - | 5 | - |
| Clothes washing m/c, dom. | 2 | - | - |
| Dishwasher m/c domestic | 2 | - | - |

considered as representative of flow rates, which have not given rise to complaints of inadequacy.

Care is required with the 'loading unit' method of calculation where usage may be intensive. This is particularly applicable to field sports showers, theatre toilets, and factory wash rooms, etc. where it is necessary to establish the likely period of constant usage and provide the flow rate to suit.

# Flow rates

To determine the design maximum simultaneous flow rate for a specific water distribution system the following process is necessary:

a. Identify the type and position of all the appliances and equipment requiring a water supply.

b. Determine the pipe routes and location for the incoming mains, cold & hot water distribution, and the locations of storage cisterns/tanks and hot water generators.

c. Sketch a scaled plan and a schematic or an isometric of the pipework distribution and plant layout.

d. Identify type, position of all fittings, i.e. couplings, elbows, tees; all valves, (isolation, service, check, double check, pressure reducing) all cisterns/tanks and vessel entry and exit arrangements.

e. Identify all types of draw-off fitting attached to appliances and equipment.

f. Establish the mains pressure available, in metres, and the cistern/tank head available in metres.

g. Identify the index run, ie. the furthest and/or highest outlet, and greatest draw-off volume.

Having established items a-g, proceed to add the sanitary and appliance loading units, loading each section of pipe with the number of loading units that it is required to carry.

This is best achieved on either a plan or isometric of the system. A useful technique is to use a four-quarter frame. See Figure 14.

The pipe size at this initial stage is provisional in order to enable the calculation to proceed. The provisional pipe size can be established by calculating the available head or pressure, in metres head and dividing it by the overall length of the index circuit, i.e. the longest pipe route with the greatest duty and least head or pressure, plus a 30% factor for, at this stage an assumed loss through fittings. The result

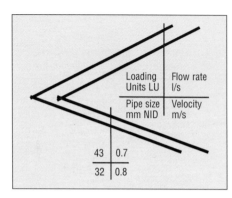

*Figure 14* Pipe section loading

of the provisional calculation is a 'head loss in metres, per metre run of pipe.' This figure can be used with the pipe sizing charts to establish the assumed or provisional pipe size. As the loading unit for each pipe section is established enter the figures into the calculation sheet. See Figure 15.

# Pipe sizing chart definitions

### Pipe reference

Numbered or lettered sections of the system identifying the start and finish.

### Loading units

Simultaneous maximum demand figure being carried by that section of pipe.

### Flow rate (l/s)

Litres per second derived from the loading unit figure.

### Assumed pipe diameter (mm)

Nominal internal diameter established from the available head divided by the index circuit length plus 30% for loss through fittings.

### Length (m)

Length of pipe, in metres of the pipe section being sized, measuring its total route length.

### Pipe losses (mh/m)

In metres head per metre of pipe, taken from the pipe sizing charts.

### Velocity (m/s)

Velocity, in metres per second of the water flowing through the pipe being sized, taken from the pipe sizing charts.

### Pipe loss (mh)

In metres head, being the multiplication of the pipe length and the metres head loss per metre run of pipe length.

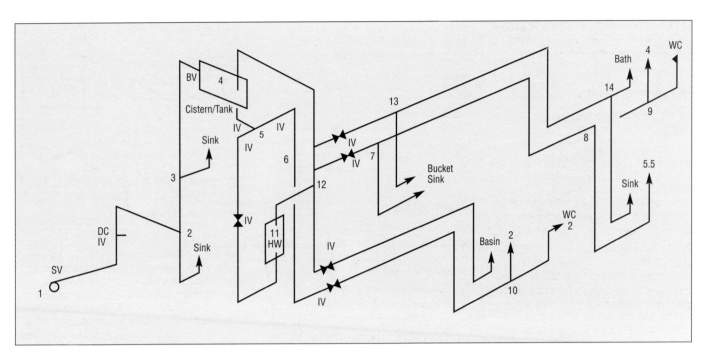

| Pipe Ref | Loading units | Flow rate | Assumed pipe dia. | Length | Pipe loss | Velocity | Pipe loss | Fittings head loss (m/h) | | | | | | | Total head loss | System head loss | Total head available | Final pipe size |
|---|---|---|---|---|---|---|---|---|---|---|---|---|---|---|---|---|---|---|
| | | | | | | | | E | T | SV | IV | BV | DO | Other | | | | |
| | | (l/s) | | (m) | (mm/h) | (m/s) | (mh) | | | | | | | | (mh) | (mh) | (mh) | (mm) |
| 1-2 | 10 + tank | .45 | 20 | 10 | .15 | 1.3 | .5 | .2 | .15 | 0.75 | | | | | 2.6 | | 15.0 | 20 |
| 2-3 | 5 + tank | .35 | 20 | 2 | .09 | 1.1 | .18 | | .08 | | | | | | .26 | | Less static | 20 |
| 3-4 | Tank | .15 | 15 | 3 | .17 | 1.0 | .51 | .01 | | | .02 | .16 | | | .7 | 3.56 | | 15 |
| 4-5 | 29 | .56 | 25 | 2 | .06 | 1.0 | .12 | .07 | .08 | | .015 | | | .07 | .355 | | | 25 |
| 5-6 | 16 | .42 | 25 | 3 | .035 | .75 | .105 | | | | | | | | .155 | | | 25 |
| 6-7 | 12 | .32 | 20 | 2 | .07 | .9 | .14 | .09 | .065 | | | | | | .295 | | | 20 |
| 7-8 | 10 | .3 | 20 | 4 | .066 | .85 | .264 | .12 | .065 | | | | | | .449 | | | 20 |
| 8-9 | 5 | .2 | 20 | 2 | .32 | .65 | .064 | | .02 | | | | | | .084 | | | 20 |
| 9-wc | 1 | .15 | 15 | 1 | .16 | 1.0 | .16 | .04 | | | .02 | .16 | | | .38 | 1.718 | 2.0 | 15 |
| | | | | | | | | | | | | | | | | | | |
| 5-11 | 13 | .35 | 25 | 3 | .25 | .6 | .075 | .06 | | | .005 | | | .03 | .17 | | | 25 |
| 11-12 | 13 | .35 | 25 | 1 | .025 | .6 | .025 | .04 | | | | | | | .065 | | | 25 |
| 12-13 | 11 | .32 | 20 | 2 | .07 | .9 | .14 | | | | .03 | | | | .17 | | | 20 |
| 13-14 | 9 (inc bath) | .3 | 20 | 4 | .07 | .9 | .28 | .07 | | | | | | | .35 | | | 20 |
| 14-bath | Bath | .3 | 20 | 1 | .07 | .9 | .07 | | | | | | | .5 | .507 | 1.262 | 2.0 | 20 |
| 6-10 | | | | | | | | | | | | | | | | | | |
| 10-basin | | | | | | | | | | | | | | | | | | |
| Continue for the remainder of the system | | | | | | | | | | | | | | | | | | |

*Figure 15* Pipework isometric and calculation sheet

### Fittings head loss (mh)

In metres head, for each pipe fitting and valve on the section of pipe being sized.

### Total head loss (mh)

In metres head, being the total sum of the pipe head loss and the fittings head loss.

### System head loss (mh)

In metres head, being the total sum of all the sections of pipe relevant to the source of head available.

### Total head available (mh)

In metres head, being either the mains or pump pressure and/or the height of the gravity feed cistern/tank. See Table 16.

### Final pipe size (mm)

In mm, nominal internal diameter, confirming the pipe size for that section of pipe.

## Loss of head through fittings

Refer to Table 19 loss of head, in metres through various pipeline fittings

and terminal outlets, against a range of flow rates and sizes.

Loss of head through Tees should be assumed to occur at the changes of direction only.

For fittings not identified reference shall be made to the respective manufactures literature.

Where the flow rate falls between the stated figures then the proportional flow rate difference between the higher and lower figure shall be equally applied to the higher and lower head loss figure.

*Table 16  Head and pressure of water*

| Metres | kNm² or kPa | Bars | Bars | kN/m²/ or kPa | Metres |
|--------|-------------|------|------|---------------|--------|
| 1 | 9.81 | 0.098 | 0.1 | 10 | 1.02 |
| 2 | 19.61 | 0.196 | 0.2 | 20 | 2.04 |
| 3 | 29.42 | 0.294 | 0.3 | 30 | 3.06 |
| 4 | 39.23 | 0.392 | 0.4 | 40 | 4.08 |
| 5 | 49.03 | 0.490 | 0.5 | 50 | 5.10 |
| 6 | 58.84 | 0.588 | 0.6 | 60 | 6.12 |
| 7 | 68.65 | 0.686 | 0.7 | 70 | 7.14 |
| 8 | 78.45 | 0.785 | 0.8 | 80 | 8.16 |
| 9 | 88.26 | 0.883 | 0.9 | 90 | 9.18 |
| 10 | 98.07 | 0.981 | 1.0 | 100 | 10.20 |
| 11 | 107.87 | 1.08 | 1.1 | 110 | 11.22 |
| 12 | 117.68 | 1.18 | 1.2 | 120 | 12.24 |
| 13 | 127.49 | 1.27 | 1.3 | 130 | 13.26 |
| 14 | 137.29 | 1.37 | 1.4 | 140 | 14.28 |
| 15 | 147.10 | 1.47 | 1.5 | 150 | 15.30 |
| 16 | 156.91 | 1.57 | 1.6 | 160 | 16.32 |
| 17 | 166.71 | 1.67 | 1.7 | 170 | 17.34 |
| 18 | 176.52 | 1.77 | 1.8 | 180 | 18.36 |
| 19 | 186.33 | 1.86 | 1.9 | 190 | 19.38 |
| 20 | 196.13 | 1.96 | 2.0 | 200 | 20.40 |
| 25 | 245.17 | 2.45 | 2.5 | 250 | 25.49 |
| 30 | 294.20 | 2.94 | 3.0 | 300 | 30.59 |
| 35 | 343.23 | 3.43 | 3.5 | 350 | 35.69 |
| 40 | 392.37 | 3.92 | 4.0 | 400 | 40.79 |
| 45 | 441.30 | 4.41 | 4.5 | 450 | 45.89 |
| 50 | 490.33 | 4.90 | 5.0 | 500 | 50.99 |
| 60 | 588.40 | 5.88 | 6.0 | 600 | 61.18 |
| 70 | 686.47 | 6.86 | 7.0 | 700 | 71.38 |
| 80 | 784.53 | 7.85 | 8.0 | 800 | 81.58 |
| 90 | 882.60 | 8.83 | 9.0 | 900 | 91.77 |
| 100 | 980.66 | 9.81 | 10.0 | 1000 | 101.97 |

The use of various units to describe pressure can cause confusion. The calculation of 'Head loss' in this Guide Section is declared in 'Metres head' as a readily usable means of measurement. Metres head can be easily converted to Bar, kN/m² and/or Pascals pressure figures as there is a close correlation between all of them. The table above provides the comparative figures for eas of reference.
1 litre of water weighs 1 kilogram, or 1000 grams.
1 cubic metre of water = 1000 litres.
1 metre head of water = 9810Pa or kN/m², or 9.81Pa or kN/m², or 0.1 bar.

*Table 17  Pipework velocities*

| Location | Noise rating NR | Pipe material | |
|----------|-----------------|---------------|---|
| | | Metal: copper, stainless steel, galvanised (m/s) | Plastic UPVC, ABS, CPV, Pb (m/s) |
| Service duct, riser, shaft, plant room | 50 | 2.0 | 2.5 |
| Service enclosure, ceiling void | 40 | 1.5 | 1.5 |
| Circulation area, entrance corridor | 35 | 1.5 | 1.5 |
| Seating area, lecture/meeting room | 30 | 1.25 | 1.25 |
| Bedroom | 25 | 1.0 | 1.0 |
| Theatre, cinema | 20 | 0.75 | 0.75 |
| Recording studio | <20 | 0.5 | 0.5 |

*Other factors than velocity need to be considered with regard to noise generated by water flows in pipework. The pipe support and brackets required to secure the pipework sufficient to restrain it and prevent contact with other elements. Where pipework passes through a hollow structure ie wall or floor, then it needs to be separated or sleeved so as not to be in contact with the structure, to avoid resonance, and resulting amplified noise to occur.*

# Pipe sizing by velocity

Where there is ample head available, or the water supply is by a pump or pump set, then pipe sizing can best be achieved by using an optimum pipe velocity.

In a gravity down feed system where the head available is a limiting factor, pipe velocities are generally low, often in the range of 0.4 to 0.8 metres/second. Where delivery is to be a pumped supply, then the pipe velocities can be allowed to increase to 1.0 to 1.5 metres/second, and possibly higher where pipes are routed in non occupied areas.
See Table 17.

Pipe velocities, ultimately are limited by either of the following:

a.  Noise

b.  Erosion/corrosion

c.  Cavitation.

Noise is a major consideration, and velocities above 1.5 metres/second in pipework passing through occupied areas, in particular bedrooms should be avoided.

Erosion and corrosion are less of an issue. If velocities are being set to limit noise then erosion and corrosion will not generally be a problem. Where velocities exceed 2.5 metres/second erosion and/or corrosion can result from the abrasive action of particles in the water. This type of water would normally be associated with a 'raw' water rather than a water supply for domestic use purposes where filtration has taken place as part of the treatment process by the Water Companies who have a duty to provide a 'wholesome' supply for domestic purposes.

Cavitation caused by velocity is not considered an issue with water supply systems as velocities should always be below the 7.0 to 10.0 metres/second where velocity cavitation can occur.

Having determined the appropriate velocity for the location of the distribution pipes, using the pipe sizing charts you can determine the pipe size by cross reference to the design flow rate, and record the pipe head loss per metre. From thereon the pipe sizing schedule for the whole system can be completed.

*Table 18a* Heat emission from insulated pipes (40°C temperature difference)

| | Value of pipework insulation thermal conductivity W/mK | | | | | | | | | | | |
| --- | --- | --- | --- | --- | --- | --- | --- | --- | --- | --- | --- | --- |
| | 0.040 | | | | 0.055 | | | | 0.070 | | | |
| | Thickness of pipework insulation (mm) | | | | | | | | | | | |
| | 12.5 | 19 | 25 | 38 | 12.5 | 19 | 25 | 38 | 12.5 | 19 | 25 | 38 |
| 10 | 9 | 7 | 6 | 4 | 12 | 10 | 8 | 7 | 14 | 12 | 10 | 9 |
| 15 | 11 | 9 | 8 | 6 | 14 | 12 | 10 | 9 | 16 | 14 | 12 | 11 |
| 20 | 12 | 10 | 9 | 7 | 16 | 13 | 12 | 10 | 19 | 16 | 14 | 12 |
| 25 | 14 | 11 | 10 | 8 | 19 | 15 | 13 | 11 | 22 | 18 | 16 | 14 |
| 32 | 17 | 13 | 12 | 9 | 22 | 18 | 5 | 12 | 26 | 22 | 19 | 15 |
| 40 | 19 | 15 | 13 | 10 | 24 | 20 | 17 | 13 | 29 | 24 | 21 | 17 |
| 50 | 23 | 18 | 15 | 12 | 30 | 23 | 20 | 16 | 34 | 28 | 24 | 19 |
| 65 | 27 | 21 | 18 | 14 | 35 | 28 | 23 | 18 | 42 | 33 | 28 | 22 |
| 75 | 31 | 24 | 20 | 15 | 40 | 31 | 26 | 20 | 48 | 38 | 32 | 25 |

*Table 18b* Heat emission from uninsulated pipes (W/m run)

| Pipe size | Copper/stainless steel | Plastic | Steel |
| --- | --- | --- | --- |
| 10 | 22 | | |
| 15 | 31 | | 42 |
| 20 | 43 | Refer | 51 |
| 25 | 53 | to | 62 |
| 32 | 64 | manufacturers | 75 |
| 40 | 75 | data | 84 |
| 50 | 93 | | 102 |
| 65 | 112 | | 125 |
| 75 | 125 | | 143 |

Pipework taken to be shiny surface, individual, with zero air movement, and a 40°C temperature difference between the pipe content and surrounding air temperature.

*Figure 16* Secondary circulation pipework isometric and calculation sheet

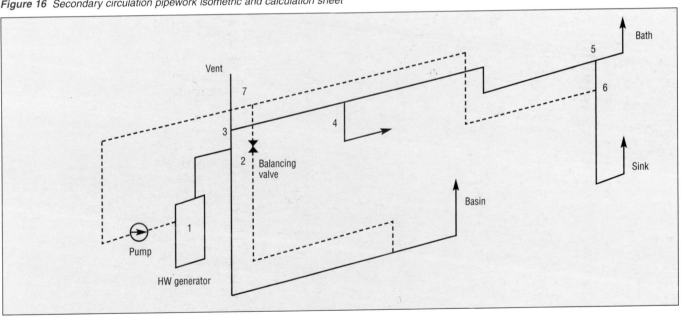

| Pipe Ref | Heat loss load (W) | Flow rate (l/s) | Assumed pipe dia. | Length (m) | Pipe loss (m/mh) | Velocity (m/s) | Pipe loss (m/h) | Fittings head loss (m/h) | | | | | | | Total head loss (m) | System head loss (m) | Total head available (m) | Final pipe size (m) |
| --- | --- | --- | --- | --- | --- | --- | --- | --- | --- | --- | --- | --- | --- | --- | --- | --- | --- | --- |
| | | | | | | | | E | T | SV | IV | BV | DO | Other | | | | |
| 1-2 (flow) | 400 | .09 | 25 | 1 | .0025 | <.5 | .0025 | .002 | | | | | | .02 | .0045 | | | 25 |
| 2-3 (flow) | 200 | .05 | 20 | 2 | .003 | <.5 | .006 | | | | .001 | | | | .007 | | | 20 |
| 3-4 (flow) | 200 | .05 | 20 | 4 | .003 | <.5 | .012 | .001 | | | | | | | .013 | | | 20 |
| 4-5 (flow) | 200 | .05 | 20 | 1 | .003 | <.5 | .003 | .002 | | | | | | | .005 | | | 20 |
| 5-6 (flow) | 200 | .05 | 15 | 1 | .02 | <.5 | .02 | .001 | | | | | | | .021 | | | 15 |
| 6-1 (return) | 200 | .05 | 15 | 7 | .02 | <.5 | .14 | .045 | | | | | | | .0185 | | | 15 |
| 7-1 (return) | 400 | .09 | 15 | 3 | .05 | 0.6 | .15 | .045 | | | | | | .02 | .195 | .264 | | 15 |

## Hot water secondary circulation

In order to maintain the correct temperature of hot water within the hot water distribution system, provision of a 'return' pipe to enable the water to be circulated back to the hot water generator is required.

Hot water circulation can be achieved by gravity or pump circulation means, although in nearly all instances a pumped system is provided.

## Secondary circulation pipe sizing

The formal method of sizing the secondary circulation pipework is to calculate the heat loss from all of the 'flow' and 'return' pipe circuits throughout the system. Calculating the heat loss allows a comparable flow rate to be established, and thereafter the head loss throughout the system is determined, and the duty of the circulating pump.

The total heat loss from each section of pipe is converted to a flow rate necessary to replace the lost heat.

$$kg/s = \frac{Watts}{4.187 \; (shc \; of \; water) \times 1000}$$

The pipework heat loss is that which is emitted through the pipe wall and insulation material. See Tables 18a and 18b for pipes with and without insulation.

A 'Rule of Thumb' method of sizing pumped HWS secondary circuits is to initially select a return pipe size two sizes lower than the flow. As a guide select smaller sizes over larger pipe sizes, and maintain a check on the HWS return pipe velocities.

Pipe circuit balancing valves will be needed where the HWS return has a number of branches and loops to serve the various parts of the circulation system. These valves restrict the flow to the circuits nearest the pump where there is greater pump pressure, forcing the HWS return to circulate to the furthest circuit. Commonly the circuit valves are a double regulating pattern which permit an accurate 'low flow' setting to be achieved and retained when the valve may be shut off and re-opened during maintenance of the system. The use of ordinary isolation valves can achieve a crude form of restricting the flow for balancing purposes, but these rarely remain effective, or return to their initial setting after being shut off.

The over-riding purpose of the balancing valve is to maintain the correct temperature within the pipework distribution system to minimise the potential for bacterial growth, in particular legionella. The Health & Safety Approved Code of Practice Guidance L8 should be applied (see earlier).

*Table 19 Loss of head through pipe fittings (expressed in millimetres, ie 1mm = 0.001 m unless otherwise stated)*

**Elbows – flow rate in litres/second**

| Pipe size nom. ID | 0.02 | 0.04 | 0.08 | 0.15 | 0.2 | 0.3 | 0.5 | 0.75 | 1.0 | 1.5 | 2.0 | 3.0 | 4.0 | 5.0 | 6.0 | 7.0 | 8.0 | 9.0 | 10.0 | 11.0 | 12.0 |
|---|---|---|---|---|---|---|---|---|---|---|---|---|---|---|---|---|---|---|---|---|---|
| 10 | 2 | 10 | 35 | 150 | 300 | | | | | | | | | | | | | | | | |
| 15 | 1 | 3 | 15 | 45 | 100 | 190 | | | | | | | | | | | | | | | |
| 20 | | 1 | 5 | 10 | 15 | 45 | 120 | 270 | | | | | | | | | | | | | |
| 25 | | | 1 | 5 | 10 | 15 | 45 | 100 | 180 | 420 | | | | | | | | | | | |
| 32 | | | | 1 | 3 | 5 | 15 | 30 | 60 | 130 | 230 | 540 | | | | | | | | | |
| 40 | | | | | 1 | 2 | 5 | 15 | 25 | 60 | 100 | 250 | 440 | | | | | | | | |
| 50 | | | | | | 1 | 2 | 5 | 10 | 20 | 35 | 85 | 150 | 220 | 320 | 450 | | | | | |
| 65 | | | | | | | 1 | 2 | 3 | 5 | 10 | 20 | 40 | 60 | 85 | 115 | 150 | 190 | 240 | 290 | |
| 75 | | | | | | | | | 1 | 3 | 5 | 10 | 20 | 35 | 50 | 70 | 90 | 110 | 140 | 170 | 200 |

**Tees – flow rate in litres/second (applicable to change of direction only)**

| Pipe size nom. ID | 0.02 | 0.04 | 0.08 | 0.15 | 0.2 | 0.3 | 0.5 | 0.75 | 1.0 | 1.5 | 2.0 | 3.0 | 4.0 | 5.0 | 6.0 | 7.0 | 8.0 | 9.0 | 10.0 | 11.0 | 12.0 |
|---|---|---|---|---|---|---|---|---|---|---|---|---|---|---|---|---|---|---|---|---|---|
| 10 | 3 | 15 | 50 | 220 | 450 | | | | | | | | | | | | | | | | |
| 15 | 2 | 5 | 20 | 60 | 150 | 280 | | | | | | | | | | | | | | | |
| 20 | | 1 | 5 | 15 | 20 | 65 | 180 | 400 | | | | | | | | | | | | | |
| 25 | | | 1 | 5 | 15 | 20 | 65 | 150 | 270 | 600 | | | | | | | | | | | |
| 32 | | | | 1 | 3 | 5 | 20 | 45 | 95 | 210 | 370 | 870 | | | | | | | | | |
| 40 | | | | | 1 | 2 | 5 | 20 | 40 | 100 | 160 | 400 | 700 | | | | | | | | |
| 50 | | | | | | 1 | 2 | 5 | 15 | 30 | 50 | 135 | 240 | 350 | 520 | 720 | | | | | |
| 65 | | | | | | | 2 | 4 | 5 | 10 | 20 | 40 | 80 | 120 | 170 | 230 | 300 | 380 | 480 | 580 | |
| 75 | | | | | | | | | 2 | 5 | 10 | 20 | 40 | 70 | 100 | 140 | 180 | 220 | 230 | 340 | 400 |

**Globe valve/Stop tap – Flow rate in litres/second**

| Pipe size nom. ID | 0.02 | 0.04 | 0.08 | 0.15 | 0.2 | 0.3 | 0.5 | 0.75 | 1.0 | 1.5 | 2.0 | 3.0 | 4.0 | 5.0 | 6.0 | 7.0 | 8.0 | 9.0 | 10.0 | 11.0 | 12.0 |
|---|---|---|---|---|---|---|---|---|---|---|---|---|---|---|---|---|---|---|---|---|---|
| 10 | 30 | 135 | 430 | 1800 | | | | | | | | | | | | | | | | | |
| 15 | 20 | 45 | 190 | 570 | 1200 | 2400 | | | | | | | | | | | | | | | |
| 20 | | 10 | 20 | 80 | 125 | 290 | 840 | 1890 | | | | | | | | | | | | | |
| 25 | | | 25 | 50 | 110 | 315 | 690 | 1340 | 2950 | | | | | | | | | | | | |
| 32 | | | | 15 | 45 | 125 | 290 | 530 | 1150 | 2010 | 4720 | | | | | | | | | | |
| 40 | | | | | 20 | 40 | 90 | 180 | 380 | 660 | 1570 | 2750 | 4020 | | | | | | | | |
| 50 | | | | | | 30 | 60 | 130 | 230 | 530 | 940 | 1400 | 2030 | 2850 | | | | | | | |
| 65 | | | | | | | 50 | 90 | 220 | 400 | 570 | 870 | 1170 | 1570 | 1900 | 2530 | 2920 | | | | |
| 75 | | | | | | | | | 50 | 100 | 180 | 280 | 420 | 560 | 730 | 920 | 1120 | 1400 | 1710 | | |

*Table 19* Loss of head through pipe fittings – continued (expressed in millimetres, ie 1mm = 0.001 m unless otherwise stated)

**Gate valves/Service valves – Flow rate in litres/second**

| Pipe size nom. ID | 0.02 | 0.04 | 0.08 | 0.15 | 0.2 | 0.3 | 0.5 | 0.75 | 1.0 | 1.5 | 2.0 | 3.0 | 4.0 | 5.0 | 6.0 | 7.0 | 8.0 | 9.0 | 10.0 | 11.0 | 12.0 |
|---|---|---|---|---|---|---|---|---|---|---|---|---|---|---|---|---|---|---|---|---|---|
| 10 | 2 | 5 | 15 | 75 | | | | | | | | | | | | | | | | | |
| 15 | 1 | 1 | 5 | 20 | 50 | 100 | | | | | | | | | | | | | | | |
| 20 | | | 1 | 5 | 10 | 20 | 60 | 135 | | | | | | | | | | | | | |
| 25 | | | | 1 | 2 | 5 | 10 | 30 | 90 | 125 | | | | | | | | | | | |
| 32 | | | | | | 1 | 5 | 10 | 20 | 50 | 85 | 200 | | | | | | | | | |
| 40 | | | | | | | 1 | 5 | 10 | 20 | 40 | 90 | 165 | 250 | | | | | | | |
| 50 | | | | | | | | 2 | 5 | 10 | 20 | 35 | 55 | 80 | 110 | 150 | | | | | |
| 65 | | | | | | | | | 1 | 3 | 10 | 15 | 25 | 35 | 45 | 60 | 75 | 95 | 115 | | |
| 75 | | | | | | | | | | 2 | 5 | 7 | 10 | 15 | 18 | 20 | 25 | 35 | 40 | | |

**Check valve – Flow rate in litres/second**

| Pipe size nom. ID | 0.02 | 0.04 | 0.08 | 0.15 | 0.2 | 0.3 | 0.5 | 0.75 | 1.0 | 1.5 | 2.0 | 3.0 | 4.0 | 5.0 | 6.0 | 7.0 | 8.0 | 9.0 | 10.0 | 11.0 | 12.0 |
|---|---|---|---|---|---|---|---|---|---|---|---|---|---|---|---|---|---|---|---|---|---|
| 10 | 5 | 20 | 70 | 300 | | | | | | | | | | | | | | | | | |
| 15 | 3 | 5 | 30 | 95 | 200 | 400 | | | | | | | | | | | | | | | |
| 20 | | | 5 | 20 | 45 | 80 | 240 | 540 | | | | | | | | | | | | | |
| 25 | | | | 5 | 15 | 30 | 85 | 200 | 360 | 840 | | | | | | | | | | | |
| 32 | | | | | | 10 | 35 | 80 | 150 | 330 | 570 | 1350 | | | | | | | | | |
| 40 | | | | | | | 15 | 35 | 70 | 150 | 260 | 630 | 1100 | 1720 | | | | | | | |
| 50 | | | | | | | | 25 | 50 | 90 | 210 | 370 | 610 | 810 | 1140 | 1500 | | | | | |
| 65 | | | | | | | | | 40 | 90 | 160 | 250 | 350 | 460 | 620 | 830 | 1010 | 1170 | | | |
| 75 | | | | | | | | | | 50 | 90 | 140 | 210 | 280 | 360 | 460 | 580 | 700 | 850 | | |

**Double check valve**

| Pipe size nom. ID | 0.02 | 0.04 | 0.08 | 0.15 | 0.2 | 0.3 | 0.5 | 0.75 | 1.0 | 1.5 | 2.0 | 3.0 | 4.0 | 5.0 | 6.0 | 7.0 | 8.0 | 9.0 | 10.0 | 11.0 | 12.0 |
|---|---|---|---|---|---|---|---|---|---|---|---|---|---|---|---|---|---|---|---|---|---|
| 10 | | | | | | | | | | | | | | | | | | | | | |
| 15 | | | | 750 | 850 | 1400 | 3000 | | | | | | | | | | | | | | |
| 20 | | | | 450 | 500 | 550 | 900 | 1800 | 3000 | | | | | | | | | | | | |
| 25 | | | | 300 | 450 | 500 | 600 | 800 | 1100 | 2400 | | | | | | | | | | | |
| 32 | | | | | | | | | | | | | | | | | | | | | |
| 40 | | | | | | | | | | | | | | | | | | | | | |
| 50 | | | | | | | | | | | | | | | | | | | | | |
| 65 | | | | | | | | | | | | | | | | | | | | | |
| 75 | | | | | | | | | | | | | | | | | | | | | |

**RPZ valves (reduced pressure zone valve) excluding filters (expressed in metres)**

| Pipe size nom. ID | 0.02 | 0.04 | 0.08 | 0.15 | 0.2 | 0.3 | 0.5 | 0.75 | 1.0 | 1.5 | 2.0 | 3.0 | 4.0 | 5.0 | 6.0 | 7.0 | 8.0 | 9.0 | 10.0 | 11.0 | 12.0 |
|---|---|---|---|---|---|---|---|---|---|---|---|---|---|---|---|---|---|---|---|---|---|
| 10 | | | | | | | | | | | | | | | | | | | | | |
| 15 | | | 8.2 | 8.8 | 8.9 | 9.2 | 10.0 | 11.2 | 14.0 | | | | | | | | | | | | |
| 20 | | | 8.1 | 8.5 | 8.7 | 8.8 | 9.3 | 9.7 | 10.2 | 11.8 | 16.0 | | | | | | | | | | |
| 25 | | | | 8.3 | 8.4 | 8.6 | 8.9 | 9.2 | 9.5 | 10.2 | 11.0 | 13.8 | | | | | | | | | |
| 32 | | | | 8.2 | 8.3 | 8.4 | 8.6 | 8.8 | 9.0 | 9.3 | 9.7 | 10.8 | 12.0 | 15.0 | | | | | | | |
| 40 | | | | 8.1 | 8.2 | 8.3 | 8.6 | 8.8 | 9.0 | 9.1 | 9.2 | 9.7 | 10.0 | 11.3 | 11.9 | 13.0 | | | | | |
| 50 | | | | 8.0 | 8.1 | 8.2 | 8.4 | 8.5 | 8.7 | 8.8 | 8.9 | 9.1 | 9.3 | 9.7 | 10.0 | 10.3 | | | | | |
| 65 | | | | | | | | 8.0 | 8.05 | 8.1 | 8.18 | 8.3 | 8.35 | 8.5 | 8.7 | 8.9 | 9.2 | | | | |
| 75 | | | | | | | | | | | 8.0 | 8.15 | 8.23 | 8.35 | 8.5 | 8.6 | 8.9 | 9.0 | 9.1 | | |

**Ball float valves – Flow rate in litres/second**

| Pipe size nom. ID | 0.02 | 0.04 | 0.08 | 0.15 | 0.2 | 0.3 | 0.5 | 0.75 | 1.0 | 1.5 | 2.0 | 3.0 | 4.0 | 5.0 | 6.0 | 7.0 | 8.0 | 9.0 | 10.0 | 11.0 | 12.0 |
|---|---|---|---|---|---|---|---|---|---|---|---|---|---|---|---|---|---|---|---|---|---|
| 10 | | | | | | | | | | | | | | | | | | | | | |
| 15 | | | 120 | 160 | 350 | 700 | | | | | | | | | | | | | | | |
| 20 | | | | 40 | 80 | 145 | 420 | | | | | | | | | | | | | | |
| 25 | | | | 10 | 25 | 55 | 155 | 340 | 670 | 1470 | | | | | | | | | | | |
| 32 | | | | | | 20 | 65 | 140 | 250 | 540 | 950 | 2220 | | | | | | | | | |
| 40 | | | | | | | 30 | 60 | 115 | 250 | 430 | 1030 | 1810 | 2840 | | | | | | | |
| 50 | | | | | | | | | 40 | 85 | 150 | 350 | 620 | 1010 | 1330 | 1880 | | | | | |

*Table 19* Loss of head through pipe fittings – continued

| Pipe size nom. ID | Vessel entry | | | | | | | | | | Vessel exit | | | | | | | | | |
|---|---|---|---|---|---|---|---|---|---|---|---|---|---|---|---|---|---|---|---|---|
| | 0.2 | 0.3 | 0.5 | 0.75 | 1.0 | 2.0 | 4.0 | 6.0 | 8.0 | 10.0 | 0.2 | 0.3 | 0.5 | 0.75 | 1.0 | 2.0 | 4.0 | 6.0 | 8.0 | 10.0 |
| 20 | 20 | 40 | 120 | 270 | | | | | | | 10 | 15 | 50 | 100 | | | | | | |
| 25 | | 20 | 40 | 100 | 180 | | | | | | | 10 | 15 | 40 | 70 | | | | | |
| 32 | | 5 | 20 | 40 | 80 | 280 | | | | | 1 | 5 | 15 | 30 | 110 | | | | | |
| 40 | | | 10 | 20 | 35 | 130 | 550 | | | | | | 5 | 10 | 15 | 50 | 220 | | | |
| 50 | | | | | 10 | 50 | 190 | 400 | 770 | 1200 | | | | | 5 | 20 | 70 | 160 | 300 | 480 |
| 65 | | | | | | 20 | 80 | 175 | 315 | 500 | | | | | | 10 | 30 | 70 | 120 | 200 |
| 75 | | | | | | | | | | | | | | | | | | | | |

| Pipe size nom. ID | Vessel inlet – tank (not ball valve) | | | | | | | | | | | | | | | | | | | | |
|---|---|---|---|---|---|---|---|---|---|---|---|---|---|---|---|---|---|---|---|---|---|
| | 0.02 | 0.04 | 0.08 | 0.15 | 0.2 | 0.3 | 0.5 | 0.75 | 1.0 | 1.5 | 2.0 | 3.0 | 4.0 | 5.0 | 6.0 | 7.0 | 8.0 | 9.0 | 10.0 | 11.0 | 12.0 |
| 10 | | | | | | | | | | | | | | | | | | | | | |
| 15 | | | | | | | | | | | | | | | | | | | | | |
| 20 | | | | | | | | | | | | | | | | | | | | | |
| 25 | | | | | | | | | | | | | | | | | | | | | |
| 32 | | | | | | Additional example tables if required | | | | | | | | | | | | | | | |
| 40 | | | | | | | | | | | | | | | | | | | | | |
| 50 | | | | | | | | | | | | | | | | | | | | | |
| 65 | | | | | | | | | | | | | | | | | | | | | |
| 75 | | | | | | | | | | | | | | | | | | | | | |

| Pipe size nom. ID | Reducers, individual or combination with tee | | | | | | | | | | | | | | | | | | | | |
|---|---|---|---|---|---|---|---|---|---|---|---|---|---|---|---|---|---|---|---|---|---|
| | 0.02 | 0.04 | 0.08 | 0.15 | 0.2 | 0.3 | 0.5 | 0.75 | 1.0 | 1.5 | 2.0 | 3.0 | 4.0 | 5.0 | 6.0 | 7.0 | 8.0 | 9.0 | 10.0 | 11.0 | 12.0 |
| 10 | | | | | | | | | | | | | | | | | | | | | |
| 15 | | | | | | | | | | | | | | | | | | | | | |
| 20 | | | | | | | | | | | | | | | | | | | | | |
| 25 | | | | | | | | | | | | | | | | | | | | | |
| 32 | | | | | | Additional example tables if required | | | | | | | | | | | | | | | |
| 40 | | | | | | | | | | | | | | | | | | | | | |
| 50 | | | | | | | | | | | | | | | | | | | | | |
| 65 | | | | | | | | | | | | | | | | | | | | | |
| 75 | | | | | | | | | | | | | | | | | | | | | |

| Pipe size nom. ID | Pillar tap draw-off fitting | | | | | | | | | | | | Bib tap draw-off fitting | | | | | | | | |
|---|---|---|---|---|---|---|---|---|---|---|---|---|---|---|---|---|---|---|---|---|---|
| | 0.02 | 0.04 | 0.08 | 0.15 | 0.2 | 0.3 | 0.5 | 0.75 | 1.0 | 1.5 | 2.0 | 3.0 | 0.08 | 0.15 | 0.2 | 0.3 | 0.5 | 0.75 | 1.0 | 1.5 | 2.0 |
| 10 | | | | | | | | | | | | | | | | | | | | | |
| 15 | | | 240 | 520 | 700 | | | | | | | | 185 | 520 | 750 | 1800 | | | | | |
| 20 | | | | 240 | 300 | 500 | | | | | | | | 210 | 330 | 750 | 1500 | | | | |
| 25 | | | | | | | | | | | | | | | | 450 | 1000 | | | | |

| Pipe size nom. ID | Manual mixer valve (only) (metres) | | | | | | | | | | | | Thermostatic mixer valve (only) (metres) | | | | | | | | |
|---|---|---|---|---|---|---|---|---|---|---|---|---|---|---|---|---|---|---|---|---|---|
| | 0.02 | 0.04 | 0.08 | 0.15 | 0.2 | 0.3 | 0.5 | 0.75 | 1.0 | 1.5 | 2.0 | 3.0 | 0.08 | 0.15 | 0.2 | 0.3 | 0.5 | 0.75 | 1.0 | 1.5 | 2.0 |
| 15 | | | 0.8 | 1.5 | 3.0 | 10.0 | 30.0 | | | | | | | 0.7 | 1.2 | 2.0 | 4.0 | 10.0 | | | |
| 20 | | | | | | | | | | | | | | | | | 1.5 | 4.3 | 10.0 | 16.0 | |
| 25 | | | | | | | | | | | | | | | | | | 2.0 | 4.0 | 9.0 | 12.0 |

*Table 20* Water supply system – pipe sizing table

| Pipe Ref | Loading units | Flow rate (l/s) | Assumed pipe dia. | Length (m) | Pipe loss (m/mh) | Velocity (m/s) | Pipe loss (m/h) | Fittings head loss (m/h) | | | | | | | Total head loss (m) | System head loss (m) | Total head available (m) | Final pipe size (m) |
|---|---|---|---|---|---|---|---|---|---|---|---|---|---|---|---|---|---|---|
| | | | | | | | | E | T | SV | IV | BV | DO | Other | | | | |
| | | | | | | | | | | | | | | | | | | |

*Graph 3* *Pipe sizing chart – copper and stainless steel.*

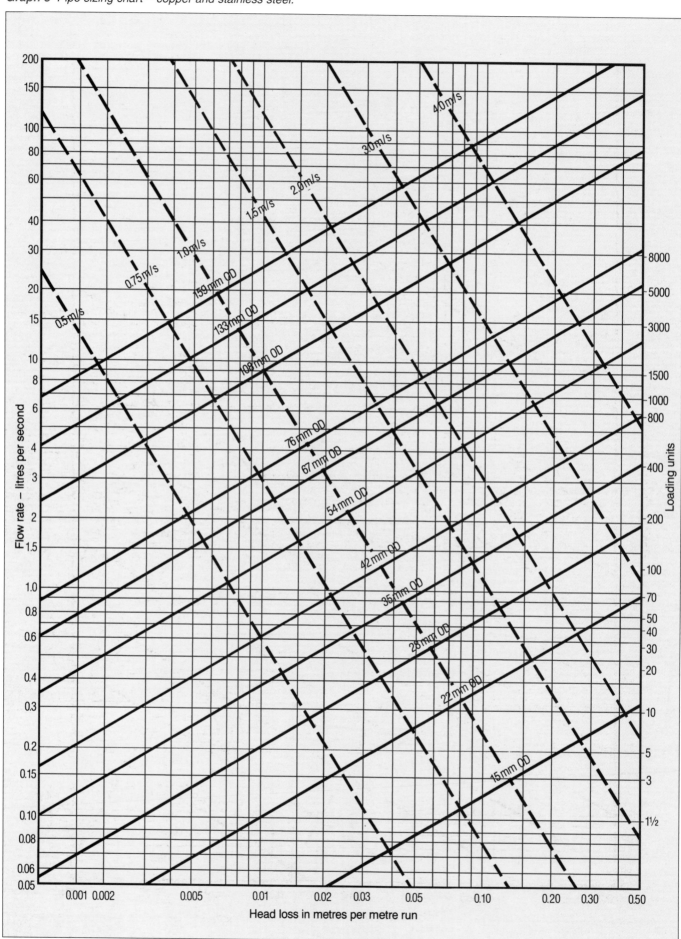

*Graph 4  Pipe sizing chart – plastic*

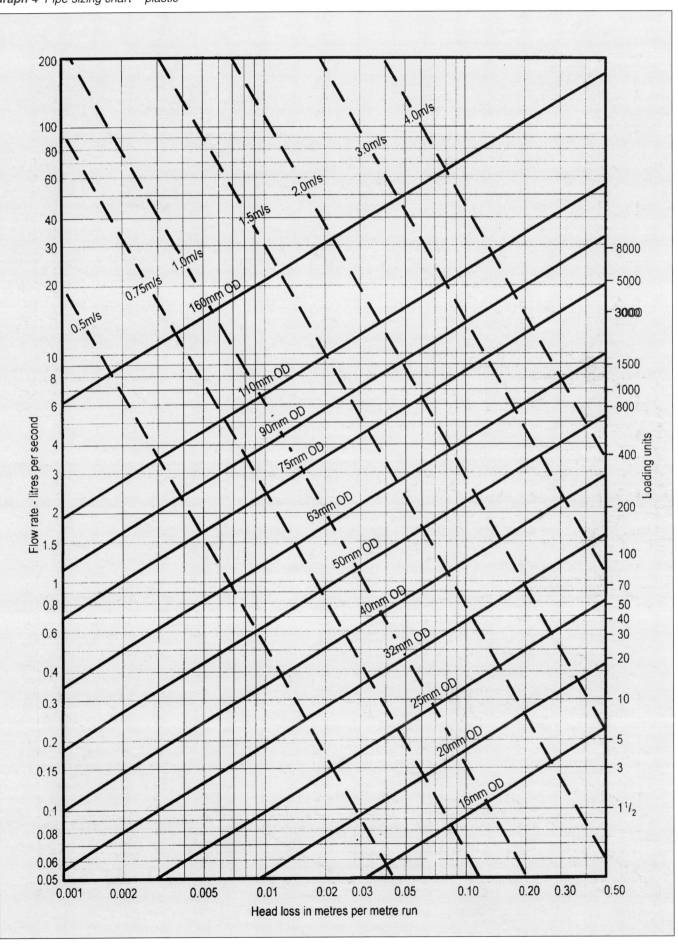

# Hard water treatment

Hard water occurs with the presence of calcium and magnesium salts in solution in the water. This occurs naturally in the water but its extent varies considerably throughout the British Isles.

The definition or a 'hard water' is generally measured in either parts per million (mg/l as calcium carbonate) or 'Clarks' scale.

When the water temperature is raised within a water supply system the salts change to solids and they are deposited as a hard rock-like scale in vessels and pipes. Hard water can lead to widespread damage incurring expensive replacement, increased maintenance and operating costs.

All water containing salts will, when heated deposit scale to a varying amount dependant on the level of hardness and heat applied. If the protection of the water supply installation apparatus is the

*Table 21  Classification of hardness*

| Category | Mg/l | Clarks |
|---|---|---|
| Soft | 0-50 | under 3.5 |
| Moderately soft | 50 –100 | 3.5 – 7 |
| Slightly hard | 100-150 | 7–10.5 |
| Moderately hard | 150-200 | 10.5-14 |
| Hard | 200-300 | 14-21 |
| Very hard | 0ver 300 | Over 21 |

*Table 22  Typical water hardness levels*

| Location | Hardness ppm |
|---|---|
| Bradford | <100 |
| Bristol | 250-350 |
| Cardiff | 100 |
| Edinburgh | <50 |
| Glasgow | <50 |
| Hartlepool | 400-580 |
| Hull | 250-400 |
| Leeds | 120-220 |
| Leicester | 250-320 |
| London | 250-320 |
| Manchester | <60 |
| Middlesbrough | 145-165 |
| Newcastle | 150-165 |
| Norwich | 300+ |
| Nottingham | 220-300 |
| Reading | 260-300 |
| Sheffield | <100 |
| Southhampton | 280 |
| Southport | 220-300 |
| Sunderland | 80-420 |
| Warrington | 70-250 |
| York | 200-300 |

prime concern, then waters having a hardness level of below 150ppm, and generally not being heated above 65°C, generally will not require treatment.

However, to assist in extending the life of the hot water generating plant a 'Water Conditioner' fitted to the cold water supply would be beneficial where the hardness level is above 100ppm.

For water above 150ppm treatment will be needed to protect the condition and maintain the expected life of the water supply system, in particular hot water plant and thermostatic valves. Either a 'water softener' or a 'water conditioner' can be used for protecting the system.

If softer water is desired by the user for washing, or manufacturing production purposes then a base exchange 'salt regeneration' water softener will be necessary. It will be required to be installed on the cold water supply to the hot water generator, or to all the water draw off points except the draw offs used specifically for drinking water.

Water conditioners are effective for the protection of the hot water system because they alter the mineral crystals, reducing their ability to adhere to the internal surfaces of the system, enabling them to pass through the water system. The effectiveness of this process is limited by time, therefore the shorter the period water is retained in the system after conditioning the better. Therefore within large water distribution systems the placing of a water conditioner immediately prior to the hot water generator, and other plant, will provide the best results possible.

# Water supply installations

The installation of the water supply system components requires planning and co-ordination prior to commencement of work to achieve the best possible integration within the building and the areas to be served.

## Materials

The correct selection of the component materials is of paramount importance. The available range of water supply installation materials is extensive, and includes numerous types of components made from metals and plastics, or a combination of both, often for similar purposes.

Some materials are more suited to particular applications than others. For

the selection of components and materials the main considerations are:

a.  Suitability

b.  Availability

c.  Appearance (if to be seen)

d.  Cost

e.  Durability

f.  Compatibility with existing

g.  User choice

h.  Spares.

The range of materials and components available from merchants held or readily available stocks are an excellent guide as to the most used and suitable in any particular regional area, and more often than not represent the best discounted cost component(s).

## Plumbosolvent (dissimilar materials)

Plumbosolvency covers the compatibility of the materials within the water system. Where there is a mix of metal materials, such as copper, stainless steel, and galvanised steel then there is the potential for corrosion to occur. This 'potential' can increase to a 'likelihood' where:

a.  The metals are widely apart on the 'galvanic' scale

b.  the water has a greater acidity or alkalinity above or below the neutral pH value of 7.5

c.  the water in contact with the two metals is warm or hot.

To prevent, or minimise the effect of corrosion through 'Galvanic' action then the selection of compatible materials for the type of water is required.

Where dissimilar metals are in direct contact, and they do not have a close Galvanic relationship, then the installation of an intermediate metal link is appropriate to reduce the likelihood of corrosion occuring.

The 'Galvanic' relationship of metals is as shown in Table 30.

*NOTE:*
*For a greater appreciation of corrosion refer to the later part of this section.*

## Pseudomonas bacteria

Pseudomonas bacteria is a potential risk to water supply systems. More common in the closed water circuits of heating and chilled water systems, but known to occur in water supply systems.

There are many different types of the

**Table 23** *Commonly used materials*

| Component | Options | | | |
|---|---|---|---|---|
| Underground mains | Soft copper | Polyethylene | UPVC | Ductile iron, lined |
| Storage tanks | Polypropylene | Glass reinforced plastic | Steel, lined | |
| Pipework | Copper | Stainless steel | Polybutylene | CPVC |
| Hot water vessels | Copper | Steel, copper or glass lined | Stainless steel | |
| Draw off fittings | Chromed brass | Brass, brass alloy | Plastic | |
| Valves | Chromed brass | Brass, brass alloy | Plastic | |

Pseudomonas bacteria that once in a water system can be difficult to eradicate. If not completely destroyed the bacteria can reappear and grow at a fast rate to form a biofilm within the system. Problems occur due to a greasy brown slime or biofilm that coats strainers, pipework, tanks etc. creating corrosive conditions which can discolour the water and can exude a noxious smell.

Pseudomonas Bacteria can grow more when it has access to a higher level of oxygen and temperatures between 20°C and 40°C, although it can grow outside this range if the water has a pH value of 7-8.5.

Pseudomonas has greater chance of occuring under the following circumstances.

a. Water used for temporary works and filling/testing of pipework coming from dirty cisterns/tanks or temporary mains with dead legs and areas of low use.

b. Non-disinfected hoses used for filling systems.

c. Systems that are filled and then left for long periods with stagnent untreated water, or are partially or fully drained down and then left for long periods with wetted surfaces.

d. Pipework installed on site where there is substantial amounts of debris.

e. If ambient temperatures are high.

Avoiding the above circumstances will greatly reduce the likelihood of pseudomonas bacteria becoming prevelent within the water supply installation.

Infected systems must be disinfected and flushed. Any excessive growth may require repeated disinfecting and flushing to effect a reduction. Ultra-violet water treatment is an effective method of killing the widest range of micro-organisms. However both ultra-violet and disinfection will only provide a temporary respite unless the causes are identified and removed.

## Frost protection

Precautions are required to be taken to prevent the water contained within the water supply distribution system freezing, as this will likely cause components to fail, or burst due to the increase in the internal pressure by the expanding volume as the water turns to ice.

To minimise the risk of 'bursts' pipework and associated components should always be located within areas where the ambient temperature will remain above freezing. In practical terms this would be 3°C and above.

Locations to avoid are:

a. All external locations, unless a minimum of 750mm below ground

b. Roof spaces, unless part of the

building's accommodation

c. Under floor voids, unless part of the building's accommodation

d. Outhouses, enclosures, sheds, and garages etc.

e. Adjacent to ventilators, air bricks, or anywhere subject to external drafts of air.

If the above, and similar locations cannot be avoided then protection will need to be provided by insulating the pipework and components, and possibly providing heating to the spaces that contain water supply installations.

Insulation alone will not ultimately prevent freezing, but only slow down the lowering of the temperature of the water. However if a suitable type and thickness of insulation is used, and it is protected from damage or moisture, then it is a worthwhile method of protection.

Reference should also be made to the guidance provided within the Water Regulation Guide.

An enhanced and very effective method of frost protection is the provision of trace

**Table 25** *Thermal conductivity of insulating materials*

| Material | Thickness, mm, W(m.K) |
|---|---|
| Rigid phenolic foam | < 0.020 |
| Polisocyanurate foam Rigid polyurethane foam | 0.020 to 0.025 |
| PVC foam | 0.025 to 0.03 |
| Expanded polystyrene. Extruded polystyrene. Cross linked polyethylene foam. Expanded nitrile rubber. Improved polyethylene foam. | 0.03 to 0.035 |
| Standard polyethylene foam Expanded synthetic rubber Cellular glass | 0.035 to 0.040 |
| Cork board | 0.04 to 0.055 |
| Exfoliated vermiculite (loose fill) | 0.055 to 0.07 |

**Table 24** *Minimum thickness of insulating material to delay freezing*

| Nominal outside diameter of pipe | Thermal conductivity (W/mK) | | | | | | | |
|---|---|---|---|---|---|---|---|---|
| | 0.035 | 0.04 | 0.055 | 0.07 | 0.035 | 0.04 | 0.055 | 0.07 |
| | Indoor installations (mm) | | | | Outdoor installations (mm) | | | |
| Up to and including 15 | 22 | 32 | 50 | 89 | 27 | 38 | 63 | 100 |
| Over 15, up to and including 22 | 22 | 32 | 50 | 75 | 27 | 38 | 63 | 100 |
| Over 22, up to and including 42 | 22 | 32 | 50 | 75 | 27 | 38 | 63 | 89 |
| Over 42, up to and including 54 | 16 | 25 | 44 | 63 | 19 | 32 | 50 | 75 |
| Over 54, up to and including 76 | 13 | 25 | 32 | 50 | 16 | 25 | 44 | 63 |
| Over 76, and flat surfaces | 13 | 19 | 25 | 38 | 16 | 25 | 32 | 50 |

*This table is reproduced from BS 6700, and lists the thermal conductivity value with an air temperature of 0°C, and the minimum thickness of insulating material that will afford worthwhile protection against freezing during the normal occupation of buildings.*
*Storage cistern and pipework in roof spaces are considered as indoor installations in this context. Pipes in the air space beneath a suspended ground floor or in a detached garage should be protected as outdoor installations.*
*All insulation requires to be vapour sealed to remain effective.*

*Table 26* General pipe insulation

| Pipe size (mm) od | Insulation material and thickness | | |
|---|---|---|---|
| | Glass fibre 0.040W/mK | Phenolic foam 0.018W/mK | Nitril rubber 0.035W/mK |
| 15 | 25 | 15 | 13 |
| 22 | 25 | 15 | 19 |
| 25 | 32 | 20 | 25 |
| 32 | 32 | 20 | 32 |
| 40 | 32 | 20 | 32 |
| 50 | 32 | 20 | 32 |
| 65 | 32 | 20 | 32 |
| 75 | 32 | 20 | 32 |
| 100 | 38 | 20 | 32 |

*Where the insulation material is located in areas requiring fire protection in accordance with the Building Regulations then it shall have a 'Class 0' classification.*

heating. This comprises of self regulating electrical heating elements in a tape form, capable of being wrapped around pipework and componants. By the selection of the appropriate type and rating of heating tape the water within pipework and componants can be kept above the freezing temperature. Trace heating is used in conjunction with insulation and weathering protection.

## General insulation

Pipework and plant componants throughout the distribution system should be provide to keep hot water hot and cold water cold. Without insulation a hot water distribution system would loose heat wasting energy, requiring a larger generating plant, and increasing the opportunity for bacteria growth and potentially failing to comply with the Legionella Codes. The impact on the cold water system would be to unneccessarly gain heat from the warmer ambient temperature and any adjacent heat sources making the water less palatable for drinking, and again increasing the opportunity for bacteria growth and a failure to comply to the Legionella Codes.

The insulation for cold water components requires them to be vapour sealed to prevent condensation forming on the cooler surfaces within the higher ambient areas.

Recommended types and thicknesses of insulation are scheduled in Table 26.

## Pipework and plant supports

Water supply pipework, plant and components require to be adaquately supported to be functional and prevent noise, vibration and general movement, which would become a nuisance and/or lead to damage to itself and other elements of the building.

For the support of plant and components,

the respective manufactures requirements and recommendations should be fully adhered to.

Pipework requires supporting throughout its length at regular and specific positions to maintain its stability, avoid movement which could result in noise or vibration, whilst enabling sufficient movement for pipework expansion and contraction. See Table 27.

## Underground pipework

The Water Supply Company mains are located below ground, and therefore the incoming mains connection to the building will also be below ground until it

can enter in to the building in its desired location.

Pipes laid below ground require to be of a suitable material. The most commonly used is polyethylene, certainly for sizes up to 50mm ID (65mm MDPE OD).

The depth of pipes required to comply with the Water Regulations is a minimum of 750mm from ground level to the top of the pipe barrel, and a maximum of 1350mm, unless in a duct. Where pipes are located below a road the depth should increase to 900mm and be ducted. Where water pipes are laid in a service strip close to other services, the National Joint Utilities guidance documents recommends that the depth of the water service is at 900mm throughout to coordinate with the depth of the other services, and enable services to cross each other. The minimum distance between the water pipework and other sevices is recommended as being 350mm.

The pipe trenches should be kept to the minimum width that is practicable and retain the trench wall to minimise ground loadings transfering onto the pipe. The trench bottom requires to be firm, level and to the correct depth. A bedding of sand is appropraite having a minimum depth of 50mm, to provide a suitable means of bedding the barrel and joints of the pipe. The trench back filling should be of a suitable material such as selected excavated or imported material, consolidated to resist subsequent

*Table 27* Pipe supports – maximum spacing

| Pipe size nominal id (mm) | Pipe material – spacing of supports in metres | | | | | | | |
|---|---|---|---|---|---|---|---|---|
| | Copper | | Stainless steel | | Polybutylene | | CPVC | |
| | Horizontal | Vertical | Horizontal | Vertical | Horizontal | Vertical | Horizontal | Vertical |
| 15 | 1.8 | 2.4 | 1.8 | 2.4 | 0.3 | 0.5 | 0.5 | 1.0 |
| 20 | 2.4 | 3.0 | 2.4 | 3.0 | 0.5 | 0.8 | 0.5 | 1.0 |
| 25 | 2.4 | 3.0 | 2.4 | 3.0 | 0.5 | 0.8 | 0.5 | 1.0 |
| 32 | 2.7 | 3.0 | 2.7 | 3.0 | 0.9 | 1.2 | 0.8 | 1.4 |
| 40 | 3.0 | 3.6 | 3.0 | 3.6 | 0.9 | 1.2 | 0.8 | 2.0 |
| 50 | 3.0 | 3.6 | 3.0 | 3.6 | 1.2 | 1.5 | 1.2 | 2.2 |
| 65 | 3.0 | 3.6 | 3.0 | 3.6 | 1.5 | 2.0 | 1.5 | 2.2 |
| 75 | 3.6 | 4.5 | 3.6 | 4.5 | 1.8 | 2.2 | 1.8 | 2.2 |

*Intermediate supports will be required at changes of direction, branches, and connections to plant. Polybutylene and CPVC pipe supports can benefit from being provided with a continuous tray, rigid bar or rail spanning between support brackets at centres similar to copper, with straps to secure the pipe to the bar.*

*Table 28* Thrust per bar internal pressure (kN)

| Nominal internal diameter of pipe | End thrust | Radial thrust on bends of angle | | | |
|---|---|---|---|---|---|
| | | 90 deg | 45 deg | 22.5 deg | 11.25 deg |
| 50 | 0.38 | 0.53 | 0.29 | 0.15 | 0.07 |
| 75 | 0.72 | 1.02 | 0.55 | 0.28 | 0.15 |
| 100 | 1.17 | 1.66 | 0.9 | 0.46 | 0.24 |
| 125 | 1.76 | 2.49 | 1.35 | 0.69 | 0.35 |
| 150 | 2.47 | 3.50 | 1.89 | 0.96 | 0.49 |

*The kN thrust figures stated are the force exerted by the pipe on it's end or radial area.*

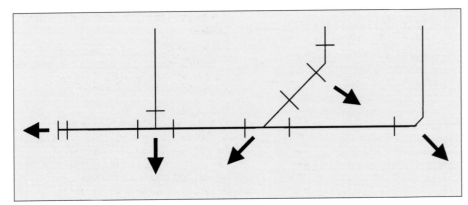

*Figure 17 Direction of thrusts developed in a pipeline due to internal pressure*

movement of the pipes. No large stones or sharp objects shall be allowed to be in contact or near the pipe material.

Below ground pipework requires to be restrained throughout it's length. To combat the thrust of the internal pressure and flows. For the greater part of the pipework this should be achieved by the weight of the backfill material but at bends, tee's, blank ends, and valves the provision of thrust blocks will be required and must be placed in a position that is in the line of the thrust developed in the pipeline due to internal pressures.

For standard fittings, the thrust can be calculated by multiplying the values given in the Table 28 for thrust in kN for a one bar internal pressure. The internal pressure can be deemed to be the maximum working pressure of the below ground pipe system.

Thrust blocks for the restraint of below ground pipework will require an adaquate bearing area to resist the thrust. Refer to Table 29 for the bearing capacity of soils for horizontal thrust.

## Entry to buildings

Pipe entries to buildings may be made by a number of methods. If entry can be made into a basement or under floor area then the pipe can pass through a pipe sleeve constructed into the section of wall below ground, into the building.

*Table 29 Bearing capacity of soils kN/m²*

| Soil type | Safe bearing load |
|---|---|
| Soft Clay | 24 |
| Sand | 48 |
| Sandstone & Gravel | 72 |
| Sand & Gravel Bondes with Clay | 96 |
| Shale | 240 |

For a building having no basement or under floor void then a pipe duct incorporating a 90° bend. If the incoming pipe size is larger than can be passed through a pipe sleeve bend, then a pit, or reduced section of floor will be required to pass the pipe into the building in a manner similar to a basement arrangement, but then rising vertically to the building ground floor level. Once the pipework is installed then the openings between the external and internal parts of the building require to be sealed. The pit can be filled with sand and topped off with a floor screed.

# Disinfection

The process of disinfection is sometimes misunderstood and described as 'sterilisation' or 'chlorination'. It is important that the terminology is understood and used correctly.

*Disinfection* describes the process of killing reducing or inactivating microorganisms, especially by chemical means.

*Sterilisation* is to render sterile, defined as completely free of living microorganisms.

*Chlorination* refers to the use of chlorine, in particular sodium hypochlorite, as a disinfectant.

## Disinfection and control methods

Disinfection is carried out whilst the system is not in use, or 'off-line'.

Control methods are used to kill bacteria and prevent their growth while the system is in use, or 'on-line'.

## Chemical disinfection - off line

The use of oxidising disinfectants is still the most commonly used method of disinfecting both new and existing domestic hot and cold water systems and is highly effective when carried out correctly. The most common oxidising disinfectant used is sodium hypochlorite (often referred to as 'chlorination') but stabilised chlorine dioxide is rapidly gaining in popularity as an alternative without the problems associated with hypochlorite's use. Other oxidising disinfectants like bromine and ozone, and non-oxidising disinfectants are commonly used for disinfecting industrial process and cooling water systems. Water containing disinfectant at concentrations greater than that approved for drinking water is classed as fluid category 3 under the Water Regulations so suitable backflow prevention is required. It is also a hazardous waste so suitable disposal procedures for used disinfectant solution must be followed and if necessary consent to discharge must be obtained from the Environment Agency.

## Thermal disinfection - off line

This method, often referred to as pasteurisation, involves raising the water temperature in the calorifier and circulating through the entire system for at least an hour, running each tap and outlet for 5 minutes, with a temperature between 60-70°C being maintained at all times in all parts of the system. Good insulation is vital, as It may be difficult to maintain a high temperature in all parts of the system for the time required. Scalding may be a significant risk, due to the high temperatures and risk control methods need to be in place. Thermal disinfection does not address the need to disinfect the cold-water storage and feed system to the calorifiers.

## Chemical dosing - on line

The most commonly used methods are the continuous dosing of chlorine or chlorine dioxide, or the release of copper and silver ions from electrodes. All can be equally effective if delivered and managed correctly and if the water conditions required for them to operate effectively are maintained. Temperature, hardness/alkalinity, pH, dissolved solids – these may all have an effect on the efficacy of some of these systems. It is therefore essential that the system is properly assessed, designed and maintained as part of an overall risk control strategy. Chemicals continuously dosed to domestic water systems will require approval for use in drinking water.

## Temperature control - on line

This requires the storage of hot water at 60°C and distribution so that a temperature of at least 50°C is attainable at all outlets within 30-60 seconds of running. Cold water storage and distribution is recommended to be at 20°C or below. For hot water systems these temperatures present a risk from scalding. Where a significant scalding risk has been identified the use of thermostatic mixing valves at the point of use to appliances should be considered.

The NHS Estates Health Guidance note on safe hot water temperatures, recommends maximum outlet temperatures for different appliances.

## Other methods

Other disinfection methods for domestic systems are available, for example ultra-violet light (UV) or ozone, but these are considered to be non-dispersive, i.e. their effect is close to the point of application, not to the system as a whole and as a consequence are not always as effective.

### Please Note

Schedule 2 paragraph 13 of the Water Supply (Water Fittings) Regulations 1999 requires that 'Every water system shall be tested, flushed and where necessary disinfected before it is first used'.

However, there are a number of factors to be considered before attempting the disinfection of any water system and approved training is required before undertaking either risk assessment or the disinfection of water systems within buildings. It is also essential to remember that disinfection and control methods are not a substitute for maintaining a high degree of water system cleanliness and carrying out good plumbing and engineering practices.

# Water quality

The quality of water is defined by chemical and bacterial analysis and where the end usage is directly or indirectly for human consumption. It should comply with recognised standards to ensure freedom from harmful bacteria, acute and long term toxic substances and in addition, the water should be clear, odourless, tasteless and wholesome.

The *International Standards for Drinking Water* produced by the World Health Organisation define the toxic limits for substances frequently found in water supplies.

Waters that satisfy the quality standards for human consumption are not always suitable for certain medical, industrial and commercial uses. They may contain levels of trace elements, high total dissolved solids contents, non-pathogenic bacteria, gases and suspended matter which necessitate some form of treatment before water can be used in activities such as food and pharmaceutical preparation, brewing, research, medicine and in many areas where heat generation and transfer take place.

Pure water exists of an equilibrium between the acid species, the hydrogen ion ($H^+$) and the hydroxyl ion (OH). In neutral water the acid concentration equals the hydroxyl concentration, and at room temperature they are both present at $10^{-7}$ gram equivalents (or moles) per litre. The purest water contains no ions at all.

Water that has $10^{-7}$ gram equivalents per litre of hydrogen ions is said to have a pH of 7.

pH is a numerical indication of the intensity of acidity or alkalinity of a solution. It is defined as $- \log 10$ ($H^+$), where ($H^+$) is the hydrogen ion concentration. The scale is logarithmic and runs from 0-14. Low numbers are acidic and high numbers are alkaline. A neutral solution exhibits pH of 7. The logarithmic nature of pH can be confusing, e.g. as the acid concentration increases, the pH value decreases. A solution of pH5 is 10 times more acidic than one of pH6 and 100 times more acidic than one of pH7.

## Deionised water

Where water is required to a higher biological and chemical purity than that supplied by the local water company, single or mixed bed deionisers are capable of producing pure and ultra pure water approaching theoretical $H_2O$. Purity

is usually measured by a conductivity monitor that measures the conductivity in microsiemens. Totally deionised water has zero conductivity (as there are no ions present to carry current).

The operation of deionisation is based on using twin bed or mixed bed columns of positive and negative charge ionised resins so that the incoming water disassociates into positively charged ions such as magnesium and calcium which exchange with the hydrogen ions of the acidic resins.

Likewise the negative ions of sulphate and bicarbonates are exchanged with the hydroxyl ions of the alkaline resins, the resultant hydrogen and hydroxyl ions combining to form theoretical $H_2O$. The exhausted resins are periodically replaced or regenerated with acid and alkaline regenerates.

As the name of the process implies, only ionisable dissolved solids and gases can be removed and the treated water is not necessarily pure or sterile. Centralised recirculating systems, local units, and both in combination where terminal polishing is required, can produce water up to the megohms at 25°C which is close to theoretical maximum.

Figure 18 shows a two bed recirculation system suitable for providing 3m$^3$/hr of deionised water up to 1 microsiemen centimetre quality.

## Softened water

Water softening in large quantities for commercial use and distribution is usually carried out using one or more of the lime or lime/soda processes. For domestic application however, the base exchange system of softening is more commonly used and only this method is described. Base exchange softening operates on a similar principle to the ion exchange described in the ionised water and functions by the process of exchanging sodium salts for those of calcium.

The action of softening can be expressed chemically as follows:

| SODIUM | CALCIUM | | CALCIUM | SODIUM |
|--------|---------|--|---------|--------|
| + | exchanges to | | + |
| ZEOLITE | CARBONATE | | ZEOLITE | CARBONATE |

And that of re-generation:

| CALCIUM | SODIUM | | SODIUM | CALCIUM |
|---------|--------|--|--------|---------|
| + | exchanges to | | + |
| ZEOLITE | CHLORIDE | | ZEOLITE | CHLORIDE |

Because the base exchange system produces water of zero hardness, it is often only necessary to soften part of the total water requirement and blend the raw and softened water together.

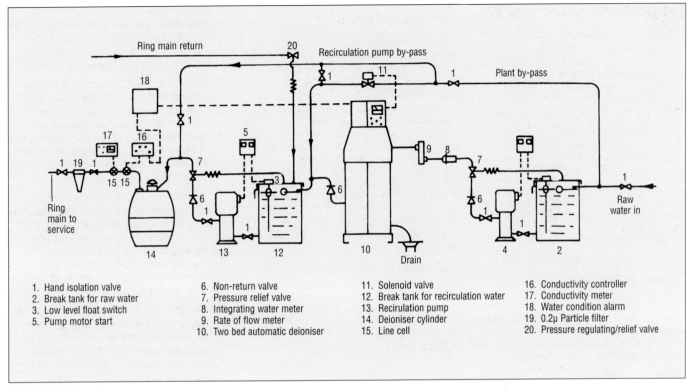

*Figure 18 Recirculation deionisation system*

1. Hand isolation valve
2. Break tank for raw water
3. Low level float switch
5. Pump motor start

6. Non-return valve
7. Pressure relief valve
8. Integrating water meter
9. Rate of flow meter
10. Two bed automatic deioniser

11. Solenoid valve
12. Break tank for recirculation water
13. Recirulation pump
14. Deioniser cylinder
15. Line cell

16. Conductivity controller
17. Conductivity meter
18. Water condition alarm
19. 0.2µ Particle filter
20. Pressure regulating/relief valve

## Operation of a base exchange water softener

The raw/hard water supply is connected into the top of the softener tank and flows downwards under pressure through the bed of softening material (zeolite) where the hardness is removed by the process of 'ion exchange'. At the same time, sediment in the water is filtered out and retained by the mineral bed. Clear soft water leaves the bottom of the tank into the water distribution system.

The softening mineral eventually becomes saturated with hardness and no longer softens the water. Regeneration of the softening material is then necessary and the three stage process is as follows:

### Backwash

Reverse the water flow through the mineral bed to remove accumulated sediment and wash to drain. A backwash controller is necessary to limit the water flow and thus prevent washing out the mineral bed.

### Brine rinse

Ordinary salt (sodium chlorine) has the ability to fully restore the softening capacity of the mineral. A measured amount of salt brine is drawn from the brine tank through the brine injector and rinsed slowly down through the mineral bed to remove the hardness, which is rinsed to drain.

### Flushing

The water flow is again reversed to re-pack the mineral bed and any trace of sediment not removed by the backwash is flushed to drain. The softener can now be returned to normal service.

# Corrosion

Corrosion is one of the major causes of premature failures in plumbing services. Not only is it responsible for increased maintenance cost but losses in efficiency, particularly in heating systems, can increase running costs.

Corrosion may be defined as the reaction of a metal with its environment resulting in damage that impairs the function of a component or system. Whilst the mechanism's of corrosion are common to different plumbing applications, methods of control and/or prevention have to be tailored to suit that particular environment.

## Causes of corrosion – basic theory

Before discussing the causes of corrosion in detail it is useful to define and clarify in simple terms some of the nomenclature used in the text.

A salt (not to be confused with common salt, NaCl) is formed by the replacement of acidic hydrogen in an acid by a metal or basic group.

$$2Na + H_2SO_4 \rightarrow Na_2SO_4 + H_2l$$

metal    acid       a salt   hydrogen

When most salts are dissolved in water they form ions which are atoms or groups of atoms carrying positive or negative charges. The resulting solution is called an electrolyte because of its ability to conduct an electrical current.

$$Na_2SO_4 \rightleftharpoons 2Na^+ + SO_4$$
a salt    positive ion  negative ion

Some salts are much more soluble than others and their solubility in water often depends to a large extent on solution temperature.

In practical terms, pH is used to measure the acidity or alkalinity of a solution. Values range from 0-14, those less than 7 being acid and those greater are alkaline.

Corrosion is electrochemical in nature and can occur by oxidation (dry corrosion) or wet corrosion. Most corrosion problems in plumbing applications are caused by wet corrosion which requires the presence of an electrolyte to allow the passage of an electric current and some agency to maintain a difference in potential. Many corrosion processes also require the presence of oxygen. Natural and supply waters contain dissolved salts that make them into electrolytes and therefore capable of carrying an electric current. The factors which may cause and will affect the rate of corrosion are as follows:

## Solution potential

If a metal is placed in an electrolyte, corrosion in the form of a chemical reaction may occur accompanied by the passage of an electric current. That part of a metal system where current, i.e. positive charges in the form of metal ions, leaves and enters the solution is called the anode while the resulting electrons (negative charges) migrate to an area of higher potential, the cathode, where they react with other ions or oxygen.

In the corrosion process it is always the anode that is dissolved. The difference in potential between the anode and the cathode at equilibrium is termed the solution potential. This potential has different values for different metals and conditions, e.g. temperature, electrolyte concentration and the surface or metallurgical condition of the metal, has a profound effect on corrosion.

## Temperature

In general, rates of chemical reaction and therefore corrosion, increase with a rise in temperature. However, some corrosion reactions, for example the corrosion of steel in aerated solution, may be controlled by the solubility and diffusion rate of dissolved gases that vary appreciably with temperature.

As the rate of corrosion of steel is partly determined by the availability of oxygen at the surface, it is found that this rate has a maximum in the range 75-85°C, which is approximately 4 times that at ambient temperatures.

With other metals, for example zinc, the variation of corrosion rate with temperature is related to the nature of the corrosion product. At temperatures that produce a continuous/adherent corrosion product, the corrosion rate is low. However, when a granular, non-adherent product is formed, the corrosion rate increases considerably.

Differences in surface temperature on the same metal component can create areas differing in potential, resulting in increased corrosion.

## Differential aeration

If part of a metal surface is shielded from air, the natural oxide film can break down. Where the oxygen availability is low, these areas become anodic to those areas to which there is greater supply. This results in localised corrosion, which can occur particularly in crevices and also underneath surface deposits, for example mill scale. This type of corrosion is called differential aeration.

## Dissolved salts

The influence on corrosion of salts dissolved in natural or supply waters is determined both by their concentration and more importantly, by the type of ion produced in solution. In general, a high dissolved solids content would be expected to exacerbate corrosion, due to the increase in conductivity, if conditions favour it. Some ions, however, for example carbonates, can be protective due to their scale forming ability on metal surfaces. Other ions, in particular chloride and sulphate, are aggressive as they interfere with the development of protective films and also allow passive films to be broken down more readily. Both ions occur naturally in source waters, with additional sources of chloride being fluxes, washing up liquids (sometimes misguidedly used to quieten noisy boilers), and malfunctioning water softeners. Sulphate ions also support the growth of anaerobic bacteria.

Although in certain conditions the overall rate of corrosion may not be increased, the attack may be more localised and therefore corrosion pits tend to be deeper. In the absence of aggressive ions, the corrosion rate of steel at different oxygen concentrations reaches a maximum, however, where appreciable levels of chlorides are present (>200mg/litre), the corrosion rate continues to increase with increasing oxygen availability.

Two indices have been developed to predict whether a carbonate scale will be deposited from a supply water of given composition. These are called the Langelier and Ryznar indices respectively; a positive Langelier index or a Ryznar index of less than 6 indicating that the water is scale forming.

Since the deposition of a carbonate scale can stifle corrosion, it often follows that these waters are less corrosive than those that tend to dissolve calcium carbonate. Their behaviour however, depends greatly on the form in which the scale is laid down, a discontinuous layer providing relatively little protective value.

When natural water runs over a metal surface, it can take up traces of that metal, which are later deposited on another metal. This may form a bimetallic couple and if the deposited metal is cathodic to the substrate, rapid corrosion will ensue. Typical examples are copper pipework upstream from galvanized cisterns and run-off from copper roofs into aluminium gutters. The high acidity of rainfall in certain areas, due to the dissolved sulphur and nitrogen oxide pollutants has generally resulted in reduced service life of exposed metal surfaces.

## Surface effects

Certain surface films are cathodic to steel and under wet conditions where there are breaks in the film, the underlying steel surface becomes the anode and will corrode preferentially.

## Ion concentration

As discussed above, the solution potential is affected by the concentration of ions in the electrolyte. The higher the concentration, the more cathodic the metal becomes. If therefore, a metal surface is in contact with an electrolyte that varies in concentration, those areas of metal in contact with dilute solution will become anodic to those areas in contact with the more concentrated solution and corrosion will be accelerated.

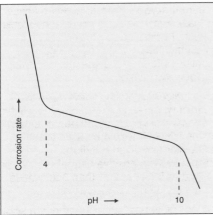

**Graph 5** *The effect of pH on mild steel corrosion rate in an open recirculating cooling system*

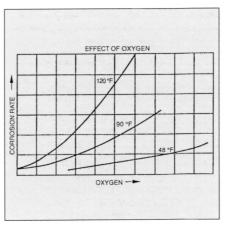

**Graph 6** *Effect of oxygen concentration on corrosion at different temperatures*

**Table 30** *Galvanic series of metals and alloys in natural waters*

| Metal | Normal electrode potential (vs standard hydrogen electrode, mV) 'Noble' or cathodic, ie protected end |
|---|---|
| Graphite (carbon) | +200 |
| Titanium | |
| Silver | |
| Nickel | |
| Monel | |
| Austenitic stainless steel (types 304/316) | |
| Copper | |
| Ferritic stainless steel (type 416) | |
| 67/33 Nickel copper | |
| Martensitic stainless steel (type 431) | |
| Aluminium bronze | |
| 70/30 Brass | 0 |
| Gunmetals, phosphor bronzes and tin bronzes | |
| 60/40 brass | |
| Chromium | −100 |
| Tin | −200 |
| Tin-lead solder | |
| Lead | −300 |
| Steel | −400 |
| Cast iron | |
| Cadmium | −500 |
| Aluminium and aluminium alloys | −700 |
| Galvanised iron | −800 |
| Zinc | |
| Magnesium and magnesium | −1300 |
| 'Base' or anodic, ie corroded end | |

## pH

Waters with a pH below 7 will dissolve most metals to an appreciable extent. This will not necessarily cause serious deterioration of the metal structure concerned, but it can produce undesirable amounts of dissolved metal in the water.

Graph 5 shows the effect of pH on the corrosion of iron. Within the acid range (pH<4), the iron oxide film is continually dissolved. The increased potential for calcium carbonate deposition with higher pH causes the corrosion rate to decrease slightly from 4-10. Above pH 10, iron becomes increasingly passive.

## Dissolved gases

The significant gases are oxygen and carbon dioxide. Oxygen is the main driving force for corrosion of steel in water. The increase in corrosion with temperature for a given oxygen concentration is due to more rapid oxygen diffusion occurring at higher temperatures.

Carbon dioxide is present in some supply waters, particularly those derived from deep wells and has the effect of lowering the pH. This will cause any protective scales to dissolve.

It must be borne in mind that plastic materials, unlike metals, are permeable to gases. This can exacerbate oxidative corrosion of iron/steel components in closed systems where plastic pipework is used for distribution or under floor heating.

## Contact with dissimilar materials

### Metals

If different metals are immersed in an electrolyte, after a period of time each will attain a characteristic potential. In this way it is possible to arrange metals in what is termed a galvanic series, however the precise order may differ slightly depending on the particular metal/alloy composition and the nature of the electrolyte.

Table 30 gives the galvanic series for metals and alloys when in contact with natural waters.

Corrosion occurring when two differing metals/alloys are in electrical contact is termed bimetallic corrosion. There are three other factors that can influence corrosion at a bimetallic junction.

The first is the relative areas of the two metals in contact. If the area of the cathodic metal is large compared with that of the anodic (corroding) metal, corrosion would be concentrated resulting in rapid attack. Conversely with a large anode connected to a small area of cathodic metal, although some corrosion will be localised adjacent to the contact area, most corrosion will be distributed over the remaining area and the relative thickness loss will be less.

The second is the conductivity of the electrolyte. In an electrolyte of low conductivity, attack will be confined adjacent to the joint area and may be relatively intense. Where the electrolyte conductivity is high, the attack will spread out more and the level of general corrosion will be greater.

The third factor concerns electrical contact between the dissimilar metals. Some metals, in particular aluminium and stainless steel, form coherent oxide films in air which are non-conductive. If they prevent a current flow between the metals then bimetallic corrosion will be prevented. In the absence of dissolved oxygen, bimetallic contact will not cause iron and steel surfaces to corrode.

### Other materials

Many non-metallic materials found in or around buildings can be responsible for corrosive attack on metals. Some woods are acidic and under damp conditions can cause attack on steel, cadmium, zinc and lead. If the wood has been treated with a copper/chrome arsenate preservative, corrosion can be accelerated and in particular aluminium alloys and zinc are attacked.

Fresh concrete is very alkaline (pH12.6-13.5) and while this is responsible for protecting steel reinforcement against corrosion, other metals, for example zinc, aluminium and lead will be attacked. Some concrete also contains chlorides, which will increase the risk of corrosion.

Bleach and some soldering fluxes contain high level of chloride ions, which will cause rapid attack on many metals including copper and stainless steel. Furthermore, some plastics on heating or degradation also give off acids and/or chlorides, which in the presence of moisture will cause corrosive attack.

Soils are complex in nature and therefore are extremely variable in corrosive activity. The most widespread form of corrosion is due to sulphate reducing bacteria. Other problems are caused by acidic conditions due to natural constituents or contamination by industrial waste, for example ashes and clinker.

Although not strictly corrosion, it is worth mentioning that other industrial wastes, for example, tar, oils, can cause failures in buried plastic pipework due to environmental stress cracking. They may also attack protection on metal pipework, thus exposing the underlying surfaces to corrosive attack.

## Bacteria

In the absence of oxygen, corrosion may continue by the cathodic reduction of sulphate, which is present in most soils and natural waters. This is facilitated by anaerobic bacteria (called sulphate-reducing bacteria, disulpho-vibrio disulphoricans) that are able to use cathodic hydrogen in their living process and convert sulphate to sulphide. This type of corrosion is responsible for the smell of 'bad eggs' (hydrogen sulphide) sometimes observed when venting radiators.

## Flow, erosion, impingement and cavitation

Corrosion can be aggravated by the nature of water flow across a metal surface. The overall rate will be controlled both by the rate of reaction and how quickly reactants and products can approach and leave the metal surface. These are termed chemical and diffusion control respectively. Flow may be stagnant, laminar or turbulent which will affect the rates of diffusion.

Where the flow is turbulent, the impingement of gas, liquid or solids or a combination of any three can cause mechanical damage, which removes or prevents formation of a protective film. If the metal or alloy is corrodible in that environment, localised attack of the surface will occur.

Cavitation is a particular type of attack that occurs when a metal surface is exposed to a high velocity, low-pressure liquid.

In areas where the pressure is sufficiently low, pockets of vapour form, which may suddenly collapse when they pass to an area of higher pressure. The shock generated is sufficient to cause

mechanical damage to the metal surface at that point and exacerbate corrosive attack. This mechanism is responsible for water hammer.

## Stray current corrosion

Stray earth currents, in particular DC, can produce cathodic and anodic areas where they enter and leave buried pipelines or other metallic structures causing severe corrosion.

## Organic matter

Organic matter, derived from their natural or industrial sources, may lower the pH and increase corrosion rates as well as preventing scale deposition. Bacteria are also often present in organic matter and these may be responsible for fouling and increased corrosive attack under both aerobic and anaerobic conditions.

It can be seen from the forgoing that corrosion phenomena are very complex in nature and are affected by many factors. Most of these factors can have a profound effect on corrosion rates and highlight the difficulties in predicting corrosion behaviour and time to first maintenance or failure. However, many techniques are now available for identifying, monitoring and controlling corrosion to acceptable limits.

# Effects of corrosive environments

Corrosion can manifest itself in numerous ways, depending on the metal or alloy and particular environment in which it is in contact. It is convenient to look back at the various metals likely to be encountered in plumbing applications and the environments that can be detrimental to their service life.

Some of these metals are also used as protective coatings and their performance together with that of the substrate is also considered.

## Aluminium and aluminium alloys

Although aluminium is a very reactive metal, it has a high resistance to corrosion because of the tenacious, inert oxide film that forms on the surface. Pure aluminium is generally stable in the pH range 4.5-8.7 but outside this range, attack can be rapid. Aluminium alloys, particularly those containing copper in

significant quantities (Duralumin), are less resistant to corrosion.

The most commonly encountered form of aluminium corrosion is pitting but the rate of propagation is very dependent on the alloy composition and nature of the solution with which it is in contact. While many neutral or weakly alkaline solutions allow self-passivation, others particularly those containing chlorides or copper ions, cause rapid propagation of corrosion pits in some alloys.

Aluminium alloys may also suffer a preferential attack at the boundaries between the grain structure that is termed intercrystalline corrosion.

Aluminium and its alloys have very good resistance to atmospheric corrosion providing the surfaces are regularly washed by rain etc. Where deposits of, for example acidic sulphates are allowed to build up on sheltered surfaces, moisture from condensation is sufficient to give an increased rate of attack.

In all environments, aluminium is very sensitive to bimetallic corrosion. Contacts with copper and copper alloys, and to a lesser extent, iron and iron alloys, should be avoided.

## Cadmium

The main application of cadmium is as a protective coating on steel. It is particularly useful as a plated finish on high strength steels where zinc finishes can heighten the risk of cracking due to hydrogen embrittlement. Its corrosion behaviour is similar to zinc and although it is less protective to steel, unlike zinc, it is stable in alkali solution.

## Cast iron

Cast irons are ferrous alloys containing generally 2-4% carbon and frequently have high silicon contents. A wide variety of compositions are available and additions of silicon, chromium and nickel can be used to improve corrosion resistance. Typical applications include boiler sections, pump housings and pipe fittings (malleable iron). Although corrosion rates are similar to those of steel, above ground corrosion is not normally a problem due to the thick sections used for cast iron components.

When in contact with some natural waters, particularly those that are slightly acidic or contain chlorides (salt), cast iron may suffer a form of attack called graphitisation. The iron corrodes leaving weak, porous structure composed of graphite and iron oxides. This can result in catastrophic failures in underground pipes where soil or ground movement causes large sections where graphitisation has occurred to crust without warning.

Although not directly associated with corrosion, it is worthwhile mentioning a common cause of premature failure in gas-fired sectional boilers. If hard-water scale is allowed to build up inside the cast iron sections, and flame impingement occurs on the outside, overheating can cause a change in the cast iron structure to a weaker 'undercooled' form. Subsequent thermal stress can result in fracture and consequent leakage from the boiler.

# Copper and copper alloys

Copper and its alloys comprise a versatile range of materials, which are used in a wide variety of plumbing applications.

Copper is used extensively for pipework and heat exchanges due to its excellent ductility and thermal conductivity. A wide range of copper alloys are available and in addition to the aforementioned applications, they are used for valve and pump components, pipe fittings, etc.

Most problems occur when these materials are in contact with water or steam containing dissolved oxygen or carbon dioxide and/or acids or chlorides, although corrosion can also result from contact with aggressive atmosphere e.g. flue gases or certain bacteria.

These environments cause a breakdown in the protective oxide film formed on the surface by contact with oxygen and water, thus allowing corrosion to proceed. Not only will this eventually result in failure of the component, but also dissolved copper can cause accelerated corrosion if it is deposited on other metals that are more anodic.

# Copper

Copper is used extensively in the form of tube for pipework and the manufacture of hot water cylinders. When in contact with natural waters corrosion can occur by a variety of mechanisms.

A major factor in the corrosion of copper is dissolved oxygen. The higher the temperature of the water the less dissolved oxygen it can contain, consequently cold water is more corrosive to copper than hot water. Typically when copper is first exposed to a water, a significant increase in the copper concentration will occur, however, within a short period of time the corrosion rate will fall to an acceptable level due to the formation of protective films or scales on a metal surface.

Waters given rise to the highest rates of

corrosion are those drawn from wells and springs (usually privately owned) which are often soft and contain dissolved carbon dioxide. Such waters are called cuprosolvent. Here the role of dissolved oxygen is less significant and corrosion is most marked when the water has been heated.

Pitting corrosion of copper is divided into three categories:

## Type 1

Type 1 pitting is characterised by broad/shallow pits. Temperature is a significant factor with corrosion more likely to occur in cold and lukewarm water than in hot water. It is most usually associated with borehole waters or waters that have been treated by flocculation. Often the total hardness of the water is greater than 100mg/l and is usually greater than 150mg/l but corrosion can occur in soft waters. It is thought that in surface derived waters, the presence of extremely low levels of organics such as polyphenols acts to inhibit this form of attack. Type 1 pitting needs initiation and used to be caused by carbon film in copper tube remaining after the drawing process. The modern use of abrasive cleaning of the tube minimises the problem.

## Type 2

Type 2 pitting is characterised by narrow/deep pits. It occurs in soft waters at temperatures above 60°C. The bicarbonate/sulphate ratio is often less than 1 with the pH less that 7.6. In the United Kingdom it is thought that the presence of manganese is contributory.

## Type 3

Type 3 pitting is characterised by pepper pot holes under a crust. This form of corrosion remains a major area of research. It is virtually unknown in England but is prevalent in Scotland where it is associated with moorland waters. The cause is uncertain however; it appears that the standard of tubing is not important. Research is concentrating on finding methods of analysis for the detection of microscopic quantities of organic acids, which it is thought, might be contributory.

Copper cylinders can be prone to pitting attack, particularly in the base sections where near stagnant conditions exists in crevices or underneath debris. In an attempt to control the problem, the incorporation of aluminium anodes, which corrode preferentially whilst a uniformly thick protective film builds up on the surface of the copper, was included in a British Standard and soon became commonplace. In most cases it was necessary only for the anode to

remain intact for approximately 3 months to fulfil its purpose.

Problems, which have been generally confined to cylinders not fully complying with BS1566 (for indirect) or BS699 (for directs), were found to arise in two ways from one cause. Poor insulation of the connection point resulted in early detachment of the anode, whereupon it fell to the base of the cylinder, causing a massive build up of oxide sludge. Normally such oxide debris would form around the extremities of the anode and be carried away by the water flowing through the vessel, however, where sludge built up, under-deposit corrosion of the base of the cylinder was initiated due to differential oxygenation. Rapid failure could occur. If failure didn't occur in this way, the absence of the anode from its proper position allowed corrosion by the mechanisms it was originally installed to prevent.

Rosette corrosion is another form of copper corrosion. The phenomenon is so named because the corroded copper has the characteristic appearance of petal shapes etched on to its surface. There are no reported instances of copper other than that associated with cylinders being affected. Research into the causes continues, but factors known to contribute to its occurrence include nitrate and the presence of an aluminium anode. There is also evidence that rosette corrosion is favoured when a copper vessel fitted with an aluminium anode has been allowed to stand full of water for an extended period.

In some parts of the country, the concentration of nitrate has risen significantly over the last few years, probably due to the permeation of nitrate based fertilisers down to the aquifers providing all or part of the mains supply water. However, it remains unproved that this is the main factor responsible for the apparent increase in rosette corrosion.

Changes to the design of cylinders to inhibit the formation of stable areas of colder water (less than 30°C) will prevent many early failures, whether they are due to Type 1 pitting, or by elimination of the aluminium anode, rosette corrosion. Standards include a test to ensure that water in the base of the cylinder is heated appropriately.

Specifiers and installers can also take sensible steps to help themselves, by installing only units correctly sized for the job, so eliminating large volumes of unused water from residing in the vessel. In regions of the country where pitting failure is known to be a problem, end users should be encouraged to periodically drain their cylinder completely. This might well be applied to cylinders filled and left in non-use situations, e.g., new unoccupied properties.

Compared with its alloys, copper generally has a lower resistance to impingement attack in waters containing oxygen and/or carbon dioxide. Where dissolved gases are absent, for example in closed heating systems, this type of attack is not a problem. Table 31 gives recommended maximum water velocities for copper pipework carrying fresh aerated water of pH not less than 7.

**Table 31** *Maximum recommended water velocities for copper tube at different temperatures (metres/second)*

| Temperature °C | 10 | 50 | 70 | 90 |
|---|---|---|---|---|
| Pipes that can be replaced | 4.0 | 3.0 | 2.5 | 2.0 |
| Pipes that cannot be replaced | 2.0 | 1.5 | 1.3 | 1.0 |
| For short connections which are used intermittently, eg taps | 16.0 | 12.0 | 10.0 | 8.0 |

Impingement attack has a distinctive appearance, the pits formed having a water swept appearance, sometimes in the shape of horseshoes and being free from corrosion products. In closed heating systems where the oxygen content is low, this type of attack does occur.

Copper can fail by stress corrosion cracking (the combination of constant stress together with a specific corrodent, (see brasses) and corrosion fatigue results from the conjoint action of fluctuating stresses, which may be caused by expansion and contraction in restrained pipework, vibration of equipment, poorly supported tubes, or pressure variations and a corrosive environment.

Occasionally, corrosion can result in copper calorifiers where large temperature differences exist. This may be between a coil carrying steam, high temperature water under pressure or immersion heater sheath and the calorifier shell. The large differences in temperature are sufficient to generate a potential difference and cause preferential attack on the hotter surface. This may be prevented by electrically insulating the shell and heater.

## Brasses

The common brasses consist of a range of copper alloys containing from 10-50% zinc and other minor alloying elements. Alloys containing up to 39% zinc from a single-phase alloy with copper is termed

α brass and in the range 47-50% zinc is another single-phase alloy termed β brass. Alloys containing 39-47% zinc content, both phases are termed α + β or duplex brasses. The latter alloys are more suitable for hot pressing or die-casting small components.

An alloy has been developed having a controlled composition so that it is suitable for processing as a duplex brass but heat treated to attain the dezincification resistance of inhibited brass (see below). This material is termed DZR (dezincification resistant) brass and fittings are marked by the Water Research Centre recognised symbol CR. It should be noted that brazing alloys containing zinc can suffer from similar forms or attack to brasses.

Brasses can suffer a form of selective corrosion called dezincification. Zinc is preferentially removed form the alloy leaving a porous mass of copper having little strength. Where the zinc corrosion products are not washed away, they may form bulky hollow shells which readily block waterways. This is termed 'meringue' dezincification. In the single-phase brasses the whole of the metal is corroded either uniformly over the surface or more commonly on the form of a 'plug'. With duplex brasses the phase which contains a higher proportion of zinc is preferentially attacked.

In general the risk and/or rate of dezincification is increased by higher proportions of zinc in the alloy, high temperature, high chloride content of the water, low pH, low temporary hardness, low water speed and the presence of surface deposits or crevices.

Where leakage or breakage of a fitting has occurred, dezincification may be suspected if the defective areas have a dull, coppery appearance.

Brasses may be inhibited against dezincificaiton by small additions of arsenic. Duplex brasses cannot be inhibited in this way and where there is a risk of dezincification, either DZR brass or gunmetal must be used.

Where brasses have a high degree of internal stress, which may be induced during manufacture, in particular those containing ammonia or ammonium compounds (in-organic or organic) can cause failure by a mechanism called stress corrosion cracking (season cracking). The corrosive environment is normally external and may result from an ammonical compounds used as light weight concrete foaming agents, in rubber lattices used as cement additives or for bonding floor tiles, and from fertilisers either as residues in aggregate or airborne pollution.

In common with copper, brasses can

suffer attack by impingement or cavitation. This may cause particular problems down stream from valves that when properly open, cause a pressure drop sufficient to create air bubbles from dissolved gasses and initiate attack. It is important therefore that valves are carefully positioned in plant so that possible damage from this type of attack is minimised.

## Bronzes (gunmetals, phosphor bronzes and tin bronzes)

Technically the term 'bronze' should refer to copper-tin alloys, but in practice a variety of copper alloys are termed bronzes, irrespective of whether they contain tin.

This wide variation in composition makes corrosion behaviour of a component difficult to predict unless the specific composition is known.

In general, copper-tin alloys have a good resistance to corrosion when in contact with both water (natural and sea) and steam and rarely suffer from the selective attack (dezincification) that brasses do.

## Aluminium bronze

These materials generally have a high resistance to corrosion, impingement attack and cavitation erosion. They are however, surprisingly prone to pitting corrosion in natural waters and can suffer selective corrosion analogous to dezincification.

## Cupro nickel alloys

Alloys containing copper and nickel have excellent resistance to corrosion and many environments, including those containing chlorides. They are more stable than brasses under flow conditions, less susceptible to stress corrosion and are used in heat exchanger applications.

## Lead

Lead and lead alloys have a good corrosion resistance due to the formation of insoluble adherent carbonate or sulphate corrosion products. These films are protected and may be formed over a wide range of pH values (3-11) in most natural and treated waters. However, in soft waters with a low carbon dioxide content, a less protective oxide film is formed which allows corrosion to proceed slowly.

Lead is generally resistant to

atmospheric corrosion but may be attacked by organic acids or free alkali. Run off from roofs bearing organic growths, acetic acid derived from wood and fresh cement, can all cause corrosive attack.

In its pure form, lead has poor mechanical properties and without small alloying additions, is susceptible to creep and fatigue failures induced by thermal movement.

# Magnesium

The only plumbing application in which magnesium is likely to be met is that of cathodic protection. The greater negative potential in relation to steel and compared to zinc or aluminium makes magnesium alloys efficient for protecting the interior of steel (either unprotected, painted or galvanised) water cisterns or the exterior of buried steel structures and pipelines.

# Soft solders (tin alloys)

Soft solders (i.e. tin alloyed with lead, antimony, silver and/or copper) are anodic to copper and therefore corrosion of solder used in capillary joints could be expected. However, due to the nature of the protective film formed, corrosion often occurs in waters of high conductivity, for example those containing chlorides. Most problems with capillary joints may be attributed to the use of soldering fluxes which leave aggressive residues at, or adjacent to the joint area.

# Stainless steels

The term 'stainless steel' covers a variety of alloys which may be simply and conveniently divided into the following three categories:

### Martensitic stainless steels

These alloys generally contain 12-14% chromium and from 0.1-2 % carbon, which confers hardenability and controls the mechanical properties. They are used for applications requiring high strength and wear resistance combined with considerable corrosion resistance.

### Ferritic stainless steels

Alloys containing 16-18% chromium and having a low carbon content are termed ferritic stainless steels. They are not hardenable and are used for flue and sink components.

### Austenitic stainless steels

Often termed 18/8 stainless steels, the common austenitic alloys contain 15-22% chromium, 6-11% nickel and 0.05-0.15% carbon and have the highest resistance to corrosion (grades 302, 304). The addition of molybdenum (2-4%) confers even greater corrosion resistance (grade 316). They are non-magnetic and not hardenable unless heavily cold worked.

The main applications in plumbing services are for pipework, boiler flues, sinks and urinals.

Stainless steels owe their high corrosion resistance to the presence of self-healing oxide films on the metal surface. However, certain environments may cause these films to break down and allow corrosion rates comparable to those of mild steel. The most common environments to cause attack are those containing chlorides and in crevices or underneath surface debris where the absence of oxygen prevents repair of the protective oxide film.

Corrosion of stainless steels is often localised. The presence of chlorides can cause rapid pitting, particularly at grain boundaries and can initiate intergranular attack and stress corrosion cracking.

# Steels (low alloy)

Low alloy steels, due to their ease of fabrication and the range of mechanical properties attainable by alloying additions, are used in a wide variety of plumbing applications. When compared with other metals in most environments, they are found to have a much lower corrosion resistance. Under certain conditions, small additions of copper, chromium and nickel improve corrosion resistance but the overall effect is often small and variable.

Steel can exhibit two entirely different types of corrosion behaviour depending on the nature of the environment with which it is in contact. In the passive state, for example when in contact with neutral or alkaline natural water free from bacteria and oxygen, the corrosion rate is negligible. However, in the active state widely differing rates of corrosion, either general or localised, can occur depending on the many factors that have been discussed earlier.

The most common cause of corrosion is exposure to water containing dissolved oxygen. The rate of attack is greatest when the water is soft and/or acidic and the corrosion products often form bulky mounds in the surface called tubercles. These overlie areas where localised attack is occurring and can seriously reduce the carrying capacity of pipes. In severe cases, iron oxides can cause contamination leading to complaints of 'red water'. In hard, neutral or slightly alkaline waters, calcium carbonate (lime scale) can deposit on steel surfaces and provide a protective coating.

Although carbon dioxide has no specific influence on the corrosion of steel, it will increase the corrosion rate by lowering the pH and also preventing the formation of protective calcium carbonate films.

In the absence of oxygen, corrosion can occur in waters where sulphate-reducing bacteria are active.

The effect of dissolved gases and calcium carbonate in fresh waters has already been discussed. Water may also contain a variety of other dissolved material present in the supply or as a result of subsequent contamination. Ions such as chloride and sulphate can interfere with the development of protective films and lead too more localised attack whereas other ions such as calcium and bicarbonate have inhibitive properties. Small concentrations of organic matter can improve the protective qualities of carbonate films; however, organic acids resulting from decomposition of vegetation can increase corrosion rates by lowering the pH. Where the pH is reduced to values below 4 as a result of acid contamination, then the corrosion rate will progressively increase with a further decrease in pH. Other surface contaminants such as oil, mill scale or deposits may not increase the overall rate of corrosion, but can localise the attack causing pitting and pinhole corrosion.

Steel pipes are not normally suitable for use in wet soils unless protected against external corrosion.

# Zinc

Zinc is used almost exclusively in plumbing applications as a protective coating on steel. It may be applied by a variety of methods, which give widely varying coating weights and consequent degrees of protection. Both zinc and zinc alloys have good resistance to corrosion under conditions of exterior exposure and when in contact with most natural waters. This resistance is due to the protective layers of zinc oxide and hydroxide, or other basic salts depending on the nature of the environment, which are formed on the metal surface.

Under atmospheric conditions, the rate of corrosion depends on the degree of pollution. Heavily polluted industrial areas containing sulphur dioxide can increase the rate of corrosion by a factor of up to 10 as compared with rural areas. Where new zinc surfaces are stored under damp conditions, an unsightly white corrosion product may be formed. This is termed 'white rust' and can be prevented by oiling or a chromate treatment.

In natural waters, the rate of corrosion is governed by the presence of dissolved salts and gases. The presence of carbon dioxide together with calcium and magnesium salts will form a basic carbonate film that is protective to the base metal. Zinc is anodic to steel and will provide protection in the form of a coating even if small areas of substrate are exposed due to damage or in fabrication.

Temperature has a marked effect on the corrosion of zinc in natural waters. Due to a change in the nature of the protective films, the corrosion rate increases in the range of 55°C to 95°C, giving a maximum increase of some 100 times at 70°C. In some natural waters where zinc is used as a protective coating on steel, a reversal of potential occurs above 65°C. The zinc then becomes cathodic to steel, stimulating attack which results in localised (pitting) corrosion and subsequent perforation.

In general zinc and copper or copper alloys are not compatible when used in natural water systems. Where waters which are cupro-solvent (e.g. those containing free carbon dioxide) flow through copper pipework, traces of copper are dissolved which can subsequently deposit as metallic copper on zinc surfaces and stimulate attack due to bimetallic corrosion. Brass fittings on galvanised steel tanks and cisterns, however, rarely cause problems due to the relatively small area of brass to zinc.

Where unprotected galvanised pipes are used below ground the most severe attack occurs in soils which are poorly aerated and/or have high acid and soluble salt contents.

In conclusion, galvanised tanks/cisterns, calorifiers and pipes should not be used at temperatures above 65°C or downstream from copper pipework. Below ground, galvanised pipework is best protected using proprietary tape wrap systems.

## Plastic and rubber components

Although polymeric materials do not corrode in the accepted sense, they may degrade when exposed to certain environments. These environments include ultraviolet light, heat, organic compounds and inorganic and metallic ions, but the wide range of materials and compositions available make specific guidance impossible.

# Prevention of corrosion

Before deciding on the most suitable course of action required, if any, to control or prevent corrosion, it is often beneficial to assess the nature of the environment to which the metal will be exposed or the rate at which corrosion will occur. In certain cases, metal loss due to corrosion may be economically acceptable providing the required service life or life to first maintenance is exceeded. Furthermore, where corrosion has occurred, there are now several non-destructive techniques that may be used to quantify the extent of the attack and metal loss.

## Assessing the corrosivity of the local environment

### External surfaces

The external surfaces of pipework, etc. may suffer attack if buried in soil, located in ductwork subject to condensation or flooding, or where exposed to rain, spray, etc.

The aggressiveness of soils to buried metals, particularly ferrous, may be assessed using resistivity data to measure the likelihood of oxidative corrosion and redox-potentials to indicate the risk of bacterial corrosion. Soils may be considered aggressive if the resistivity is less than 200Ωcm at the specified depth or the mean redox-potential is less than +0.400 volts (standard hydrogen scale) when corrected to pH = 7 (+0.430 volts if the soil is predominantly clay).

Accelerated corrosion may also be caused by the presence of stray electrical earth currents from for example, DC railway systems or rectified induced AC from high voltage transmission systems, and these may be identified from the measurement of voltage differences in the soil.

Where metal surfaces may be exposed to natural waters, either due to immersion, condensation or rainfall, corrosion can be severe particularly if salts or other pollutants are present. The likely corrosivity of these environments can be assessed using a variety of electrical and electrochemical techniques.

### Internal surfaces

The nature of the water in contact with the metal surfaces may be most conveniently assessed or monitored by chemical analysis of representative samples. The analysis required depends

to a certain extent on the particular situation in which the supply or circulating water is being used.

It must be stressed that conclusions from analytical results should be drawn very carefully and expert consideration needs to be given to the many factors involved. It is only then possible to formulate the most appropriate treatment to control corrosion and also scale deposition, which may affect the efficient operation of a system.

The data given should only be used as a guide and no indications have been given as to the relative importance of the different factors.

## Wholesome (supply), hot and cold domestic waters

The ability of these waters to deposit a protective film of calcium carbonate scale on internal metal surfaces can play an important part in controlling corrosion. As described earlier, the Langelier and Ryznar indices indicate whether a particular water will dissolve or deposit a protective scale.

A negative Langelier index indicates that the water will tend to dissolve scale and promote corrosion while a positive index indicates that a protective film will be deposited.

The Ryznar index is a modified form of the Langelier index that is claimed to be more reliable. Using this index, a water is considered to be corrosive when the index exceeds approximately 6 and scale forming when it is less that 6. Where the water is used to feed heating plant, then the hardness value will determine the need for chemical treatment/softening to minimise scale deposition.

### Primary and secondary heating waters - chilled water systems

These systems, whether open vented or sealed, should use little or no make-up. Problems can arise when there are excessive water losses, air ingress, and aggressive residues from fabrication or cleaning operations. Flushing will be necessary to reduce the risk of corrosion. Guidance on system cleansing is given in BS 7593: 1992, *'Treatment of water in domestic hot water central heating systems'* (the advice is equally suited to chilled systems). Analytical data can be used to assess the waterside condition.

### pH – Aluminium

A pH less than 5.0 or greater than 8.5 is liable to be detrimental to aluminium. A pH outside these limits is unlikely to have occurred naturally. If the pH is lower than

5.0, an acid is present. If higher than 8.5, the water is alkaline, either due to the presence of an alkaline treatment, e.g. caustic soda, or in some circumstances due to alkali generated within the system naturally.

### Conductivity

If the system water has a higher conductivity than the supply water, this indicates that the water has been treated with an inhibitor or contaminated. The levels of concentration to be expected in the other analyses can be estimated from this comparison, e.g. a high conductivity is likely to be associated with high levels on the other tests.

### Chloride

Chloride is naturally present in all supply waters. A high level may indicate the presence of residues from acid de-scaling or chloride based fluxes. It should be noted that the chloride concentration in a towns mains supply water is liable to fluctuate, however, a level more than 25 mg/l greater or 50% greater in the system, is strongly suggestive of flux contamination.

### Sulphate

Sulphate is naturally present in all supply waters. A low level (<10 mg/l) in the system may indicate the presence of sulphate reducing bacteria.

### Hardness

Towns mains supplies are categorised in Table 22

Generally speaking, hard water is present in 60% of the country (especially in the Eastern, Central and Southern areas of England) and to varying degrees in the rest of the United Kingdom and Northern Ireland. The water for some northern cities is supplied from naturally soft water reservoirs in Wales and the Lake District.

Most calcium salts form a scale when heated. Comparison with the system water will indicate if scale has been formed. If a high level of hardness is present in the system water after it has been heated, it may be because of water loss and subsequent make-up.

### Iron

As a heating system corrodes, iron will dissolve or form corrosion debris and hydrogen gas will be generated. The amount of any debris present (visible as suspended solids) is a factor in determining the seriousness of a corrosion problem. In terms of dissolved iron, an increase of 0.5mg/l over that in the supply water is significant, with an increase of more than 3mg/l very high.

If the test sample contains rust particles, they will be dissolved when the test is carried out. The iron reading will then be the dissolved iron plus the iron due to the particles. Care should be taken to ensure that the suspended solids are representative of the overall system conditions.

### Copper

A dissolved copper concentration of 0.2mg/l more in the system than in the supply water is significant.

### Aluminium

Where aluminium components are present, an aluminium concentration of 0.3mg/l or more in the system water than in the supply water indicates that some corrosion has taken place. If the pH lies between 5.0 and 8.5, the aluminium surfaces will be passive and further corrosion will not be occurring. Any given concentration of aluminium is not a problem in itself, but an increase over a period should be noted and would require corrective action.

More significance should be attached to the aluminium concentration when an aluminium heat exchanger is fitted. Where aluminium radiators are concerned, concentrations above 0.5 mg/l do not present any special problem, provided there is no deterioration.

## Steam boilers and water heaters

BS 2486: 1997 *'Treatment of water for steam boilers and water heaters'* gives recommendations for the control of waterside conditions of steam boilers and water heaters and also for the preparation of feed water for such plant. Categories covered are:

a. Hot water systems i.e. water above 120°C (HTHW), water below 100°C (LTHW), water at 100-120°C inclusive (MTHW)

b. Electrode boilers

c. Shell (fire tube) boilers operating at pressures up to 30 bar

d. Water tube boilers operating up to critical pressure

e. Once through boilers, including 'coil' and 'hairpin' types, operating up to critical pressure

## Cooling waters

Cooling for air conditioning systems is most commonly achieved by evaporation of water, normally 1-1.5% of the circulation rate being used to cause a

temperature drop of 5-8°C. This evaporation leaves behind both dissolved solids that build up until deposition occurs and aggressive ions, for example chlorides, which will exacerbate corrosion. In addition the cooling water may become contaminated by atmospheric pollution resulting in acid corrosion due to the reduced pH.

## Corrosion control and prevention

### External surfaces

A variety of methods are available for protecting pipework etc. When their external surfaces are exposed to a corrosive environment.

Organic coatings such as paints, plastic coatings or tape wrap systems may be applied to the metal surface which has been prepared by grit blasting and/or the application of a suitable primer. In general the more severe the conditions of service, the thicker and more resistant the coating needs to be. These types of coatings can be very susceptible to mechanical damage and this should be borne in mind during installation.

Both tanks and pipes can be repaired and protected using either glass reinforced plastic (GRP) or specially formulated concrete linings.

Metal coatings, for example zinc and aluminium, may be applied to steel surfaces by hot dipping or spraying, which gives the thickest coating, diffusion or in the case of zinc, electro-deposition. These metals will corrode, albeit at a rate much slower than steel and therefore the coating thickness required depends on the aggressiveness of the environment. In severe cases, an additional paint coating may be applied.

Another method of protecting underground pipelines is that of cathodic protection. Two methods are available each of which produce a counter current sufficiently large to neutralise the currents responsible for corrosion. The first uses a more electro-negative metal, the most common being either magnesium, aluminium or zinc, in the form of sacrificial anodes which are connected electronically to the metal requiring protection. The second uses an impressed current from a generator in conjunction with auxiliary anodes of iron, steel, graphite, lead or platinised titanium.

### Internal surfaces

All internal surfaces that store or carry water, for example pipes, tanks, calorifiers, heat exchangers, radiators etc. may be subject to corrosive attack.

There are many different possible approaches to preventing corrosion and it is of utmost importance that the correct method is chosen to suit each particular situation. In most cases, proprietary blends of chemicals are available which fulfil some or all of the required preventative treatment.

Other factors may also need to be considered for example toxicity when treating wholesome waters or if there is a risk of crossover between primary heating and domestic supplies.

Both polyphosphates and sodium silicates may be used as a non-toxic, tasteless, odourless and colourless treatment for domestic waters. They both prevent iron corrosion discolouring the supply water (commonly known as 'red water') and inhibit the deposition of scale by forming a thin film on the metal surfaces, which acts as a barrier. They are dosed either in liquid form using a proportional dosing pump or as slowly dissolving crystals from a suitable dispenser.

Storage tanks/cisterns may be protected internally using cathodic protection. Sacrificial anodes, normally magnesium for steel or aluminium for copper, are connected to and suspended in the tank. While aluminium anodes in copper tanks only have to last for sufficient time to form a permanent protective film, magnesium anodes in steel tanks need to be replaced when consumed.

### Primary and secondary heating waters – chilled water systems

These systems, because they are essentially closed recirculating systems, may be treated with either oxygen scavengers, which act by the removal of oxygen responsible for the corrosion process, or inhibitors which slow down the corrosion reactions to acceptable levels, sometimes in conjunction with pH control.

Inhibitors need to be chosen carefully to suit the system under consideration. Some inhibitors may reduce corrosion in one environment while increasing it in another, while others only work effectively in a certain concentration range, actually intensifying corrosion outside this range. Sulphate reducing bacteria may be controlled by maintaining a specified level of biocide in the system.

With the current trend towards very low content boilers, it is also advisable to use sludge conditioners to prevent scale deposition inside boiler sections and tubes. These materials should be used with caution in older systems as they may dislodge scale and corrosion products highlighting weaknesses at

joints and causing leaks. Where larger systems suffer continuous water loses due to the presence of leaks, it can be beneficial to use softened water for make-up to reduce the need for frequent scale removal.

### Cooling waters

Corrosion may be controlled by dosing the system with a suitable inhibitor. This needs to be carried out continuously at a rate proportional to the bleed-off required to prevent scale deposition and excessive levels of aggressive ions building up. The treatment should also include sludge conditioners to prevent localised scale deposition and biocides to control bacteria and algae (slime) growth.

In hard water areas, the cost of water and treatment chemicals can be high and therefore consideration should be given to using a softened make-up supply. Disposal of bleed-off water also needs to be considered as some treatment chemicals are toxic and cannot be drained into local sewerage systems.

### Steam rising plant

Steam boilers are treated by ensuring that the boiler water is alkaline at all times and by removing dissolved oxygen to maintain a protective film of magnetite (magnetic iron oxide) on steel surfaces. In addition, treatment may also be necessary to prevent corrosion in condensate lines, which is most commonly caused by the presence of dissolved oxygen and carbon dioxide gases.

Dissolved oxygen in boiler water may be removed by means of a physical de-aerator or oxygen scavenger, the chemicals most commonly used being catalysed sodium sulphite, certain selected tannins or hydrazine. Condensate corrosion may be controlled by the addition of volatile amines which either neutralise the acidity caused by the presence of carbon dioxide, or form a protective film on the metal surfaces.

Caustic cracking, which used to be a fairly common phenomenon particularly in riveted boilers, can occur if concentrations of sodium hydroxide greater than 5% exist. This may be prevented by either:

i.  maintaining the ratio of sodium nitrate to total alkalinity (in terms of calcium carbonate) at a minimum value of 0.32 at all times

ii. maintaining the ratio of sodium sulphate to caustic alkalinity (in terms of calcium carbonate) at a minimum value of 2.0 at all times.

In high-pressure boilers, the level of chloride ions needs to be limited to

minimise corrosion. In addition to treatment for the prevention of corrosion, sludge and scale deposition also needs to be carefully controlled to maintain efficiently and steam purity, particularly as the trend in modern boilers is towards a lower water content and higher heat transfer rates. In brief, the concentration of solids in the boiler water may be controlled by the following methods depending on the quality of supply water:

i.  Softening and filtration of the feed water to remove dissolved and suspended solids.

ii. Precipitation of hardness salts as a mobile sludge in the boiler by maintaining a controlled reserve of either carbonate or phosphate in solution in the boiler water. In addition, organic sludge conditioners may be added to ensure that the precipitated salts are non-adherent and mobile.

iii. Maintaining the total dissolved solids below the maximum level applicable to the particular boiler and operating conditions (usually below 3500mg/l) by 'blowing down'. Blowdown may be either intermittent or continuous.

iv. Cleaning the boiler when shut down.

## Cleaning and descaling of boilers and associated plant

In newly installed systems, it is often necessary to remove internal contaminants, for example flux residues, metal filings and other builder's debris by flushing. Even if carried out in accordance with recommended procedures, it is unlikely that all will be removed due to either their insolubility or the internal geometry of the system. This highlights the need to adopt working procedures that negate the need for flushing, for example using non-aggressive fluxes and cutting rather than sawing copper tubes.

In older systems, particularly where there has been water losses or air ingress; scale and sludge may have deposited, which will affect the efficiency. In the worst case, particularly where low water content boilers are used, overheating will lead to eventual failure of sections or splitting of tubes.

If inspection indicates that de-scaling is necessary, the nature of the deposits should be determined to ascertain the best method of removal.

Loose deposits may be removed manually or mechanically but hard deposits will normally require chemical removal. Table 32 indicates chemicals that may be used to remove the most

*Table 32* Cleaning and descaling treatments

| Treatment | Carbonate | Phosphate | Sulphate | Silicate | Copper & oxide | Millscale | Magnetite | Oil | Grease |
|---|---|---|---|---|---|---|---|---|---|
| Hydrochloric acid (inhibited) | × | × | | | | × | × | | |
| Hydrochloric/hydrofluoric acids (inhibited) | × | × | × | | | × | × | | |
| Sulphuric acid (inhibited) | × | | | | | × | × | | |
| Sulphamic acid | × | | | | | | | | |
| Citric adic | | | | | | × | × | | |
| Ammonium citrate with oxidising agent (pH 9.5) | | | | | × | | | | |
| Formic acid | × | × | | | | × | × | | |
| Tetra sodium salt of EDTA (ethylene diamine-tetra acetic acid) | × | × | × | | | | | | |
| Tetra-ammonium salt of EDTA | × | × | × | × | × | × | | | |
| Sodium hydroxide/sodiuim phosphate | | | | | | | | × | × |

common types of deposit. If scaling is present in a confined part of the system, for example the boiler, then treatment should be isolated to that part of the system. Progress of the cleaning should be strictly monitored, care being taken to ensure that all aggressive chemical residues are removed after completion of the de-scaling operation. Throughout the treatment, adequate safety precautions need to be observed and the effluent disposed of in accordance with statutory and other requirements.

## Plant shutdown

When plant and associated equipment is taken out of service for any length of time, steps need to be taken to prevent damage due to internal corrosion.

In the case of heating and chilled water systems, they should be left completely filled with water containing oxygen scavengers or corrosion inhibitors and a biocide maintained at a high pH. In this situation, precautions may also need to be taken to prevent frost damage. Plant should only remain in a drained down condition if left and maintained completely dry internally, otherwise rapid localised attack, particularly in for example steel panel radiators, can occur resulting in premature failure.

Cooling towers need to be drained and where necessary dismantled to prevent seizure of pumps etc. When they are brought back on line, treatment with suitable biocides is recommended to control bacteria.

## References

Water Regulations Guide, including the Water Byelaws 2000 (Scotland), ISBN 0-9539708-0-9; Water Regulations Advisory Scheme, Fern Close, Pen-y-Fan Industrial Estate, Oakdale, Newport, NP11 3EH.

The HSE's ACOP and Guidance document – L8 2001.

The Department of Health's code of practice HTM2040 – *the control of legionella in healthcare premises.*

BS6700:1997 – *Specification for the design, installation, testing and maintenance of services supplying water for domestic use within buildings and their curtilages.*

The Institute of Plumbing - *Legionaire's Disease - good practice guide for plumbers.*

# Legionnaires' disease

# Introduction

Over 16 species of the genus *Legionella* have been shown to be associated with respiratory tract infections in Man. The term legionellosis is given to the disease caused by these micro-organisms. The severity of the disease ranges from Legionnaires' disease, an acute severe pneumonia with low attack rate and relatively high death rate, to Pontiac fever, a mild non-pneumonic, flu-like infection with high attack rate but no fatalities. It would be noted that *L. pneumophila* serogroup 1 is the most common cause of human infection.

# Systems associated with outbreaks

Epidemiological investigations have associated outbreaks of Legionnaires' disease with cooling towers, hot water systems, whirlpool spa baths, clinical humidifiers in respiratory equipment, supermarket vegetable sprays, natural spa baths, fountains and potting compost. Although there are many sporadic cases of Legionnaires' disease associated with domestic water systems, in Britain almost all of the major *Legionella* outbreaks have been associated with cooling towers and large domestic water systems.

A study carried out a few years ago by the Public Health Laboratory Service on the presence of *Legionella* in man-made water systems found *Legionella* in 60% of all water systems examined and the most virulent type, *L. pneumophila* serogroup 1, was found in over 20% of these systems.

# Parameters which influence the growth and survival of *Legionella* in natural and man-made water systems

Temperature is the most important factor in the survival and growth of *Legionella*. The micro-organisms can grow at temperatures between 20-45°C, the optimum temperature for growth and virulence being 36°C. *Legionella* can survive at temperatures below 20°C but it can't grow, and at temperatures above 60°C *Legionella* are rapidly killed. Humidity is also an important factor considering the ability of *Legionella* to survive in aerosols. As the humidity increases the ability of *Legionella* to survive increases.

The nutrients available in water systems from plumbing materials or organic matter may also increase the capacity for *Legionella* growth.

Biofilm formation in water systems provide protection from adverse conditions like biocide concentration and shear forces of water. Moreover the presence of other micro-organisms will, depending on the type present, increase the ability of *Legionella* to survive. For example *Flavobacterium* will provide nutrients for the *Legionella* to grow on. Moreover, it is well documented that *Legionella* can grow inside amoebae. The amoebae provide a protective environment for the *Legionella*. Amoebae can encyst and this makes them very resistant to environmental stress and biocides and so if the *Legionella* are inside the amoebae they will also be more resistant to these factors.

# Events leading to an outbreak

An outbreak of sporadic infection of *Legionella* can occur if a viable pathogenic strain of *Legionella* is introduced into the water systems. This can happen from contaminated water or from aerosolised water droplets containing *Legionella*. The strain must then be able to multiply in the water system. The water containing the micro-organisms has then to be aerosolised and the aerosol carried to susceptible humans.

# Factors shown to increase susceptibility

Various sections of the population are more susceptible to *Legionella* infection than others. The elderly, males, people with existing respiratory illness and people with illness which reduces the body's defence systems, smokers because of impaired lung function and people on immunosuppressive drugs which again reduces the host defences are all more susceptible to *Legionella* infection.

## *Legionella* infection

There are two routes of *Legionella* infection. One involves *Legionella* getting into the planktonic phase of the water system and then onto surfaces or inside amoebae and the other is infection into humans which involves aerosolisation of *Legionella*-infected water followed by water droplet inhalation by a susceptible host. The micro-organism can then infect various cells in the body. *Legionella* infection in humans involves inhalation of the micro-organism in water droplets or aerosols. The droplets must be small enough (<5µm) to get down into the lung bronchioles where the *Legionella* become lodged/deposited and can subsequently cause infection.

If detected quickly, Legionnaires' disease is curable. Erythromycin, which halts biosynthesis in *Legionella*, is the recommended antibiotic therapy for *Legionella*. Patients who have a mild infection are treated orally and those who are moderately or severely ill require intravenous treatment. Treatment should continue for 3 weeks. The use of another antibiotic Rifampicin, which has a similar mode of action to Erythromycin, in conjunction with Erythromycin is advocated where patients with *Legionella* pneumonia are critically ill, severely immunocompromised or have lung abscesses.

## *Legionella* preventative measures

To effect control on *Legionella* infection it is necessary to understand about the events leading to an outbreak, as described previously. To know where *Legionella* may exist in the environment, to understand the mechanism of entry into the water system and the various means by which *Legionella* survive disinfection. We also need to know the mechanisms enabling *Legionella* to grow in water systems and how it survives in aerosols. Many of these issues have yet to be resolved but with existing knowledge a set of guidelines for the control of *Legionella* in man-made water systems have been set up.

## Outbreak control: duties of the responsible person

The permanent duties of the responsible person and the maintenance team need to eliminate the recurrence of Legionnaires' disease in buildings are summarised as follows:

a.  All cold water supplied (other than drinking water) and water storage should be disinfected to ensure that water delivery to every cold water outlet in the building complies with the requirements of the disinfection control technique to be used.

b.  All cold water storage cisterns (commonly known as tanks) should be regularly inspected, maintained and disinfected in the manner specified.

c.  Where water is distributed to water outlets at the recommended distribution temperatures i.e. 55-60°C a warning notice should be displayed at each such outlet because there is a risk of scalding at these temperatures.

d.  All apparatus likely to produce contaminated aerosols such as humidifiers, cooling towers etc. should be scheduled and a detailed system of cleaning and disinfecting by chlorination carried out at regular intervals.

e.  The Responsible Person should ensure regular testing and inspection. All such testing should be recorded in an agreed manner.

f.  In conjunction with other staff, such as administrators, production personnel, senior officers, cleaners etc., a system should be initiated which ensures that any department, rooms and areas in the building, if left unoccupied for a week or more, should be thoroughly tested before bringing back into service.

g.  Special attention to items e and f should be observed concerning shower equipment and spray taps. For drinking water – all drinking outlets in the buildings should have been checked that they are connected to the drinking water mains and have been clearly labelled. All drinking water mains in the building must be connected directly to the mains water to ensure that they are not fed through any storage or

tank system. It has been determined in the United Kingdom that no chlorination or form of disinfection is required for existing drinking water mains or outlets except for initial disinfection in the commissioning of a new building or pipework. It is important that when requests for additional drinking water outlets are received, the maintenance staff should check that connections are in fact made to drinking water mains and that the outlets are labelled as such. All new pipework should be disinfected before being put into use. (In the National Health Service this is recommended in HTM 2040). B.S. 6700 and other appropriate documents.

## Cold water storage systems and tanks

It is intended that, when necessary, modifications to pipe and storage systems should take place so that only one unit for continuous disinfection need be installed.

Wherever possible the cold water storage system and storage tanks should store water at below 20°C. The Responsible Person should eliminate the possibility of any conditions which produce abnormally high temperature rises. Advice should be sought on the method to be used to control any temperature rise.

Cold water storage systems and tanks for wholesome water supply, shall be installed and maintained in a workmanlike manner and, flushed, tested and disinfected where necessary before bringing into use as required by 'The Water Supply (water fitting) Regulations 1999'. Part 2 Regulation 4(5) and Schedule 2 Paragraph 13.

It is essential that all cold water storage systems and all storage tanks should be thoroughly cleaned out at least annually.

The cold water storage system is sometimes associated with pressurised vessels and storage tanks, which should be disinfected as appropriate. All equipment should then be drained to waste and the system refilled. A continuous system of disinfection should be constantly maintained. An official log book should be maintained by the Responsible Person and the readings of disinfection effectiveness in the cold water storage system recorded daily. At least once a week the Maintenance Team should examine and sign the log book and in the event of the disinfection level falling below the minimum effective levels take appropriate action.

Testing should be carried out using the appropriate testing equipment and the Responsible Person should ensure that all members of his staff are trained to carry out this test efficiently.

## Continuous chlorination plant

The continuous chlorination plant should be located in a suitable position and this should be permanent. The use of chlorine gas is potentially hazardous so it is recommended that sodium hypochlorite solution be used for chlorination. the Responsible Person should arrange for the inclusion in his Planned Preventive Maintenance system of daily inspections of the chlorination plant. The Responsible Person should also order and obtain all spare parts, chemical etc. necessary to ensure that the equipment can be rapidly returned to service in the event of breakdown.

*NOTE:*
*It should be noted that sodium hypochlorite solution will lose its strength if stored for a long time, or in a warm place.*

## Thorough testing of all outlets

It is recommended that during one week in each year, a thorough test of very hot and cold water outlets, including all thermostatic mixing valves etc should take place and a suitable log retained. In the case of cold water outlets these should indicate between 1-2mg/l chlorine strength within one minute of running the waste.

In the case of hot water outlets these should indicate temperatures of between 50-60°C within one minute of running to waste. If connected to a dosing pump, 1-2mg/l chlorine strength should be achieved. All thermostatic mixing valves, shower heads and spray taps etc. should be tested by first running hot water to waste without recording temperatures for a minimum of one minute, then running cold to waste, when a chlorine strength of between 1-2mg/l chlorine strength should be achieved. Recording of test results should be carried out by the supervising engineer to the approved schedule. Any outlet which fails these test conditions should be recorded and details submitted to the engineer who must rectify the fault.

It is intended that in addition to the testing proposed above, more frequent testing of selected outlets, both hot and cold, should be carried out in a similar manner. Chlorine levels, hot and cold water temperatures should be tested once weekly to maintain observation on the current situation.

Recording of test results should be carried out by the supervising engineer to an approved schedule of outlets, which will be determined by a responsible body of people, and any outlets which fail the test conditions should be recorded and brought to the attention of the engineer.

# Water softening and hot water storage system

If the site contains only one main central storage tank, this should be modified so that one compartment, if possible, is allocated to contain soft water only for the hot water supply system.

If necessary, existing pipework should be altered so that mains water is connected directly to the water softening plant and then to the continuous chlorine injection unit to provide the softened water with chlorine to approximately 1-2mg/l at the outlets. The softened and chlorinated water should be delivered to the appropriate compartment of the central storage tank prior to distribution to calorifiers.

The softened water storage compartment should be cleaned and chlorinated to 50mg/l every year in the first week of April in a similar manner to that specified for the raw water compartments. In addition, all associated pipework, pumps and equipment which can be segregated from hot water calorifiers etc. should also be similarly chlorinated each year.

NOTE:
*The water softener unit itself should not be subjected to chlorination.*

At each of the calorifiers the water should be stored at a temperature high enough to give a flow temperature of 60°C and suitable thermometers installed in flow and return pipework and aim for a maximum temperature deviation of 5°C.

Where these conditions cannot be obtained, a schedule of calorifiers should be prepared, clearly indicating

discrepancies and their effect on hot water outlet temperatures. This schedule should identify the remedial action required to bring the system to the approved standard and given to the Responsible Person for *immediate action.*

Any showers found to be infrequently used should be taken out of use.

All shower positions in the building should be regularly run to waste weekly.

Each shower fitting should be run for five minutes during which, in the first two minutes hot water should be passed, and for the remaining time, cold chlorinated water.

This procedure should be the responsibility of a nominated person in each department and a list of staff nominated kept by the Administrator.

# Stagnant water positions – unoccupied

From time to time cases arise where departments or individual rooms in the building are left unoccupied for various reasons. It is essential that a policy be devised so that accommodation cannot be returned to general use until a full test of hot and cold water outlets has been carried out.

The engineer will be required to certify that all hot and cold water outlets, including thermostatical outlets, have been tested in the manner previously specified.

# Domestic hot water calorifiers

Where *Legionella pneumophila* has been identified, it is recommended that the calorifiers should be thoroughly cleansed and the following guidelines should be followed:

1. Isolate the calorifier from the system. If more than one is involved, select the one that is most infected.

2. Do not disturb the other calorifiers i.e. putting them on or off line.

3. Drain and clean the calorifier to be treated, refill with clean treated water and then decide which of the following techniques is to be applied.

To make the calorifiers safe, one of the following may be undertaken:

a. Attach a clear PVC hose pipe to the drain cock ensuring that the end of the hose is right in the drain, (this is to prevent the inhalation of infected aerosol), and drain off as much water as is required to make room for the disinfection solution to be added. This should be measured according to the amount of water in the system to achieve 50-60mg/l dependent on the requirements of the chemical user. Other techniques such as U.V., iron deposition and irradiation should be dosed to the requirements of the manufacturers Instructions.

b. Make sure the domestic hot water flow valve is closed (DHWF), leave the remaining valves open, i.e. the domestic hot water return valve (DHWR), the cold water supply make up valve (CWS). The primary heating source, flow and return must be closed.

Remove or disconnect any 'over temperature control stats'. Raise the temperature of the water in the calorifier by turning on the primary heat source so that a temperature of 70°C is reached all over the casing of the calorifiers, then let the calorifier stand for a minimum of 24 hours or longer if possible. This is to enable the heat to penetrate through the scale and sludge and kill of any *Legionella*. It will be noticed that the temperature will fall very slowly owing to the lagging. Drain to waste, as before, with the hose pipe inserted right into the drain.

4. Remove primary heating (coil(s) for insurance requirements and thoroughly mechanically clean out.

5. Refix all heating coils etc. in the calorifier and fill up with water. Make sure the domestic hot water flow valve remains closed.

6. Reconnect the high limits stats and turn the heat back on, the temperature control to be set at approximately 60°C.

7. If it is proved that bacterial growth can still be found at the tap and shower outlets, then washers should be changed on the taps to a Water Regulations Advisory Scheme approved type.

# Cooling towers

It is highly recommended that wet cooling towers should be replaced by air to water or other approved types of coolers. If any existing wet cooling towers are to be refurbished, specialist cleaning advice should be sought and applied.

# Humidifiers

There are a number of different types of humidifiers, i.e. steam, battery-spray, spinning disc, and simple 'pouring water' humidifiers. These are normally found in the heating and ventilation systems of big office blocks, computer rooms and sometimes in hospitals, particularly in operating theatre areas. Up until now none of these humidification systems has been implicated as the source of *Legionella* infection. However, the manufacturers' advice should be sought for maintenance cleaning purposes.

# Major plant

| | |
|---|---|
| Cooling towers | Water treatment, cleaning |
| Air handling units | Filtration |
| Humidifiers | Cleaning, water treatment |
| Chill coil/drip trays/ drains | – Tundish |

# Summary

To minimise risk of *Legionella* infection: avoid release of water sprays, avoid water temperatures which may encourage the growth of *Legionella* and other micro-organisms, avoid water stagnation, don't use materials which can harbour bacteria or provide nutrients for growth, maintain cleanliness throughout the systems, use water treatment techniques and ensure correct and safe operation and maintenance of the waste system and plant.

# Practical prevention and solutions

## Wholesome water

| | |
|---|---|
| Drinking fountains | check mains supply |
| Vending machines | Mains supply/disinfection |
| Drinking water taps | Mains supply – label |

## Cold water services

| | |
|---|---|
| Break tank (pressure set) | Air vent, locked access |
| Storage tanks | Lead-lag, capacity, lids, overflow |
| Down services | Dead legs |
| Taps | Sprays scale |
| Showers | Scale |

## Hot water services

| | |
|---|---|
| Calorifiers | Annual clean |
| Taps | Washers |
| Showers | Mixers/strainers |
| Dishwashers | Flexible hand spray |

# Heating

# Introduction

Modern central heating systems have to be capable of meeting the user's expectations of providing an adequate level of heating in an efficient manner. An efficient system is one that provides the correct amount of heat at the correct place at the correct time, burning the fuel used in the most efficient way possible and switches off the boiler when the demand is satisfied. Achieving this objective will require correct system design, avoiding inefficient oversizing of plant, and the use of appropriate controls. However, the more sophisticated the system the greater the potential for problems and so good design often requires a compromise between what is the ideal solution and what is advisable in terms of operational and maintenance considerations. The recommendations in this Guide relate primarily to domestic and small commercial installations with boiler input ratings not exceeding 60kW, although much of the content will also be applicable to larger systems. For a greater understanding of efficiency requirements reference should be made to the Resource efficient design section.

# Building design/ construction

## New buildings

In designing a new building, there are many considerations which will have a direct impact on the design of the heating system and its operational efficiency, such as fabric selection, constructional details, orientation, internal layout, nature of occupancy/use, domestic hot water loading and provision for plant installation, access & maintenance.

To maximise the desirable influences and ameliorate those that have an undesirable effect on the building operational efficiency, the heating engineer should, ideally, have an early involvement in the design of the building.

## Existing buildings

With existing buildings, insulation levels may be far from satisfactory and the design engineer should determine what cost effective insulation measures can be taken in order to reduce heat losses and therefore the size and capital cost of the installed heating system, such as :

a. Increase insulation levels within roof voids to 200mm thickness.

b. Ensure window and door openings are adequately draught proofed and un-used chimneys closed off. Ensure that there is still adequate ventilation to prevent odour/moisture build-up and if closing off a chimney, leave just sufficient ventilation to protect the internal fabric of the chimney from deterioration.

c. Insulate flat roofs by the application of insulation on top of the existing roof waterproofing membrane.

d. Insulate external walls. There are several types of material used for cavity wall insulation and solid walls can be insulated internally or externally, although the choice of method needs careful evaluation.

e. Consider replacing window frames in poor condition with sealed double-glazed units, possibly using low emissivity glass where there are potential solar radiation gains. It is not cost effective to install double-glazing simply to reduce energy consumption.

## Surveying an existing building

With an existing building, the pre-requisite of a successful heating system design is the carrying out of a detailed survey, which should provide the necessary information for the heat loss calculations and for the system preliminary design. The following details the various aspects that should be covered by the survey and could form the basis of a check list.

### Occupancy

Details of pattern of occupancy – preferred temperatures.

### Building layout

Orientation, positions of windows, doors and major items of furniture – party and external walls (load bearing ?). For each room, ceiling height, floor dimensions, skirting and cill height, window size and type of glazing – wall and roof construction. Floor construction – if suspended, direction and depth of floor joists and position of any steel beams – if solid, type of construction (e.g. reinforced concrete, beam and pot). Details of any natural ventilation shafts (e.g. open chimneys) and/or ventilation fans. Possible locations for any envisaged equipment, taking access for installation/ maintenance into consideration.

### Insulation

Existing levels of insulation and draught proofing (if any). Adequate, or do they need improving?

### Boiler

Preferred type of boiler – combined primary storage unit (cpsu), fuel (location of nearest supply – storage), floor/wall mounted, conventional/balanced flue. Possible locations (including any ancillary equipment), taking into account possible pipe routes, flue requirements – conventional/ balanced and fan assisted balanced flues – condensate drainage provision (condensing boilers).

### F & E cistern

Position for F & E cistern – routes for cold feed and safety vent pipes and location of rising main for float valve supply. Alternatively, space for sealed system expansion vessel and pressurisation set.

### Electrics

Source of electrical supply and position for controller, thermostats, etc. Adequacy of existing earthing. Position of socket outlets, etc. Equipment/lighting loads?

### Pipe routes

Possible/acceptable pipe routes (concealed/exposed?) including drops for between floor connections.

### Heaters

Client preference for type of system/ components and reasons?

# Calculation of heating loads

The heating load of a building is dependant upon fabric heat loss and ventilation heat loss due to air infiltration. In commercial installations there may be offsetting internal gains from people, equipment, lighting, etc., but this is only taken into account if it is continuous during the pre-heat and heating periods. Such gains are normally ignored in domestic situations, as are solar radiation gains.

# Heat transfer theory

Heat is a form of energy and its transfer occurs through three basic processes – conduction and convection, which both require a medium through which the heat is transmitted, and radiation which occurs from one body to another and does not require a medium. All three processes require a temperature difference for heat transfer to occur.

Conduction is a process whereby heat is transferred without an appreciable movement of the molecules within the medium concerned. For a solid material, the rate of heat transfer is directly proportional to the area (A) across which the heat is being conducted and the temperature gradient $(t_1 - t_2)$. It is inversely proportional to the thickness of the material (l).

$$Q = \frac{\lambda A(t_1 - t_2)}{l}$$

Q = heat transfer rate in Watts

A = area in $m^2$

l = thickness in metres

t = temperature in °C (or Kelvin)

$\lambda$ = thermal conductivity in $\dfrac{W}{m°C}$

The thermal conductivity for a material can vary, depending upon its mean temperature, moisture content and density. For liquids and gases, it will also depend upon pressure. Good insulators have low thermal conductivity.

The reciprocal of the conductivity gives the resistivity of the material

Dividing the conductivity of a specific material by its thickness gives its thermal conductance and its reciprocal gives the thermal resistance 'R'.

$\dfrac{\lambda}{l}$ = thermal conductance – its reciprocal

$\dfrac{l}{\lambda}$ = thermal resistance 'R'

## Convection

Convection is a process whereby heat is transferred as a result of the actual movement of the fluid molecules within the medium.

## Radiation

Radiation is the transfer of heat between two bodies at different temperatures due to electromagnetic radiation waves passing through the intervening space and the rate of radiant heat transfer depends upon their shape, orientation and their relative emissivities and absorptivities.

## Emissivity Factor (E)

Emissivity Factor (E) is the ratio of heat emitted by a unit surface area of a material to that emitted by a unit area of a perfect black surface at the same temperature – most building materials have an emissivity of 0.9 – 0.95 – shiny/reflective surfaces have a low emissivity of around 0.05.

# Heat loss calculations and 'U' values

Calculation of the rate of heat loss (Q) from a building is straightforward. It involves calculating the area (A) of each constructional element of the building through which heat is going to flow, such as the wall, roof, floor and windows – different areas of the same element may be of different construction and so the heat loss across each area must be separately calculated. The area is then multiplied by the temperature differential across each element $(t_1 - t_2)$ and the 'U' value.

$$Q = UA(t_1 - t_2),$$

The constructional elements considered are usually those which form the boundary between the inside and outside of the building, with the temperature difference being that between the inside and outside design temperatures. In some cases it may also be necessary to calculate the heat loss from one internal space to another, if they are at significantly different temperatures (say 3°C or more) – an example would be a bathroom at 22°C with an adjacent bedroom or hallway at 18°C. Alternatively, the adjacent area may be unheated, such as a garage beneath a bedroom, and so the likely temperature of the unheated space has to be determined. This can be calculated, but in most instances it is sufficient to make a reasoned 'guess'. The temperature in an unheated garage within the envelope of a house is likely to be some 5°C to 8°C above outside design temperature – if it has an exposed roof and walls, then 2°C may be more appropriate.

Consideration must also be given to the additional heating load resulting from air infiltration.

It is worth noting that whilst temperatures are usually quoted in degrees Centigrade (°C), temperature differences are often quoted in degrees Kelvin (°K). One degree difference in the Centigrade scale is the same as one degree difference in the Kelvin scale, but they are not the same for actual temperatures: 0°K is –272°C!

## 'U' value

The 'U' value is a measurement of the rate of heat flow across one square metre of the element of the structure in consideration, with a 1°C temperature differential across that element and assuming steady state heat transfer conditions. It can be written as:

$$U = \frac{1}{R_{si} + \dfrac{l_1}{\lambda_1} + \dfrac{l_2}{\lambda_2} + \ldots R_a + R_{so}}$$

where $R_{si}$ and $R_{so}$ are the internal and external surface resistances; $R_a$ is the resistance of any airspace; $l_1$, $l_2$, etc. are the thicknesses of each of the structural elements (in metres, not millimetres) and $\lambda_1$, $\lambda_2$, etc. are the conductivities of the respective materials.

The lower the 'U' value of a material, the better its thermal insulating properties – do not confuse with electrical insulation.

Tabulated 'U' values for specific constructions, or Thermal Conductivities for various materials can be found in a variety of sources including the CIBSE. Guide, Building Regulations Section L1, Insulation Industry Handbook, HVCA/CIBSE/IoP Domestic Heating Design guide, manufacturers' literature and many other sources.

## Building Regulations

The Building Regulations (reference Approved Documents L1 and L2), that apply to replacement and new systems stipulate that 'reasonable provision shall be made for the conservation of fuel and power in buildings. For domestic dwelling designs, as covered by L1, this requires:

a. Limiting heat loss through the building fabric; from hot water pipes and hot air ducts and from hot water vessels

b. Providing space heating and hot water systems which are energy efficient

c. Providing lighting systems with lamps and controls that use energy efficiently.

For buildings other than dwellings, as covered by L2, in addition to the above, there are requirements relating to the provision of mechanical ventilation, air conditioning, lighting systems and more.

# 'U' value calculation

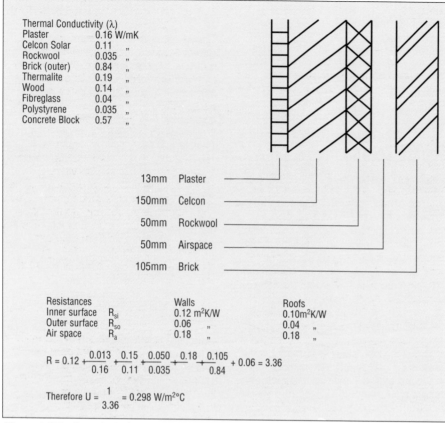

Thermal Conductivity (λ)
| | |
|---|---|
| Plaster | 0.16 W/mK |
| Celcon Solar | 0.11 " |
| Rockwool | 0.035 " |
| Brick (outer) | 0.84 " |
| Thermalite | 0.19 " |
| Wood | 0.14 " |
| Fibreglass | 0.04 " |
| Polystyrene | 0.035 " |
| Concrete Block | 0.57 " |

| | |
|---|---|
| 13mm | Plaster |
| 150mm | Celcon |
| 50mm | Rockwool |
| 50mm | Airspace |
| 105mm | Brick |

| Resistances | | Walls | Roofs |
|---|---|---|---|
| Inner surface | $R_{si}$ | 0.12 m²K/W | 0.10m²K/W |
| Outer surface | $R_{so}$ | 0.06 " | 0.04 " |
| Air space | $R_a$ | 0.18 " | 0.18 " |

$$R = 0.12 + \frac{0.013}{0.16} + \frac{0.15}{0.11} + \frac{0.050}{0.035} + \frac{0.18}{} + \frac{0.105}{0.84} + 0.06 = 3.36$$

$$\text{Therefore } U = \frac{1}{3.36} = 0.298 \text{ W/m}^2\text{°C}$$

*Figure 1* '*U' value calculation*

All new housing and conversions must have an energy rating, calculated in accordance with the Government's Standard Assessment Procedure (SAP) and which has to be declared for Building Regulations approval.

For domestic dwellings, the Building Regulations (Section L1) details three methods of demonstrating that the Regulations have been complied with in respect to the building heat loss – the Elemental method; Target U-value method and Carbon index method. Full details of the methods of calculation are given in Section L1, together with example calculations.

For other buildings, the Building Regulations (Section L2) details three methods of demonstrating that the Regulations have been complied with in respect to the building heat loss – the Elemental method; a Whole building method and Carbon emissions calculation method.

The calculated heat flow rate based on the 'U' value is for steady-state conditions and for the majority of situations, will give a perfectly adequate indication of the mean rate of heat loss from the structure. However, in reality the heat flow rate will vary in response to fluctuations in internal temperature, external temperature and variations in structural thickness and/or density. If considering the dynamic performance of a structure (normally in relation to heat gain calculations) then it is necessary to take into account three factors in addition to the 'U' value: Surface Factor (F), Admittance Factor (Y-value) and Decrement Factor (f).

## Design temperatures

The temperature sensed by a body depends upon the surrounding air temperature and the mean radiant temperature (MRT) of all the surrounding surfaces – a similar level of comfort can be achieved with a high air temperature and low MRT, or with a lower air temperature and higher MRT.

To only consider air temperature when carrying out heat loss calculations may give unsatisfactory results, so either 'environmental' or 'dry resultant' temperatures are normally used, which take into account both air and mean surface temperatures.

For normal situations, where air movement is low, the dry resultant temperature is used, and recommended values for various situations are given in the CIBSE Guide, NHBC Guide and BS5449. In domestic situations it is necessary to consider whether designing for adjacent areas to be at considerably varying temperatures is reasonable. In practice, communicating doors are frequently left open, and so to calculate on the basis of one room being at 21°C and an adjacent communicating room being at 16°C may be unrealistic – with the door open the adjacent room temperature is likely to stabilise at around 18°C-19°C.

The environmental temperature is weighted in favour of the mean surface temperature and is generally used in dynamic heat transfer calculations, where the heat exchange between the surfaces and the enclosed space is considered.

## Air change rates

In a building of normal construction there will be air infiltration occurring at various points through the building structure (e.g. window and door frames) and this has to be allowed for in the heat loss calculations. Actual infiltration rates may vary considerably, depending upon the age of the building, level of insulation and exposure. Empirical values of air change rates for various situations are given in the HVCA/CIBSE/IoP Domestic Heating Guide. The procedure for calculation is straightforward – the volume of the room is calculated (V) and multiplied by the air change rate (N), the specific heat of air (0.33 W/m³°C) and the inside/outside temperature difference.

Modern buildings are increasingly being constructed with higher standards of insulation and draught proofing and as a result, the air change rate can drop to considerably less than that required to adequately control moisture and odour build-up. Under these circumstances, some form of mechanical extract and/or supply ventilation should be considered.

The provision of mechanical extract from domestic kitchens, bath/shower rooms and some toilets is now mandatory under the Building Regulations (reference Approved Document F) and literature from domestic fan manufacturers gives guidance on requirements.

In commercial properties it is also necessary to take into account the number of occupants and ensure that an adequate supply of fresh air is available. The recommended fresh air supply rate in offices, where it is minimal or no smoking, is 5–8 l/s per person. Installation of a fresh air ventilation system may be required. Alternatively, the use of through-wall heat recovery ventilator units, could be considered.

Wherever mechanical ventilation is used,

its effect on the heat loss must be considered and allowed for.

## Heat loss calculations

Accurate heat loss calculation is essential for efficient operation. Using 'rule of thumb' methods or a simple disc calculator will invariably result in system oversizing, with increased capital and running costs. A number of radiator manufacturers now offer free of charge heat loss programmes which can be run on a PC, but it is essential to understand the 'manual' method of calculation, if only to do 'spot checks'.

Examples of design calculation worksheets can be found in the HVCA/CIBSE/IoP Domestic Heating Design Guide.

It must be remembered that the calculation of heat losses is not an 'exact' science, since there are many variables involved, such as variations in standard of construction and in the constructional materials and their moisture content (e.g. bricks)

The heat losses are calculated a room at a time and for rooms over 5m height a percentage addition is made to the calculated heat loss, dependant upon the type of system (convective/radiant).

The calculated heat loss for each room forms the basis for the sizing of the heat emitters and the total of all the calculated heat losses forms the basis for sizing of the primary heat source. However, whilst the individual room heat losses all include for the effect of air infiltration, the rooms into which air will be infiltrating at any given time will depend upon the wind direction. Air will infiltrate into rooms on the windward side, pass through the building and exit the building from the rooms on the leeward side, thus the air infiltrating into the leeward side rooms, will have already been heated by its passage through the rooms on the windward side. The fact that the air entering the leeward side rooms has been pre-heated cannot be taken into account in the sizing of heat emitters for the rooms – a change in wind direction may reverse the situation – but it can be considered when sizing the primary heat source. With a property having two or more exposed elevations and internally partitioned, the primary heat source basic load can be reduced by up to 50% of the calculated ventilation heat loss. The actual reduction allowed will be dependant upon the building configuration – if a domestic property has a through lounge, exposed at both ends to the outside, then a 50% reduction in respect of this room would not be appropriate, but it may well be in respect of bedrooms at first floor.

# Types of heating system

Heating systems generally fall into one of four categories – wet, dry (warm air), radiant and electric storage and a building could have a combination of any of these.

## Wet system

In a wet system, the heat source is invariably a boiler burning gas, (natural or LPG), oil or solid fuel, or an electric storage boiler. Water is heated in the boiler and then pumped via a piping distribution system to the heat emitters, where the heat is given out. The cooled water then returns to the boiler for re-heating. Wet systems are adaptable, extendable (subject to capacity) and fully controllable and in domestic situations they usually also provide domestic hot water heating via an indirect cylinder.

Heat emitters are usually radiators or natural or fan assisted convectors, or underfloor heating may be installed, in which hot water is circulated through a network of underfloor pipes. This gives a very even level of heating, with no heaters to occupy wall space and the maintenance requirement and potential leakage risk is reduced. Underfloor heating can be installed within new floors and over all types of existing floors and offers proven energy consumption reductions in the order of 15-20%, compared to normal wet heating systems. The installation is usually carried out by specialist contractors.

Wet systems can be either open vented or sealed. With an open vented system a feed and expansion (F & E) cistern is

located at least 1m above the top of the highest heater or section of circulating pipework and connected to the system by a cold feed and expansion pipe. The purpose of the cistern is to keep the system topped up with water and to accept the increase in system water volume as it heats up. The F & E cistern capacity to waterline should be not less than 18 litres plus 1/20th of the water content of the system, and the cold feed pipe should ideally be sized to contain the expansion volume of the system (usually means 22mm minimum size) and connected to the circulating part of the system with an anti-gravity loop. Terminating over the F & E cistern is the safety open vent pipe which must have an unobstructed path back to the heat generator and the function of which is to vent any air liberated from the heat generator and provide a relief for any steam produced as a result of a boiler thermostat failure.

With an open vented system the positioning of the pump in relation to the safety open vent and cold feed connections is very important if problems of pumping over, open vent aeration or suction leaks are to be avoided. As a general rule, position the pump on the flow after the safety open vent connection. In low head situations a combined safety open vent and cold feed is permitted, provided the boiler has a high limit safety thermostat. Always fit a diaphragm type safety valve if there is a risk of freezing.

A sealed system has no F & E cistern, cold feed or safety open vent pipe. The system is usually filled direct from the mains via a filling loop incorporating a double check valve, isolating valve and, ideally, a pressure reducing valve, to a pressure of approximately 0.5 bar above the static head from the fill point to the highest point in the system.

**Figure 2** *Typical open vented system*

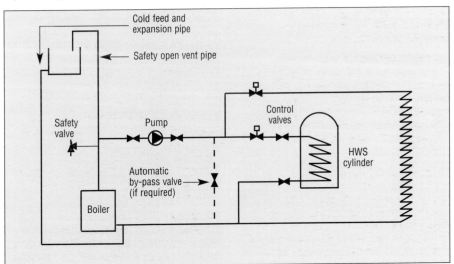

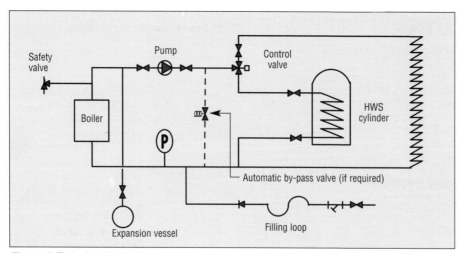

*Figure 3* Typical sealed system

To accommodate the expanded water volume as the system heats up, an expansion vessel is connected to the system, which must also be fitted with a non-adjustable safety valve (diaphragm type) set at 3 bar. All boilers connected to sealed systems must have high limit thermostats. All gas combination boilers are of the sealed type, with the expansion vessel, safety valve and high limit thermostat all built into the unit and a number of ordinary boilers are now available as 'system boilers' with all necessary sealed system components built in.

A sealed system avoids the risk of freezing of the F & E cistern and associated pipework; overcomes problems associated with positioning of the cold feed and open vent connection to the system – a particular problem with low water content boilers – and drastically reduces the corrosion problems due to oxygenation of the system.

With any wet heating system, the pipework requires protection from damage/frost.

## Dry (warm air) system

With a dry (warm air) system, air is heated by passing through a heater, which can be directly heated (e.g. gas or oil fired) or indirectly heated by a heater battery through which hot water is circulating. The heated air is discharged, either directly or via a ducting system, into the areas requiring heating. Depending upon the application, the air having given up its heat, may pass back to the heater, via a ducting system or by natural ventilation paths, to be re-heated, or it may be discharged to outside (e.g. toilet extract system) and fresh outside air supplied to the heater.

Warm air systems give rapid heat up but may lack control flexibility (particularly

domestic) and ducted systems may be difficult to extend without major building works.

Commercially, ducted systems can be zoned, possibly with individually controlled heaters for each zone and/or motorised zone dampers and mixing boxes, but in domestic situations, due to cost limitations, they only offer a limited degree of control and separate provision has to be made for domestic hot water heating.

## Radiant heating

Radiant heating systems are suited to situations with very high ceiling levels, or very high air change rates, with heaters usually of the gas fired 'radiant plaque' or 'tube' type.

Gas-fired radiant heating systems can be highly efficient and economical, with running costs of between 20% and 40% lower than alternative types of system. However, to realise these savings it is essential to correctly control the heaters (non-adjustable black bulb type thermostat) and consideration of access to the heaters for maintenance purposes must always be considered when evaluating the economics. The potential savings in running costs could be negated by the cost of installing a tower to give access for maintenance/repair.

## Electric storage

Electric storage heating is possibly the cheapest to install, but lacks the inherent control flexibility of wet systems and is therefore invariably less efficient, unless used only for 'background' heating. They are suited to very well insulated properties with a heat loss around 4kW or less and re-furbishment in properties where the installation of gas could present a potential hazard (e.g. high-rise flats). Most modern heaters incorporate

charge and output controls and some electricity supply companies have tariffs which provide a mid-afternoon boost, as well as radio controlled charging periods.

# Heat sources

With wet heating systems the heat source is invariably a gas or oil fired boiler, although solid fuel boilers may be found in areas without a natural gas supply.

## Solid fuel boilers

Solid fuel boilers can be quite economical, especially the 'smokeater' type units, which can burn bituminous coals in smokeless zones, but usually much more expensive to operate for heating the domestic hot water only during the summer – use electric heating for summer DHW, unless large quantities required. They need frequent maintenance, plus fuel storage facilities and, since the heat cannot be turned on and off in the same way as with gas or oil, they must have 'heat-sink'. They are not suited to fully automatic control.

The suitability for use of an existing chimney must be checked. Flue gas temperatures from solid fuel boilers will be considerably higher than with gas boilers and flues must be capable of withstanding these temperatures (around 1,200°C if any tar deposits catch fire) – suitable types are twin wall S/S insulated (some with additional ceramic lining) and refractory block flues. Existing chimneys must be checked for suitability for use – can be lined with insulating refractory concrete liners of 'cast-in-situ' refractory liner – single skin flexible liners must not be used. Consult a specialist if in doubt.

## Gas fired boilers

Gas fired boilers, both natural gas and LPG fired, are available as floor or wall mounted models with conventional or balanced flues. Balanced flue boilers can be located in any room, and fan assisted balanced flue boilers do not have to be located on outside walls – some flues can be extended by up to 30m. There are limitations in the siting of conventionally flued boilers, particularly in relation to bathrooms, shower rooms and sleeping accommodation and reference must be made to the current Gas Safety (Installation and Use) Regulations. There are also restrictions on under stairs installation of boilers, as there are in relation to the manner and positioning of flue terminations.

For domestic and commercial boilers with atmospheric burners (flue gas temperatures up to 260°C), flues can be of single wall or flexible stainless steel type. To comply with the Gas Safety Regulations, one should never, generally, connect a new appliance to an existing flue liner – the liner should always be renewed at the same time.

For solid fuel boilers, commercial boilers with pressure jet burners and certain DFE fires, where flue gas temperatures can be up to 540°C, flues must be twin wall insulated or of refractory block/liner.

In commercial situations a 'Monodraught' type flue or fan diluted flue system can overcome problems of boiler location and fluing. The choice of system depends on location and it is advisable to seek the manufacturers advice relating to design/installation requirements.

## Oil fired boilers

Oil fired boilers are available as conventional or balanced flue units, both floor standing or wall mounted. They require the provision of an oil storage tank (accessible for filling) plus connecting pipework to the boiler and safety controls. For conventional flues, check with boiler manufacturer for correct type, as this will depend on flue gas temperature – aluminium/ceramic/clayware are not normally suitable.

See Building Regulations (Part J) and BS 5410 for detailed installation requirements.

## Electric boilers

Some electric boilers are similar to a normal night storage heater, but incorporate a pump, heat exchanger and pipework for connection to the central heating distribution system. Since all the heat is stored in one unit the distribution of the heat output is far more flexible than with individual storage heaters and, provided any 'boost' consumption at the higher general tariff rate can be kept to an absolute minimum, although economical to run, they can be quite bulky and heavy.

## Condensing boilers

Conventional boiler efficiencies are limited to around 80% to 83%, to keep the flue gas temperatures around 220°C and prevent condensation occurring in the boiler or flue. The annual efficiency of a conventional boiler will be around 67% (with a badly controlled system this can easily drop to well below 60%) compared to 87% for a gas fired condensing boiler,

rising to at least 94% when fully condensing.

The only major difference between a condensing boiler and a fan assisted balanced flue boiler is that the condensing boiler has a corrosion resistant aluminium or stainless steel heat exchanger, with a very high heat exchange surface area, and a condensate collection and drain point. Installation is no more difficult than for a conventional boiler, the only additional requirement being a plastic drain pipe to a suitable drain connection. Do not run the condensate piping in copper, or connect it to copper or lead piping, since the condensate is mildly acidic and will corrode copper and lead. When the condensing boiler is working at its most efficient, 'flue pluming' is most prevalent.

System design is to normal parameters, as with a conventional boiler. Oversizing of heat emitters is not economically justified – 50% oversizing only improves efficiency by 2.4%. Even without entering the condensing mode, the boiler will still achieve an efficiency of around 87% compared to around 77% for a modern floor standing unit. With the cost of boilers steadily reducing, the increased capital cost can be quickly recovered through reduced running costs.

Condensing boilers are also available for operation with LPG (Propane), and oil.

## Direct fired air heaters

Direct fired air heaters are available as balanced flue gas fired room heaters; conventional or balanced flue gas fired unit heaters; oil fired conventionally flued heaters and radiant gas heaters. There are numerous variations to suit different applications and they are usually quite efficient, due to them being individually controlled.

Note that in garages/workshops the combustion air supply to the burners should be ducted from outside.

Electric quartz radiant heaters, operating on normal tariff rates, will be very expensive to run, although they may be the ideal solution in certain areas requiring localised and intermittent heating.

# Alternative heat sources

Three alternative primary heat sources which could be considered are: heat pumps, combined heat and power (CHP) units and solar heating.

## Heat pump

A heat pump operates in the same way as a domestic refrigerator, but in reverse – heat is removed from some 'inexhaustible' source (e.g. outside air, ground water) and discharged into the heating system, in the same way that heat is removed from the icebox and given out at the condenser coil at the back of the refrigerator cabinet.

## CHP units

CHP units are usually gas-fired and comprise of a gas driven internal combustion engine linked to an electrical generator. A high percentage of the energy that would otherwise be wasted as heat from the engine unit can be used to power the heating system, giving an operational efficiency in excess of 85%. For a client with a fairly constant electrical and heating demand, this can be an extremely efficient method of electrical generation.

## Solar heating

Although fairly high levels of solar radiation are available in the UK, even in cloudy winter days, solar heating will only provide what is generally termed a 'low grade' heat source, such as is suitable for pre-heating domestic hot water and for heating of swimming pools.

All the above alternatives offer a variety of permutations and combinations, and it is essential to obtain independent and unbiased professional advice if any of these options are being considered.

# Combustion air

With any fuel burning appliance it is vital that there is an adequate provision for combustion, cooling and flue dilution air. Full details of requirements are given in the Building Regulations, Gas Safety (Installation and Use) Regulations and relevant British Standards – the following summarises the basic requirements.

## Unflued appliances

The concentration of carbon dioxide must not exceed 2800ppm where people may be present and ventilation must be provided by natural ventilation via permanent openings at high and low level, or by mechanical ventilation with airflow safety interlock.

## Open flued appliances

These require permanent ventilation openings, either directly to outside or via adjacent room(s). Vents must be non-closeable; must not incorporate any screens that could be blocked by dirt, insects, etc. and must not be positioned where they could be blocked by leaves, snow, etc. Vents through cavity walls **must be sleeved**. Always check effect of any extract ventilation fans on the operation of the flue. To correctly size the grilles, check the manufacturers' information on the percentage of 'free area'.

## Balanced flue (room sealed) appliances

The design of these appliances places the air inlet and flue discharge in the same pressure zone. The only ventilation requirement may be for cooling purposes

if the appliance is located in a compartment – some appliances do not require compartment ventilation – see manufacturers' requirements.

**Inadequate ventilation can be lethal, particularly with gas fired appliances. it is the installer's responsibility to ensure that the complete gas installation and connected appliances are safe to use. A contractor working on a gas installation would be committing a criminal offence if he does not belong to a class of persons approved for the time being by the Health and Safety Executive.**

**Carbon monoxide** poisoning causes cherry red appearance in victims face – remove victim from contaminated area and ensure continued breathing – administer oxygen if possible. See Table 1.

# Boiler sizing

Boiler size is normally based upon the calculated heat loss plus 10% (or 15%), but with intermittently occupied buildings a margin of 20–25% may be more appropriate. If there is a great amount of pipework which is not giving off useful heat (e.g. beneath suspended or intermediate floors or passing through unheated voids or cupboards) an additional allowance must be included.

In domestic situations an additional 2 or 3kW is often added to the boiler load for domestic hot water heating, but with a well insulated domestic dwelling this could represent around 30% of the total load and seriously reduce the boiler efficiency.

In the average domestic situation, with a well controlled system and with a low capacity very high recovery cylinder (at least 20kW heat transfer capacity) and hot water priority, the inclusion of an additional

hot water heating margin is unnecessary. With the full boiler output switched to hot water heating, the short period of loss of space heating will not be noticed.

Where there is a requirement for a high performance shower, the domestic hot water heating load will be greater and is likely to constitute the largest element of the total boiler heating load. Calculation of DHW storage capacity is therefore a matter of achieving an economic balance between storage capacity and boiler re-heat capacity, assuming a very high recovery cylinder with heat transfer capacity >boiler output capacity.

The following can be used to evaluate requirements:

Specific heat of water = 4.18kJ/kg°K.

1 Joule  = 1 Watt for 1 sec.

1kW/h  = 3,600kJ.

Assumed cold water supply at 10°C and mixed water temperature at 40°C.

Useful energy stored in cylinder (H1 kJ.):

H1 = storage volume (litre = kg.) × (storage temp. – 40)°C × 4.18kJ/kg°K.

Re-heat potential from boiler (H2kJ.):

H2 = boiler output (kW) ×

$$\frac{\text{draw off duration (min.)}}{60 \text{ min}} \times 3,600\text{kJ.}$$

Required energy (H3 kJ.) :

H3= Draw off volume (litre = kg.) ×

(40 – 10)°C × 4.18kJ/kg°K.

To meet load, H3 = H1 + H2

# Heat emitter selection

## Types of heat emitters

The common steel panel radiators are available with single or double panels and with fins welded to them to further increase output. Radiators manufactured from steel are also available in a variety of shapes and designs, as are ones manufactured from aluminium, copper, cast iron and even plastic, but they are more expensive than the steel panel type. In certain circumstances, such as with the elderly, infirm or young children, it is necessary to use low surface temperature radiators. Radiators give approx. 80% of their output by convection and 20% by radiation.

There should be at least 100mm clearance from the top of the radiator to

*Table 1*

| % Saturation of haemoglobin with carbon monoxide | Symptoms |
|---|---|
| 0.005 | Threshold value |
| 0.01 | Slight headache in 2–3 hours |
| 0.02 | Mild headache, dizziness, nausea and sleepiness after 2–3 hours |
| 0.04 | Frontal headache and nausea after 1–2 hours; risk of death after 3 hours |
| 0.08 | Severe headache, dizziness, convulsions after 45 minutes; unconsciousness within one hour; risk of death after 2–3 hours |
| 0.16 | Headache, dizziness and nausea within 20 minutes; unconsciousness, risk of death after 1–2 hours |
| 0.32 | Headache, dizziness and nausea in 5–10 minutes; risk of death after 15 minutes |
| 0.64 | Severe symptoms after 1 to 2 minutes; death within 10–15 minutes |
| 1.28 | Immediate symptoms; death within 1 to 3 minutes |

any cill above and 150mm clearance below for the pipework and connections. A long, low radiator will give better heat distribution than a tall one (note emission penalty) and avoid locations covered by furnishings. Natural convectors will give a quicker heat-up than a radiator and can be either wall mounted or of the skirting or under floor type.

Fan convectors will give an even faster heat up and can be time/temperature controlled. They are very compact and can be built into fitted units, bench seats or stairways; mounted at high level or recessed into floors. Significant savings can result if the operation of the fan convector can be linked to a touch activated timer control or occupancy detector. Ensure the path of the airflow is not obstructed by any furniture.

## Choice and positioning of heaters

Heat is given out in two ways – by radiation and by convection. With radiant heating, the heat rays given out strike any surfaces in their path, such as people, furniture, and walls, and warm them up – these surfaces then in turn heat the surrounding air. With convective heating the heat warms the air which in turn heats the surfaces it comes into contact with, as it circulates around the room. Occupancy pattern/use of area will influence selection of emitter type.

Comfort depends not only on the air temperature but also the average radiant temperature (Mean Radiant Temperature – MRT) of all the surrounding surfaces – the lower this average temperature the higher the air temperature must be to give comfortable conditions. Around 20% of the heat output from a radiator is by radiation and the remaining 80% is given out by convection – a reasonable balance for most domestic situations, where the radiant level will balance the effect of colder external wall surfaces. With highly insulated buildings, a faster responding convective heater may be more appropriate.

If radiators are positioned on outside walls, significant savings (5–10%) can be achieved by putting reflective foil faced insulation behind the radiators.

Avoid obstructing any electrical socket outlets. If using a fan convector, ensure the path of the airflow is not obstructed by any furniture.

## Heat emitter sizing

To size a heater it is first of all necessary to decide on the system flow and return water temperatures. The 'conventional' temperatures for low pressure systems are 82°C flow and 71°C return (180°F/160°F) giving a mean water temperature of 76.5°C for heaters on a two-pipe system, it is worth considering basing the design on 82°C/68°C flow and return, in order to reduce pipe sizes and flow rates. There is no reason why the temperature differential cannot be even higher, but attention must be given to any limitations imposed by the boiler manufacturer, and the saving in pipe sizing may be offset by the necessary increase in radiator size.

The generally accepted method of sizing radiators is to add 10% to the calculated room heat loss and select the nearest sized radiator. With the variations in the UK Winter climate during recent years, a 15% margin may be considered more appropriate., especially if heating is very intermittent. It is not normal in domestic situations to consider internal heat gains from people and equipment, since these can be intermittent.

Prior to 1-7-97, radiator outputs were based on BS 3528:1977 which specified a mean water to room temperature difference of 60°C and pipe connections at top and bottom opposite ends (TBOE). With normal system flow and return temperatures of 82/71°C the outputs will therefore be lower. Table 2 gives the correction factors with which the manufacturers figures must be multiplied for 82/71°C flow and return temperatures and varying room temperatures, plus other correction factors for varying methods of installation.

All the correction factors below are cumulative, so for a radiator with a rated output of 1500W installed in an open recess in a room at 20°C with BOE connections, its output will reduce to 1500 × 0.9 × 0.85 × 0.90 = 1032W.

From 1-7-97, radiator outputs have had to comply with EN-442 which requires that quoted outputs are based on a mean water to room temperature difference of 50°C – this will result in the quoted outputs being reduced by around 20%. Also, testing has to be carried out, or quoted outputs adjusted, to equate to pipe connections at top and bottom same ends (TBSE), thus requiring a deduction of 8-9% from quoted outputs to allow for bottom opposite end connections – the normal in the UK. Virtually all UK radiator manufacturers still quote outputs based upon 60°C temperature difference, the figures shown in their catalogues being adjusted from the 50°C difference at which testing is carried out.

Oversizing will result in reduced system efficiency due to temperature overshoot. As a general guide one heater will satisfactorily cover up to 20sq. metres.

## Piping system design and sizing

The most common type of heating distribution system is a two-pipe system, although there are many older single-pipe systems still in existence.

## Two-pipe system

The two-pipe system will have separate flow and return pipes with the flow and return connections to each heater connected to the respective flow and return pipes.

Two-pipe systems are always pumped and have the advantage of a positive (pumped) flow of water through each heater. Copper piping systems of 15–28mm size are referred to as 'small-

*Table 2* *Correction factor for radiator outputs*

| Room temperature | Correction factor for radiator outputs |
|---|---|
| 16 | 1.00 |
| 18 | 0.95 |
| 20 | 0.90 |
| 22 | 0.87 |
| Connections top bottom same ends (TBSE) | 1.04 |
| Connections bottom opposite ends (BOE) | 0.85 |
| Radiator length greater than 5 x its height | 0.93 |
| Radiator in open fronted recess | 0.90 |
| Radiator in recess with front grille | 0.80 and lower |
| Radiator shelf above | down to 0.90 |
| Metallic paint finish | from 0.9 to 0.8 |

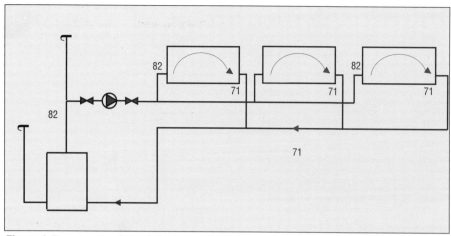

*Figure 4  Two pipe circuit circulating temperatures °C*

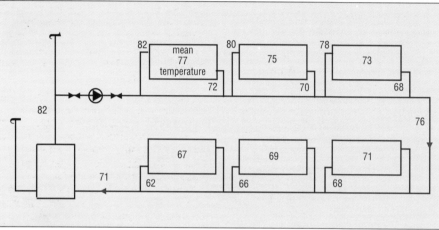

*Figure 5  Single pipe circuit circulating temperatures °C*

# Pipe layout and sizing

Before sizing a piping system, it is necessary to decide upon the position of heaters etc. in order that pipe routes can be decided, with due regard to the constructional details of the building and any client requirements. If installing a heater in a bathroom, it is a good idea to connect it from the outlet side of the pump before any control valves. It will then heat up whenever the boiler comes on and not be dependant on the remainder of the house requiring heating. If installing a solid fuel boiler, at least one heater must be connected on a separate gravity circuit from the boiler to provide a 'heat sink'. If most of the heaters can be picked up on one or two pipe loops, then it may be worth considering a single pipe system. Heaters will have to be sized to take account of the reducing water temperature, and they must be connected top bottom opposite ends and always with the return connection downstream of the flow. Convectors and hot water cylinders cannot be put on a single pipe circuit. Mixing microbore and smallbore is quite permissible, provided the pipework and pump are correctly sized.

Always connect a hot water cylinder primary return to the combined heating and DHW return pipe downstream of the last heating return connection, to avoid possible reverse circulation problems.

Correct pipe sizing is essential if problems of insufficient water flow to the farthest radiators on the system are to be avoided. Having determined the piping layout, the heating load on each section can be calculated and the provisional pipe size can be determined from Table 3, which is based on a flow rate corresponding to an 11°C. system temperature drop and also shows the heat loss from uninsulated and insulated pipe.

For domestic systems it is generally unnecessary to carry out a detailed pipe sizing, with proportioning of mains losses, etc., as one would do for a commercial situation. However, it is a good idea to carry out an accurate pressure drop calculation, in order to check the adequacy of the pipe sizing and check the pump duty.

The procedure for this can be summarised as follows:

1.  Total heating loads in each pipe section and convert to flow rate in l/s (same as kg/s). The following conversion formula can be used:

bore'. An option (usually for domestic situations) is a 'microbore' system in which the main flow and return from the boiler, connect to manifolds from which the radiators are individually connected by 8mm or 10mm pipes. Being flexible, the pipes can be 'threaded' between floor joists etc. in much the same way as electrical cables, so avoiding having to use fittings. Installation is simplified, but the system has to be very carefully designed and a more powerful pump is needed to circulate the water through the small pipes as well as specially designed 'twin- entry' radiator valves.

There are several variations for commercial installations, including 'ladder' or 'reverse return' configurations.

## Single pipe systems

With single pipe systems, water circulates around one or more single pipe loops with the radiator flow and return connections connected from the same pipe loop, the return connection being downstream of the flow. Whilst circulation is usually pump assisted, the circulation of water through each radiator is primarily by gravity, although it can be aided by the use of diverter tees, and

connections must be top/bottom opposite ends (TBOE). Although there is less pipework to install, a single-pipe system must be carefully designed and it cannot be used with convectors, which must have a pumped flow of water through them to achieve the rated output.

Since the water temperature around the pipe loop(s) will progressively drop as it passes each radiator, the radiators towards the end of the circuit will have to be larger than they would be for the same output on a two-pipe system, where there would be little variation in flow temperature from one end of the system to the other.

A variation on the basic single pipe system is the 'loop-in' system whereby the pipework loops in and out of a single two connection valve on each radiator – the valve incorporates a by-pass so that some of the water enters the radiator whilst the remainder goes through the by-pass and is joined by the cooler water leaving the radiator – and the mixed water leaves the valve through the second connection and passes to the next radiator on the circuit. This gives a more positive flow through each radiator.

*Table 3* Heat losses

| Pipe diameter (mm) | Maximum load (watts) | Heat loss/m | |
| --- | --- | --- | --- |
| | | Bare (watts) | Insulated (watts (9mm thick)) |
| 6 | 650 | 20 | 4 |
| 8 | 1300 | 27 | 6 |
| 10 | 2100 | 32 | 7 |
| 15 | 5500 | 46 | 10 |
| 22 | 11000 | 63 | 12 |
| 28 | 18000 | 78 | 14 |
| 35 | 28000 | 95 | 15 |

$$\text{Load in kW} \times \frac{0.23825}{\text{Design temp drop K}} = \text{flow in l/s}$$

2. Measure length of each section of pipe and add allowance for equivalent length of fittings.

*NOTE:*
*This is a simplification of the procedure of multiplying the pipe equivalent length at a particular flow rate by the fitting velocity pressure loss factor.*

3. Determine pressure drop in Pa/m for the flow rate in the pipe size concerned and multiply by the total length from 2 × 2 (flow & return) – this gives the pressure drop in that section of pipe. If the resultant velocity >1m/s or pressure drop >400Pa/m, then increase pipe size.

4. Total all calculated pressure drops from the boiler to the radiator at the end of each of the distribution circuits, adding the resistance of the boiler and any control valve – some circuits may have common sections of piping. The circuit with the highest resistance is the Index Circuit and gives the required pump head at the system flow rate – the pump selection can then be made.

A reduction can be made in the heater sizing for each metre run of exposed copper pipe, based on the outputs in the preceding table. These figures will vary depending upon room and water temperatures, etc. but are sufficiently accurate to be used with the normal range of water and room temperatures. If the pipe emission is too high, the efficiency of the system control could be adversely affected.

## Gas and oil piping installations

Gas piping systems must be designed and installed in accordance with the requirements of either BS 6891:1998 'Installation of low pressure gas pipework up to 28mm. in domestic premises' or Institution of Gas Engineers publication IGE/UP/2 'Gas installation Pipework, Boosters and Compressors on Industrial and Commercial premises'. The requirements for LPG is covered in the CITB Study Notes Publication ME 210.

Oil supply systems should be in accordance with BS 5410:Part 1:1977 – CoP for Oil fired installations up to 44 kW output or Part 2 for above 44kW.

# Domestic hot water – types of system

## Vented (storage) systems

In domestic premises with a heating system, the normal method of providing domestic hot water is via an indirect hot water storage cylinder, with the cold water supply from a cold water storage cistern. The efficiency of such a system will vary considerably – it is essential that the cylinder is very well insulated . Building Regulations require the use of factory applied insulation. Primary heating pipework between the boiler and cylinder must also be insulated.

A very basic system, with time switch control, gravity circulation to the cylinder coil, and no controlling thermostat on the cylinder to shut off the boiler when the temperature of the stored water is hot enough, may have an efficiency as low as 30% during 'hot water only' heating. If the primary heating pipes are

uninsulated, even lower efficiency will result. The efficiency will improve with the addition of full thermostatic control.

The efficiency of a fully pumped system can be considerably increased by installing a cylinder with a low storage capacity which has a very high recovery rated coil cylinder, far in excess of a normal BS cylinder.

With low storage capacity and very high heating coil surface area (heat exchange capacity up to 30kW or more), heat is transferred to the stored water as fast as the boiler can provide it. The boiler does not cycle 'on' and 'off' during the heating period and a hot water only system efficiency of well in excess of 75% can be achieved. The use of a high recovery cylinder enables the boiler input to be taken into account when calculating domestic hot water storage requirements, since it will be re-heating the water to a significant extent, even during a relatively short draw-off period.

With a typical 60 litre cylinder and a gas fired boiler of 17kW output, the entire contents will be heated from cold to 60°C in around 15 minutes if the boiler is hot to start with, and 18 minutes if starting from cold. With a 22kW boiler, these times reduce to 10 minutes and 17 minutes The very fast recovery means baths can be run at around 10-15mins. intervals, but use with a 'hot water priority' control system. The inclusion of a pump over-run thermostat to transfer residual boiler heat to the cylinder, will further increase the system efficiency, by around ½-1%.

### Advantages

i. Large quantities of hot water available quickly

ii. Once heated, availability of water unaffected by gas or electric supply failure.

### Disadvantages

i. Water pressure may be inadequate for a good shower

ii. Considerable re-heat time once hot water drawn off (unless a high recovery cylinder)

iii. Requires cold water storage cistern, with consequent frost protection problems if located in a roof void

iv. Wasteful heat loss from stored hot water when no demand

v. Space required for storage cylinder.

## Unvented (mains pressure) systems

All cold water outlets and the hot water storage system are fed directly from the mains, giving very good outlet pressures, suitable for high resistance terminal fittings, such as single lever operation taps – balanced hot and cold pressures will result in improved mixing and less wastage of water, with consequent reduced running costs.

Water is heated directly or indirectly in a purpose designed insulated storage cylinder, either of copper or lined steel. Expansion is accommodated in a small expansion tank and a number of special safety controls are fitted. Suitable cylinders with expansion tank and safety controls are available as packaged units to serve just a few basin taps or a complete dwelling. Direct gas fired units are also available, although these would normally be used for larger installations.

Mains pressure hot water can also be provided by combination boilers, multipoint water heaters (gas or electric) and point-of-use electric heaters. If installing a combination boiler, ensure the gas supply is adequate – input can be >35kW for DHW heating. When comparing different makes, ensure you compare like with like – DHW output claims may be based on 25°C, 30°C or 35°C temperature rise.

### Advantages

i. Cold water storage cistern not required

ii. Possible cheaper installation cost

iii. Removes problems of freezing of roof pipework etc

iv. Reduced running costs

v. Very good water pressure at outlets and better shower performance.

### Disadvantages

i. Requires annual maintenance check of all safety controls by qualified plumber

ii. May show up defect in existing piping installations when converted to the higher pressure un-vented operation.

## Mains fed instantaneous systems

Usually supplied by a wall mounted multipoint gas fired water heater or combination gas fired boiler. Some multipoint units have fan assisted flues and can be located up to 3m from the outside wall. Outputs can be up to 35kW and most units will also supply a shower, in conjunction with a suitable thermostatic mixer. In hard water areas a water treatment unit should always be installed on the mains supply to the heater. It is also advisable to insulate any long runs of hot water supply pipework to reduce heat loss between the heater and taps.

### Thermal storage system

A thermal storage system provides mains pressure hot water to all points of use, in the same way as a multipoint heater. Heating water from the boiler is passed through the shell side of the cylinder and the mains water is passed through the coil to supply all the taps – the volume of heated water is small, so all the safety devices of an 'unvented system' can be omitted, although the installation of a small expansion vessel to act as a 'shock arrestor' is advisable, as is a thermostatic mixing valve. The heating circuit is separately pumped, either from the shell side, or via the second coil. See below. Such a system may give improved boiler part load efficiency and the thermal store provides rapid response to both hot water and heating system demand. The primary circuit pump will be of a low head type and the potential for system aeration problems will be reduced. The inclusion of a pump over-run thermostat will further increase the system efficiency. The heating circuit could be a completely separate sealed system with its own expansion vessel and safety valve, whilst the boiler remains on a low head open vented system. The latest packaged units combine both a condensing boiler and thermal store in one insulated unit, together with purpose designed controls, and have a resultant energy saving potential.

### Electric water heaters

Electric mains fed instantaneous water heaters are generally restricted to supplying a single outlet and small electrically heated 'point of use' storage units of 7 litre capacity. capacity can be installed above or below a working surface – they require special taps to provide a vent and prevent pressure build-up. They avoid having to heat a large quantity of stored water at a time when only a small amount is required. Inlet water treatment should be considered in hard water areas, although the majority of electric heater elements are easily removed for de-scaling.

## Alternatives and design considerations

Where the points of demand are a considerable distance apart, or demand is of a low level, consideration should be given to the installation of individual 'point of use' heaters. In a large dwelling, with an en-suite bathroom remote from the main area of demand at the kitchen and main bathroom, consideration could be given to the installation of two independent low storage/high recovery cylinders.

Another option would be to install a single cylinder with a self-regulating electric trace heating cable on the very long dead-legs.

In the majority of small commercial situations demand is low, and can be met by local point-of-use heaters, but occasionally one is involved in a project requiring large quantities of water. Under these circumstances, a dedicated gas fired water heater may be the answer, which can be cistern or mains fed. If the high demand is on a very intermittent basis (e.g. showering) and there is a heating system installed, then another option would be to install a non-storage system with a plate heat exchanger, which is heated on a priority basis by the boiler plant.

### Advantages

i. Cold water storage cistern not required (unless for c/w outlets)

ii. No space required for hot water storage (except thermal storage)

iii. Hot water always available at the turn of a tap

iv Possibly cheaper installation cost than a storage system (except thermal storage)

v No wasteful heat loss from stored hot water

vi High water pressure available at outlets.

### Disadvantages

i. For a gas multipoint heater an adjacent outside wall and a gas supply is required

ii. Slower delivery rate of hot water than with a storage system

iii. Electric heaters are expensive to run if quantities of water are required – they need a separate electrical supply.

When designing any mains-fed system, storage or instantaneous, it is essential that the adequacy of the cold water main supply is checked for maintenance of adequate flow/pressure under periods of high demand/drought.

Water Regulations are very explicit in their requirements to avoid wastage or contamination of water supplies and everyone who is involved with the design, specification, installation and maintenance of domestic water systems must ensure that they comply with the requirements of the various legislative documents relating to the prevention of Legionella.

# Piping installation

1. Avoid placing bends or other fittings close to the inlet or outlet of pumps, as this can cause cavitation under certain conditions. If possible, aim for a 450mm length of straight pipe both sides of the pump.

2. Fittings which offer a high resistance to the flow of water can give rise to noise generation and problems of inadequate flow. Generally, compression elbows and end feed elbows have a far tighter radius than integral solder ring elbows, and therefore offer a higher resistance to flow. Note that microbore pipes are vulnerable to damage and blockage and there may also be noise problems due to high water velocities at any restrictions.

3. Always consider requirements for venting and pre-commissioning cleansing and maintenance, and include adequate provision for drainage. At least two 15mm valved full bore drain points should be provided at low points in the system to enable it to be adequately flushed through, positioning with regard to flushing paths, avoiding short circuiting.

4. Generally, the maximum safe depth for notching a floor joist is 0.15 × the joist depth, with a maximum width of 1.5 × the pipe width, and a maximum of two pipes in a single notch. The maximum diameter for a hole drilled through a joist is 0.25 × the joist depth, with the centre line between 0.25 and 0.4 of the joist depth down from the top.

5. Indicate on the floorboards with a felt marker pen the route of pipes under suspended floors.

6. Ensure all high points are adequately vented and that air vent points, compression joists and any other potential sources of water leakage are not positioned over any electrical equipment.

7. Do not use softened water to fill a system (or add washing-up liquid !!) – the high salt content can result in serious corrosion problems.

8. Only use the very minimum amounts of flux when making soldered joints and use a pre-commissioning cleanser.

9. If there is a risk of the installation being left switched off during freezing conditions, use an anti-freeze as well as a corrosion proofer or provide frost protection controls.

10. Always connect the DHW cylinder primary return as the last connection on the return pipe to the boiler, after any heating return connections to avoid reverse circulation problems.

11. Install pumps vertically, to self-purge of air, and with the shafts horizontal (not below) to reduce bearing load and wear. Fit valves each side and do not position at system low point.

12. If installing a combined cold feed and open vent, in order to comply with British Standard 5449:Pt1:1990 the boiler must be fitted with a high limit safety thermostat.

13. Do not install a new boiler or equipment into an existing system without cleansing it thoroughly. Avoid fabricated or aluminium heat exchangers if the system is not chemically cleaned. Consider the requirement for a strainer on the return to the boiler.

14. Use reflective radiator film over pipes which are immediately below floor boards to avoid degradation of floor covering.

15. Always fuse the control system at 3A and mark the plug/connection unit accordingly.

16. The electrical supply to an immersion heater must be run directly from the distribution board, and must not feed any other equipment.

17. When an existing system cannot be drained, a self cutting tee can be used to provide a drain point.

18. Use pipe clips that completely enclose the pipe and metal strapping for suspending pipes below floor joists.

19. Use good quality lever operated quarter turn ball valves rather than gate valves for ease of future maintenance.

20. Install temporary equipotential bonds if breaking electrical continuity of existing pipework, to protect operatives and third parties.

21. Use non-dezincifiable fittings on domestic water services.

## By-pass connection

For boilers fitted with pump over-run thermostats it is essential that there is always an open circuit for the water to be pumped around. If all circuits can be closed off by motorised or thermostatic valves, a by-pass is required – use an automatic pressure operated by-pass valve to avoid loss of boiler operating efficiency. If the system has a three-port motorised control valve, or if there is some other permanently open circuit, such as via a bathroom radiator (without hand-wheel valve), there is generally no requirement for a by-pass connection, but check with boiler manufacturer.

# Controls

However well designed a system, its ultimate efficiency will depend upon the method of control. The basic requirement of any control system is to provide the correct amount of heat in the right place at the required time, and to ensure that the boiler is switched off when there is no system demand for heat.

The main components of a control system will usually be a programmer to enable selection of system operating times; thermostats to control the space and, where applicable, domestic hot water storage temperature and motorised valve(s) to control the circulation of heating water to the different circuits (e.g. space heating and domestic hot water heating).

Modern programmers are of the electronic type (rather than electro-mechanical) and either battery operated or mains operated with a battery reserve (alkaline or rechargeable). Some are very basic in operation, whilst others offer three or more switching cycles a day, with separate times for heating and hot water plus separate programming for each day of the week or weekdays and weekends. Such flexibility offers greater potential for energy saving, but consideration of the occupants ability to operate the unit must be taken into account.

## Thermostats

Modern room thermostats can be either of the electro-mechanical type, (with either a bi-metallic strip or vapour- filled bellows) or electronic type. Electro-mechanical type thermostats often incorporate accelerator heaters (requiring a neutral connection) to reduce the temperature overshoot with radiator systems and some also have a night set-back facility. Modern electronic room thermostats achieve much better control, with a differential of around 0.5°C. Since each 1°C rise in temperature above that required will increase fuel consumption by about 7%, the energy saving potential of the electronic thermostat is readily apparent. Cylinder thermostats are invariably of the electro-mechanical type with a differential of around 6-10°C to prevent excessive boiler cycling.

### Programmable thermostats

Programmable room thermostats comprise a single channel electronic programmer and a room thermostat in one casing. They are often used where the boiler does not provide domestic hot water storage (e.g. the 'combi' type), or for zone control. Being of the electronic type, they give close temperature control and offer programming on a daily basis with as many as six timed periods a day, each at a different temperature setting. They all have battery back-up, or are battery operated. The 'off' periods are determined by selecting a timed period at a reduced temperature (e.g. 14°C), effectively giving frost protection.

## Thermostatic radiator valves

Thermostatic radiator valves are simple to install, requiring no electrical supply, and can be installed to give temperature control in individual rooms. They should not be installed on all radiators as there would be no means of automatically stopping the boiler and pump when the demand in all areas is satisfied, with the valves having closed. The energy saving potential of the valves can be completely lost due to the continued operation of the pump, with water circulating via a continuously open or automatic by-pass valve controlled by-pass loop, and inefficient cycling of the boiler under the control of its thermostat. The Building Regulations require the installation of a room thermostat, to shut the boiler off when demand is satisfied. The thermostat must be located in an area that is representative of the temperatures in the property and there must be no thermostatic radiator valves in that area.

Their use should be limited to selected locations which are subject to external heat gains, or areas which require keeping at reduced temperature for long periods (e.g. spare bedrooms).

## Motorised valves

Motorised valves will either be of the two-port or three-port type. Two-port valves are also called 'zone valves' and can be used to control the flow of water around individual circuits (space heating or domestic hot water heating). There may be a boiler requirement for by-pass, particularly where it has a pump-over-run thermostat, to ensure that there is always an open path for water circulation.

Three-port valves have one inlet port, connected from the boiler flow (usually via the pump) and two outlet ports. The outlet ports will, typically, connect to the hot water cylinder heating flow and the radiator circuit flow, although they could both connect to two different zone heating circuits. The valves are either of the diverting (two position) or mid-position type. A diverting valve is driven by its motor to allow water to flow to one or other of the two outlet ports, as required by the controlling programmer/thermostat – usually give priority to the hot water cylinder heating. A mid-position valve allows the water to flow to either of the outlet ports, or both at the same time. Use of a three-port valve ensures that one port will always be open to maintain a flow path for the water and may avoid the need for a boiler by-pass.

## Electronic controllers

There is an increasing use of more sophisticated electronic controllers in domestic systems and these fall into three categories: compensated control; optimising time control, and boiler short-cycling control.

### Compensated control

Compensated control is a method whereby the amount of heat that is put into the building is automatically varied, depending upon the outside temperature and therefore the rate of heat loss from the building. This is achieved by either varying the temperature of the water flowing around the heating circuit, over-riding the boiler thermostat, or by varying the length of the boiler 'on' periods. This method of control is more efficient than a simple room thermostat control, and overcomes the problem of siting the room thermostat in a position that is truly representative of the average conditions in the house.

### Optimising time control

Optimising control is well proven in the commercial/industrial sector, and now coming into the domestic sector. The basic principle of operation is that you programme the occupancy period and required temperature and the controller then calculates the latest switch 'on' time, based on the preceding ambient temperature. Can also provide optimum 'off' control.

### Boiler short cycling

Boiler short cycling controls operate in conjunction with a normal room thermostat controlled system, and delays the boiler firing for a timed period. Some are simply electronic delay timers which delay boiler firing for a timed period, regardless of level or frequency of demand, whilst others take into account demand frequency. They have little energy saving potential and their use with certain types of systems may actually increase energy consumption.

# Underfloor heating systems

There is available a complete range of low pressure hot water underfloor heating systems suitable for all types of buildings. This includes different floor constructions such as screed, concrete and timber suspended.

Systems are also available for the refurbishment market using special thin screeds and dry construction techniques.

The design principles, however, are common to all systems and need to be understood.

Underfloor systems operate by means of embedded loops of pipe connected via a manifold to the flow and return sides of the heat source. See Figure 6.

Each loop or circuit can usually be controlled and/or isolated on both the flow and return.

Systems will normally be designed to operate at low water temperatures of between 40°C and 60°C and a temperature drop of between 5 and 10°K across the system.

Virtually all systems today use non-ferrous plastic pipe instead of ferrous or copper material. By laying modern polymer plastic pipe in continuous coils without joints it is possible to avoid many of the problems associated with systems in the past. Modern polymers do not corrode or attract scale and are in many cases capable of outliving the useful life of the building.

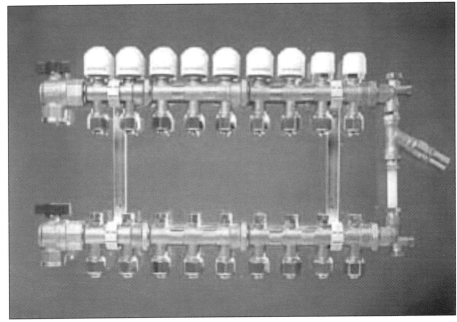

*Figure 6* Typical manifold

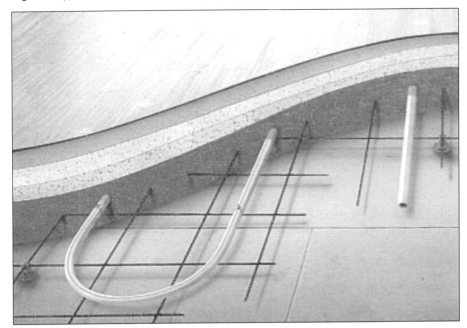

*Figure 7* Solid floor construction

## Solid floor construction

Typical floor make up:

a. Oversite

b. Concrete slab

c. Insulation

d. Underfloor heating pipes

e. Floor screed

f. Final floor finish.

On some buildings, the insulation will be fitted below the slab in which case the pipes can be installed within the concrete slab. See Figure 7.

The above construction is used for both ground bearing and suspended slabs.

## Floating floor construction

Typical floor make up:

a. Oversite

b. Concrete slab

c. Pre-grooved insulation fitted with heat emission plates

d. Underfloor heating pipes

e. Floor boarding

f. Final floor finish.

This design is often used on pot and beam construction where the finished floor is flooring grade chipboard laid over the underfloor heating system.

The specially adapted insulation, which is usually pre-grooved to accept the pipe and heat emission plates, is designed for full floor loading. The use of heat emission plates ensures that the floor temperature will be even across the whole floor area. See Figure 8.

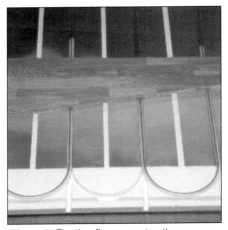

*Figure 8* Floating floors construction

The most common materials in use today are:

PEX: Cross linked Polyethylene

PP: Co-Polymer of Polypropylene

PB: Polybutylene

All pipes should ideally incorporate a diffusion barrier, which can be either integral or applied to the outside of the pipe as a coating. The purpose of the barrier is to reduce the amount of oxygen that can migrate through the pipe wall. Pipes without a diffusion barrier will pass much higher rates of oxygen thereby providing a highly oxygenated water circulation around the heating system. If the heating system is not fully protected by a corrosion inhibitor then rapid corrosion of any steel components within the heating system can occur.

Better insulation standards in our buildings have meant that most floors are now insulated as standard. This means that for most buildings the installation of the underfloor heating will be no more difficult than any other form of heating.

The basic form of floor construction in most buildings is solid concrete, floating or suspended. There are many different ways in which various underfloor heating manufacturers design their systems and it is only possible to deal with some of the standard methods of construction in this publication.

The following are typical floor sections of the three most common types.

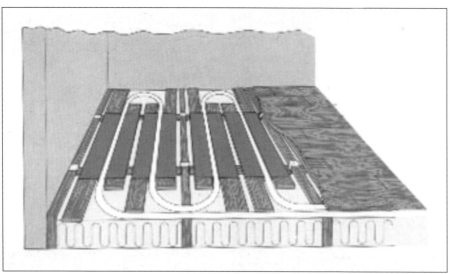

**Figure 9** *Suspended floors*

## Suspended floor construction

Typical floor make up:

1. Timber joists or battening

2. Insulation between joists

3. Cross battens

4. Heat emission plates fitted to cross battens

5. Underfloor heating pipes

6. Floor boarding

7. Final floor finish.

This design is suitable for most types of joisted or battened floors. The cross battening fitted at 90° to the joists means that a consistent pipe centre can be maintained irrespective of the joist centres. This particular system also avoids any notching of the joists.

There are many variations on all the standard floor sections and there are systems available today which can be adapted in a variety of ways to meet the building design.

Insulation would be fitted to most floors irrespective of the construction method and this would need to meet the requirements of the Building Regulations. The downward heat transmission can be calculated in several ways. For ground bearing slabs the most common formulae used is:

$$U_{slab} = \left\{ 0.05 + \left( 1.65 \times \frac{P}{A} \right) \right\} - \left\{ 0.6 \times \frac{P^2}{A} \right\}$$

Where:

$U_{slab}$ = U value of un-insulated slab W/m²K

P = External Perimeter of Building m

A = Total Area of Floor m²

By using the above formula, the 'U' value of the un-insulated slab can be calculated. Once this value is known the amount of insulation required to bring the floor up to the standard required can be calculated.

For an insulated slab the formula would be:

$$U_{insulated} = \frac{1}{\left( \dfrac{1}{U_{slab}} \right) + R_{insulation}}$$

Where:

$U_{insulated}$ = U value of an insulated slab W/m² K

Uslab = U value of un-insulated slab W/m²K

$R_{insulation}$ = The thermal resistance of the insulation W/m²K

The selection of a suitable insulation material will normally be made in conjunction with the architect to ensure the material will meet the floor loading requirements in addition to the level of insulation required.

For suspended floor slabs, the calculations are more complex since an enclosed air space is introduced below the slab, which can often have a high infiltration rate.

It must be remembered that with underfloor heating a solid screed or concrete floor will have a higher mean temperature than a floor constructed without underfloor heating. For this reason most floors will require a degree of insulation to be fitted to offset any downward losses.

# Design considerations

The human foot is a highly effective thermostat for the whole body. In the colder areas of the world human kind has been keen to 'take the chill off the floor' since ancient times. The techniques used to achieve this range from the simplest rugs and skins to the more sophisticated hypocaust system of the Greeks and Romans.

Research shows that a basic temperature of 21°C on the floor surface will give an ideal sensation of comfort. International Standards indicate that the comfortable range is between 19–26°C and dependant upon the required air temperature, floor heating systems should stay within this band.

Most areas are permitted with design floor temperatures up to 29°C. Temperatures up to 35°C are acceptable for specific areas such as pool surrounds, changing rooms, bathrooms and the first metre of space adjacent to walls with high fabric losses. This may occur where you have for instance extensive floor to ceiling glazing where it is necessary to offset as much as possible the cold down draught that occurs.

The sensitivity of the human foot will perceive a temperature above 29°C as 'uncomfortable' at normal room temperatures of 18–22°C and should be avoided.

Other limiting factors to the surface temperature may be the particular floor covering and for some materials such as timer the maximum manufacturers temperature should be observed.

Modern well insulated buildings no longer need high surface temperature in order to provide sufficient output to meet the heat losses of a typical building. Average floor emissions of between 50 and 75 watts per m² will often be more than sufficient. Low temperature floor systems provide inherent, passive self regulation. Floor temperatures generally need only be 3–5°K higher than room air. Any rise in air temperature due to solar gain or increased occupancy means the air will begin to approach the floor temperature. As this temperature difference decreases the heat emission from the floor reduces. This process is rapid and precise. Heat emission from the floor will begin to decrease as soon as air temperature rises. Given an air temperature of 20°C and a floor temperature of 23°C, heat emission from the floor will decrease by about a third for each degree of temperature that the air temperature rises. A three degree rise in air temperature will thus be sufficient to neutralise the system. Theoretically, this inherent self regulation makes it possible to design self an underfloor heating system with no other form of room temperature control.

# Design criteria

To evaluate comfort purely in terms of temperature requires consideration of the following:

1. Wet Bulb temperature

2. Dry Bulb temperature

3. Rate of air movement

4. Mean radiant temperature.

There are various accepted methods for the measurement of temperature including globe, equivalent, effective, radiant, environmental, dry and wet bulb.

The most commonly used measure of comfort for heating systems is the dry resultant temperature which in the absence of high rates of convection can give accurate indications as to the level of comfort that can be anticipated.

The dry resultant temperature is defined as:

$$t_{res} = \frac{t_r + T_{ai}\sqrt{10v}}{1 + \sqrt{10v}}$$

Where the internal rate of air movement v is less than 0.1m/s then the above equation can be simplified as follows.

$t_{res} = 0.5t_{ai} + 0.5t_r$

where:

$t_{res}$ = dry resultant temperature °C

$t_{ai}$ = inside air temperature °C

$t_r$ = mean radiant temperature °C

The inside air temperature can be assumed to be the dry bulb temperature with the mean radiant temperature as a calculation derived from the shape of the room, it's area, surface emmisivity and temperature.

The radiant temperature is significant to a feeling of comfort since it is the exchange of radiation with our surrounding that has the most effect on our perception of 'thermal comfort'.

With convective systems, the air temperature will always be higher than the dry resultant temperature and this difference can be as much as 5°K in buildings with high fabric losses such as glass walled structures.

Conversely in floor radiant systems the air temperature will always be lower than

the dry resultant temperature and is not so affected by the rate of fabric loss.

This means that the floor radiant systems lower dry resultant temperature can safely be used for the calculation of heat losses.

This difference can account for a reduction of 5-10% for most types of buildings.

In addition, it is not necessary to allow any margins for height factors in buildings when considering the use of radiant floor heating systems.

In order to prepare a design for a building it is necessary to calculate the heat losses in an acceptable form.

Many of the modern computer programs allow for the use of resultant temperatures in conjunction with floor radiant systems. These will give a more accurate reflection of the steady state heat losses.

Once the heat losses are known and tabulated then the underfloor heating system can be designed. Since there is an upper limit on the surface temperature the maximum output from the floor is restricted.

For general purposes, a figure of 11 Watts/$m^2$ K can be used to determine the maximum floor emission. Where K is the difference between surface and air temperature.

For example:

| | |
|---|---|
| Room area | 10$m^2$ |
| Heat loss | 540 Watts |
| Heat required | 54 Watts/$m^2$ |
| Air temperature | 20°C |
| Floor temperature | 26°C |
| Output required | 54/(26-20)<br>= 9 Watts/$m^2$K |

In the above example, the heat required is within the design parameter of 11 Watts/$m^2$K.

The calculation should be repeated for each of the rooms or areas to determine whether there are any areas, which cannot be, heated within the permitted design limits of the maximum floor surface temperature.

The water flow temperature required to achieve a given surface temperature is dependant upon the following:

1. Surface temperature required

2. Type of floor construction

3. Depth of pipe below floor surface

4. Floor covering.

All of these determine the total thermal resistance above the pipe, which will determine the drop in temperature between the pipe and the surface of the floor.

To achieve a set output from a floor means that we can either vary the pitch of the pipe and operate at a set water temperature or we can fix the pipe pitch and operate at different water temperatures.

Constant water temperature is sometimes introduced into the design by choice but more often is a function of only 'one' water temperature being available regardless of different floor constructions. The main disadvantage of this approach will be encountered during installation when the installer will have to create different pipe pitches. Many projects – especially domestic ones – feature different floor structures with, for example, the ground floor being concrete and the upper storeys wooden suspended floors. Water temperature required can differ by more than 15°C between the floors and such a temperature difference is difficult to meet using constant water temperature. Altering the pitch of pipes to meet requirements from area to area also presents potential future problems when floor covering materials are replaced e.g. switched from tiles to wall-to-wall carpet. In such circumstances, the pipe pitch cannot be altered retrospectively and heat transfer may not be sufficient to achieve design temperatures.

If the pipe pitch is kept constant, it will result in varying water temperatures. This method leads to easier design and installation. It must be borne in mind that there is always an upper limit to the desirable water temperature and in extreme cases different pipe pitches and loop configurations may need to be considered. Clearly there are an unlimited number of combinations of construction methods and floor finishes, each of which will give a different overall thermal resistance.

The temperature drop across the pipe loops should be kept low i.e. approximately 5–10°K in order to maintain even floor temperatures.

Different pipe sizes also require equivalent adjustments to water temperatures however this adjustment is very small. The difference between a 15mm and a 20mm pipe result in only a 2% increase in flow temperature for the 15mm pipe.

Three main types of loop configuration are used for underfloor heating. The construction techniques used for the building will effect selection of the most suitable type for the individual project. In general when pipe layout plans are formulated, attention should be paid to routing the supply flow to the external wall or other potentially cold areas.

## Serpentine coil layout

Temperature variations within local areas are kept to a minimum. The main advantage of this configuration is that it is adaptable to all kinds of floor structures and can be easily modified for different energy requirements by altering the pitch of the pipes. This configuration is the most suitable for underfloor heating installations serving domestic premises. However, a flexible pipe is required.

## Double coil layout

The characteristic of this configuration is that supply and return pipes in the layout run in parallel.

This provides an even mean temperature, but will result in a higher variation of temperature within small areas. It is suitable for heating larger areas with higher heat demands e.g. churches, hangers, or even for external use under paths and driveways.

## Spiral coil layout

Supply and return pipes are run parallel, but in the form of a spiral in this variation. This approach is suitable for buildings with a higher heat demand, but is less suitable for installation in association with wooden floor structures.

Studies show that a naked human foot cannot detect a temperature variation of less than 2°C. A serpentine layout with a pipe pitch of 250–300mm keeps the temperature comfortably within this range, so that no variation in floor temperature can be detected.

A number of different approaches may be applied to the control of water temperature in underfloor heating systems.

One of the simplest means of control is to maintain a constant supply water temperature from the boiler to the system by means of self-regulating control valve and mixing circuit.

This type of circuit works by mixing some of the return water from the underfloor heating with the water from the boiler to maintain a fixed supply water temperature.

Whilst this is satisfactory for small building such as domestic housing heat demand for a building will vary principally

*Figure 10  Serpentine coil layout*

*Figure 11  Double coil layout*

*Figure 12  Spiral coil layout*

as a function of outdoor temperature. One of the main advantages using outdoor temperature compensation is the shorter reaction time particularly for systems installed in concrete floors. The lower the water temperature is in the system the smaller the heat sink effect of the floor and the quicker the response, a disadvantage being the possible rapid changes in the outside air temperatures.

Maximum comfort requires room temperature control. Different areas of the building will have differing heat requirements depending upon external factors, including the orientation of the building, wind direction etc. or internal influences including open fires, number of occupants etc. Underfloor heating installations can, with the right controls, meet all of these requirements. Water circulation in each loop of the underfloor system can be controlled individually by means of actuators and room

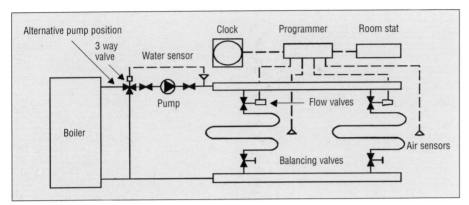

*Figure 13* Control circuit for fixed supply temperature

thermostats. This gives the end user individual control over each room or area.

The U value of a building directly relates to the performance of the underfloor heating system, which serves it. If the building is poorly insulated energy will be wasted and response times will be affected by the undesirable heat losses. Floor structure also affects response time. In buildings with concrete screeded floors, the screed will serve as an energy store, however by comparison a wooden suspended floor has little thermal store potential and therefore reacts much quicker.

Careful consideration should be given to the location of the manifolds at the outset of the project. They should be located as centrally as possible within the building so that the length of pipe routing between manifolds and the individual heating zones is kept to a minimum. This will help to balance the system and improve the temperature control of individual rooms. The manifolds can be concealed in cupboards, or suitable voids, so aesthetics are not a major issue.

Care should be taken however, to ensure that the manifolds are located in such a way as to provide easy access for further maintenance. Underfloor heating systems, with an oxygen diffusion barrier, can be used safely in association with other heating systems and air conditioning.

Complementary heating systems should be set up in such a way that they do not interfere with temperature control of the underfloor heating system.

# Resource efficient design

Resource Efficient Design: Energy Efficiency (excluding section on Plate Heat Exchanger): this has been contributed by the government's Housing Energy Efficiency Best Practice Programme, and Crown Copyright is reserved

# Introduction

Conservation has been described as the careful management and preservation of natural resources and the environment. Environmental Issues such as climate change, ozone layer destruction along with air and water pollution are having a greater impact on building designs than in the past. For Building Services, regulations are in place to help in the design of space heating and hot and cold water services. The Institute of Plumbing (IoP) supports all initiatives that seek to reduce the use of energy and to rely where possible on renewable energy sources. This section of the Guide has been compiled to give a broad view on aspects of installations where these valuable resources can be saved. Some of these aspects are covered elsewhere throughout the Guide, but this section has greater detail to give the designer/installer a better understanding, helping to achieve that all-important Resource Efficient Design.

# Energy efficiency

## What energy efficiency means

'Energy efficiency' is a measure of the benefit obtained from the consumption of a unit of energy. The energy efficiency of a building depends upon how well it is insulated and how well the heating is controlled, as well as the efficiency with which its heating and hot water systems can convert fuel to heat.

The fabric of the building has an important influence on the amount of energy required to keep it comfortable. If it is badly insulated, even the most efficient heating system will require a great deal of energy to keep it warm. Although it may not always be possible to improve building fabric insulation, the heating installer should always be aware of opportunities for improved insulation and bring them to the client's attention. Better insulation will improve comfort and client satisfaction and may lead to opportunities for a more competitive quotation.

Excessive ventilation, caused by air leakage through the building fabric, also contributes to unnecessary heat loss. It is essential to comply with requirements for ventilation and supply of combustion air to heating appliances and for the ventilation of kitchens and bathrooms, but opportunities to reduce draughts around windows and doors should

always be taken. Draught sealing around loft hatches is particularly important as warm moisture-laden air from occupied rooms can cause condensation in lofts.

Pipework for heating must be insulated wherever it runs outside the heated living space; e.g., under floors or in garages. Hot water systems should also be insulated to minimise heat loss from storage cylinders and primary circuits; heat output from them may contribute to space heating requirements in the winter but in summer it is wasted and may make the building uncomfortably warm.

## Professional responsibility

The IoP's Code of Professional Standards requires members to safeguard the environment, as does the Engineering Council's Code of Practice *Engineers and the Environment*. As greenhouse gas emissions are one of the principal environmental concerns of the present time, following the Code means that members must take all reasonable steps to pursue energy efficiency in the work they undertake.

Aspects of heating system design and installation are subject to the legal requirements relating to energy efficiency set by the Building Regulations, which apply to all material alterations to heating systems, including those in existing buildings. In many cases, the customer relies on the installer for advice both on compliance with the Regulations and on options for reducing environmental impact. Professional responsibility must therefore rest on awareness of legislation and an appreciation of the wider factors contributing to energy efficiency.

## The environmental rationale

The combustion of fossil fuels, such as gas, oil and coal, is responsible for a large proportion of all carbon dioxide ($CO_2$) emissions to the atmosphere. The concentration of $CO_2$ in the global atmosphere has risen by about 30% since the start of the industrial revolution. In recent times, climatologists have reached a consensus view that the 'greenhouse effect' arising from $CO_2$ and other man-made gases in the atmosphere is likely to cause global warming and consequent changes on climates around the world. This has led to agreements under the auspices of the United Nations Organisation to limit further emissions of greenhouse gases. Most notably, at the World Climate Conference in Kyoto in 1997, it was agreed that developed nations should achieve an overall reduction of 5.2% relative to 1990 levels over the

succeeding 15 years, with the European Union contributing 8%, the USA 7% and Japan 6%.

Following an agreement reached between the member states of the European Union, the United Kingdom is committed to reducing its greenhouse gas emissions to 12.5% below the 1990 level by 2010. The heating of buildings accounts for around a third of all UK $CO_2$ emissions and is expected to contribute a similar proportion of the necessary reductions. Savings can be achieved from better insulation in new and existing buildings, more efficient heating and hot water systems and electrical appliances.

## The benefits of energy efficiency

Energy efficiency produces benefits both for building occupants and for the environment.

For the occupants of buildings, the benefits are lower fuel bills and more comfortable conditions. A well-insulated building needs less heat to bring it up to a comfortable temperature and cools down more slowly when the heating system is turned off. And an efficient, well-controlled heating system uses less fuel to produce a given amount of heat. Both these attributes combine to reduce the total amount of fuel needed and hence the cost. Affordable heating is of particular importance in the social housing sector, which increasingly caters for households with low incomes. Consequently, contractors working for housing associations and local authorities need to pay particular attention to energy efficiency.

Energy efficiency contributes to reduced environmental impact through the use of less fuel and lower emissions of atmospheric pollution. But it is also important to remember the difference in emissions between fuels, particularly the high emissions associated with electricity use. Electrical energy is already in a form that can be converted to heat with 100% efficiency and can operate motors, lights and electronic circuits without further conversion. But that versatility comes at a price: electricity has been generated from fuel consumed at power stations with an average thermal efficiency of around 40%. The energy used overall to provide 1kWh of delivered electricity is therefore considerably greater at around 2.5kWh. The total energy used to provide the supply is known as the 'primary energy', which takes account of the energy overhead required for generation and distribution. It should be noted that there are also energy overheads associated with the production, refining and distribution of oil, gas and solid fuels, although these are much smaller than for electricity, typically around 5%. The distinction between 'delivered energy' (as metered and paid for by the consumer) and primary energy is important when considering environmental impact, which arises from primary energy consumption. Table 1 gives $CO_2$ emissions per unit of delivered energy for electricity and heating fuels in the UK.

*Table 1: $CO_2$ emission factors for delivered energy in the UK*

| Fuel | $CO_2$ emissions in kgC/kWh |
|------|------------------------------|
| Gas (mains) | 0.053 |
| LPG | 0.068 |
| Heating oil | 0.074 |
| Solid fuels | 0.079 – 0.106 |
| Electricity | 0.113 |

## Fuel choice

Space and water heating can be provided using a range of different fuels, including electricity. Fuel price is generally the most important factor for consumers in making a choice of fuel. Standard tariff electricity is generally very expensive, at around 5 times the price of gas in delivered energy terms. Heating oil has varied considerably with the price of crude oil over the past 3 decades, from being the most economical fuel at times to considerably more expensive than gas at others. LPG is generally expensive and tends to follow oil price trends rather than the price of natural gas. The relative price of fuels for heating may be obtained from Table 12 in the Standard Assessment Procedure (SAP), which is updated periodically: an abbreviated version is shown here in Table 2.

*Table 2: Typical fuel costs, including VAT but not standing charges (SAP 2001)*

| Fuel | pence per kWh |
|------|---------------|
| Gas (mains) | 1.4 |
| LPG (bulk) | 3.1 |
| Heating oil | 1.7 |
| Solid fuels | 1.7 – 2.8 |
| Electricity (standard) | 7.4 |
| Electricity (7 hour on-peak) | 7.9 |
| Electricity (7 hour off-peak) | 3.0 |

Advice given by installers on the choice of fuel for heating should be based on both relative costs and $CO_2$ emissions, as an increasing proportion of clients are now concerned about environmental impact. Table 1 (above) may be used to provide a comparison between alternatives in terms of $CO_2$ emissions. Comparisons of both running cost and $CO_2$ emissions must take account of the

efficiency of the heating system, which has the effect of reducing the relative disadvantage of electricity to some extent.

## Building Regulations

Part L of the Building Regulations (Part J and Part F in the corresponding legislation for Scotland and Northern Ireland, respectively) requires that 'reasonable provision shall be made for the conservation of fuel and power' in buildings. It specifically requires limiting heat loss through the fabric of the building, from hot water pipes and hot air ducts used for space heating, and from hot water storage vessels. Other requirements of particular relevance to heating installers are that space and water heating systems should be energy efficient and that building occupiers should be provided with sufficient information to allow them to operate their heating and hot water services efficiently. Part L was revised during 2001, with new requirements in force from April 2002 (Part L1 deals with dwellings, Part L2 with other buildings).

Under Part L, heating became a 'controlled service' from April 2002, and for the first time the provisions applied to 'material alterations' carried out to existing heating systems. So heating installers must take account of the Regulations not just in new buildings but also when renewing systems in existing buildings: failure to do so will leave them exposed to action from aggrieved customers and Building Control authorities.

*Approved Document L* gives detailed practical guidance showing how the requirements may be met. In Part L1, for dwellings, three alternative ways of demonstrating compliance with the insulation requirements are shown, including a 'Carbon Index Method', in which the level of insulation required depends on the choice of fuel and the heating system efficiency. A minimum heating system efficiency is required for other cases, as shown in Table 3. Boilers should meet specified SEDBUK efficiencies, depending on type and fuel used, and there are minimum standards for cylinders and controls. For non-domestic buildings, there are also three alternative ways of showing compliance, which are broadly analogous to those for dwellings. The main difference is in the calculation methods specified, which take account of the different building services systems used.

Apart from boiler efficiency, the most relevant requirements for heating system installers are those concerning controls, commissioning, and provision of

operating and maintenance instructions. The requirement for control of heating systems in dwellings may be met by zone controls, timing controls and boiler interlock. The interlock requirement will be satisfied if the boiler can only operate when either a space heating thermostat or a hot water cylinder thermostat is calling for heat. In practice, this means that thermostatic radiator valves alone are not enough, and should be supplemented by at least one room thermostat.

The requirement for commissioning of heating systems was introduced for the first time in the year 2000 revision, and applies to both new and existing buildings. Responsibility for commissioning rests with the person carrying out the work and includes the recording of system settings and performance test results. A certificate must be made available to the client and the building control body; the certificate issued under the Benchmark Code of Practice for the Installation, Commissioning and Servicing of Central heating systems is considered suitable for this purpose.

*Table 3: Minimum SEDBUK boiler efficiencies to be used with elemental U-values in Part L1*

| Central heating system fuel | SEDBUK % |
|------------------------------|----------|
| Mains natural gas | 78 |
| LPG | 80 |
| Oil | 85[2] |

*For boilers for which SEDBUK is not available, the appropriate seasonal efficiency may be obtained from Table 4b of the SAP*

*For oil-fired combination boilers a SEDBUK value of 82%, as calculated by the SAP 98 method, would be acceptable.*

## The Standard Assessment Procedure (SAP)

A home energy rating is a measure of the energy efficiency of a dwelling, intended to give information on the relative energy efficiency of different houses. SAP is the UK Government's standard methodology for home energy rating. The SAP rating is based upon running costs for space and water-heating, which are calculated taking account of the form of the building, its thermal insulation, which fuel is used and the performance of the heating system. SAP ratings are expressed on a range of 1-120, the higher the better. They allow comparisons of energy efficiency to be made, and can show the scope for improvements. The SAP process also delivers a carbon index, in the range 0-10, to indicate carbon emissions. Using energy ratings, designers, developers, house-builders, and home owners can take energy efficiency factors into consideration both for new dwellings and when refurbishing existing ones. Energy ratings can be used at the design stage as a guide to energy efficiency and the potential reduction of future fuel bills and $CO_2$ production. The Building Regulations require that every new dwelling be given a SAP energy rating, which must be displayed in the form of a notice.

The heating designer has an important opportunity to influence the SAP rating and the carbon index through the choice of fuel, boiler, hot water system, and controls. When the carbon index is used to show compliance with Part L of the Building Regulations, the performance of the heating system can contribute significantly, leading to less stringent requirements for insulation.

## SEDBUK

SEDBUK is an acronym for 'Seasonal Efficiency of a Domestic Boiler in the UK'. The method used in SEDBUK was developed under the Government's Energy Efficiency Best Practice Programme with the co-operation of boiler manufacturers, and provides a basis for fair comparison of different models. It was specifically designed to provide efficiency values for use in SAP calculations, and has been used in SAP assessments since July 1999.

SEDBUK is the average annual efficiency achieved in typical domestic conditions, making reasonable assumptions about pattern of usage, climate, control, and other influences. It is calculated from the results of standard laboratory tests together with other important factors such as boiler type, ignition arrangement, internal store size, fuel used, and knowledge of the UK climate and typical domestic usage patterns. SEDBUK figures for most boilers currently on sale can be seen on the website www.boilers.org.uk, which is updated monthly.

For estimating annual fuel costs SEDBUK is a better guide than laboratory test results alone. It can be applied to most gas and oil domestic boilers for which data is available from tests conducted to the relevant European standards. The SEDBUK method is used in SAP, which is described below.

As a simple guide to boiler efficiency for consumers, a scheme has been created with bands on an 'A' to 'G' scale. (see Table 4) The band may be used on product literature and labels, though there is no legal requirement for manufacturers to do so. The scheme is

temporary, as it will be withdrawn when a European directive on boiler energy labelling is introduced.

*Table 4: SEDBUK efficiency bands*

| Band | SEDBUK range |
|------|--------------|
| A | 90% and above |
| B | 86%-90% |
| C | 82%-86% |
| D | 78%-82% |
| E | 74%-78% |
| F | 70%-74% |
| G | below 70% |

## Specifying efficient systems

How can purchasers specify efficient heating systems? To help them *Central Heating System Specifications (CHeSS)* have been published under the Energy Efficiency Best Practice Programme as General Information Leaflet 59. They have been written with assistance from the relevant trade associations and the manufacturers of heating products. The specifications cover the efficiency-critical components of domestic wet central heating systems (boilers, cylinders, controls), with an emphasis on ensuring good levels of energy efficiency using well proven and cost-effective techniques and products. At present (CHeSS in year 2000) there are four, summarised in Table 5. It is intended that purchasers should refer to CHeSS when seeking quotations for installation work: as well as calling for good or best practice this is an aid to making quotations comparable.

*Table 5: CHeSS (2000) reference systems*

| CHeSS reference | Type of system |
|-----------------|----------------|
| HR1 | Good practice; system with regular (i.e. non-combi) boiler |
| HC1 | Good practice; system with combi boiler |
| HR2 | Best practice; system with regular (i.e. non-combi) boiler |
| HC2 | Best practice; system with combi boiler |

## Boiler efficiency

The efficiency of the boiler is the main factor affecting the energy efficiency of gas and oil-fired wet central heating systems. Guidance on boiler types (especially the relative advantages of regular and combi boilers) and system design is given in Good Practice Guide 284 *Domestic central heating and hot water: systems with gas and oil-fired boilers*. Information on the efficiency of both current and obsolete boilers, gas

and oil, can be seen on the Boiler Efficiency Database at www.boilers.org.uk.

Minimum standards of efficiency for most types of boiler are imposed by law, which in the UK is the *Boiler (Efficiency) Regulations 1993* (UK legislation implementing the European Union Boiler Efficiency Directive).

Boiler efficiency depends on the design of the boiler and the conditions under which it operates. Boiler design features affecting efficiency include:

a. Size (surface area) of heat exchanger

b. Water content of the heat exchanger

c. the method of ignition, especially whether or not it relies on a permanent pilot flame

d. The type of burner control (on/off, gas modulating or gas/air modulating)

e. Whether or not the boiler is designed to operate in condensing mode

f. Flue shape and length.

Operating conditions affecting boiler efficiency include:

a. The size (power rating) of the boiler in relation to the design heat load and radiator sizes

b. The heating system controls

c. Flow and return water temperatures.

All three are at least in part within the control of the designer. Installation and commissioning are also important to the realisation of the designer's intentions. Regular servicing and maintenance are also necessary to ensure that efficiency is sustained, particularly for oil fired boilers.

## Condensing boilers

The heat exchanger in a condensing boiler is designed to extract maximum heat from the flue gases. As a consequence of doing so, the temperature of the flue gases may fall below the dew point, which causes water vapour to condense on the surfaces of the heat exchanger, a situation that is deliberately avoided in other boilers. The presence of condensation in large quantities means that the heat exchanger must be made of corrosion-resistant materials and that a drain must be provided to dispose of the liquid condensate.

Condensing boilers are always more efficient than non-condensing boilers, which must be designed to operate with flue gas temperatures high enough to avoid the accumulation of condensate that would cause corrosion. Even the least efficient condensing gas boiler is about 3% more efficient than the best non-condensing boiler, and the difference is typically about 13%. Condensing boilers are most efficient when operating with low return water temperatures, which induce high levels of condensation. But they remain more efficient than other boilers even while not condensing. Although it is possible to increase the proportion of time boilers operate in condensing mode by installing larger radiators and using lower flow and return temperature, it is neither necessary nor to be recommended; field trials have shown it to be not cost-effective.

From the installer's point of view, there are two particular considerations to be taken into account when specifying condensing boilers: the provision of a drain for the condensate and the acceptability of 'pluming'– the production of a visible cloud of water droplets - from the flue. The condensate drain does not normally cause a problem, although care must be taken to ensure that it can be kept clear. Pluming can be a real problem, however, when the flue discharges into an area close to neighbouring property. Pluming may be perceived as much less acceptable than the less visible and more buoyant combustion products from a non-condensing boiler. Condensing boilers are thought by some installers to be more difficult to maintain and less reliable but there is no reason why a condensing boiler should be different from any other modern boiler in these respects. There is little difference in complexity and the only additional maintenance task is to ensure that the condensate drain is clear.

For gas installations, condensing boilers should be specified unless the additional costs outweigh the benefits or where there are serious difficulties with terminal siting, pluming or connection to a drain. For oil installations, condensing boilers have less of an advantage over non-condensing types and until recently the market for them has not been developed to the same extent as for gas.

## Hot water cylinders

Two points require consideration to ensure the energy efficiency of hot water storage cylinders. Firstly, they should be well insulated, as heat lost to their surroundings cannot contribute usefully to space heating requirements when no heat is required in summer and may cause uncomfortably high temperatures. Insulation is especially important if the cylinder is located in an unheated space. Secondly, the heat exchangers in indirect cylinders should have sufficient surface

area to provide rapid warm-up, as poor heat exchanger performance causes the boiler to be on for long periods at low loads. Apart from providing poor service to the household, a slow response reduces boiler efficiency and increases heat losses from the primary circuit. It is also important to ensure that cylinders have sufficient storage capacity; apart from the inconvenience caused by lack of capacity, system energy efficiency will be impaired if the boiler has to be called upon frequently to reheat the cylinder.

As a minimum, the designer should always specify hot water cylinders that comply with BS 1566 or BS3198. 'High performance' cylinders, which have fast recovery heat exchangers and are usually also better insulated, are recommended (see CHeSS (2000) notes 5, 6 and 7). 'Medium duty' cylinders should always be avoided as they are usually badly insulated and have poor heat exchanger performance, and do not comply with Building Regulations.

## Controls for heating systems

The output required from a heating system varies considerably, particularly in response to external temperature. Controls are needed to ensure that the system provides the appropriate output for all conditions, including those where little or no additional heat is required. Controls contribute significantly to the efficient operation of a heating system, by allowing the desired temperatures to be achieved in each room at the times required. The selection of appropriate controls also plays a key part in the overall running costs of a heating system. For example, upgrading controls on older heating systems can save up to 15% on energy bills. The recommended minimum set of controls is given in Good Practice Guide 302 Controls for domestic heating and hot water systems. See also General Information Leaflet 83 Domestic boiler anti-cycling controls – an evaluation concerning claims made for boiler anti-cycling devices.

## Insulation

Insulation is relevant to the heating installer in two different contexts. Firstly, as noted above, the extent to which the fabric of a building is insulated affects the design heating load. Consequently, opportunities for improving insulation should be explored before undertaking heating system design – the cost of the insulation may well be offset by reductions in the cost of the heating system, as well as energy cost savings throughout the life of the installation. Secondly, parts of the heating system itself require insulation, regardless of the

extent to which the building is insulated.

Guidance for the insulation of pipes and ducts is given in Section 1.52 of Approved Document L1. Pipe work located outside the insulated building fabric should be insulated with a thickness, equal to the outside diameter of the pipe (up to a maximum of 40mm) with insulation material having a thermal conductivity not exceeding 0.035 W/m.K. Pipes connected to hot water storage vessels, including the vent pipe and the primary flow and return to the heat exchanger, should be similarly insulated for at least 1 metre from their points of connection. Additional insulation may be required to prevent freezing of pipes passing through unheated areas. Guidance on suitable protection measures is given in the BRE publication Thermal insulation: avoiding risks.

## Solar water heating

Solar water heating panels are widely used around the world to provide domestic hot water, particularly where sunshine is plentiful and fuel is relatively expensive. In the UK, the great majority of installed systems are in dwellings.

The efficiency of solar collector panels depends on number of factors, including the type of collector, the spectral response of the absorbing surface, the extent to which the panel is insulated and the temperature difference between the panel and the ambient air. Efficiency declines sharply as panel temperature increases above air temperature, and the surface finish of the collector is important. Evacuated tube collectors are able to maintain their efficiency at high temperatures, although they may be no more efficient at low temperature rises.

A typical solar water heating installation consists of one or more roof-mounted panels, a hot water storage cylinder and a means of transferring heat from the panels to the cylinder. Very simple systems, used where sunshine is abundant, rely on gravity circulation but systems designed for a typical UK climate require a pumped primary circulation. BS5918 gives guidance for the design and installation of such systems. Some systems used in the UK have separate storage cylinders for solar heated water, which can be kept at an intermediate temperature to maximise the amount of heat collected. Others rely on an additional heating coil in the main hot water cylinder, which is also heated by a central heating system or by an electric immersion heater. The circulation pump is usually controlled by a differential temperature sensor, which causes the pump to operate whenever the temperature of the collector exceeds the temperature of the stored water in the cylinder by a pre-set margin of 2 or 3°C.

The energy content of the hot water produced annually per unit area of solar water heating panel depends upon several factors, including the collector efficiency, storage volume and usage patterns. BS 5918 gives a method for sizing solar hot water systems for individual houses, taking account of climate, panel orientation and collector performance. It shows that the optimum panel orientation is just West of South but that there is little effect on output within 45° of the optimum. Optimum tilt for the UK is around 33° but there is little difference within ±15°, which includes most pitched roofs in the UK. A rule of thumb is that a house requires 2-4m² of panel area, which will yield around a 1000kWh per year of heat and meet around half of annual hot water requirements. A set of European Standards is currently under development.

An Energy Efficiency Best Practice Programme report[i] on solar hot water systems in new housing was published in June 2001.

Solar panels are also well suited to heating swimming pools. The low temperature required and the very large thermal capacity of the pool water makes it possible to achieve relatively high collector efficiency using simple unglazed panels. Typical installations in the UK (covered by BS 6785) have a panel area of around half of the pool surface area and produce an average temperature rise above ambient air temperature of around 5°K provided the pool is covered at night or indoors.

# Thermal storage

Energy storage may be used either to cope with peak loads or to take advantage of lower energy prices at certain times of day. Heat is stored using either solid cores or hot water vessels. The most common application of thermal storage is in dwellings, in which solid core storage is charged with heat at off-peak rates for a 7 or 8 hour period. Guidance for the design of such systems is contained in the Electricity Council (later the Electricity Association) publication *Design of mixed storage heater/direct systems*.

Gas fired systems relying on hot water storage vessels are also available for use in dwellings. Three generic types are recognised:

a. Combined primary storage units (CPSU) provide both space and water heating from within a single

appliance, in which a burner heats a thermal store. The water in the thermal store is circulated to radiators to provide space heating, while a heat exchanger is used to transfer heat to incoming cold water at mains pressure to provide a supply of domestic hot water.

b. Integrated thermal stores also provide both space and water heating from within a single appliance. However, they differ from CPSUs in that a separate boiler is used to heat the primary water.

c. Hot-water-only thermal stores use thermal storage only for production of domestic hot water. As for the two types described above, the domestic hot water is provided by a heat exchanger working at mains pressure.

Also, some models of combination boiler contain a small thermal store to overcome the limitation on flow rates for domestic hot water.

Thermal storage for larger buildings must rely on purpose-designed storage vessels with capacity and storage temperature optimised for the heat load. Other design parameters that must be considered are insulation of the storage vessel, arrangements for dealing with expansion and the control strategy for coupling the store to the rest of the system.

Thermal stores may contribute to improved energy efficiency by allowing the installation of a smaller heat source that can operate closer to its maximum load and hence with improved efficiency. However, heat losses from the energy store need to be taken into account; if insulation is not of a very high standard, then any gains in efficiency from the sizing effect can be cancelled out.

# Plate heat exchanger

A plate heat exchanger is a device used to transfer heat from one liquid (or gas) flowing in one direction (primary) through the heat exchanger to cold water flowing the opposite direction (secondary). The two sets of water are kept separate by numerous stainless steel plates through which the heat is conducted. Each waterway can operate typically up to 10 bar pressure, although models are available to take far higher pressures. A typical plate heat exchanger measuring only 20 × 7 × 12cm can transfer heat at over 100kW – enough to heat 45 litres per minute of hot water from 12-42°C.

## Isolation

The ability of plate heat exchangers to transfer heat from a high pressure circuit

to a low pressure circuit makes them the perfect choice for applications where the operating pressures vary through a system. A typical example would be the use of a vented boiler system to heat mains pressure water. They are also useful if there is a need to isolate chemically treated water in one circuit from separate systems. A plate heat exchanger allows the two systems to operate separately, while providing sufficient heat transfer for correct operation.

## Plate heat exchanger sizing

When selecting plate heat exchangers, they must be large enough to provide the required rate of heat transfer, at the desired temperatures, and must also be large enough to ensure that pressure drops across the heat exchanger are not too high. Connection sizes will have an effect on pressure drops, however they are usually sized to suit the internal arrangement of the plates. The relationship between power, flow rate and temperature rise of water flowing through a plate heat exchanger can be calculated from the equation:

Power (kW) = 4.2 × Temperature change (°C) × Flow rate (l/s)

Although the temperatures and flow rates will be different on the primary side of the heat exchanger to those on the secondary, the power will be the same (energy out = energy in).

## Example

To work out the basics for a heat exchanger required to feed a shower with hot water, we know the shower flow rate to be about 8 litres per minute, the incoming mains water temperature to be 10°C, and the required water temperature is 42°C:

Power Out = 4.2 × (42 − 10) × (8/60)
= 17.92kW = Power In

Assuming the temperature of the primary water being used to provide the heat is 75°C, and we would like to aim for a temperature drop of 10°C, we can work out the required flow rate by reversing the previous equation:

$$\text{Flow Rate} = \frac{\text{Power}}{(4.2 \times \text{Temperature change})}$$

$$= \frac{17.92}{(4.3 \times (75 - 65))}$$

$$= 0.42 \text{ l/s}$$

This is generally enough information required to select a heat exchanger, however one may find that the flow rate requirement or pressure drop on one side of the heat exchanger is too high. Increasing the size of the heat exchanger will allow reduced primary flow rates, with accordingly lower return temperatures. The only other alternative is to increase the size of the primary pump and/or pipework. The correct balance has to be found between heat exchanger size and primary pump size.

Applications required to work with lower temperature differences across the heat exchanger, such as using a heat exchanger to transfer heat from a boiler system at 75°C to a radiator circuit at 50°C will also require larger heat exchangers. To size jobs accurately requires access to various pump curves as well as heat exchanger software – both of which can be obtained from manufacturers and often free on the Internet. On small output systems, under 100kW, it may be far easier and more economical to choose a heat exchanger that is slightly oversized, but off-the-shelf and hence relatively cheap.

## Limescale

The plates within the heat exchanger are embossed with a corrugated pattern, designed to maximise turbulence and heat transfer. Providing flow rates are reasonable, the turbulent flow prevents scale deposits from sticking to the plates. In addition, the slight flexing of the plates during operation helps to break up any deposits that do form.

## Swimming pools

Heating swimming pools poses additional problems due to the levels of chlorides and bromides often added to kill germs and bacteria in the water. Chlorine and bromine both attack metals, including copper, iron and steel. If a copper brazed plate heat exchanger is used on treated water then the copper is open to attack and may result in the failure of the heat exchanger. An alternative is to use Nickel brazed plate heat exchangers that are far more resistant.

## Heat pumps

Heat pumps are available in a number of different forms and exploit different sources of low grade heat, with the effect that they can produce significantly greater energy output than is supplied to them by fuel or electricity input. The performance of a heat pump may be characterised by its coefficient of performance (CoP), which is the ratio of the heat output to the power input. Although heat pumps clearly reduce requirements for delivered energy, they should be considered in terms of primary energy if an overall gain in energy efficiency is to be established. For heat pumps driven by electricity, a good CoP is required to overcome the primary energy ratio of the electricity.

### Air source heat pumps

Air source heat pumps may be used to extract heat either from outside air or from ventilation exhaust air. When outside air is used as a heat source, the coefficient of performance declines as the air temperature drops. There can also be problems with icing of the heat exchanger where the outside air is of high humidity, which is frequently the case in the UK. This requires periodic defrosting, which is often achieved by temporary reversals of the heat pump and reduces the CoP. Because of those factors, air-to-air heat pumps have a relatively low CoP (in the range of 2.0-2.5) when used for heating in a typical UK climate. As CoP declines with outside temperature, it is not economic to size air-source heat pumps for the coldest conditions, but to include some supplementary heating by electrical resistance coils.

### Ground or water source heat pumps

Ground or water source heat pumps extract heat from the ground, or from bodies of water either at ambient temperature or with temperature raised by the outflow of waste heat. They have the advantage over air source heat pumps in that their heat source has much greater specific heat than air and, provided it has sufficient mass, varies much less with outside temperature. Small ground source heat pumps have a seasonal CoP of around 3.5 in a typical UK climate.

The CoP figures given above are for electrically driven vapour compression cycle heat pumps. Absorption cycle heat pumps have a much lower CoP but have the advantage that they can be powered directly by gas. When used for heating, the CoP obtainable in practice (of around 1.4) still offers a considerable advantage over a boiler. Domestic sized absorption heat pumps are currently being evaluated in field trials in the Netherlands; they are compact enough to be considered as a replacement for a boiler, silent in operation and offer output equivalent to that from a boiler of 140% efficiency.

Many heat pumps used for heating in commercial buildings in the UK are reversible and also provide cooling in summer at no additional capital cost.

## Micro CHP

Combined heat and power (CHP) is the name given to systems designed to generate heat and electricity simultaneously. This may be done on a large scale, whereby an electricity generating station is located in an urban area and heat, which would otherwise have gone to waste, is distributed to buildings nearby. A similar approach may be adopted on a large campus site, such as a hospital or industrial complex, which has a continuous need for both heat and electric power. Smaller units are suitable for individual buildings, such as sports centres or hotels. Large CHP systems tend to be based on gas turbine technology, while small units are more likely to use reciprocating engines.

Micro CHP describes very small units designed to operate in an individual house or other small building, often relying on a Stirling engine to drive the generator. Fuel cells, which generate electricity directly from gas passed over electrodes, are currently expensive but offer a promising long term alternative form of generation. Micro CHP is technically feasible and is currently undergoing field tests in the UK and elsewhere. However, there are problems in matching short-term heat and electricity demand that could inhibit commercial exploitation. In particular, if the unit were sized to replace a boiler, there would be a significant surplus of electricity that would need to be exported and sold at a reasonable price. Alternatively, if the unit were sized to meet the base electrical load, the heat produced would not match the needs of the household and a separate boiler would still be required.

# Water efficiency and conservation

Water is a precious resource; it is required to sustain life and is used extensively in modern lifestyles. Water is consumed in the sense that it is transformed from a drinking water to a lower grade wastewater containing pollutants. This section examines methods of water conservation within and around domestic, commercial and industrial buildings.

In the UK, water supplied by the public supply main is abstracted from streams, rivers, lakes and reservoirs, as well as groundwater from aquifers. These are fed by an average rainfall of 1000mm of water each year of which half returns to the atmosphere by evaporation and transpiration by plants. The hydrological cycle is the process by which water moves from the atmosphere to surface waters (by precipitation) and aquifers, and then into the sea.

Water conservation has become increasingly important in the UK as demand for water has increased and shortfalls in supply have occurred. Also, public awareness of the scarcity of water in some areas of the UK and the economic value of water has increased.

The benefits of conserving water include:

1.  Maintaining the availability of the water supply during drought periods

2.  Reduced pumping and treatment costs (with associated energy savings)

3.  Wastewater reduction

4.  The protection of the environment and the possible reduction in costs to the consumer.

Throughout the world the use of water is increasing. Since 1950 the use of water has more than tripled to about 4340km$^3$ each year. In the UK, water consumption in households has risen by 70% over the last 30 years to around 140 litres/person /day of which only about 2.5 litres is used for drinking purposes. In order to match these increases in demand new sources of water have to be created. However, in recent years in the UK there have been regular shortfalls in supply resulting in 178 drought orders being issued between 1989 and 1991. Building new reservoirs is expensive and can have significant effects on the environment. An alternative new approach to the problem is to reduce the demand for water.

## Water supply in the UK

In England and Wales, water abstracted to provide a public water supply is provided by the ten regional water service companies and around seventeen water companies as well as

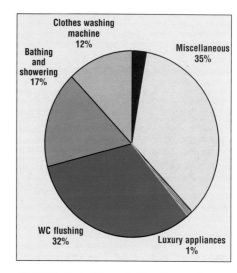

*Figure 3  Typical household water use in the UK*

NOTE:
1.  There is considerable variation in water-use between household size, socio-economic group and from region to region.
2.  External use includes water used for gardening and car washing.

small private abstractors. They supply water either metered or unmetered. Figure 2 shows uses of abstracted public water supplies in the UK.

## Domestic water consumption

Presently domestic water bills are based either on the rateable value of a building or the volume of water consumed for metered buildings. In 1991 only 2% of households in England and Wales were metered. By 2000, 18% of households were metered. Domestic demand for water has increased over the past decade. This has been alongside the population increase by 2.5% and other factors, which include:

a.  The increase in low occupation density dwellings, (as the number of occupants in a dwelling decreases the water consumption for each person of that dwelling increases)

b.  The increasing use of water using appliances, such as clothes washing machines and dishwashers.

The largest single use of water in homes is for WC flushing, as is shown in Figure 3, which gives a breakdown of water consumption in a typical household in the UK.

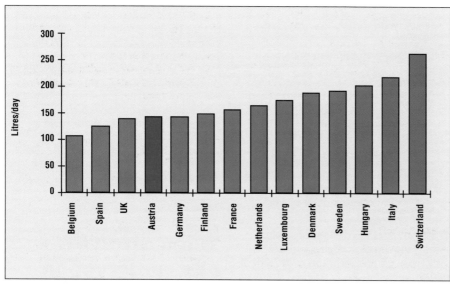

*Figure 1 Comparison of water consumption rates in Europe (1989/90)*

*Figure 2 Volume of public water supplied in the UK*

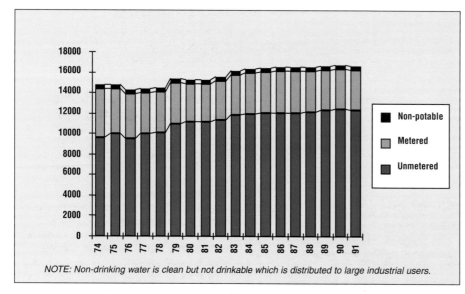

NOTE: Non-drinking water is clean but not drinkable which is distributed to large industrial users.

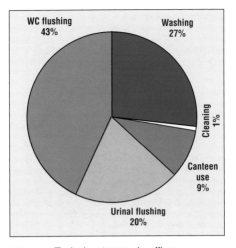

Figure 4 *Typical water use in offices*

## Office water consumption

Most water used in commercial buildings is charged on a metered basis and therefore there is a financial benefit in reducing consumption. The single most common use of water in offices is for WC flushing (43%) followed by urinal flushing. Previous Water Byelaws and now Water Regulations, stating that new flushing cisterns can only be in operation when the building is in use, have recently addressed the frequency of flushing urinals. Other uses of water in offices are shown in Figure 4. External use of water, e.g. for landscape irrigation purposes, is not accounted for in Figure 4.

## Industrial water-use

Most of the water used in industrial buildings is metered. This means there is already a financial incentive for water conservation. The main uses of water are:

a. In industrial processes

b. Cooling

c. Sanitation

d. Landscape irrigation.

## Programmes for water conservation

To identify the need for water conservation a review of current water using practices and current conservation measures should be undertaken. The evaluation of existing water conservation techniques should consider the volume of water conserved and if this can be improved. Water conservation should not only be justified on an economic basis (although it is likely that initial conservation measures need to be cost effective) but on a complete cost-benefit analysis which takes an holistic view.

Any water supply problems should be identified. The type of problems that may occur on a water supply network include:

a. Short term - drought, supply contamination

b. Long term - leakage, inadequate reserves, inadequate source of supply, inadequate distribution capacity or pressure

c. Seasonal shortcomings - such as summer high demands.

## User education and co-operation

For a water conservation programme to be successful the co-operation of water consumers is required.

Since, traditionally water has been supplied on an unmetered basis many consumers are unaware of the volume of water they use. A programme of promoting water efficiency and conservation and the benefits it can bring together with an awareness of water consumption could instil a conserving ethic amongst water users. This could be based upon a public information scheme that includes the education of school children in the importance of water.

## Identifying scope for water conservation

Current and future water supply and demand should be estimated so that the long term water conservation techniques have a sound basis. The projected forecast of population increase or decrease and the use of a region for residential, industrial, agricultural or commercial purposes should be used to predict future water demands. This information can be used to match the water system sizing with the predicted demand. This is important for new developments, and can also be used for the renovation or upgrading of water supply systems.

## Legal and statutory considerations

The following will have a bearing on any long term water conservation programme:

a. Water Industry Act 1991

b. Codes of practice for water supply such as British Standards BS 6700

c. Water Supply (Water Fittings) Regulations

d. Existing water and energy conservation programmes

e. Building Regulations

f. BREEAM (Building Research Establishment's Environmental Assessment Method).

## Present requirements for reducing waste of water

The Water Supply (Water Fittings) Regulations 1999 and the Water Byelaws 2000 (Scotland) are in place to prevent waste, undue consumption, misuse contamination or erroneous measurement of water supplied by the water undertakers. The Regulations that are relevant to water conservation cover water fittings that are used to convey water as well as water using appliances. They set a fine for each non-compliance plus a fine each day until it is rectified. In

Figure 5 *Water demand (with projections to 2021)*

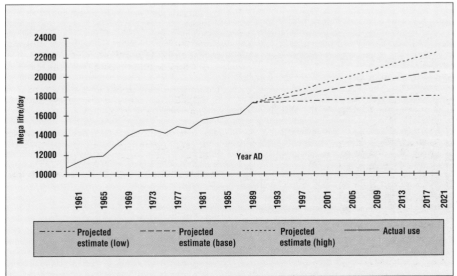

addition, the Water Regulations Advisory Scheme (WRAS) assesses compliance of fittings with the Regulations. This allows the selection of water fittings that will comply with the requirements and minimise the possibility of contamination or waste of water.

## The Water Supply (Water Fittings) Regulations 1999

The Secretary of State for the Environment, Transport and the Regions (DETR, now DEFRA) used powers under the Water Act to replace the individual water companies' Water Byelaws with Water Regulations. *Note:* The Water Supply (Water Fittings) Regulations 1999 came into force in July 1999. They are not retrospective, which means that they do not apply to any fitting lawfully installed with regard to the Byelaws before July 1999. The Regulations apply only to England and Wales. However, new Byelaws have been introduced in Scotland that, subject to compliance with Scottish law, imposes similar requirements. Similar Regulations have been introduced in Northern Ireland.

The efficient use of public water supplies and their prevention from contamination are crucial to the protection of public health as well as water resources. The Regulations embrace this idea and impact upon all water fittings, including retrofitting and new construction within domestic, commercial and industrial plumbing systems.

### Performance based requirements

Technically, the Regulations do not introduce many changes to the requirements of the Byelaws that they replaced. The two main exceptions are (a) backflow prevention and (b) requirements for water closets (WCs). The requirements of the Regulations are based largely on performance standards, rather than the prescriptive approach adopted in the Byelaws. Compliance is primarily based upon satisfying relevant British and European Standards. Mechanisms are in place to update these standards to reflect changes in technology and permit innovation.

### Water-efficient WCs

From 1 January 2001, the maximum flush volume for newly installed WCs was reduced to 6 litres. Such WCs must meet the requirements specified in DEFRA's WC Suite Performance Specification. WCs can be flushed using any mechanism that passes this performance standard. Therefore, it will no longer be necessary to use a siphon.

The use of dual flush mechanisms for

WCs is now permitted. The reduced flush must be not more than two-thirds of the maximum flush volume and clear operating instructions must be provided. Also, alternatives to traditional external overflow arrangements for WC cisterns will be permitted.

### Backflow prevention

An example of the application of European Standards is the introduction of new backflow prevention requirements. The Water Regulations reflect the approach being adopted in draft European Standard EN1717. It is the responsibility of the system designer to select the backflow prevention device appropriate to the fluid risk (i.e. a performance based approach). This allows for the introduction of new methods to prevent backflow. The Regulations recognise risks associated with five fluid categories.

### Installation

Installation issues are similar to those covered previously in the Byelaws. Fittings should be installed as intended; i.e. the fitting should operate as required by the Standards with which it is required to comply. In addition, the Regulations include requirements for not connecting materials that might lead to contamination through galvanic action or leaching. They also include procedures for pressure testing and disinfecting systems before they are used.

### Notifications

There are new notification requirements in the Regulations. The type of work that is required to be notified includes the extension of plumbing systems in non-domestic premises, where there is a material change of use of a building. In addition, notifiable work includes appliances that consume high volumes of water for discretionary uses, for example swimming pools. Where high water consumption fittings are to be installed, the water authority may consider metering the customer.

### Disagreement and disputes

Water companies are still responsible for enforcing the Regulations. In addition, there is a procedure for resolving disputes. Where a water authority will not endorse an application for a relaxation, or refuses consent following a notification, or applies conditions to the consent, the customer can appeal to DEFRA as to whether the action was reasonable.

### Approved Contractors

The Regulations include the concept of Approved Contractors. This is a non-mandatory scheme whereby a contractor may choose to become a member of an Approved Contractor Scheme. Such schemes are administered by water authorities or other organisations including the IoP's own scheme, that are appointed by DEFRA or National Assembly for Wales. Some of the notification requirements are waived for Approved Contractors. An Approved Contractor will issue a certificate for the work.

# Water conservation measures

A number of water conservation measures have been identified that would be applicable in the UK, as well as other techniques that would require further research to exploit there full potential. The examination of water conservation methods was based on various attributes such as:

## Types of conservation measures

To achieve water conservation, changes are required in the way water is used, by altering the pattern of use, by the installation of efficient appliances or a combination of the two. The simplest distinction that can be drawn between measures is to divide them into those that are:

a. products which relate to items, such as, WCs, taps and automatic car washes

b. techniques, such as, using air to move waste products instead of water and water pressure reduction

c. services that cover water-use audits and water-use labelling.

Examples of these measures are given in the following sections.

### Products

This includes all types of device that can be used to save water ranging from the simple flow restrictor, through low-water-use washing machines to fully recycling automatic car washing equipment.

i. Flow restrictors are readily available and can be fitted to many appliances, but their use has to be appropriate.

Where taps can be left on by careless users and where items are washed under running water they are a cheap way of reducing water wastage. However, a more effective, but more expensive, solution would be to install taps operated by proximity sensors.

ii. The average amount of water used for a conventional shower is approximately 30 litres, whilst a bath requires about 80 litres. It initially appears showering is more energy and water efficient, but the fact is that households with showers use them more frequently than non-shower households use their baths. Also pumped and multi-head showers are not as efficient as conventional showers. Households whose water use is metered could use suitable showering products as a method of reducing total water consumption.

iii. Conventional showerheads can discharge water at between 0.3-0.5 l/s. Low-flow showerheads can reduce this to below 0.2 litre/sec depending on the supply pressure. Research conducted in the USA has shown that the use of low-flow showerheads can save approximately 27 litre each day each person (for a person who mainly showers rather than takes baths). This equates to an energy saving in hot water of 444kWh ($1.6 \times 109$ J) each person each year for water heated by gas (or 388kWh for water heated by electricity). The cheaper alternative to low-flow showerheads is to fit a flow restrictor to the supply to an existing showerhead, although this may increase the showering time.

iv. WC cistern water displacement devices, called dams, which are inserted into cisterns, are available to reduce the volume of water flushed. Although these are relatively inexpensive they can interfere with the correct and efficient operation of the cistern. They do not fit easily into UK cisterns with a syphon flush mechanism because they are designed primarily for use in cisterns fitted with flap valves. If all the volume of water in the cistern was necessary to clear the WC pan, a reduced flush volume may not be effective and the user will flush the cistern again and hence increase the use of water, instead of reducing it.

v. WCs can be flushed with water using compressed air assistance. Some such cisterns use the pressure of the mains water supply to compress a volume of air above the stored water. When the water is released into the bowl it has a much greater velocity than from a conventional gravity operated cistern. These products are not readily available in the UK but are used in parts of France and the USA. To be used efficiently these cisterns need to be matched to WC pans that can use the higher velocity water effectively. Another type of water and compressed air toilet, uses water to rinse the bowl and compressed air to evacuate the contents. This type is used in many types of buildings in the USA.

vi. Toilets that use no water for flushing are available. The most common type in the UK is the composting toilet. In its domestic form this toilet is usually electrically powered heating the waste material to enable composting action to occur. The major problem with this type of toilet is its size; the smallest domestic model is about twice the size of a conventional WC suite. Large (greater than 15m³) composting toilets do not usually require the external input of energy for the process, as the aerobic decomposition is sufficiently exothermic to be self-sustaining. Large composting toilets may be environmentally acceptable as they consume only a small volume of water, require no drainage pipework and produce compost that can be used in the garden. However the questions of adequate hand washing facilities if there is no available water supply and the safety of children using toilets with open chutes needs to be considered.

vii. Urinal flushing cistern controllers have been widely used in the UK for some time. Water Regulations state the maximum rate at which cisterns may be filled. Since 1989 new cisterns are required to be refilled only when the urinal is in use. There are various methods of sensing use and operation. Some use changes in water pressure to identify operation of taps and therefore by association the use of urinals. Others use passive infra-red (PIR) detectors to detect movement of persons in the room, some sense the temperature of urine in the urinal traps and many use various forms of proximity detector. The essence of these devices is they all obviate the flushing of urinals when the premises are not being used and are usually an improvement over the use of the traditional 'pet-cock' that has to be set to drip water at the required rate into the cistern.

viii. The use of an occupancy detector to isolate the water supply to a washroom when unoccupied is another application of PIR technology. This can minimise the waste in urinal flushing and that caused by taps being left on.

ix. Automatic leak detectors are becoming increasingly available in the UK. These devices are fitted into the incoming mains and close when a leak is detected, preventing both the waste of water and damage to property. Some operate by sensing a high flow rate and others use conductivity detectors to activate valves.

x. Automatic closure taps can produce water savings in commercial and public buildings where there is a risk of taps being left on accidentally.

xi. Presently, 85% of households possess a washing machine and 10% a dishwasher, consuming, in total, about 12% of domestic water. The ownership of these previously luxury goods are increasing. Water Regulations govern the maximum permissible volume of water used for a wash; between 150 and 180 litre for a washing machine (depending on drum size) and about 196 litre for an average dishwasher. These levels are above current consumption of about 100 litre and 25 litre respectively). The Water Regulations maxima could be brought in line with the water consumption of current production models.

Other products include drip-proof taps and drip feed irrigation systems.

### Techniques

A technique is defined as the application of a collection of associated products (e.g. a vacuum drainage system), education or legislative policies, changes in cultural habits or the use of alternative fluids for various processes.

i. In most drainage systems in the world water is used as the transport medium. This is mainly due to historical reasons as most drainage systems involved removal of waste into rivers. However, water is becoming increasingly valuable and in some circumstances it is very wasteful to use water of drinking quality to flush toilets and drains. An established alternative is the vacuum drainage system. This uses air as the main transport medium. Some systems also use special appliances that use little water, such as, the vacuum WC and urinal.

ii. Education programmes to change the public's uses of water have been used at various times in most developed countries of the world. Education of all ages is needed but education programmes in schools help produce a new generation with an awareness of the problem.

iii. Metering of supplies is a technique

that has social, political and financial implications. Presently, the majority of domestic water used in the UK is charged on a tariff that was related to the rateable value of a building. A charge based on the volume of water consumed is an alternative to the rate method; this requires some form of metering. Commercial and industrial buildings are generally metered.

iv. Long pipe runs are to be avoided because water contained in them may have to be run off before the water reaches the desired temperature. The insulation of hot water pipes can reduce this problem. It is common practice to run water from hot taps to waste until it is up to temperature and then add cold water. If the initial cooler water was utilised reductions could be achieved. Other ways of reducing water wasted in pipe runs would be to use point of use water heaters, and to use unvented hot water systems which operate on higher water pressures than traditional vented water heaters and can be used with smaller bore piping.

v. One of the most popular techniques presently used for saving water is to use rainwater for tasks where drinking water would normally be used. These include WC flushing, garden and window box watering.

vi. Recycling of wastewater is possible but may give rise to problems. Wastewater from sinks, baths and basins may be used for irrigation purposes but if it is used for WC flushing the cisterns mechanism may suffer due to deposits of soap and other contaminants. Other problems associated with recycling wastewater are storage, contamination and separation from the existing drinkable water supply.

## Services

These are not product based but involve knowledge that can be applied or utilised.

### Audit
An audit of water using appliances, especially in large organisations, may reveal many areas where savings can be made. Companies that offer these services usually market devices such as WC dams, tap flow restrictors and are able to offer the audits at negligible cost to the clients. In New York City, USA, the use of a voluntary water audit in 5200 buildings has shown potential water savings of 28 million litres per year. The audit consisted of a leak and waste inspection with free replacement of showerheads, aerating taps and WC cistern dams.

### Economical products
To help in the selection of water economical products, water-use labelling of appliances is being adopted in Australia. It is analogous to fuel consumption figures for motor cars. A prospective purchaser is able to compare the relative amounts of water that different appliances use. This scheme would require the testing of appliances to an agreed standard and would add to the cost of the product. Currently, products that are covered in the Australian scheme include:

i. Shower heads

ii. Taps

iii. Flow restrictors

iv. Dish washing machines

v. Clothes washing machines

vi. WCs

vii. Urinals

viii. Domestic garden equipment.

In the UK, the Bathroom Manufacturers Association, represents many sanitaryware manufacturers.

### Toilet rebate programmes
Toilet rebate programmes have been used to great effect in parts of the USA. They involve offering payments to users who exchange their existing WC for a low-water-use WC from a specified list. Not only does this result in water savings but also increased WC and bathroom suit sales and is an incentive to the industry. Experience in San Simeon, California, USA has shown a 39% reduction in total water-use after a toilet rebate scheme had been implemented. This required the replacement of the existing 1198 WCs for low-water-user WCs (less than 7.2 litre). A rebate scheme for gas-fired condensing boilers is already operated in the UK by the Energy Savings Trust.

### Efficient landscaping
Efficient landscaping can reduce the amount of water required for irrigation and the watering of plants. Presently the external use of water for gardening runs at between 2% and 3% of total water consumption for domestic properties. Many commercial and public buildings have extensive landscaped areas. Low transpiration plants native to the Mediterranean can be used for ornamental gardening. Large areas are also given over to recreational uses, such as golf courses. Efficient watering systems that monitor wind speed and air temperature can vary irrigation rates so water is more fully utilised and evaporation is reduced.

BRE has developed a water efficient specification for new housing which meets the Water Regulations requirement and is given below.

BRE water efficiency specification:

i. WCs (6 litre)

ii. Dual flush WCs (6/4 litre) or (6/3 litre)

iii. Low volume baths

iv. Water butts (for garden irrigation)

v. Spray taps on handwash basins

vi. Reduced flowrate taps on handwash basins

vii. Water efficient dishwasher

viii. Water efficient washing machine

ix. Water efficient showerhead.

### Water metering
Metering trials have been conducted in twelve areas in England. These sites cover a range of geographical areas and social groups; a total of approximately 56,570 households. A survey carried out by Ofwat indicated that there was a high level of acceptance of water metering by 72% of those questioned. The installation of water meters and their use for the charging of water on a volume used rather than on a flat rate basis could be used to encourage water conservation. The actual tariff system adopted for metered dwellings will affect the potential water savings that can be achieved. The relative contributions to the total water bill from standing charges and charges related to the volume of water used are important for creating financial incentives for water conservation.

The majority of metered householders (59%) in the study attempted to reduce their water consumption by some means. This was achieved by a number of methods including:

i. Less plant watering

ii. Less toilet flushing

iii. Taking showers instead of baths

iv. Using washing machines less frequently

v. Sharing baths, bath water, or showers.

Even though installation of meters may be costly in existing buildings, there are hidden benefits, such as detecting existing leaks during installation. Presently, many new buildings are automatically fitted with a water meter or provided with suitable connections for installation later, although trends show an increase in unmetered water consumption.

Evidence from the USA suggests that water savings from the installation of water meters produced savings in the

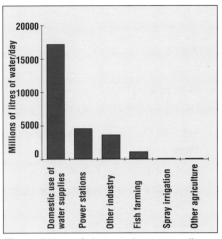

*Figure 6 Uses of abstracted water supplies in the UK*

region of 13% to 45% of supplied water. These trials were carried out between 1955 and 1975 and were based on water susceptible to differences and variations due to particular seasonal requirements. Also in the USA, the proportion of the water used for external purposes (37%) is greater than in the UK (3%). Therefore there is more scope to conserve water used externally for domestic purposes.

*Reductions in industrial water usage*
The methods to reduce water consumption in industry will be similar to those for domestic and commercial buildings. The water used in industrial processes can be reduced by various methods:

i.   The use of a water audit to locate leaks and any process which uses more water than it may require

ii.  The reuse of water (or reclaiming wastewater)

iii. The use of a closed circuit cooling system instead of a once-through system

iv.  The use of efficient cleaning processes which utilise less-clean water first.

An audit of process water requirements should also examine the quality of water that is needed for each operation. This allows effluent from one operation to be matched to a demand for lower-grade water for another operation. On-site treatment of wastewater could also be beneficial in aiding this procedure (also matching output from the water treatment plant to water demand thereby avoiding excessive peaks and the requirement for make-up water from the mains). This can reduce overall water consumption for a process as well as reducing sewerage charges.

Since cooling water is a high component of water used in industry it should be targeted for reuse. As cooling water is not normally degraded (except for mineral content), it can be reused for processes, such as cleaning, which do not require drinking water.

## References

The Building Regulations 2000 *Approved Document L Conservation of Fuel and Power* HMSO 2001.

*The Governments Standard Assessment Procedure for Energy Rating of Dwellings* BRECSU 2001.

Energy Efficiency Best Practice Programme, *General Information Leaflet 59 'Central Heating System Specifications (CHeSS)'.*

Energy Efficiency Best Practice Programme, *Good Practice Guide 284 'Domestic central heating and hot water: systems with gas and oil-fired boilers'.*

BS 1566-1:1984 *Copper indirect cylinders for domestic purposes. Specification for double feed indirect cylinders.*

BS 1566-2:1984 *Copper indirect cylinders for domestic purposes. Specification for single feed indirect cylinders.*

BS 3198:1981 *Specification for copper hot water storage combination units for domestic purposes.*

Energy Efficiency Best Practice Programme, *Good Practice Guide 302 'Controls for domestic heating and hot water systems'.*

Energy Efficiency Best Practice Programme, *General Information Leaflet 83 'Domestic boiler anti-cycling controls'.*

BRE report BR 262, *Thermal Insulation: Avoiding risks*, 2002 edition.

SERI *Engineering principles and concepts for active solar systems* Solar Energy Research Institute 1988 ISBN 0-801 16 855 9 (Hampshire Publishing Corporation).

BS 5918:1989 *Code of practice for solar heating systems for domestic hot water.*

EN 12975: 2000 *Thermal solar systems and components – Solar Collectors.*

EN 12976: 2000 *Thermal solar systems and components – Factory made systems.*

DD ENV 12977: 2001 *Thermal solar systems and components – Custom built systems.*

BS 6700: 1997 *Design, installation, testing and maintenance of services supplying water for domestic use within buildings and their curtilages.*

Energy Efficiency Best Practice Programme, *General Information Report 88 'Solar hot water systems in new housing – a monitoring report'.*

BS 6785:1986 *Code of practice for solar heating systems for swimming pools.*

Electricity Council, *Design of mixed storage heater/direct systems.* Technical Information DOM-8. 1980 (revised 1984 and 1989).

The Water Supply (Fittings) Regulations 1999 and Water Byelaws 2000 (Scotland).

# Piped gas services

# Natural gas

The piped gas provided for domestic purposes and for commercial and industrial utilization is currently supplied primarily from gas fields in the British sectors of the North Sea, with additional supplies from other fields, eg. Morecambe Bay.

Substitute natural gas (SNG) is manufactured as a direct substitute for natural gas and as a means of providing additional gas to meet peak loads. It can be made from a range of feed stocks in a number of different types of plant. Feed stocks commonly used are liquefied petroleum gas (LPG) and naphthas.

The properties of these gases compared with their methane content are given in Table 1.

## The flow of gas in pipes

The Pole formula is used in the gas industry for determining the flow rate of gas in pipes. It is a simplification of the Darcy fluid flow formula.

The friction coefficient (f) applied in the Darcy formula is taken as a constant ie.

f = 0.0065 for gas pipes of the diameter used for domestic supplies.

Pole Formula (SI units)

$$Q = 0.0071 \frac{\sqrt{d^5 \times h}}{s \times l}$$

where   Q = flow (m³/hr)

d = diameter of pipe (mm)

h = pressure drop (millibar)

l = length of pipe (m)

s = specific gravity of gas

Factors affecting pressure loss

By re-arranging the metric version of the Pole formula:

$$H = \frac{Q^2 \times s \times l}{D^5(0.0071)^2}$$

It can be seen that a pressure drop of h;

varies with length $= \frac{1}{l}$

varies with quantity $= Q$

varies with specific gravity = s

varies with $\frac{l}{d}$ (ie. inversely as diameter)

The pipe friction is assumed to be constant and the specific gravity can also be assumed constant.

The following example is based on using 15mm copper tube to Manufacturers Reference (EN 1057-250 – 15 × 0.7mm) with an internal diameter of 13.567mm.

### Example

Find Q (m³/h) when d = 13.56mm, h = 1 mb, l = 9 m, s = 0.58

$$Q = 0.0071 \frac{\sqrt{d^5 \times h}}{s \times l}$$

$$= 0.0071 \frac{\sqrt{13.56^5 \times 1}}{0.58 \times 9}$$

$$= 0.0071 \times 296.356$$

$$= 2.104 /m^3/h$$

## Gas flow tables

When using Tables 2, 3, 4, 15a, 15b and 15c to solve practical problems, the pressure drop allowed for must include the losses of the measured pipe run plus an addition for fittings in the line from Table 5.

*Table 1  Efficiency rating figures*

| Miscellaneous data | Natural gas | SNG | Methane |
|---|---|---|---|
| CV BTU/ft³ | 1065.64 | 1000.00 | 995.00 |
| CV mJ /m³ | 39.70 | 38.00 | 37.00 |
| Specific gravity | 0.58 | 0.555 | 0.56 |
| Wobbe No mJ/m³ | 52.12 | 51.00 | 49.44 |
| Air/Gas volume/volume | 10.00 | 10.00 | 9.60 |
| Flame speed | 36cm/sec | 36cm/sec | 36cm/sec |
| Temp. for ignition | 704°C | 704°C | 704°C |

*Table 2  Pipe sizing table*                                                                                                 *Natural gas*

| Size of tube in mm | | | Length of tube in metres / Discharge rate in m³/h | | | | | | | | | |
|---|---|---|---|---|---|---|---|---|---|---|---|---|
| Wall thickness (mm) | Nominal size (mm) | I/D (mm) | 3 | 6 | 9 | 12 | 15 | 20 | 25 | 30 | 40 | 50 |
| 0.6 | 6 | 4.76 | 0.266 | 0.188 | 0.154 | 0.133 | 0.119 | | | | | |
| 0.6 | 8 | 6.76 | 0.639 | 0.452 | 0.369 | 0.320 | 0.298 | 0.248 | 0.221 | 0.202 | 0.175 | 0.156 |
| 0.6 | 10 | 8.76 | 1.222 | 0.844 | 0.705 | 0.611 | 0.547 | 0.473 | 0.423 | 0.387 | 0.354 | 0.299 |
| 0.6 | 12 | 10.76 | 2.044 | 1.445 | 1.180 | 1.022 | 0.914 | 0.791 | 0.708 | 0.646 | 0.559 | 0.500 |
| 0.7 | 15 | 13.56 | 3.644 | 2.577 | 2.104 | 1.822 | 1.630 | 1.411 | 1.262 | 1.152 | 0.998 | 0.893 |
| 0.9 | 22 | 20.15 | 9.810 | 6.937 | 5.664 | 4.905 | 4.387 | 3.799 | 3.393 | 3.102 | 2.686 | 2.403 |
| 0.9 | 28 | 26.15 | 18.822 | 13.309 | 10.867 | 9.411 | 8.417 | 7.290 | 6.250 | 5.952 | 5.154 | 4.610 |
| 1.2 | 35 | 32.54 | 32.511 | 22.791 | 18.756 | 16.243 | 14.528 | 12.581 | 11.253 | 10.273 | 8.896 | 7.957 |
| 1.2 | 42 | 39.54 | 52.914 | 37.416 | 30.550 | 26.457 | 23.664 | 20.494 | 18.332 | 16.733 | 14.491 | 12.961 |
| 1.2 | 54 | 51.54 | 102.647 | 72.582 | 59.263 | 51.323 | 45.905 | 39.755 | 35.558 | 32.460 | 28.111 | 25.143 |
| 1.2 | 66.70 | 64.23 | 177.692 | 125.838 | 102.747 | 88.981 | 79.587 | 68.924 | 61.648 | 56.277 | 48.737 | 43.592 |
| 1.5 | 76.10 | 73.03 | 245.522 | 173.469 | 141.637 | 122.661 | 109.711 | 95.013 | 84.982 | 77.578 | 67.184 | 60.091 |
| 1.5 | 108.00 | 104.93 | 607.061 | 429.257 | 350.487 | 303.530 | 271.486 | 235.114 | 210.292 | 191.969 | 166.250 | 148.699 |
| 1.5 | 133.00 | 129.80 | 1033.166 | 730.559 | 596.499 | 516.583 | 462.046 | 400.143 | 357.899 | 326.716 | 282.944 | 253.073 |
| 2.0 | 159.00 | 154.80 | 1604.763 | 1134.739 | 926.510 | 802.381 | 717.672 | 621.522 | 555.906 | 507.470 | 439.482 | 393.085 |

*(Discharge in a straight horizontal copper tube with 1.0mbar differential pressure between the ends, for gas of relative density 0.6 (air = 1) Natural gas copper tube to EN1057 – R250  Previous designation BS2871 Part 1 Table X 1971*

*Table 3*   *Pipe sizing table*                                                *Natural gas*

| Size of tube in mm | | | Length of tube in metres — Discharge rate in m³/h | | | | | | | | | |
|---|---|---|---|---|---|---|---|---|---|---|---|---|
| Wall thickness (mm) | N.S. (mm) | I/D (mm) | 3 | 6 | 9 | 12 | 15 | 20 | 25 | 30 | 40 | 50 |
| 2.3 | 8 | 8.70 | 1.201 | 0.849 | 0.693 | 0.600 | 0.537 | 0.465 | 0.416 | 0.379 | 0.329 | 0.294 |
| 2.3 | 10 | 12.20 | 2.798 | 1.978 | 1.615 | 1.399 | 1.251 | 1.083 | 0.969 | 0.884 | 0.766 | 0.685 |
| 2.6 | 15 | 15.90 | 5.425 | 3.836 | 3.132 | 2.712 | 2.426 | 2.101 | 1.879 | 1.715 | 1.485 | 1.329 |
| 2.6 | 20 | 21.40 | 11.402 | 8.063 | 6.583 | 5.701 | 5.099 | 4.416 | 3.950 | 3.605 | 3.122 | 2.793 |
| 3.2 | 25 | 27.00 | 20.388 | 14.417 | 11.771 | 10.194 | 9.118 | 7.896 | 7.062 | 6.447 | 5.583 | 4.994 |
| 3.2 | 32 | 35.70 | 40.987 | 28.982 | 26.664 | 20.493 | 18.330 | 15.874 | 14.198 | 12.961 | 11.224 | 10.039 |
| 3.2 | 40 | 41.60 | 60.078 | 42.481 | 34.686 | 30.039 | 26.867 | 23.268 | 20.811 | 18.998 | 16.453 | 14.716 |
| 3.6 | 50 | 52.60 | 108.006 | 76.371 | 62.357 | 54.003 | 48.301 | 41.830 | 37.414 | 34.154 | 29.578 | 26.455 |
| 3.6 | 65 | 68.20 | 206.749 | 146.194 | 119.366 | 103.374 | 92.461 | 80.073 | 71.620 | 65.379 | 56.620 | 50.643 |
| 4.0 | 80 | 80.10 | 309.075 | 218.549 | 178.445 | 154.537 | 138.222 | 119.704 | 107.067 | 97.738 | 84.281 | 75.707 |
| 4.5 | 100 | 104.30 | 597.990 | 422.843 | 343.250 | 298.995 | 267.429 | 231.600 | 207.150 | 189.101 | 163.766 | 146.477 |
| 5.0 | 125 | 128.70 | 1011.966 | 715.179 | 583.941 | 505.708 | 452.319 | 391.719 | 350.364 | 319.838 | 276.987 | 247.745 |
| 5.0 | 150 | 154.10 | 1586.683 | 1121.954 | 916.072 | 793.341 | 709.586 | 614.519 | 549.643 | 501.753 | 434.531 | 388.656 |

*(Discharge in a straight horizontal steel pipe (to Table 2, medium, of BS 1387: 1967) with 1.0mbar differential pressure between the ends, for gas of relative density 0.6 (air = 1))*
*Steel tube medium grade – BS 1387 General purpose tube to the quality assurance requirement of (ISO 9002/BS 5750 Part 2)*

*Table 4*   *Pipe sizing table*                                                *Natural gas*

| Size of tube in mm | | | Length of tube in metres — Discharge rate in m³/h | | | | | | | | | |
|---|---|---|---|---|---|---|---|---|---|---|---|---|
| Wall thickness (mm) | N.S. (mm) | I/D (mm) | 3 | 6 | 9 | 12 | 15 | 20 | 25 | 30 | 40 | 50 |
| 0.8 | 6 | 4.36 | 0.213 | 0.151 | 0.123 | 0.106 | 0.095 | 0.082 | 0.074 | 0.067 | 0.058 | 0.052 |
| 0.8 | 8 | 6.36 | 0.549 | 0.388 | 0.317 | 0.274 | 0.245 | 0.212 | 0.190 | 0.173 | 0.150 | 0.130 |
| 0.8 | 10 | 8.36 | 1.087 | 0.769 | 0.627 | 0.543 | 0.486 | 0.421 | 0.376 | 0.343 | 0.297 | 0.266 |
| 0.8 | 12 | 10.36 | 1.859 | 1.314 | 1.073 | 0.929 | 0.831 | 0.720 | 0.644 | 0.588 | 0.509 | 0.455 |
| 1.0 | 15 | 12.96 | 3.244 | 2.301 | 1.879 | 1.627 | 1.455 | 1.260 | 1.127 | 1.029 | 0.891 | 0.797 |
| 1.2 | 22 | 19.55 | 9.096 | 6.431 | 5.251 | 4.548 | 4.067 | 3.520 | 3.150 | 2.876 | 2.491 | 2.228 |
| 1.2 | 28 | 25.55 | 17.760 | 12.558 | 10.254 | 8.880 | 7.942 | 6.878 | 6.152 | 5.616 | 4.863 | 4.350 |
| 1.5 | 35 | 31.94 | 31.032 | 21.943 | 17.916 | 15.516 | 13.878 | 12.018 | 10.750 | 9.813 | 8.498 | 7.601 |
| 1.5 | 42 | 38.94 | 50.929 | 36.012 | 29.404 | 25.464 | 22.776 | 19.725 | 17.642 | 16.105 | 13.947 | 12.475 |
| 2.0 | 54 | 49.94 | 94.864 | 67.079 | 54.770 | 47.432 | 42.424 | 36.740 | 32.862 | 29.998 | 25.979 | 23.237 |
| 2.0 | 66.7 | 62.63 | 167.085 | 118.147 | 96.467 | 83.542 | 74.723 | 64.712 | 57.880 | 52.837 | 45.758 | 40.927 |
| 2.0 | 76.1 | 72.03 | 237.010 | 167.591 | 136.837 | 118.505 | 105.994 | 91.793 | 82.102 | 74.949 | 64.907 | 58.055 |
| 2.5 | 108.0 | 102.93 | 578.547 | 409.094 | 334.024 | 289.273 | 258.734 | 224.070 | 200.414 | 182.952 | 158.441 | 141.714 |

*Copper Tube to EN 1057-R250 half hard straight lengths and EN 1057-R220 Soft Coils.*
*Previous designation BS 2871 Part 1 Table (Y) 1971*

*Table 5*   *Pipe sizing table*

| Nominal size | | | | Approximate additional lengths to be allowed | | | | | |
|---|---|---|---|---|---|---|---|---|---|
| Cast iron or mild steel | | Stainless steel or copper | | Elbows | | Tees | | 90° bends | |
| (mm) | (in) | (mm) | (in) | (m) | (ft) | (m) | (ft) | (m) | (ft) |
| Up to 25 | 1 | Up to 28 | 1 | 0.5 | 2 | 0.5 | 2 | 0.3 | 1 |
| 32 to 40 | 1¼ to 1½ | 35 to 42 | 1¼ to 1½ | 1.0 | 3 | 1.0 | 3 | 0.3 | 1 |
| 50 | 2 | 54 | 2 | 1.5 | 5 | 1.5 | 5 | 0.5 | 2 |
| 80 | 3 | 76.1 | 3 | 2.5 | 8 | 2.5 | 8 | 1.0 | 3 |

*(The effects of elbows, tees or bends inerted in a run of pipe [expressed as the approximate additional lengths to be allowed])*

In the example given, h = 1 mb and l = 9m, from which pressure loss

$$mb/m = \frac{1}{9} \quad 0.1111 \text{ mb/m}.$$

Referring to Table 2, it will be seen that the flow rate at this pressure loss and at the internal pipe diameter given, (d = 13.6mm) is 2.10 m³/h agrees with the calculated result to 2dp.

*Table 6  Pipe supports*

| Nominal size | | | Interval for vertical runs | | Interval for horizontal runs | |
|---|---|---|---|---|---|---|
| Cast iron, mild steel | Stainless steel | | | | | |
| (mm) | (mm) | (in) | (m) | (ft) | (m) | (ft) |
| 15 | 15 | ½ | 2.5 | 8 | 2.0 | 6 |
| 20 | 22 | ¾ | 3.0 | 10 | 2.5 | 8 |
| 25 | 28 | 1 | 3.0 | 10 | 2.5 | 8 |
| 32 | 35 | 1¼ | 3.0 | 10 | 2.7 | 9 |
| 40 | 42 | 1½ | 3.5 | 12 | 3.0 | 10 |
| 50 | 54 | 2 | 3.5 | 12 | 3.0 | 10 |
| 80 | 76.1 | 2 | 3.5 | 12 | 3.0 | 10 |
| 100 | 108 | 4 | 3.5 | 12 | 3.0 | 10 |

*Maximum interval for cast iron, mild steel and stainless steel pipes*

*Table 7  Pipe supports*

| Nominal size | | Interval for vertical runs | | Interval for horizontal runs | |
|---|---|---|---|---|---|
| (mm) | (in) | (m) | (ft) | (m) | (ft) |
| Up to 15 | Up to ½ | 2.0 | 6 | 1.2 | 4 |
| 22 | ¾ | 2.5 | 8 | 1.8 | 6 |
| 28 | 1 | 2.5 | 8 | 1.8 | 6 |
| 35 | 1¼ | 3.0 | 10 | 2.5 | 8 |
| 42 | 1½ | 3.0 | 10 | 2.5 | 8 |
| 54 | 2 | 3.0 | 10 | 2.7 | 9 |
| 66.70 | 2½ | 3.5 | 12 | 3.0 | 10 |
| 76.1 | 3 | 3.5 | 12 | 3.0 | 10 |
| 108 | 4 | 3.5 | 12 | 3.0 | 10 |

*Maximum interval for light gauge copper pipes*

## Domestic properties

Normal gas usage would be satisfied by the following meter size:

*Table 8a  Meter characteristics*

| Model type | Capacity per hour | | Standard working pressure | | Pressure loss at capacity | | Capacity per revolution | | Proving dial/circle | | Meter connections |
|---|---|---|---|---|---|---|---|---|---|---|---|
| | (ft³) | (m³) | (psi) | (mbar) | ("wg) | (mbar) | (ft³) | (dm³) | (ft³) | (dm³) | |
| U4/G2.5 | 141 | 4 | 0.7 | 50 | <0.5 | <1.22 | .043 | 1.25 | 1 | 10 | 1″ screwed to BS 746 |
| U6/G4 | 212 | 6 | 0.7 | 50 | <0.5 | <1.22 | .071 | 2.0 | 1 | 10 | |

## Commercial properties

Usage will vary but the following Table would generally give a meter size to suit requirements:

*Table 8b  Meter characteristics*

| | U16 | | U25 | | U40 | | U65 | | U100 | | U160 | |
|---|---|---|---|---|---|---|---|---|---|---|---|---|
| Capacity per hour | 16m³ | 565ft³ | 25m³ | 833ft³ | 40m³ | 1412ft³ | 65m³ | 2296ft³ | 100m³ | 353ft³ | 160m³ | 5650ft³ |
| Std. working Pressure | 75mbar | 1.0psi | 75mbar | 1.0psi | 75mbar | 1.0psi | 75mbar | 1.0psi | 75mbar | 1.0psi | 75mbar | 1.0psi |
| Mean pressure loss | 1.22mbar | 0.5″wg | 1.62mbar | 0.65″wg | 1.22mbar | 0.5″wg | 2.36mbar | 0.95″wg | 1.32mbar | 0.53″wg | 2.91mbar | 1.17″wg |
| Capacity per revolution | 4dm³ | 0.142ft³ | 10dm³ | 0.353ft³ | 20dm³ | 0.714ft³ | 25dm³ | 1.0ft³ | 50dm³ | 2.0ft³ | 71.4dm³ | 2.5ft³ |
| Proving circle (1 pulse =) | 100dm³ | 1ft³ | 100dm³ | 10ft³ | 100dm³ | 10ft³ | 100dm³ | 10ft³ | 100dm³ | 10ft³ | 100dm³ | 10ft³ |
| Standard connections | 1¼″ screwed to BS746 | | 2″ screwed to BS746 | | 2″ screwed to BS746 | | 65mm flanged BS4505.1 16/1 | | 80mm flanged BS4505.1 16/1 | | 100mm flanged BS4505.1 16/1 | |
| Shipping weight | 9.43kg | 20.75lb | 16.40kg | 36lb | 28kg | 61.5lb | 41.8kg | 92lb | 70kg | 154lb | 75kg | 165lb |

*Standard working pressure is shown at 75mbar (1.0 psi) – meters can be supplied for higher working pressures.*

**Heat energy rates**

The rate at which gas is used and heat produced in gas appliances may be expressed in several ways. The heat input rate can be calculated by multiplying the gas rate in m³ or ft³ by the relevant calorific value (CV). The relevant cv may vary seasonally slightly from region to region.

The current CV's are generally expressed as follows:

a.  cv Btu/ft³  =  1065.64

b.  cv MJ/m³  =  39.70

The gas discharge rate tables expressed as m³/h, can be converted to energy input rates using one or more of the listed conversion calculations from 1-8 and 9 for thermal efficiency.

It is essential however, that the heat output of appliances are kept reasonably constant and the gas quality maintained within close limits. The wobbe number will give an indication of the heat output from burners using any of the three family gases. The wobbe number can be derived using the following formula:-

$$\text{Wobbe No} = \frac{(cv)}{(\sqrt{sg})}$$

Therefore if using natural gas with a cv of 39.70 and a sg of 0.58

$$= \frac{(39.70)}{(\sqrt{0.58})} = 52.12$$

$$\text{Wobb No} = 52.12$$

*Table 9*  *Typical equipment gas consumption figures*    *Natural gas*

| Appliance | Gas consumption | | |
|---|---|---|---|
| | (m³/hr) | (ft³/hr) | (litres/sec) |
| 45 litre boiling pan | 2.5 | 90 | 0.7 |
| 90 litre boiling pan | 3.4 | 120 | 0.95 |
| 135 litre boiling pan | 4.3 | 150 | 1.2 |
| 180 litre boiling pan | 5.0 | 175 | 1.4 |
| 1200mm hot cupboard | 2.7 | 95 | 0.75 |
| 1800mm hot cupboard | 3.0 | 110 | 0.85 |
| Steaming oven | 2.1 to 2.9 | 80 to 100 | 0.6 to 0.8 |
| Double steaming oven | 5.75 | 200 | 1.6 |
| 2 tier roasting oven | 2.9 | 100 | 0.8 |
| Double oven range | 10.0 to 12.0 | 350 to 400 | 2.75 to 3.2 |
| Roasting oven | 1.7 | 60 | 0.47 |
| Gas cooker | 4.30 | 150 | 1.2 |
| Hot cupboard | 1.0 | 35 | 0.275 |
| Drying cupboard | 0.3 | 10 | 0.08 |
| Gas iron heater | 0.3 | 10 | 0.08 |
| Washing machine | 1.1 | 40 | 0.31 |
| Wash boiler | 1.7 to 2.9 | 60 to 100 | 0.47 to 0.8 |
| Bunsen burner | 0.15 | 5 | 0.04 |
| Bunsen burner, full on | 0.6 | 20 | 0.16 |
| Glue kettle | 0.6 | 20 | 0.16 |
| Forge | 0.85 | 30 | 0.23 |
| Brazing hearth | 1.7 | 60 | 0.47 |
| Incinerator | 0.36 to 1.2 | 12 to 40 | 0.1 to 0.32 |

# Conversion examples

1. Btu to ft³ $= \dfrac{Btu}{cv} = ft^3$

2. ft³ to Btu $= ft^3 \times cv = Btu$

3. m³ to ft³ $= m^3 \times 35.31 = ft^3$

4. m³ to Btu $= m^3 \times ft^3 \times cv$

   $= 1m^3 \times 35.31 \times 1065.64$

   $= 37628$ Btus

5. m³ to kW $= \dfrac{m^3 \times cv}{MJ/kW}$

   $= \dfrac{1m^3 \times 39.70}{3.60}$

   $= 11.028kW$

6. kW to m³ $= \dfrac{kW \times Btu/kW}{cv \times Btu/MJ}$

   $= \dfrac{11.028 \times 3412}{39.70 \times 947.80}$

   $= \dfrac{37628}{37628} = 1m^3$

7. kW to Btu $= kW \times Btu/kW$

   $= 1kW \times 3412$

   $= 3412$ Btu

8. kW to MJ $= \dfrac{MJ/m^3}{kW/m^3} = MJ$

   $= \dfrac{39.70}{11.028}$

   $= 3.60MJ$

9. Heat input rate example:

Assuming an appliance has a heat input rate of 2.5m³/h and a calorific value of 39.70mj/m³

Then:  $= \dfrac{m^3/h \times cv}{MJ/kW}$

   $= \dfrac{2.5 \times 39.70}{3.60}$

   $= 27.57kW/h$

Or    $= 27.57kW \times 3412$

   $= 94069$ Btu/h

10. Thermal efficiency example:

Thermal efficiency

$= \dfrac{heat\ output \times 100}{heat\ input}$

Therefore a gas water heater has a gas rate of 2.5m³/h and delivers 8 litres of water per minute raised 43°C assuming a cv = 39.70 MJ/m³.

Heat output  = 8 litres = 8kg/minute

   $= 8 \times 60 = 480kg/h$

$= 480 \times 43$
$\times 4.186kJ/kg/°C$

$= 86399.04$ kJ/h

$= 86.399$ MJ/h

Heat input  $= 2.5m^3/h \times 39.70MJ/m^3$

$= 99.25MJ/h$

% Efficiency  $= \dfrac{86.399 \times 100}{99.25}$

$= 87\%$

# Liquefied petroleum gas installations

## Introduction

Liquefied petroleum gas (LPG) is a generic term used to describe gases (predominantly $C_3$ and $C_4$ hydrocarbons) which exist as vapour at normal atmospheric temperature and pressure but which can be liquefied at only moderate pressure. When the pressure is released, the gas returns to its vapour state.

The two main liquefied petroleum gases in general use are commercial butane and commercial propane, both conforming with BS 4250. All persons involved with LPG installations should be familiar with the properties of commercial butane and commercial propane and the potential hazards involved, both for their own safety and that of others in the vicinity, including those involved in fire-fighting and control.

## Building control and planning permission

It is essential that the local Building Control and Planning Departments are consulted at an early stage in any proposal to site LPG storage vessels, either cylinders or tanks. Planning permission is required and the Planning Department will normally consult with the Environmental Health Department, Health and Safety Executive and Fire Brigade. If in doubt, ask – a telephone call to the local Planning Department could save considerable expense if the installation has to be changed later in order to comply with the Regulations.

Typical properties of commercial butane and propane gases, based on Appendix 1 in LPGITA Code of Practice No 1 are as Table 10 above:

*Table 10* *Liquid and vapour phase comparisons*

| | Commercial butane | | Commercial propane | |
|---|---|---|---|---|
| **Liquid phase** | | | | |
| Relative density (to water) of liquid at 15.6°C | 0.57 | | 0.51 | |
| Litres/tonne | 1750 | | 1960 | |
| Kg/litre | 0.57 | | 0.51 | |
| Imperial gallons/ton | 390 | | 440 | |
| lb/imperial gallon | 5.7 | | 5.1 | |
| **Vapour phase** | | | | |
| Relative density (to air) at 15.6°C and 1015.9mbar | 2.0 | | 1.5 | |
| Ratio of gas to liquid volume at 15.6°C and 1015.9mbar | 240 | | 270 | |
| Boiling point at atmospheric pressure | −2°C | | −45°C | |
| **Vapour pressure (abs) (max)** | (bar) | (psig) | (bar) | (psig) |
| 20°C | 2.5 | 40 | 9.0 | 130 |
| 50°C | 7.0 | 100 | 19.6 | 283 |
| **Limits of flammability at atmospheric pressure** | | | | |
| (% gas in air) | 1.8 to 90 | | 2.2 to 10 | |
| Calorific values (gross) (net) | 121.8MJ/m³ 112.9MJ/m³ | | 93.1MJ/m³ 86.1MJ/m³ | |

# General properties

All personnel working with LPG should receive adequate initial and refresher training as appropriate. The notes in this Guide are not intended to cover all aspects of LPG installations but are a guide to the extent of information personnel engaged in small industrial, commercial and domestic installations would be expected to fully understand.

For reference and further information, the Codes and Standards listed at the end of this Section should be consulted. The values of the physical characteristics of the product have been 'rounded' to facilitate remembering; for exact values, refer to British Standards, LPGITA or the suppliers of the gas.

LPG is normally stored at ambient temperature as a liquid in steel vessels (or special lightweight alloy cylinders for touring caravans) under pressure. There are special applications where the liquid is stored under refrigerated conditions at a lower pressure but these applications do not normally apply to the type of projects being considered here.

The liquid is colourless and is approximately half the weight of an equivalent volume of water. If LPG is spilled on water, it will float on the surface before vapourising. The liquid occupies about 1/250th of the volume needed if the product was stored as a gas. It is more practical therefore, to store and transport the product as a liquid under pressure than as a gas. However, a leakage of a small quantity of the liquid product can lead to large

volumes of vapour/air mixtures and possible hazard.

LPG vapour is denser than air, commercial butane being about twice as heavy as air and commercial propane about one and a half times as heavy as air. Leakage of LPG will therefore flow to low points, for example, along the ground to the lowest level of the surroundings, into basements or into drains without water seals. If the air is still, any LPG vapour will disperse slowly and could be ignited a considerable distance from the original leakage, the flame travelling back to the source of leakage.

When LPG vapour is mixed with air in certain proportion, a lower flammable mixture is formed. Within the range of 2% (lower limit) to 10% (upper limit) of the vapour in air at atmospheric pressure, there is a risk of explosion. Outside this range, any mixture is either too weak or too rich to propagate flame but it is important to understand that over-rich mixtures can become diluted with air and becomes hazardous. At pressures higher than atmospheric, the upper limit of flammability is increased but the increase with pressure is not linear, eg. doubling the pressure does not double the upper limit of flammability.

**ON NO ACCOUNT SHOULD A NAKED FLAME BE USED TO DETECT A LEAK**

An explosimeter, properly calibrated for LPG, must be used for testing the concentration of LPG vapour in the air. LPG vapour is slightly anaesthetic and may cause suffocation if present in sufficiently high concentrations. Extreme caution must be taken when testing for leaks and there should always be a

second person stationed outside the area to supervise. The LPG supplier should be consulted if a leak is suspected, particularly a leakage of liquid product. There is no acceptable percentage or degree of leakage with LPG.

LPG is normally odorised by the manufacture by the addition of an odorant such as ethyl mercaptan or dimethyl sulphide which give LPG its characteristic odour and enable leaks to be detected by smell at concentrations down to 0.4% of the gas in air (ie one-fifth of the lower limit of flammability). There are special applications where the LPG is not odorised, eg. where the odorising material is harmful to a process or does not serve any useful purpose as a warning agent. In such applications, extra precautions and safety procedures must be taken in respect of marking storage vessels, installing pipelines externally, inspections daily, provision of automatic flammable gas detectors etc.

Vessels are never completely filled with liquid, the maximum percentage fill varying between 80-87% depending on the vessel size. The space above the liquid level allows for liquid expansion (due to temperature changes) and for a supply of compressed vapour for drawing-off by the consumer. When the pressure of the vapour in the space above the liquid falls, the liquid boils to produce more vapour and restore the pressure. The boiling point of propane is around −45°C at atmospheric pressure. The liquid takes heat (latent heat of vapourisation) from the liquid itself, the metal of the vessel in contact with the liquid and from the surrounding air. This cooling effect may cause condensation and even freezing of the water vapour in the air local to a leakage. This effect may show as a 'white frost' at the point of escape and make it easier to detect leakage. Leaks can sometimes be seen as a 'shimmering' due to the refractive index of LPG.

LPG, particularly liquid product, can cause severe frost burns (for reasons similar to those outlined in the previous paragraph) if brought into contact with the skin. Goggles, gloves and protective clothing should be worn if exposure to this hazard is likely to occur.

A vessel which has contained LPG and is 'empty' may still contain LPG in vapour form. In this state, the pressure in the vessel is approximately atmospheric and if the outlet valve is left open or is leaking, air can diffuse into the vessel forming a flammable mixture and creating a risk of explosion. Alternatively, LPG may diffuse from the vessel to the atmosphere.

# LPG bulk tank location and safety distances

This section covers LPG bulk storage installations at industrial, commercial and domestic consumers' premises where the LPG is stored in a tank or tanks larger than 150 litres water capacity. For installations in refineries, bulk plants and large industrial plants, reference should be made to the publications issued by the Health and Safety Executive and the LPGITA.

Storage tanks should normally be installed above ground in the open air in a well ventilated position and should NOT be installed in basements or open pits. Tanks should not be installed one above the other. Vertical cylindrical storage tanks are commercially available and although used extensively abroad, vertical tank installations in the UK are not generally commonplace and are generally more expensive. However, a vertical tank may solve a problem on a restricted site but the LPG supplier should be consulted at an early stage.

Tanks may be installed underground but most LPG suppliers would prefer not to put tanks underground mainly because such installations have to be accessed for full internal visual examination and ultrasonic or hydrostatic testing every 5 years instead of every 10 years for an above ground tank. The cost of the associated attendances may make underground tank installations prohibitive.

Storage tanks should be sited and located in accordance with Table 11. Note that details for underground tanks have been omitted for clarity but details for these can be obtained from the LGPITA.

*A fire wall may be used under certain circumstances to reduce (to approximately half) the minimum separation distances shown above. For details see LPGITA publications.

The number of tanks in one group should not exceed six, subject to the maximum total capacity of a group given in Table 11. If more than one group is required, then any tank in one group should be at least 7.5 metres from any tank in another group unless a radiation wall is erected between the groups or adequate fixed water spray systems are provided.

Separation distances are intended to protect the LPG facilities from the radiation effects of fires involving other facilities as well as to minimise the risk of escaping LPG being ignited before being dispersed or diluted. The distances given are minimum recommendations and refer to the horizontal distance in plan between the nearest point on the storage tank and the nearest point of a specified feature (eg. an adjacent storage tank, building, property line etc).

Radiation walls or adequate fixed water drenching systems may be provided to enable separation distances for above ground tanks to be reduced, but specialist advice should be obtained. If separation distances are reduced. It may be necessary to provide diversion walls or kerbs (maximum height 500 mm) to ensure that the path of leaking gas from a storage site to a specified feature is not less than that shown in Table 11.

Conventional bunds (an enclosure capable of retaining the total capacity, plus 10% margin, of all the vessels within the enclosure) around LPG storage tanks should NOT be used.

No LPG storage tank should be installed nearer than:

a. 6 metres to the bund wall of any tank containing a flammable liquid with a flash point below 32°C

b. 6 metres from any tank containing a flammable liquid with a flash point between 32°C and 65°C

c. 3 metres from the top of the bund wall of any tank containing a flammable liquid.

LPG storage tanks should be installed well away from tanks containing liquid

oxygen or other toxic or hazardous substances (eg. chlorine) – distances between 6 and 45 metres are not uncommon depending on the relative sizes of the vessels – but specialist advice should always be obtained.

No LPG storage tank should be installed within the bunded enclosure of a tank containing a flammable liquid, liquid oxygen or any other hazardous or cryogenic (producing low temperatures) substances. No LPG storage tank should be located in any bund where there is a permanent source of heat (eg. steam mains) or within the bunded enclosure of a heated storage tank (eg. fuel oil tank).

The vicinity of LPG storage tanks should be free of pits and depressions which might form gas pockets and affect the safety of the tanks. The ground beneath storage tanks should be either compacted or concreted and should be sloped to;

a. Prevent the accumulation of any liquid, including rainwater and cooling water applied under fire-fighting conditions, beneath the tanks

b. Ensure a flow of any liquid away from tanks so that other vessels or important areas are not affected.

LPG storage vessels should not be sited in locations known to be susceptible to flooding eg. near rivers and streams which could overflow their banks during abnormal weather conditions.

To prevent tampering and possible vandalism, storage tanks should be enclosed by an industrial type fence which is at least 1.8 metres high and at a distance of not less than 1.5 metres from the LPG tanks, unless it is a boundary fence when the distances given in Table 12 will apply.

Around the immediate vessel area, fences should have at least two non-self locking gates, not adjacent to each other and preferably at diagonally opposite corners of the fenced enclosure, opening outwards to provide easy means of exit in an emergency situation. It is preferable that the padlocks fitted to these gates should suit the master key system operated by most LPG suppliers as this can prevent problems and delays during deliveries. The gates must be unlocked when the compound is occupied.

The provision of a fence need not apply to tanks of 9,000 litres water capacity or less which are provided with a hinged, lockable cover to deny access to valves and fittings. However, should it be elected to erect a fence to prevent unauthorised interference, then the full provisions of the previous paragraph must be applied including the provision

*Table 11 Minimum recommended safety distances for LPG storage vessels
Maximum water capacity*

| Maximum water capacity of any single tank in a group | Nominal LPG capacity | Maximum total water capacity of all tanks in a group | Minimum separation distance | |
|---|---|---|---|---|
| | | | From building boundary, property line (whether built or not) or fixed source of ignition* | Between tanks |
| (litres) | (tonnes) | (litres) | (metres) | (metres) |
| 150 to 500 | 0.05 to 0.25 | 1,500 | 2.5 | 1.0 |
| >500 to 2,500 | 0.25 to 1.10 | 7,500 | 3.0 | 1.0 |
| >2,500 to 9,000 | 1.10 to 4.00 | 27,000 | 7.5 | 1.0 |
| >9,000 to 135,000 | 4.00 to 60.00 | 450,000 | 15.0 | 1.5 |

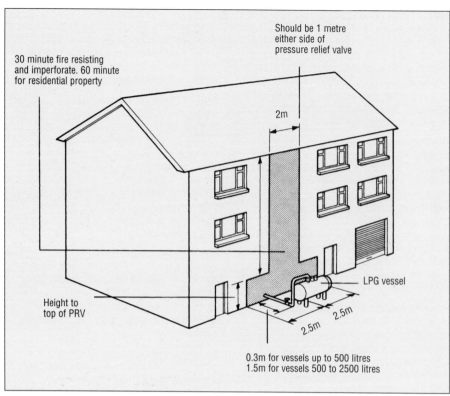

Figure 1: *Small bulk vessel adjacent to building*

Within the figure:
- 30 minute fire resisting and imperforate. 60 minute for residential property
- Should be 1 metre either side of pressure relief valve
- 2m
- LPG vessel
- Height to top of PRV
- 2.5m
- 2.5m
- 0.3m for vessels up to 500 litres
- 1.5m for vessels 500 to 2500 litres

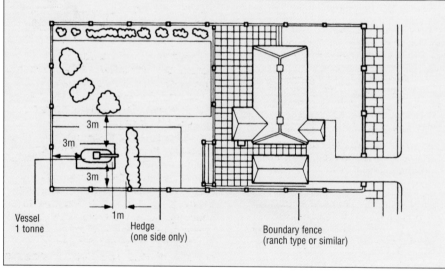

Figure 2: *Small bulk vessel at domestic premises*

Within the figure:
- 3m
- 3m
- 3m
- 1m
- Vessel 1 tonne
- Hedge (one side only)
- Boundary fence (ranch type or similar)

area within 3 metres of any storage tank of up to 2,250 litres of water capacity and within 6 metres of larger vessels. Certain weed killers are a potential source of fire hazard and should not be used.

An effective earthing point and/or bonding connection should be provided at the consumer's storage site for discharging static electricity from bulk tanker vehicles prior to commencing the delivery operation. Consumer vessels greater than 2,250 litres water capacity should be electrically earthed as a protection against the accumulation of static electricity. The earthing point for the bulk tanker vehicle and the earth for the storage vessel should have electrical continuity and should be a common earth. The resistance to earth should not exceed $1 \times 10^6$ ohms.

Access is required for delivering and positioning the tanks. The smaller domestic tanks may be off-loaded from the delivery vehicle using the onboard vehicle crane and then man-handled into position using a tank trolley. A separate crane may be required to off-load and position larger tanks. Bulk LPG delivery tankers normally carry a 30 metre long hose which means that the tank has to be within approximately 25 metres from the road or hard standing for the tanker. Extended fill pipes are practicable but are normally used as a last resort in difficult commercial and industrial sites.

The tanker driver must be able to stand at the storage tank or filling point and be able to observe the vehicle whilst he is filling the tank. Access to the premises for a bulk tanker vehicle may be required under some site conditions. If the bulk tanker vehicle has to negotiate difficult bends or steep gradients, it is usually advisable to arrange for the LPG supplier to make a 'dummy delivery' before any work commences. Suppliers may charge more for the LPG if it is necessary to send a helper with the driver for deliveries to awkward sites.

Figure 1 shows the layout of a typical small bulk vessel adjacent to a building and Figure 2, a 1 tonne bulk vessel at domestic premises.

## Storage tanks and fittings

Storage tanks are designed, fabricated and tested in accordance with British Standards, AOTC Rules and other recognised pressure vessel codes. Storage tanks are normally purchased or hired from the LPG supplier, who should assume responsibility for ensuring that the tanks, tank supports, protection against corrosion, testing and provision of tank fittings all comply with the rules and regulations.

of two means of exit. Where there is surveillance at industrial premises, the site perimeter fence may suffice for security.

Where there is a possibility of mechanical damage to LPG storage and associated equipment from vehicles (eg. in goods delivery yards, near site roads etc.), suitable protection must be provided by the use of crash barriers, vehicle impact bollards or a non-continuous wall not more than 500mm in height.

At least two NON SMOKING OR NAKED LIGHTS notices in red on white

background shall be fixed to the outside of the compound surrounding wall or fence or, if these have not been provided, the notices shall be attached to the tank. The size of the lettering shall be such that notices can be clearly read at the safety distances applicable to the installation and from points of access to the storage site.

Each storage tank shall be clearly and boldly marked:

**HIGHLY FLAMMABLE – BUTANE
(or PROPANE as appropriate)**

Long grass, weeds and combustible material should be kept clear from an

The pressure of the vapour within a bulk storage vessel, under normal UK weather conditions, can vary between 2 and 9bar depending on the liquid product temperature. On average, the vapour pressure is about 7bar when liquid product temperature is 15°C. Safety pressure relief valves protect the vessel against excessive pressure due to exposure to heat in adjacent facilities.

A first stage regulator, mounted on the tank at the vapour off-take, reduces the varying high pressure to 0.75bar. A second stage regulator reduces the intermediate pressure of 0.75bar down to 37mbar which is the industry standard propane operating pressure for domestic appliances.

The second stage regulator incorporates safety features to protect the appliances against excessive pressure.

Tanks are sized in accordance with three main criteria:

### Vapour offtake capacity

The tank must be able to boil-off liquid product faster than the vapour product is being drawn-off when all the gas appliances are operating at maximum capacity. This rate of gas production is known as the vapour offtake capacity of the tank and is a function, amongst other things, of the surface area of the tank; the larger the tank the larger the offtake capacity. It is normally quoted in cubic metres per hour (m³/hr) or in kilograms per hour (kg/hr). Sometimes two figures are quoted; a figure for intermittent offtakes and a lower figure for continuous offtakes.

### Storage capacity required

To ensure continuity and security of gas supplies under adverse weather conditions, storage should be sufficient for a minimum of six weeks gas supply at maximum use. (This allows for the tank being partially full, some of the gas being used and for three weeks adverse weather conditions in the UK when it may not be possible for delivery vehicles to get to the site). The consequences of the gas supply failing during adverse weather conditions, industrial action, etc should be considered (eg. hospitals, old persons homes, etc) and additional storage provided if necessary.

### Location for tank

Tanks must be located in accordance with the Codes of Practice and Regulations.

Each tank should be provided with at least one each of the following fittings suitable for LPG service over the range of pressures and temperatures

**Table 12** Storage tank dimensions

| Nominal LPG capacity (kg) | Water capacity (litres) | Diameter (mm) | Overall length (mm) | Approx. overall height (mm) | Continuous off-take (m³/hr) |
|---|---|---|---|---|---|
| 200 | 450 | 610 | 1675 | 900 | 2.26 |
| 600 | 1400 | 1000 | 1985 | 1310 | 5.66 |
| 1000 | 2250 | 1000 | 3042 | 1460 | 7.08 |
| 2000 | 4500 | 1220 | 4100 | 1685 | 10.19 |
| 7000 | 16000 | 1700 | 6782 | 3580* | 28.30 |
| 1200 | 28000 | 2172 | 8600 | 3910* | 39.62 |

*including platform and guard rails

appropriate to the operating conditions in service:

i. Pressure relief valve connected directly to the vapour space

ii. Drain or other means of removing the liquid contents

iii. A fixed maximum level device and preferably also an independent contents gauge

iv. A pressure gauge connected to the vapour space if the vessel is over 5,000 litres water capacity

v. A suitable earthing connection if the vessel is over 2,500 litres

vi. A filling connection.

It should be noted that some LPG suppliers provide a combination valve for certain sizes of tanks which includes:

i. A threaded filling connection incorporating a manual shut-off valve, a spring loaded back check valve, a relief valve to prevent pressure build up between the back check valve and the manual shut-off valve and a protective cap to prevent thread damage and ingress of foreign matter.

ii. A vapour off-take connection controlled by a diaphragm valve which can be fitted with a first stage regulator and pressure gauge.

iii. A fixed liquid level gauge incorporating a replaceable control valve.

For a detailed specification of tank fittings and piping, consult the references at the end of this section.

Figure 3 and Table 12 show typical LPG storage tank dimensions. For exact dimensions and a copy of a certified drawing, consult the LPG supplier of the tanks.

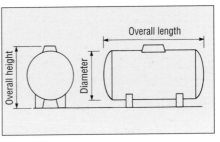

**Figure 3** Storage tank dimensions

## LPG storage in cylinders

The basic principles detailed in previous sections in respect of safety when handling and storing propane in tanks also apply to installations where the propane is stored in cylinders.

For permanently piped domestic installations with a low offtake rating, eg. single cooker, two 19kg propane cylinders with a change-over regulator should be sufficient. Larger domestic and small commercial and industrial installations, with a higher offtake rating, eg. central heating boilers and fires, bunsen burners in laboratories etc, may require four 47kg propane cylinders. Each cylinder is fitted with a valve; the handwheel is turned anti-clockwise to open and clockwise to close. An excess pressure relief valve is also provided. The four cylinders, at the container pressure of up to 9 bar, are connected to a change-over valve by means of pigtails (see Figure 4). The change-over valve incorporates a regulator to reduce the pressure to 37 mbar for the supply to the appliances. The change-over valve connects two cylinders to the pipework system and, when these two cylinders are empty, the valve automatically changes over to the two reserve cylinders and indicates that these have been brought into use.

For indoor applications, eg. portable domestic cabinet heaters where the cylinder is contained in or close to the unit, butane must be used.

Manufacturers of LPG may have different sizes and ranges of sizes of cylinders. Table 13 gives details of the popular

*Table 13* Cylinder sizes

| Cylinder capacity | Overall height | Maximum diameter | Cylinder offtakes | |
|---|---|---|---|---|
| (kg) | (mm) | (mm) | Intermittent (m³/h) | Continuous (m³/h) |
| **Propane** 3.9 | 337 | 28 | 0.28 | 0.17 |
| 13.0 | 584 | 318 | 0.57 | 0.28 |
| 19.0 | 800 | 318 | 0.85 | 0.42 |
| 47.0 | 1289 | 375 | 1.69 | 0.85 |
| **Butane** 4.5 | 337 | 248 | 0.17 | 0.08 |
| 7.0 | 495 | 256 | 0.21 | 0.10 |
| 15.0 | 584 | 318 | 0.28 | 0.14 |

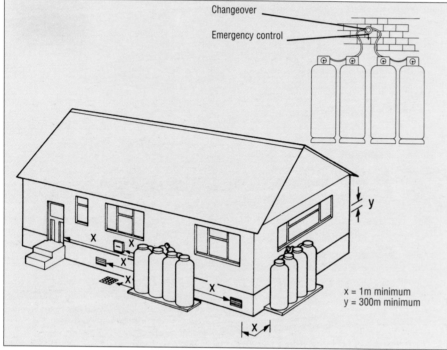

Changeover

Emergency control

x = 1m minimum
y = 300m minimum

*Figure 4* Cylinder storage

sizes for a range of four propane cylinders and three butane cylinders.

## Pipe sizing

The industry standard operating pressure for propane is 37mbar and in order to obtain this pressure at the appliance, pipework must be of adequate diameter to pass the required rate of gas flow when all the appliances are operating at maximum output, without significant pressure drop due to friction losses. A pressure drop of not more than 2.5mbar between the second stage regulator and the appliance at maximum gas flow rates has been proven to give satisfactory results.

Consideration should be given when sizing main runs of pipework to future extensions and/or appliances being added to the installation.

Table 14 gives recommended sizes for short final connections to individual domestic appliances.

Tables 15a, 15b and 15c give pipe sizes and flow rates in longer runs and higher rates of flow, with a 2.5 mbar pressure drop. These tables should be used to determine the diameter of the main run.

Copper pipe to EN 1057 R250 with capillary and compression fittings to EN 1254 Parts 1-5 are suitable for LPG.

Galvanised screwed steel pipe, medium weight, to BS 1387: 1987 with screwed fittings to BS 143: 1968 are also suitable for LPG installations. PTFE tape or a jointing compound specifically made for LPG must only be used. General purpose jointing materials with hemp are not suitable for LPG. Existing joints on pipework being converted to LPG must be examined and if made with general purpose jointing materials and hemp, must be dismantled and remade or the pipework scrapped.

Polyethylene may be used for underground pipework but the manufacturer's instructions for jointing must be followed. Polyethylene must not be exposed to strong sunlight during transit and pending installation.

Underground pipework must be a minimum of 500mm below finished ground level. Trenches should be dug deeper than 500mm and all stones should be removed from the bottom of the excavation before backfilling and compacting the bottom 75mm of the trench with sifted material. The pipework should be supported with sifted material and a warning tape should be laid 150mm above the pipework to prevent possible damage during future excavations. All backfill should be carefully selected to remove all stones which could cause damage to the pipework due to settlement and compaction. Pipework should be protected if installed in corrosive soil conditions.

Pipework installations must be pressure tested and proved to be leak-free before connecting to the tank(s) or cylinder(s).

When installing Polythene pipework to convey gas it is recommended that advice from the pipe manufacturer is sought because there could be a

*Table 14* Guide to pipe sizes for appliances

| Appliance | Metric (mm) | Imperial (in) |
|---|---|---|
| Central heating boilers | 22 | ¾ |
| Cookers, domestic | 15 | ½ |
| Lights | 6 | ¼ |
| Portable fires | 10 | ¼ |
| Fixed fires | 10 | ⅜ |
| Water heaters | | |
|     Single-point instantaneous | 10 | ⅜ |
|     Multi-point instantaneous | 15 | ½ |
|     Bath heaters | 15 | ½ |
|     Optional single or multi-point | 10 | ⅜ |
|     Sink storage | 6 | ¼ |
|     Circulators | 6 | ¼ |

*Table 15a  Steel tube medium grade – BS1387*                                                                           LP gas

| Size of tube in mm | | | Length of tube in metres  Discharge rate in m³/h | | | | | | | | | |
|---|---|---|---|---|---|---|---|---|---|---|---|---|
| Wall thickness | NS (mm) | ID (mm) | 3 | 6 | 9 | 12 | 15 | 20 | 25 | 30 | 40 | 50 |
| 2.3 | 8 | 8.70 | 1.181 | 0.835 | 0.682 | 0.590 | 0.528 | 0.457 | 0.409 | 0.373 | 0.323 | 0.289 |
| 2.3 | 10 | 12.20 | 2.751 | 1.945 | 1.588 | 1.375 | 1.230 | 1.065 | 0.953 | 0.870 | 0.753 | 0.673 |
| 2.6 | 15 | 15.90 | 5.334 | 3.772 | 3.080 | 2.667 | 2.385 | 2.066 | 1.848 | 1.686 | 1.460 | 1.306 |
| 2.6 | 20 | 21.40 | 11.211 | 7.927 | 6.472 | 5.605 | 5.013 | 4.342 | 3.883 | 3.545 | 3.070 | 2.746 |
| 3.2 | 25 | 27.00 | 20.046 | 14.174 | 11.573 | 10.023 | 8.964 | 7.763 | 6.944 | 6.339 | 5.489 | 4.910 |
| 3.2 | 32 | 35.70 | 40.298 | 28.495 | 23.266 | 20.149 | 18.022 | 15.607 | 13.959 | 12.743 | 11.036 | 9.871 |

*General purpose tube to the Quality Assurance requirements of ISO9002/BS5750 Part 2*

*Table 15b  Copper tube to EN1057-R250*                                                                                  LP gas

| Size of tube in mm | | | Length of tube in metres  Discharge rate in m³/h | | | | | | | | | |
|---|---|---|---|---|---|---|---|---|---|---|---|---|
| Wall thickness | NS (mm) | ID (mm) | 3 | 6 | 9 | 12 | 15 | 20 | 25 | 30 | 40 | 50 |
| 0.60 | 6 | 4.76 | 0.261 | 0.184 | 0.151 | 0.130 | 0.116 | 0.101 | 0.090 | 0.082 | 0.071 | 0.064 |
| 0.60 | 8 | 6.76 | 0.628 | 0.444 | 0.363 | 0.314 | 0.281 | 0.243 | 0.217 | 0.198 | 0.172 | 0.154 |
| 0.60 | 10 | 8.76 | 1.201 | 0.849 | 0.693 | 0.600 | 0.537 | 0.465 | 0.416 | 0.380 | 0.329 | 0.294 |
| 0.60 | 12 | 10.76 | 2.009 | 1.421 | 1.160 | 1.00 | 0.898 | 0.778 | 0.696 | 0.635 | 0.550 | 0.492 |
| 0.70 | 15 | 13.56 | 3.583 | 2.533 | 2.068 | 1.791 | 1.602 | 1.387 | 1.241 | 1.133 | 0.981 | 0.877 |
| 0.90 | 22 | 20.15 | 9.645 | 6.820 | 5.568 | 4.822 | 4.313 | 3.735 | 3.341 | 3.050 | 2.641 | 2.362 |
| 0.90 | 28 | 26.15 | 18.505 | 13.085 | 10.684 | 9.252 | 8.275 | 7.167 | 6.410 | 5.851 | 5.067 | 4.532 |

*Previous designation BS2871 Part 1 Table X 1971*

*Table 15c  Copper tube to EN1057-R250 half hard straights*                                                             LP gas

| Size of tube in mm | | | Length of tube in metres  Discharge rate in m³/h | | | | | | | | | |
|---|---|---|---|---|---|---|---|---|---|---|---|---|
| Wall thickness | NS (mm) | ID (mm) | 3 | 6 | 9 | 12 | 15 | 20 | 25 | 30 | 40 | 50 |
| 0.8 | 6 | 4.36 | 0.210 | 0.148 | 0.121 | 0.105 | 0.093 | 0.081 | 0.072 | 0.066 | 0.057 | 0.051 |
| 0.8 | 8 | 6.36 | 0.539 | 0.381 | 0.311 | 0.269 | 0.241 | 0.209 | 0.187 | 0.170 | 0.147 | 0.132 |
| 0.8 | 10 | 8.36 | 1.069 | 0.756 | 0.617 | 0.534 | 0.478 | 0.414 | 0.370 | 0.338 | 0.292 | 0.261 |
| 0.8 | 12 | 10.36 | 1.828 | 1.292 | 1.055 | 0.914 | 0.817 | 0.708 | 0.633 | 0.578 | 0.500 | 0.447 |
| 1.0 | 15 | 12.96 | 3.199 | 2.262 | 1.847 | 1.599 | 1.431 | 1.239 | 1.108 | 1.011 | 0.876 | 0.783 |
| 1.2 | 22 | 19.55 | 8.943 | 6.232 | 5.163 | 4.471 | 3.999 | 3.465 | 3.097 | 2.828 | 2.449 | 2.190 |
| 1.2 | 28 | 25.55 | 17.462 | 12.347 | 10.081 | 8.731 | 7.809 | 6.763 | 6.049 | 5.522 | 4.782 | 4.277 |

*Copper tube to EN1057-R220 soft coils. Previous designation BS2871 Part 1 Table Y 1971*

variance between the internal dimensions (ID) and various manufacturers. The discharge rate for any manufacturers pipe can be ascertained when applying the specific internal diameter using poles formula as shown earlier at the front of this section.

# Compressed air

## Compressing the air

There are many different types of machines for compressing air-reciprocating, rotary-vane, screw and turbine compressors. This section will cover reciprocating and rotary vane compressors only; turbine types are normally used only where extremely large quantities of compressed air are needed, often at relatively low pressures, and are outside the scope of the normal industrial installation.

The reciprocating compressor may have one or several stages. The rotary-vane compressor consists of a rotor, having blades free to slide in radial slots, rotating off centre in a cylindrical chamber. Rotation causes the blades to be thrown out by centrifugal force and to sweep the compression chamber. A small amount of oil is admitted to the chamber to seal and lubricate the blades and to act as an internal coolant. Again, there may be one or more stages.

The screw compressor is a rotary positive displacement machine in which two intermeshing rotors each in helical configuration, displace and compress the air. Available in lubricated and non-lubricated (oil-free) construction, the discharge air is normally free from pulsation. The machine has a high rotation speed, and is available in single or twin stages.

There is no hard and fast rule about the choice of single or multi-stage

*Table 16* Final temperature (°C) of adiabatic compression from free air at 1.013 bar at 20°C (SI metric units)

| Gauge pressure (bar) | Single stage (°C) | Two stage (°C) |
|---|---|---|
| 3 | 164 | 85 |
| 4 | 192 | 97 |
| 5 | 218 | 106 |
| 6 | 240 | 116 |
| 8 | 278 | 129 |
| 10 | 310 | 141 |
| 14 | 365 | 160 |

*Table 17* Effect of altitude on compressor volumetric efficiency (SI metric units)

| Altitude (m) | Barometer pressure (mbar) | Percentage relative volumetric efficiency compared with sea level | |
|---|---|---|---|
| | | (4 bar) | (7 bar) |
| Sea level | 1013 | 100.0 | 100.0 |
| 500 | 945 | 98.7 | 97.7 |
| 1000 | 894 | 97.0 | 95.2 |
| 1500 | 840 | 95.5 | 92.7 |
| 2000 | 780 | 93.9 | 88.0 |
| 2500 | 737 | 92.1 | 87.0 |

*Table 18* Cooling tank capacities

| Compressor capacity (dm³/h free air) | Tank capacity (litres) | Compressor capacity (cfm free air) | Tank capacity (gallons) |
|---|---|---|---|
| 10 | 170 | 25 | 40 |
| 25 | 370 | 50 | 80 |
| 50 | 700 | 100 | 150 |
| 70 | 1020 | 150 | 225 |
| 100 | 1600 | 200 | 360 |
| 140 | 2200 | 300 | 480 |
| 200 | 3000 | 450 | 700 |
| 280 | 3800 | 600 | 850 |
| 350 | 4500 | 800 | 1000 |

compressors. A multi-stage machine will use less power to compress a given quantity of air, the power required being appreciably less as the pressure rises. But a multi-stage compressor can be more costly to purchase and so there must be an economic balance beween the initial cost and the running cost.

It is therefore usual to find that for simplicity and low initial cost, single stage compressors are used for small duties and pressures up to about 7bar (100psi), whereas for pressures above this and for higher duties, compressors having two or more stages are used.

There is also considerable difference in the air temperature leaving a single or two stage compressor as Table 16 will show. The sizing of compressors is outside the scope of this Guide, but there are a number of points which should not be forgotten when sizing and choosing a compressor. One of these points covers the effect of altitude on the volumetric efficiency of the compressor, as shown in Table 17. Other aspects which should be considered include the following:

a. Future expansion requirements

b. Maximum and minimum pressures required in the system

c. Type of cooling required

d. Type of compressor

e. Running cost

f. Initial cost

g. Space

h. Type of control to meet anticipated plant requirement

i. Protection devices.

## Compressor cooling

Because of the temperature rise which takes place when air is compressed, some form of cooling is required so that the temperature is not too high for satisfactory lubrication and to avoid excessively high thermal stresses in the machine structure. Cooling may be either by air or water.

Nowadays, air cooled compressors may have capacities up to 350dm³/s (750cfm), or be rated on continuous duty up to 14 bar (200psi). Air cooled cylinders are finned and additional cooling is provided by arranging for the flywheel or a fan to direct a stream of air onto the cylinder. Such compressors should not be run in a confined space, otherwise the high ambient temperature will prevent adequate air cooling.

A common method of compressor cooling is of course, to provide a water jacket. There are a number of ways in which such a jacket could be supplied with cooling water. It should however be remembered that, although the colder the water the more effective the inter or after cooler, cold water fed to the compressor jackets can be harmful. This is because it can cause water vapour in the compressed air to condense to the detriment of cylinder lubrication and also lead to possible corrosion.

## Thermo-syphon circulation

Thermo-syphon circulation is satisfactory for small single-stage compressors and relies on convection to circulate the water which is heated by the compressor. The water circulates from the compressor jacket to a holding tank where the heat is lost. It is essential that the flow and return pipes have a fall from the tank to the compressor to ensure good circulation. Even a horizontal pipe will reduce the flow rate and may induce air locks. Preferably, the tank should be placed in the open-air and the top should be open to provide maximum cooling effect; however, adequate protection of the tank from birds etc must be ensured.

A tank having a large water surface area loses heat more quickly than a tall narrow tank. The drawback of such a tank is that it is liable to freeze if the compressor is shut down in cold weather. A stop valve should therefore be fitted in the cold water make-up line and on the tank outlet so that the compressor cooling jacket can be drained. To avoid draining an overnight shutdown, it is a good idea to fit a small electric immersion heater in the tank.

## Pump assisted circulation

For larger single stage compressors, thermo-syphon circulation is too slow to dissipate the heat and a circulating pump must be installed to increase water velocity. The required water tank capacity should be discussed with the compressor manufacturer, but where information is not available, Table 18 can be used as a rough guide for compressors running at up to 7 bar (100psi).

# Closed cycle cooling

It is usually better, particularly with larger compressors, to operate them on a closed circuit, the heat being dissipated either through a cooling tower or through a mechanical cooler.

A further advantage is that a closed circuit can eliminate jacket scaling, particularly if the water is treated. The use of the closed circuit does not mean that temperature control is unimportant. With the closed circuit, it is usually preferable to use a 'three-way temperature control'. It is also important to remember that in severe winter conditions, it is not uncommon for cooling towers to freeze solid. Should this be the case, the compressor must be shut down.

Freezing of the sump in the cooling tower may be prevented by fitting a heating coil. To prevent the tower becoming a solid mass of ice, the line from the diversion control valve should be so valued that it can return the water from the compressor direct to the sump instead of to the top of the tower in such low temperature conditions. Under these circumstances, sufficient cooling can usually be maintained due to heat losses from the sump itself.

A mechanical cooler, where the cascade of water is cooled by forced or induced air draught, is much smaller than the cooling tower and the elements are almost totally enclosed offering less risk of freezing when shut down. However, any ice which does form will usually melt within seconds of the compressor starting up.

# Rotary compressors

Where the compressor is of the rotary-vane or oil lubricated screw type it should be noted that oil is usually injected into the compression chamber to form a seal between the blades and the casing and to act as an internal coolant. The oil is removed from the air by a separator at the discharge and is then passed back to the sump by way of a water cooled heat exchanger.

# Cooling the air

The whole purpose of the compressed air installation is to deliver air to the point of use in the best possible condition – clean, dry and with the minimum loss of pressure. If it fails on any one of these counts, then there is likely to be increased wear on tools, poor performance particularly of items such as paint spray equipment, and the operating costs will inevitably be higher than they ought to be.

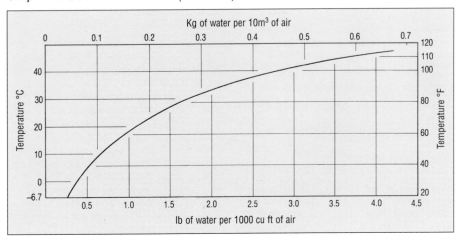

*Graph 1  Moisture content of air (100% RH)*

# Removing moisture

Atmospheric air always contains a proportion of water vapour, the amount depending on the relative humidity. In Britain, this may be between 50 and 70% (RH), this being highest in foggy or rainy weather or if the inlet of the compressor is adjacent or over a pond, stream or other damp area. It is important to note this latter point when installing compressors.

The amount of water which can be held by a given volume of air will depend on its temperature. The moisture carrying capacity of air increases with a rise in temperature, and at this stage, possibly of greater importance, it decreases with a fall in temperature (see Graph 1). Its moisture carrying capacity also falls as the pressure is increased. So, when 'free air' containing water vapour under average conditions enters the compressor, two things will happen. Its ability to hold the water will decrease as the air is compressed to a smaller volume but will increase because of the higher temperature resulting from the compression. Under average conditions, the air will leave the compressor, just able to carry its initial water content.

It will follow that any cooling which then takes place must cause the air to shed its excess water vapour by condensing and this can be accelerated by introducing artificial cooling devices such as intercoolers and aftercoolers.

Although it is customary to lag steam mains to retain heat, it is a potentially bad practice to lag the compressed air main between the compressor and the first major cooling plant (ie. aftercooler or receiver). If the pipework is lagged, the high discharge temperature of the compressed air may be sufficient to spontaneously ignite the deposits of oil, dirt, scale etc. commonly found in this first section of pipe. Once the air has cooled to near ambient temperature, this

danger will not arise. An intercooler is fitted between the stages of a multi-stage compressor; its purpose is to cool the air between the stages and in cooling the air, it also serves the very useful purpose of condensing out the surplus water vapour which, if allowed to pass to the next compression stage, could condense on the cylinder wall with resultant damage to the compressor.

It is essential that the water is drained away from the intercooler and this can best be done automatically using one of the range of compressed air traps. An aftercooler should be fitted immediately following the compressor so as to remove as much water as possible before the air reaches the receiver.

The water must be drained from the bottom of the aftercooler, and this is best done automatically. Manual drains will work only if they are attended to regularly. Rarely, if ever, is this possible, and an automatic drain trap is the best way of ensuring that the system operates properly.

The most efficient aftercoolers are usually water cooled and the lower the air temperature they can produce, the better. However, there is a point of maximum efficiency so, for reasons of economy, where mains water is used, it is well worth fitting a temperature control to the water outlet to keep consumption within reasonable bounds.

For those areas where cooling water is either not available or is too expensive, the air blast aftercooler becomes the first choice. Ambient air is blown by an electric motor fan over a bank of finned tubes, through which the compressed air flows. Although the compressed air discharge temperature is likely to be on average, approximately 6°C (10°F) higher than for a water cooled aftercooler, the unit will still require automatic drainage by a trap.

**Example** (SI metric units)

How much moisture will separate out from air if the compressor inlet conditions are 20°C and 70% relative humidity; the compressor delivers 1m³/sec of free air compressed to 7 bar to the system at 25°C.

Compressor takes in 1m³/sec

From Graph 1, water taken in will be:

$$\frac{0.18 \times 70}{10 \times 100} = 0.0126 \text{kg/s}$$

Compression ratio at 7 bar = 7.91 (Table 19).

Next, we must find the volume of air after compression. Since its volume is proportional to the absolute temperature and to

$$\frac{1}{\text{compression ratio} \times 1\text{m}^3}$$

will occupy:

$$\frac{1}{7.91} \times \frac{(273 + 25)}{(273 + 20)} = 0.128 \text{m}^3$$

From the graph, 10m³ of air at 250°C can carry 0.24 kg of water

Therefore, 0.128m³ can carry:

$$0.128 \times \frac{0.24}{10} = 0.00307 \text{ kg}$$

Therefore, the amount of water which will separate out is:

$$0.0126 - 0.00307 = 0.00953 \text{kg/s}$$

# Receivers

Important as aftercoolers are, it would be very unusual for all the water vapour in the air to condense at this point. Further cooling almost always takes place in the receiver as well as from the distribution system. The water vapour, (and oil mist, if the compressor is of the lubricated type) condenses in the receiver and collects at the bottom. On those installations where the compression plant is small, an aftercooler may not be fitted, thus making the receiver the point at which most condensed liquid will be found. If these liquids are allowed to build up, carry-over into the mains system is likely. There is also the possibility of corrosion of the receiver itself.

It is therefore, important to ensure that these collected liquids and solids (atmospheric dust, pipe scale, carbon, rust etc.) are automatically removed as they collect. As the trap and its protective strainer will have to handle varying proportions of water, oil, emulsion, dirt, etc., regular cleaning is essential.

If excessive amounts of oil are being carried over from the compressor, it generally indicates that maintenance of the compressor is required. If a manual drain cock is fitted to the receiver a short

distance above the drain trap outlet, oil and scum floating on the water surface (which might foul up the trap) can be periodically drained off.

Apart from the receiver's ability to cool the air and hence deposit liquid (that is why it is better to site the receiver where the ambient temperature is low), it performs two other functions. For some applications, it is important that the pressure pulses produced by a reciprocating compressor be eliminated as far as possible. The receiver therefore acts as a pulsation damper. The receiver also acts as a power storage vessel, allowing intermittent high demands for compressed air to be met from a smaller compression set.

Being a pressure vessel and thus subject to regular inspection, a receiver is fitted with inspection covers and manholes. These also allow any solid contaminent build–up to be removed. To comply with Factory and Safety Acts, a receiver must be fitted with an adequately sized safety valve and generally a pressure gauge is also fitted.

On small horizontal receivers generally supplied with the smaller industrial or garage type compressor, automatic drainage may be more difficult. The drain point is often in the centre of the dished end of the receiver or on the top. In each case, an internal dip pipe is fitted to allow the air pressure to displace the collected liquid when the manual drain is opened. An automatic trap can be used.

It is also worthwhile considering the capacity of the receiver. This is usually sized on the actual output in 1 minute from the compressor, but where consumption is high and fairly constant, the air is in the receiver for too short a time to cool down very much. Where this is so, the storage capacity is obviously low and it is better to size the receiver on plant consumption rather than on compression output.

One compressor manufacturer recommends the following as a guide to receiver size:

Receiver capacity (m³)

$$= \frac{\text{m}^3 \text{ of free air required}}{\text{Allowable pressure drop (bar)}}$$

and also;

Receiver capacity (cu ft)

$$= \frac{\text{cu ft of free air required} \times 14.7\text{psi}}{\text{Allowable pressure drop (psi)}}$$

**Example 1**

A machine requires 3m³; available pressure is 7 bar and the minimum suitable pressure is 5.5 bar.

By using the formula to determine the receiver capacity;

$$\frac{3}{1.5} = 2\text{m}^3$$

**Example 2**

A machine requires 100 cu ft; available pressure is 100psi and the minimum suitable pressure is 80psi.

By using the formula to determine the receiver capacity;

$$\frac{100 \times 14.7}{20} = 73.5 \text{ cu ft}$$

# Layout

Although in an ideal system, all cooling and condensing should be carried out before the air leaves the receiver, this is not very often achieved in practice. It is in fact impossible where aftercoolers are not fitted. The whole of the compressed air mains therefore become additional cooling surfaces, the amount of condensing which takes place depending on the efficiency of moisture extraction before the air leaves the receiver and the temperature in the mains system itself.

It is useless to provide a compressed air gun to blow out particles of swarf after a machining operation if, every time the operator used the gun, he squirts water all over the finished job. Equally, it can be very expensive to pass this water through compressed air operated tools.

Care must therefore be taken in the layout of the mains so that adequate fall is given to proper drainage points.

The general layout of the building will dictate the best positions for drain points but in general, the main should be given a fall of not less than 1m in 100m in the direction of air flow and the distance between draining points should not exceed 30m (100ft).

It is a good idea to form a distribution system as a ring main to help reduce pressure losses. It also makes the alteration of extension of the existing system easier. Drainage points should be provided by using equal tees and it assists in the separation of the water if these are arranged to change the direction of the flow as shown in Figure 5. Whenever a branch line is taken off the main, it should leave the top of it, so that any water in the main doesn't fall straight into the plant and the bottom of the falling pipe should be drained as in Figure 5.

## Separators

Whilst automatic drain traps will effectively deal with any water which has collected at the bottom of the main or in a receiver of some kind, they can do nothing for the mist of water droplets which may be suspended in the air. For most everyday applications, much of this water can be removed by fitting a separator in the distribution mains as Figure 5.

When a separator is fitted in a ring main system, install it to allow for the normal direction of flow.

## Dryers

There are applications where the air must not only be clean, but have a reduced dew point. This may call for more sophisticated and expensive methods to lower the dew point of the compressed air. There are three common systems used for this purpose.

### Adsorption dryers

These consist of two pressure vessels filled with water adsorbing chemical. Wet compressed air is passed through one chamber until the chemical is saturated. Whilst this first chamber is being regenerated by heat and/or a purge of the ultra dry air, the second chamber is adsorbing moisture. An automatic control system alternates the chambers, one operation, one regeneration.

### Absorption dryers

These consist of a container of chemical through which compressed air passes. The chemical absorbs the water vapour, forming a solution which drains to the bottom of the container. This solution has to be discharged periodically by a drain trap, and the level of the desiccant then requires topping up. A domestic salt cellar is typical of this type.

### Refrigerant or chiller dryers

These units are heat exchangers which will cool the air down to a theoretical dew point of 1 to 3°C (34 to 37°F) and thus precipitate out the moisture. The system is a straight mechanical refrigeration unit with one extra facility included. This is a second heat exchanger whereby the outgoing cold, dry air is used to pre-cool the incoming compressed air supply. In doing so, the outgoing cold air is warmed up to around ambient temperature.

All these units incur running costs of a kind, whether it be compressed air for purging, steam or electrical power to reactivate chemicals, or the replacement of desiccant.

## Main pressure reduction

It is often necessary to reduce the mains pressure when supplying groups of plant or complete workshops. This requires a pressure reducing valve having quite a large capacity and very good flow characteristics. This unit is somewhat different from the small regulators used for individual items of plant.

## Sizing compressed air mains

The compressed air mains are the all-important link between the compressor and the point of usage. It is thoroughly bad to install mains which are too small and cause high pressure drop. If for example, a compressor has to work at 8bar (120 psi) to cater for pressure drop conditions whereas 7bar (100 psi) would normally meet the case, it calls for an additional power input of as much as 10%.

Mains which are too small also cause high velocity, making it difficult to separate the water from the air because much of the condensed vapour running as a stream of water along the bottom of the pipe, will be whipped up by and carried along with the fast moving air stream. Whilst a watchful eye must be kept on the pressure drop, it is common practice to size compressed air mains on velocity and a reasonable figure for all practical problems is 6-9m/s (20-30ft/sec) which is sufficiently low to prevent excessive pressure drop on most systems and will allow moisture to precipitate out without re-entrainment.

Many compressed air systems are working inefficiently because the demand has outgrown the supply – new pneumatic plant has been added from time to time without addition to the compressor plant or mains.

In designing a new plant, some thought might be given to possible future demands and allowances made in the mains sizes. Sizing by velocity presents an easy form of determining pipe size for a given duty, but it must be remembered that the duty of a compressor and the demand of the equipment is usually expressed in $dm^3/s$ of free air and that when compressed, the volume will be less.

Table 19 shows that the ratio of compression and the actual volume occupied at any given pressure can be found by dividing the volume of free air by the ration of compression.

### Example 1 (SI metric units)

At a gauge pressure of 8bar, Table 16 shows the ratio of compression as 8.9 so if we have $190dm^3$ of free air compressed to 8bar it will occupy a space of:

$$\frac{190}{8.9} = 21.35 \ dm^3$$

By adding the equivalent lengths to the actual length of pipe, the loss in each section of a system can be easily found by reference to the Table 20.

**Graph 2** *Compressed air sizing nomogram*

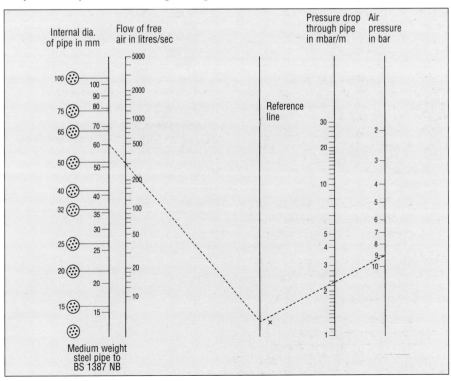

*Table 19* *Ratio of compression (metric units)*

| Gauge pressure (bar) | 0.5 | 1 | 2 | 3 | 4 | 5 | 6 | 7 | 8 | 10 | 12 | 14 | 18 |
|---|---|---|---|---|---|---|---|---|---|---|---|---|---|
| Ratio of compression | 1.5 | 1.99 | 2.97 | 3.96 | 4.95 | 5.94 | 6.92 | 7.91 | 8.9 | 10.87 | 12.85 | 14.82 | 18.77 |

*Table 20* *Resistance of pipe fittings (equivalent length in m)*

| Type of fitting | Nominal size (mm) | | | | | | | | | |
| | 15 | 20 | 25 | 32 | 40 | 50 | 65 | 75 | 100 | 125 |
|---|---|---|---|---|---|---|---|---|---|---|
| Elbow | 0.26 | 0.37 | 0.49 | 0.67 | 0.76 | 1.07 | 1.37 | 1.83 | 2.44 | 3.2 |
| 90° bend (long) | 0.15 | 0.18 | 0.24 | 0.38 | 0.46 | 0.61 | 0.76 | 0.91 | 1.2 | 1.52 |
| Return bend | 0.46 | 0.61 | 0.76 | 1.07 | 1.2 | 1.68 | 1.98 | 2.6 | 3.66 | 4.88 |
| Globe valve | 0.76 | 1.07 | 1.37 | 1.98 | 2.44 | 3.36 | 3.96 | 5.18 | 7.32 | 9.45 |
| Gate valve | 0.107 | 0.14 | 0.18 | 0.27 | 0.32 | 0.40 | 0.49 | 0.64 | 0.91 | 1.20 |
| Run of standard tee | 0.12 | 0.18 | 0.24 | 0.38 | 0.40 | 0.52 | 0.67 | 0.85 | 1.2 | 1.52 |
| Through side outlet of tee | 0.52 | 0.70 | 0.91 | 1.37 | 1.58 | 2.14 | 2.74 | 3.66 | 4.88 | 6.4 |

*Table 21* *Formula for converting volume of compressed air to volume of free air*

Air tools are usually rated in cfm of free air. Where ratings of other air equipment are not given in terms of free air consumption, the following formulae may be used to convert.

$$q = q_1 \frac{P + 1.033}{1.033}$$

$$Q = Q_1 \frac{Q_1(P + 101325}{101325}$$

$$Q = Q_1 \frac{P_1 + 14.7}{14.7}$$

| | | |
|---|---|---|
| q = Litres free air | Q = Cubic metres free air | Q = Cubic ft. of free air |
| $q_1$ = Litres compressed air | $Q_1$ = Cubic metres compressed air | $Q_1$ = Cubic ft. of compressed air |
| $p_1$ = Compressed air pressure in kg/cm² | $P_1$ = Compressed air pressure in Newtons/metre² | $P_1$ = Compressed air pressure psig |

*Weight and volume of pure air. Pure air at 32°F (0°C) and 14.7psi (101.325Kn/m² absolute (atmospheric pressure). Weight 0.08073 lb/ft² (1.29g/litre). Volume 12.381ft²/lb (772 litres/kg).*

The nomogram shown in Graph 2 gives a ready means for determining pressure drops through pipes often found in industry. It is based on the following formula which can also be used for pipe sizes outside those shown in the table.

$$\text{Pressure drop (bar)} = \frac{KLQ^2}{R \times d^{5.3}}$$

Where K = 800

L = length of pipe (m)

Q = volume of free air passing through the pipe (l/sec)

R = ratio of compression

d = internal pipe diameter (mm)

## Example 2

Determine the size of pipe needed to pass 300 litres/sec free air with pressure drop of not more than 300mbar in 125m of pipe run, air pressure is 9bar.

300mbar in 125m is equivalent to

$$\frac{300}{125} = 2.4\text{mbar/m}$$

Join 9 bar on the air pressure line to 2.4mbar/m on the pressure drop line and produce to cut reference line at X. Join X to 300 litres/sec and produce to cut pipe size line at approximately 61mm.

Select pipe having a minimum bore of at least 61mm (a 65mm nominal bore pipe to BS 1387 has a bore of 69mm and would therefore be suitable with some margin).

Table 22 shows the amount of water which will accumulate every 8 hours in a compressed air system using 47 litres/sec of compressed air at different air temperatures and air pressure. For example, at 5.4bar, with a temperature of 32.2°C (90°F), a compressed air system would contain 7.419 litres of water in vapour form every 8 hours.

Ascertainment of peak capacities for compressed air systems is largely a matter of judgement. It is necessary to consider the probable use factors, determined by the devices requiring compressed air, the estimated number of people who will be drawing air from the system and the pattern of air use, with special attention paid to periods of high load. For example, compressed air demand in a two-man laboratory may reach 9 litres/sec of free air per laboratory, depending on the number of air outlets (⅛ inch orifices) in use.

*Graph 3* *Compressed air – laboratories*

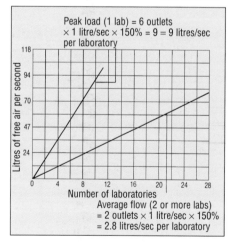

Peak load (1 lab) = 6 outlets × 1 litre/sec × 150% = 9 = 9 litres/sec per laboratory

Litres of free air per second

Number of laboratories

Average flow (2 or more labs) = 2 outlets × 1 litre/sec × 150% = 2.8 litres/sec per laboratory

*Table 22* Relative discharging capabilities of steel tubes to BS 1387

| Nominal dia. of larger pipe | | Nominal diameter of smaller pipe in in. and mm | | | | | | | | | | | | | | |
| --- | --- | --- | --- | --- | --- | --- | --- | --- | --- | --- | --- | --- | --- | --- | --- | --- |
| | | ⅛ | ¼ | ⅜ | ½ | ¾ | 1 | 1¼ | 1½ | 2 | 2½ | 3 | 4 | 5 | 6 | (in) |
| | | 3 | 8 | 10 | 15 | 20 | 25 | 32 | 40 | 50 | 65 | 75 | 100 | 125 | 150 | (mm) |
| (in) | (mm) | Approximate number of small pipe flows served by larger pipe | | | | | | | | | | | | | | |
| ⅛ | 6 | 1 | – | – | – | – | – | – | – | – | – | – | – | – | – | |
| ¼ | 8 | 2.1 | 1 | – | – | – | – | – | – | – | – | – | – | – | – | |
| ⅜ | 10 | 4.5 | 2.1 | 1 | – | – | – | – | – | – | – | – | – | – | – | |
| ½ | 15 | 8 | 3.8 | 1.8 | 1 | – | – | – | – | – | – | – | – | – | – | |
| ¾ | 20 | 15 | 8 | 3.6 | 2 | 1 | – | – | – | – | – | – | – | – | – | |
| 1 | 25 | 30 | 15 | 6.6 | 3.7 | 1.8 | 1 | – | – | – | – | – | – | – | – | |
| 1¼ | 32 | 60 | 25 | 13 | 7 | 3.6 | 2 | 1 | – | – | – | – | – | – | – | |
| 1½ | 40 | 90 | 40 | 20 | 10 | 5.5 | 2.9 | 1.5 | 1 | – | – | – | – | – | – | |
| 2 | 50 | 165 | 75 | 35 | 20 | 10 | 5.5 | 2.7 | 1.9 | 1 | – | – | – | – | – | |
| 2½ | 65 | 255 | 120 | 55 | 30 | 16 | 8 | 4.3 | 2.9 | 1.6 | 1 | – | – | – | – | |
| 3 | 75 | 440 | 210 | 100 | 55 | 27 | 15 | 7 | 5 | 2.7 | 1.7 | 1 | – | – | – | |
| 4 | 100 | 870 | 400 | 190 | 100 | 55 | 30 | 15 | 10 | 5.3 | 3.4 | 2 | 1 | – | – | |
| 5 | 125 | 1500 | 720 | 330 | 180 | 90 | 50 | 25 | 17 | 9 | 6 | 3.5 | 1.8 | 1 | – | |
| 6 | 150 | 2400 | 1130 | 530 | 300 | 150 | 80 | 40 | 28 | 15 | 9 | 5.5 | 2.8 | 1.6 | 1 | |

*Table 23* Discharge of air through orifices

| Gauge pressure (bar) | Discharge of free air in litres/sec for various orifice diameters in mm | | | | | | |
| --- | --- | --- | --- | --- | --- | --- | --- |
| | 0.5 | 1 | 2 | 3 | 4 | 10 | 12.5 |
| 0.5 | 0.06 | 0.22 | 0.92 | 2.1 | 5.7 | 22.8 | 35.5 |
| 1.0 | 0.08 | 0.33 | 1.33 | 3.0 | 8.4 | 33.6 | 52.6 |
| 2.5 | 0.14 | 0.58 | 2.33 | 5.5 | 14.6 | 58.6 | 91.4 |
| 5.0 | 0.25 | 0.97 | 3.92 | 8.8 | 24.4 | 97.5 | 152.0 |
| 7.0 | 0.33 | 1.31 | 5.19 | 11.6 | 32.5 | 129.0 | 202.0 |

*Table 24* Receivers for compressed air systems

| Compressor capacity | | Receiver dimensions | | | | | |
| --- | --- | --- | --- | --- | --- | --- | --- |
| | | Diameter | | Length | | Volume | |
| ft³/min | m³/min | (in) | (m) | (ft) | (m) | (ft³m) | (m³) |
| 45 | 1.27 | 14 | 0.355 | 4 | 1.22 | 4.5 | 0.127 |
| 110 | 3.12 | 13 | 0.33 | 6 | 1.83 | 11 | 0.312 |
| 190 | 5.38 | 24 | 0.61 | 6 | 1.83 | 19 | 0.538 |
| 340 | 9.63 | 30 | 0.76 | 7 | 2.13 | 34 | 0.963 |
| 570 | 16.14 | 36 | 0.91 | 8 | 2.44 | 57 | 1.614 |
| 960 | 27.19 | 42 | 1.07 | 10 | 3.05 | 96 | 2.719 |
| 2115 | 59.90 | 48 | 1.22 | 12 | 3.66 | 151 | 4.276 |
| 3120 | 88.36 | 54 | 1.37 | 14 | 4.27 | 223 | 6.315 |
| 4400 | 124.61 | 60 | 1.52 | 16 | 4.88 | 314 | 8.892 |
| 6000 | 169.92 | 66 | 1.68 | 18 | 5.48 | 428 | 12.121 |

*Table 25* Vapour chart

| Temperature of air °C | °F | Compressed air pressure in bars (litres of water) | | | | | | | | | | | |
| --- | --- | --- | --- | --- | --- | --- | --- | --- | --- | --- | --- | --- | --- |
| | | 2 | 2.7 | 3.4 | 4 | 4.8 | 5.4 | 6 | 6.8 | 7.5 | 8.2 | 8.8 | 10 |
| 0 | 32 | 2.176 | 1.635 | 1.362 | 1.060 | 0.946 | 0.871 | 0.795 | 0.681 | 0.643 | 0.530 | 0.492 | 0.454 |
| 4.4 | 40 | 2.839 | 2.271 | 1.892 | 1.628 | 1.438 | 1.249 | 1.136 | 1.098 | 0.984 | 0.908 | 0.871 | 0.795 |
| 10 | 50 | 4.353 | 3.369 | 2.877 | 2.460 | 2.082 | 1/817 | 1.628 | 1.514 | 1.400 | 1.287 | 1.211 | 1.098 |
| 15.6 | 60 | 5.980 | 4.883 | 4.050 | 3.520 | 3.104 | 2.687 | 2.385 | 2.082 | 1.779 | 1.703 | 1.628 | 1.514 |
| 21.1 | 70 | 8.213 | 6.548 | 5.678 | 4.921 | 4.353 | 3.899 | 3.558 | 3.255 | 2.914 | 2.725 | 2.612 | 2.157 |
| 26.7 | 80 | 10.977 | 9.046 | 7.570 | 6.737 | 5.980 | 5.413 | 4.807 | 4.353 | 3.899 | 3.709 | 3.482 | 3.066 |
| 32.2 | 90 | 15.524 | 12.415 | 10.447 | 9.160 | 8.176 | 7.419 | 6.548 | 5.980 | 5.450 | 5.110 | 4.769 | 4.164 |
| 38.2 | 100 | 20.174 | 16.768 | 14.156 | 12.188 | 10.901 | 9.765 | 8.706 | 8.176 | 7.570 | 6.964 | 6.548 | 5.905 |
| 43.3 | 110 | 26.495 | 21.764 | 18.547 | 16.086 | 14.194 | 12.642 | 11.431 | 10.447 | 9.841 | 8.993 | 8.251 | 7.381 |
| 48.2 | 120 | 35.958 | 28.198 | 24.792 | 20.893 | 18.433 | 15.540 | 15.216 | 13.929 | 12.642 | 11.961 | 11.128 | 9.803 |

*Table 26  Volume of compressed air carried by medium grade steel pipes, of minimum bore, to BS 1387 at given velocities*

| Velocity M/s | Flow of air (litres/sec) through medium grade steel pipe to BS 1387, minimum bore | | | | | | | | | | | |
|---|---|---|---|---|---|---|---|---|---|---|---|---|
| | 15mm | 20mm | 25mm | 32mm | 40mm | 50mm | 65mm | 75mm | 100mm | 125mm | 150mm | 200mm |
| 3.0 | 0.6 | 1.1 | 1.7 | 3.0 | 4.1 | 6.5 | 10.9 | 15.1 | 25.7 | 39.2 | 56.2 | 98.5 |
| 3.5 | 0.7 | 1.3 | 2.0 | 3.5 | 4.7 | 7.6 | 12.7 | 17.6 | 30.0 | 45.7 | 65.5 | 115.0 |
| 4.0 | 0.8 | 1.4 | 2.3 | 4.0 | 5.4 | 8.7 | 14.6 | 20.1 | 34.2 | 52.3 | 74.9 | 131.0 |
| 4.5 | 0.9 | 1.6 | 2.6 | 4.5 | 6.1 | 9.8 | 16.4 | 22.6 | 38.5 | 58.8 | 84.2 | 147.0 |
| 5.0 | 1.0 | 1.8 | 2.8 | 5.0 | 6.8 | 10.8 | 18.2 | 25.1 | 42.8 | 65.4 | 93.6 | 164.0 |
| 5.5 | 1.1 | 2.0 | 3.1 | 5.5 | 7.4 | 11.9 | 20.0 | 27.6 | 47.1 | 71.9 | 103.0 | 181.0 |
| 6.0 | 1.2 | 2.1 | 3.4 | 6.0 | 8.1 | 13.0 | 21.8 | 30.1 | 51.3 | 78.5 | 112.0 | 197.0 |
| 6.5 | 1.3 | 2.3 | 3.7 | 6.5 | 8.8 | 14.1 | 23.7 | 32.6 | 55.6 | 85.0 | 122.0 | 213.0 |
| 7.0 | 1.4 | 2.5 | 4.0 | 7.0 | 9.5 | 15.1 | 25.5 | 35.1 | 59.9 | 91.5 | 131.0 | 230.0 |
| 7.5 | 1.5 | 2.7 | 4.3 | 7.5 | 10.1 | 16.2 | 27.3 | 37.6 | 64.2 | 98.0 | 140.0 | 246.0 |
| 8.0 | 1.6 | 2.8 | 4.5 | 8.0 | 10.8 | 17.3 | 29.1 | 40.1 | 68.5 | 105.0 | 150.0 | 263.0 |
| 8.5 | 1.7 | 3.0 | 4.8 | 8.5 | 11.5 | 18.4 | 31.0 | 42.6 | 72.8 | 111.0 | 159.0 | 278.0 |
| 9.0 | 1.8 | 3.2 | 5.1 | 9.0 | 12.2 | 19.5 | 32.8 | 45.1 | 77.1 | 118.0 | 169.0 | 296.0 |

*Table 27  Equivalent volume of compressed air at common pressure*

| Volume free (litres) | Equivalent volume (litres) when compared to gauge pressures of | | |
|---|---|---|---|
| | 4 bar | 5 bar | 7 bar |
| 5 | 1.01 | 0.84 | 0.63 |
| 10 | 2.02 | 1.68 | 1.26 |
| 15 | 3.03 | 2.52 | 1.90 |
| 20 | 4.04 | 3.37 | 2.53 |
| 25 | 5.05 | 4.21 | 3.16 |
| 30 | 6.06 | 5.05 | 3.79 |
| 35 | 7.07 | 5.89 | 4.42 |
| 40 | 8.08 | 6.73 | 5.06 |
| 50 | 10.1 | 8.42 | 6.32 |
| 60 | 12.1 | 10.1 | 7.58 |
| 70 | 14.1 | 11.8 | 8.85 |
| 80 | 16.2 | 13.5 | 10.1 |
| 90 | 18.2 | 15.1 | 11.4 |
| 100 | 20.2 | 16.8 | 15.8 |
| 125 | 25.2 | 21.0 | 15.8 |
| 150 | 30.3 | 25.2 | 19.0 |
| 175 | 35.3 | 29.5 | 22.1 |
| 200 | 40.4 | 33.7 | 25.2 |
| 225 | 45.4 | 37.9 | 28.4 |
| 250 | 50.5 | 42.1 | 31.6 |
| 275 | 55.5 | 46.3 | 34.8 |
| 300 | 60.6 | 50.5 | 37.9 |
| 350 | 70.7 | 58.9 | 44.2 |
| 400 | 80.8 | 67.3 | 50.6 |
| 500 | 101.0 | 84.2 | 63.2 |
| 750 | 151.0 | 126.0 | 95.0 |
| 1000 | 202.0 | 168.0 | 126.0 |
| 1250 | 252.0 | 210.0 | 158.0 |

*Table 28  Typical equipment consumption of compressed air*

| Appliance | Consumption free air (litres/sec) | Gauge pressure (bar) |
|---|---|---|
| Air motors  per kW | 16-22 | – |
| Contractors' tools, breakers, diggers, etc. | 2-35 | 5.5 |
| Controls, typical | 0.005-0.01 | 1.0 |
| Laboratories, bench outlets | 5-15 | 1.5-5.5 |
| Workshop tools, blast clearers, small | 10-13 | 6.5 |
| Workshop tools, blast clearers, large | 100-110 | 6.5 |
| Percussive, light | 2-8 | 5.5 |
| Percussive, heavy | 10-15 | 5.5 |
| Rotary (eg drills, etc.) | 2-15 | 3.5-5.0 |
| Spray guns | 0.5-10 | 2-5 |

# Vacuum

There are three elementary questions that are always asked in connection with this subject; what is it, what is it used for and by whom?

In layman's terms, it can be described as a piped distribution system from a prime mover (this generally takes the form of an electrically operated vacuum pump), terminating in a number of outlet points which give facilities for obtaining a vacuum or negative pressure service. Hospital personnel also refer to this type of service as the medical suction system.

The uses for such a service are vast and varied. There is the simple school laboratory system where students carry out elementary filtrations under reduced pressure to speed up the filtration time cycle. On the other hand, we have the complex research and industrial systems whereby a vacuum of better than 10 torr is required. In between these two extremes, there is the complete medical field for ward suction, operating theatre, dentistry and x-ray bolus. Most hospitals also have a separate laboratory system for pathology and pharmacy work.

This section does not cover in detail, the rather specialized high vacuum systems (below 1 torr) which for reasons such as outgassing of line material and vapour pressure problems, form the subject of more specialized publications. It is written with the object of familiarising the plumbing engineer with the basic facts relating to the design and installation of a piped vacuum system. It is also important that the consultant who is asked to plan initially what is loosely termed a vacuum system, should know exactly what the client is going to use the system for, and it must firstly be determined what degree of vacuum is expected at the outlet points. This in itself is sometimes difficult to establish (very often because the user himself does not know), and is complicated further because vacuum can be identified in inches of mercury, millimetres of mercury or water gauge, and we also have the international term, torr (which for the purposes of this Guide, is equivalent to the millimetre of mercury).

Vacuum specialist firms always measure the degree of vacuum with atmosphere at 30in or 760 torr, and ultimate vacuum as 0, whereas the engineer thinks of vacuum in reverse, whereby atmospheric

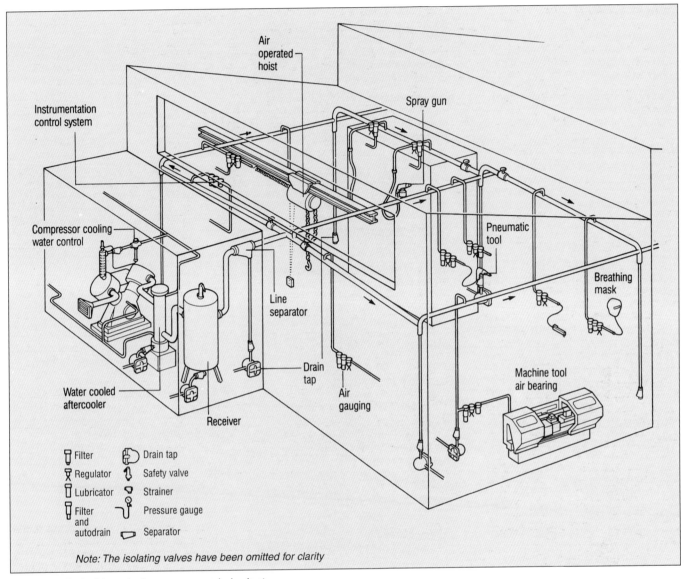

*Figure 5 Typical layout of a compressed air plant*

pressure is 0 and the ultimate is 760 torr or 30 inches of mercury. Also, manufacturers of vacuum gauges produce scales calibrated in both ways.

This guide therefore uses 0 as ultimate and 30in or 760 torr as atmosphere for the remainder of this summary.

## The hospital system

Apart from the scientific and industrial fields, the main usage of vacuum is in the medical and medical research field which covers five main areas:

a. Ward suction

b. Theatre suction

c. X-ray bolus

d. Dental suction

e. Pathology and pharmacy laboratories.

As any hospital engineer will confirm, the provision of an efficient central vacuum system will cut his maintenance work considerably.

## Ward suction

The free air displacement required at the bedside outlet varies of course, depending on the type of ward being served. For instance, in the respiratory ward, suction is required for quick removal of sputum etc, from the throat, and is not generally in use for long periods, whereas in the post-thoractomy wards, the suction may be required for long periods of continuous duty. Therefore the outlet displacements can be anything from 1 litre per minute to an estimated maximum of 40 litres per minute (free air) at approximately 250 torr.

## Theatre suction

The free air displaced in the theatre is naturally much higher than for general ward usage, and it is quite possible for the surgeon and anaesthetist to require suction to be available at up to 80 litres per minute in the theatre at any one time, and also at a pressure of 250 torr.

## X-ray bolus

This is a technique using the suction system to evacuate bags filled with granules that are placed in position around the limb to be X-rayed, and on applying the suction, it is found that the limb will be held firmly in the pre-set position. The free air displaced here is quite small once the initial evacuation has taken place, and the degree of vacuum need not exceed 150 torr.

## Dental suction

The usage here is mainly one of removal of saliva and water, the latter being sprayed on to the dentist's drill and the site of drilling.

There are at present two techniques used, the first involves a high degree of vacuum (30 torr) at low flows and known as the aspiration technique. This has one main disadvantage which is that the suction tube must be held very close to the tissues of the mouth in order to 'pick up' the fluid accumulating within the mouth, and sometimes these tissues can block the suction orifice and can both damage the mouth tissues and stop the water from being drawn away.

The second method, known as the high flow technique, employs suction at a great velocity, of the order of 50m/s, but the degree of vacuum required is only about 700 torr maximum. The 'pick up' bridge between fluid and sucker orifice in this case is approximately 12mm, and no damage to mouth tissues occurs. It is therefore essential to establish which technique is being employed.

## Pathology and pharmacy laboratories

Generally speaking, the pathology laboratory user and the pharmacist are the only case where a fairly high degree of vacuum would be required ie. 10-15 torr, and it should always be borne in mind when planning hospital systems, that the medical suction system should never be interconnected to the laboratory system.

The former requires a fairly high flow at relatively moderate suction pressure, ie. rarely better than 125 torr, whereas the latter requires a low flow rate at a relatively high degree of vacuum (10-15 torr). There is also the fear that bacteria from laboratory experiments could find their way to patients if the systems were linked.

When considering a pipeline installation to serve these types of area, especially ward and theatre suction and X-ray bolus, it must be borne in mind as a rough guide that to remove 1 litre of liquid rapidly will require a free air displacement at atmosphere of approximately 4 litres per minute.

The modern trend of providing an efficient suction system for ward and theatre usage is to have what is known as a twin standby pumping set. This generally consists of two prime movers interconnected to a common reservoir with all necessary cycling and safety gear, which enables the second pump to operate if either the first pump fails or cannot maintain the pipeline system within the predetermined pressure, in which case, both pumps will operate until the vacuum in the system builds-up, and the two pumps will cut out in sequence.

Facilities are also provided by most manufacturers for alternating the duty pump. There is no reason why a series of pumps cannot be interconnected in this way and linked in pairs to pressure switches to enable further capacity to be provided as and when the new extensions are added to the system.

## Siting of pumps

Preferably, the central vacuum pipeline pumping equipment should be grouped in one area to save the hospital engineer and his staff precious time in maintaining hospital equipment at various points in the building, and the actual positioning of the vacuum units is important on three counts.

The first is the noise factor. Not all vacuum pumps are silent, so it is imperative that any noise or vibration is not transferred to areas where such inconvenience could not be tolerated. Noise carried through the walls of the pipeline can be eliminated by interposing a simple rubber sleeve connection close to the prime mover. Alternatively, vacuum bellows with demountable vacuum union connections are sometimes used but are naturally more expensive.

The second is the case of maintenance. The pumps will need to be positioned for accessibility of servicing and running of water cooling lines if necessary.

Thirdly, the exhaust of gasses and perhaps equally important, the pump exhaust system. This should be run conveniently direct to atmosphere but away from windows, fresh air intake or any area where ignition would be possible should flammable vapours be discharged. It must be remembered that any rising exhaust line must be trapped to avoid condensates from running down into the pumping gear and more important, to prevent a back pressure. The length of the exhaust line must be related to the bore of the exhaust pipe; for example, it may be quite permissible to run a 15mm bore exhaust line direct to atmosphere at low level through an exterior wall, but if the exhaust could only be piped to atmosphere via the roof at say 13m high, then the bore of pipe could easily be increased to 42mm bore or greater. One answer to this problem is to site the problem gear on the top floor, but this is only possible if weight of pumps and availability of running services permit.

## Pipelines

The actual pipelines that are provided must be designed to allow displacement of the required flow of air, and at the same time, be leak-tight at better than the ultimate vacuum required by the user.

For very low pressure or rough suction systems, ie. in the order of 450 torr, it is quite possible to obtain a satisfactory result by using gas-barrel tube with threaded fittings suitably sealed on the threads, but this material will be quite unsuitable for systems where better than 200 torr is required. One of the most reliable and well tried materials is copper tube with capillary fittings.

Some of the modern materials such as uPVC pipe and stainless steel tube are also quite suitable for most systems, but one has to be careful that the vapours and condensates pumped over are not solvents of the line material, and they will only be accepted where the risk of destruction by fire or heat does not apply. In general, copper tube is used by most vacuum specialist firms.

If the client is likely to pump over actual liquids, it is necessary to incorporate traps that would preclude such liquids from entering the pumping gear. On a multi-storey building, such traps can be conveniently placed at the base of each riser; also they should preferably be of a design whereby they can be emptied without interference of the main vacuum line. If the building is so designed that there are no main risers, ie. single storey buildings, then it is preferable that each branch should be individually trapped.

## Laboratory systems

The design of vacuum installations to serve university and college laboratory systems is far more critical; the demand of the user calls for a much more accurate control of the line pressure, because the student often has to carry out long term experiments at a controlled pressure and therefore cannot tolerate the wide pressure differentials that can be allowed with absolute safety on the medical suction system.

There exists a resistance by some heads of departments in some of our premier academic establishments, to the central vacuum system. They are suspicious of replacing the well-tried water jet pump with which they could control their vacuum by adjustment to the water tap pressure. (This pressure should ideally be constant at between 2 and 2.8bar). The fact is that even the latest water jet pumps will consume between 0.15 and 0.19 litres of water per second and the very suggestion of running a new university chemistry block with up to 400 laboratory places fitted with water jet pumps is not permissible by with the Water Companies in most areas.

Even if the case is put that only a quarter of these outlets would be in use for say four hours per day, the possible water consumption is going to be about 270m³ per day. Due to this, the central vacuum pipeline system is here to stay for sometime.

To overcome the water shortage, the obvious solution is to first look at a water recirculation system, but this has two main disadvantages. The ultimate vacuum obtainable is dependent upon the vapour pressure of water, and provided the water is maintained at an ambient temperature of 15°C, then a vacuum of 15 torr can be expected.

However, the distribution pipes and tanks need to be internally treated and unless the recirculating water is filtered and cooled, the temperature will rise, thus affecting the ultimate vacuum obtained, ie. if the water temperature rose to 50°C, then the ultimate vacuum would be in the order of 100 torr as against the 15 torr at 15°C.

It may be permissible to allow a minimum number of water jet pump positions which could be reserved for pumping really corrosive vapours that would otherwise be detrimental to the working mechanism of the central vacuum pump, and this compromise may be accepted if it can be demonstrated that adequate protection is provided to prevent backflow in the water system. Most laboratories will require a pressure at the bench outlets at least as good as a water jet pump, namely between 12 and 15 torr absolute, and the speed of evacuation found to be most suitable is about 6 litres per minute, which is a little faster than most water jet pumps.

The consultant or planning authority can generally base laboratory requirements on these figures, but a close check should be made during discussion with the client and establish quite clearly what pressure is to be provided, and if a pressure of better than 12 torr is wanted, say for instance 1 torr, then the problems increase considerably, and these cases will be discussed later.

We are now at the stage where the pipelines and accessories should be discussed, having established that a standard system is wanted for normal filtration through buncher flasks and possibly, some distillations etc, are to be carried out. If the system is to maintain a vacuum of 12-15 torr, then the lines, joints, isolation valves, traps and most important, the bench valves, must be proved free from vacuum leakage at

better than 10 torr. Nowadays, many contracts are split into mains services and then bench furniture and services separately. This is not a convenient arrangement for most services, but in case of vacuum, it is not at all satisfactory.

If, upon completion of the laboratory, only 50 torr vacuum can be created at the bench outlet, where is the fault? The vacuum pump, the main distribution system, the bench pipe run or the bench outlet? Such a situation could involve up to four different contractors, and to find a small leak in an already completed vacuum system can be a very tedious and expensive business.

One should check that the specification states quite clearly, the degree of vacuum at which the whole installation is to undergo a pressure rise test, and also the operating pressure at which the line will be maintained.

## Bench outlets

There are several good vacuum bench valves on the market in this country and the types that give a good flow control and easy replacement of working parts are preferred. For instance, never install metal-to-metal cone-type vacuum cocks with a grease seal where hydrocarbon vapours are present, because the vapours will quickly dissolve the grease and a pressure rise will take place, causing the pumping unit to cycle at frequent intervals.

Valves having a stuffing-box shaft seal are not considered suitable.

The push-in or bayonet type of outlet is very practical provided that flow control is not essential and is favoured on industrial projects. Its use in the teaching or research field is limited and its leak tightness in some cases is suspect.

The sizing of the bench runs is not difficult in this pressure range, and as a guide, a 15mm copper line could serve up to four outlets on a 4 metre bench, a 22mm line would serve up to eight outlets and a 28mm line up to 16 outlets. A 15mm line to each bench valve is preferred, and if elementary work is being carried out or the laboratory is to be used for a high density of students, then under-bench traps should be incorporated at a convenient position in each bench run. These traps should be designed to incorporate an isolation valve and an air admittance facility to enable the trap to be emptied without interference to the vacuum system. The laboratory steward would no doubt be responsible for emptying these traps, and it is most important that they are not installed in inaccessible positions where

major work has to be carried out before the trap is exposed.

In senior and research laboratories, traps are not considered necessary because this calibre of student using the vacuum system would interpose his own trap on the bench top between the process being carried out and the bench valve, and this trap would be charged with a suitable desiccant to neutralize the particular vapour being pumped.

The sizes of the main runs do, of course, depend upon the total number of outlets to be served, and on the general layout of the building. If, for example, there is a tower block of laboratories four storeys high, having 50 outlets on the first two floors, 10 on the third and 40 on the top floor, a suitable arrangement would be a 54mm diameter riser to the second floor and 42mm extending to the top floor. This riser must be suitably trapped at the base.

The first two floors would have 42mm subsidiary mains reducing at the bench runs, the third floor would only require a 28mm diameter floor run but the top floor would probably be best served by a 42mm main floor run.

As with the hospital system, copper tube with capillary fittings has been found trouble-free in this pressure range, but again, a rigid PVC line can be maintained at better than 10 torr, but it is essential to study the vapour content likely to be pumped to make sure that the material chosen for the line will not be adversely affected by vapours pumped over.

## Pumping units

Vacuum pump manufacturers in this country whose pumps can achieve the desired pressures are limited, and all have merits of their own. The three most essential points to look for in a vacuum pump to serve laboratories are:

a. That it will achieve and maintain the pressure required

b. That it is designed to discharge, or has facilities for dealing with corrosive vapours pumped over

c. That its noise will not give cause for complaint.

It is not essential that a twin standby unit is provided, although many modern colleges are favouring this arrangement. However, it must be decided whether the prime mover is to be automatically controlled or manually operated.

The automatic unit is designed to provide a 'vacuum on tap' service at all times of the night and day, and is generally controlled by switches which operate from a vacuum bellows. Thus, the pump only runs when a pressure rise takes place in the line. The differential between the cutting-in and cutting-out pressure can be limited to about 5 torr if necessary. This type of controlled system is ideal for laboratories or research areas that have intermittent use.

The manually operated plant has to be turned on when vacuum is required, and this does mean that there is a time delay (which varies depending on pump speed and line capacity) in pumping out the system. It also means that a lower pressure can eventually be achieved provided that the line is leak tight. The main advantage with this type of system, as opposed to the automatic one is cost; also the manually operated unit is most suitable for large teaching laboratories where the vacuum service is only required for a short period each day but because of the high percentage of bench valves in use simultaneously, there is no real point in providing an automatic pumping unit. In fact, if automatic gear is provided in such areas, there is sometimes a risk that because of frequent cycling of the pumps, the starters and switch gear could become overloaded.

## High vacuum systems

In certain laboratories, there may be a call for vacuum to be provided at better than 1 torr. An example would be for a rotary evaporator in pharmaceutical research work. This is a special requirement and to obtain such conditions, it will be necessary to take great care in the planning and installation of the system.

Although this pressure is still within the viscous flow range, it will be necessary to install the vacuum pump as close to the outlets as possible and keeping the bore of the pipelines as wide as possible. It is not practicable to try and obtain a 1 torr working system from a central pumping set as previously described, and each bench run would therefore have to be provided with its own pump and pipeline system. This presents two problems, the first is to make suitable arrangements to house the pump within the bench area without the noise level interfering with the user, and secondly, to run the pump exhaust to atmosphere at a convenient place.

As this type of system would generally consist of a small rotary oil-sealed high vacuum pump and motor and would be manually controlled, ie. no safety or cycling switches, it must be firmly established that the personnel using the system will interpose a desiccant flask

between their process and the bench outlet which will preclude any liquids being accidentally pumped over and also that the vapours being pumped will be partially dried by the desiccant. If this simple precaution is taken, it will ensure that the small pump will not become contaminated by carelessness; this will add considerable life to the rotary pump.

When providing these small systems with individual pumps, the biggest hazard is to the working parts of the pump; for example, if soluble organic acids are to be pumped, the oil film in the pump gives no protection at all to the working parts and formic and acetic acids will cause quite severe corrosion depending on the number of outlets in use. The only way to prevent such acids from entering the pump is by the use of conical flasks on the bench tops, these containing sodium hydroxide pellets mixed with indicating soda lime.

The question of explosion risk in small rotary pumps is sometimes raised, especially when ether-air mixture is present, but the risk is very small because the temperature at which automatic ignition takes place would be about 180°C which is at least twice the maximum running temperature of most conventional vacuum pumps.

If requests are made for a central vacuum system calling for bench outlet pressures of better than 0.5 torr, then the problems are increased even further because at these pressures, we are moving from the viscous flow to molecular flow and such conditions are not generally accepted as economically practical on a pipeline system.

Certainly, the use of 90° elbows and sharp tees would not be permissible and the lines would possibly have to be in some other material such as glass, and these problems would cover outgassing of the line material, vapour content to be pumped, and speed of displacement required at any specific pressure.

## Pipe sizing

The difficulty experienced in trying to calculate pipeline sizes is bound up with the fact that is very rarely that the designer really knows what materials are going to be pumped in a particular pipeline system. It may be that the system will be required to deal with high vapour pressure materials which even at the pipeline pressure, produces very large quantities of vapour which obviously have to be handled by the mechanical pump and pipeline systems, and this makes the whole question of accurately sizing pipelines a very difficult one to resolve.

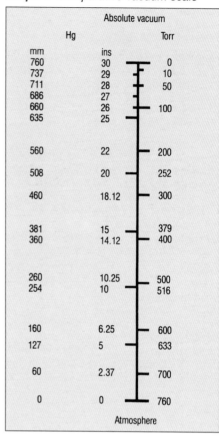

***Graph 4*** *Comparative vacuum scale*

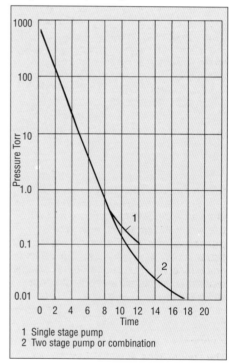

***Graph 5*** *Pump sizing*

1 Single stage pump
2 Two stage pump or combination

*Graph 6* *Vacuum pump sizing, copper tube to EN 1057-250*

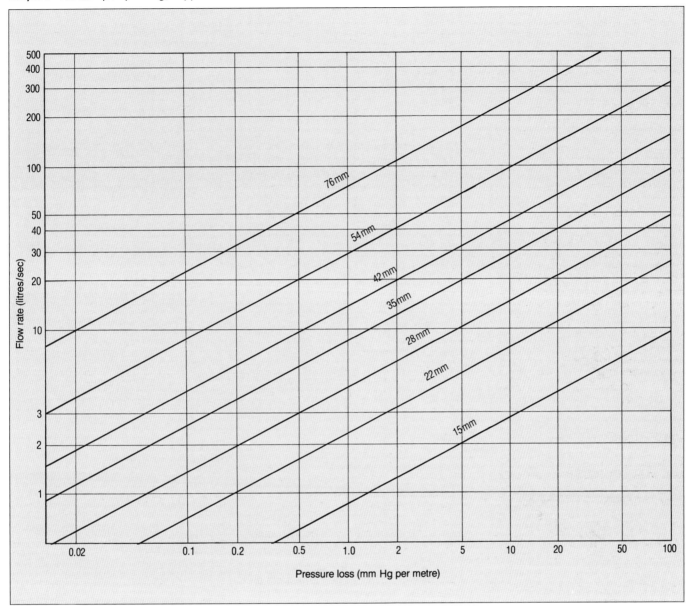

As a crude example, a gramme of water at, say 10 torr, will evolve about 100 litres of water vapour in the system, and other vapours will have a similar or even greater volumetric effect on the system. It has been found that the best approach is one based on discussion with the user, in order that the possible vapour content can be considered, and this, coupled with previous experience gained, should enable a sensible sizing of the lines to be possible.

The suggestions already given for pipe sizing may form a useful guide for those persons who have to design or install a piped vacuum system. It must be remembered however that there is no straightforward scale on pipe sizing for vacuum systems unless of course, the system is only going to handle clean, dry

air, which for 99% of the time, will not be the case.

## Summary

Figure 5 is indicative of air which is fairly dry, and consideration must be taken of excess moisture that may be generated. First establish usage and determine what pressures and displacements are required.

Clarify these usages, ie. medical or laboratory.

Discuss the various types of outlets, the siting of the pumps, the provision of an efficient exhaust system, and choose a line material which is both leak-tight at the desired pressure and one that is functional in use.

## Pump sizing for individual chamber work

T = pump-down time (excavation time)

F = pump-down factor from Graph 5 for given pressure

S = pump speed (free air displacement)

V = system volume

*NOTE*
*V and S must be consistent units (ie. litres and litres/min).*

*To calculate the time taken to reach certain pressure in a given system with a given pump:*

$$T = \frac{F \times V}{S}$$

*To calculate pump speed required to reach a given pressure in a given time:*

$$S = \frac{F \times V}{T}$$

### Example

Pump size required to excavate a chamber of 60 litres to 1 torr in 3 minutes.

Pump speed $S = \frac{F \times V}{T}$

From Graph 5, F = 7

Hence, $S = \frac{7 \times 60}{3}$

$\qquad$ =140 litres/min

Therefore, pump with displacement of 140 litres/min and ultimate vacuum better than 1 torr is required.

Graph 5 enables pump-down time or pump size to be evaluated for any clean, leak-tight rotary pumped system down to 0.1 torr.

Due allowance made for change of pump volumetric efficiency with reduction in pressure but impedance of connecting pipelines neglected.

For recommended plant layouts, consult specialized manufacturers and for medical vacuum, consult current Health Technical Memorandum.

## Medical gases

The term medical gases covers the following:

1. Medical compressed air (oil and moisture free)

2. Vacuum suction

3. Oxygen

4. Nitrous oxide

5. Nitrous oxide/oxygen mixture $N_2O/O_2$.

Oxygen and vacuum are used extensively throughout most hospitals and are usually required in the following areas:

1. In-patient departments

2. Operating suites

3. Maternity departments

4. Accidents and emergency areas including out-patients.

Vacuum and compressed air are required in dental suites, and operating suites for patient ventilators and operating surgical tools.

Nitrous oxide is required in operating suites, maternity units and accidents and emergency areas. In addition, $N_2O/O_2$ is usually required in maternity delivery rooms.

## References

### LP Gas Association Codes of Practice

No. 1 – Installation and maintenance of bulk LPG at consumer's premises.

Pt. 1 – Design and installation.

Pt. 2 – Small bulk installations for domestic premises.

Pt. 3 – Periodic inspection and testing.

No. 3 – Prevention and control of fire involving LPG.

No. 22 – LPG Piping systems – Design and installation.

No. 24 – The use of LPG cylinders at residential premises.

No. 25 – LPG Central storage and distribution systems for multiple consumers.

# Sanitary plumbing and drainage

# Design of sanitary pipework systems

A good sanitary pipework system should be designed and installed to provide the following attributes:

1. Prevent the transmission foul air in to the building.

2. Minimise the frequency of any blockage, and provided with adequate pipe access to enable the effective clearance of any such blockage.

3. Provide efficient conveyance of discharge from sanitary, kitchen, laundry and wash-down facilities, to enable the correct function of each appliance.

4. Where any sewer is likely to surcharge, minimise the risk of flooding to any part of a building where the floor level is located below normal ground level.

Sanitary discharge pipework should therefore be kept as short as possible, with few bends, and with adequate gradient.

## Location

Discharge stacks and discharge branches should be installed inside buildings, although for buildings up to three storeys it is permissible to place them externally.

## Design basis

The sanitary discharge system, terminology, and method of sizing previously used in BS 5572 has now been replaced by Part 2 of BS EN 12056. This section therefore incorporates these changes. The new harmonised Standard is designed to be applicable in all EN member countries. The design engineer has a choice of four system types, as shown in Table 1.

*Table 1*

| System | Typical practice in |
|---|---|
| I | Germany, Austria, Switzerland, Belgium |
| II | Scandinavia |
| III | United Kingdom |
| IV | France |

In addition to the generic System requirements, the design engineer must also comply with the relevant National Annexe, which each country is allowed to incorporate in their own published version. The content of this Section is based on System III, the UK National

Annexe, and the 2002 edition of the Building Regulations Approved Document H.

## Terminology

The term 'domestic wastewater' refers to all the water, solid particles, and urine, which may be conveyed by a sanitary discharge system. It includes condensate water, and (where permitted) rainwater.

'Black water' is wastewater containing faecal matter or urine.

The documented definition for 'grey water' is wastewater which excludes faecal matter and urine; although some design engineers may also wish to exclude any macerated solids, such as food.

Therefore, the effluent conveyed by a typical discharge stack in the UK is domestic wastewater. Some countries have retained the two-pipe system, where one stack is used for black water, and a second stack is used for grey water, this method is also used where recycling of grey water is required.

## Discharge pipe systems

For the purpose of stack sizing, there are essentially two piping methods:

Primary ventilated stack; or
Secondary ventilated stack.
Figures 1-4 show the typical configurations in diagrammatic form.

The primary ventilated system (previously known as the single stack system) is shown in Figure 1. Where any branch piping does not comply with the requirements for unventilated branches, branch vent piping would be required, as shown in Figure 2. For primary ventilated systems there are limits (see Figure 5) on the vertical distance between the invert of the drain connection and the centre line of the lowest discharge branch connection to the stack. A primary ventilated stack may require additional venting at the base of the stack where the sewer connection is likely to surcharge or where the stack is the only means of ventilating an interceptor trap.

The secondary ventilated system (previously known as the ventilated stack system) is used to increase the flow capacity of a given discharge stack size, (see Figure 3). The additional vent stack, incorporating a connection to the discharge piping on every storey, alleviates excessive pressure fluctuations by allowing air movement within the system. Where any branch piping does not comply with the requirements for unventilated branches, branch vent

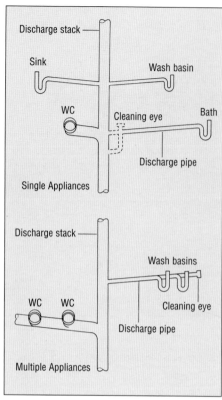

*Figure 1*   *Primary ventilated system*

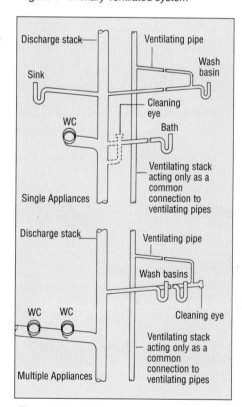

*Figure 2*   *Modified primary ventilated system*

piping would also be required, as shown in Figure 4.

At the base of any discharge stack, the drain connection should be achieved by using two 45° bends, or a single swept bend with a centre line radius of not less than 2 times the pipe bore, (see Figure 5).

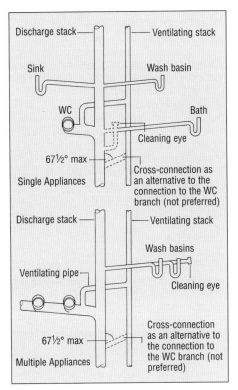

*Figure 3  Secondary ventilated system*

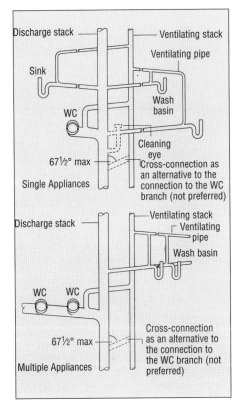

*Figure 4  Modified secondary ventilated system*

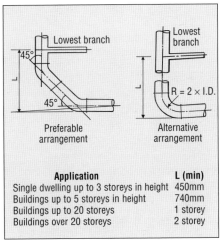

| Application | L (min) |
|---|---|
| Single dwelling up to 3 storeys in height | 450mm |
| Buildings up to 5 storeys in height | 740mm |
| Buildings up to 20 storeys | 1 storey |
| Buildings over 20 storeys | 2 storey |

*Figure 5  Requirements at the base of primary ventilated discharge stacks*

## Offsets

In large buildings, it is often be necessary for the discharge stack to offset. Vent piping to relieve the offset pressure fluctuation would be required (see Figure 6) where systems are heavily loaded, or serving more than three stories. The bore of the vent pipe should be not less than half the bore of the discharge stack. Where offsets are incorporated, the bends should have a centreline radius of not less than 2 times pipe bore, and no discharge branch connection should be made to the offset between the vent connection points. Where offset venting is used, the stack should still be sized as a primary ventilated system, unless vent connections to every storey are included. Offsets above the highest discharge connection to the stack do not require venting or the use of large radius bends.

## Air admittance valves

Air admittance valves may be used in either primary or secondary ventilated systems, providing they are used within the application limits contained in the approval document issued by a European Technical Approvals body, such as the BBA and WIMLAS. These valves are available in a range of sizes, and can be used to terminate stack vent pipes inside the building, and to prevent siphonage problems for branch discharge pipes or individual appliances. The valves open automatically on sensing negative air pressure within the system; thus allowing air ingress only. They should not be used where positive pressure ventilation is required, such as when the stack connects to a septic tank, intercepting trap, or where a sewer is prone to surcharge.

## Termination of ventilation pipes

At the top of a discharge stack, the vent pipe diameter should be equal to the stack's. However, on stacks serving 1 or 2 storey housing, the vent pipe may be reduced to 75mm diameter. Each pipe should be fitted with a durable and secure domical cage, which is resistant to bird nesting and movement by vermin. Ventilation pipes should terminate outside the building, positioned where the emission of foul air does not cause a nuisance. This is generally achieved, if the termination point is not less than 900mm above the top of any window or natural ventilation opening if within a horizontal distance of 3m. Consideration should also be made in relation to adjacent roof structures likely to cause

*Figure 6  Offset venting*

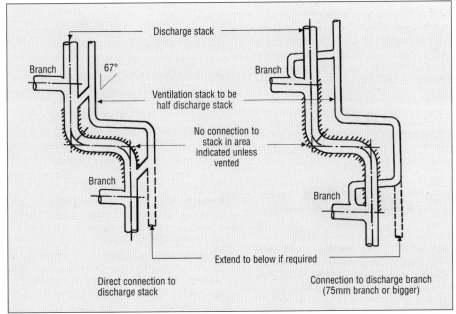

wind based fluctuating pressure zones and mechanical ventilation inlets.

## Stub stacks

Stub stacks may be used as a method to connect discharge branches from ground floor appliances to drain. They are essentially a short vertical extension from a 100mm drain, and there are limits on the height of branch connections, (see Figure 7). They can be used to connect the discharge from a group of appliances in a bathroom and kitchen, but should be limited to a cumulative load of 5 l/s. They may be installed either internally or outside the building, and should be terminated with an access cap. If the stub stack is located inside the building, and it is not possible to comply with the dimensional or flow limitations, then an air admittance valve should be used instead of an access cap. The length of the branch drain serving the stub stack should be limited as required for correct drainage accessibility, and should be connected to a drain, which is adequately ventilated.

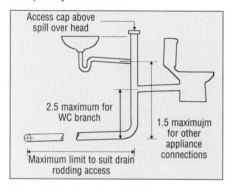

*Figure 7* *Stub stack vertical limits*

## Stacks serving only urinals

Stacks serving urinals and no other appliances should be avoided, as regular pipe access to clear deposition is usually necessary. It is advantageous to connect other appliances, to allow flushing, preferably including hot water discharge.

## Stacks serving only kitchen sinks and/or washing machines

Stacks serving only kitchen sinks and/or washing machines should be avoided, as deposition (particularly with soft water) and problems due to foaming detergents can occur. If these stacks are unavoidable, then they should be located where regular access will not pose a threat to hygiene, and the avoidance of a stack connection on the bottom storey is desirable.

## Waste traps

Every sanitary appliance should be provided with a trap, either as an integral part of the appliance, or attached directly to the appliance outlet, or fitted in close proximity to the appliance. On showers, for ease of maintenance, a trap may be positioned up to 750mm from the outlet. An alternative method to a trap is to use a proprietary valve (see Figures 22-26). The purpose of the trap is to provide a non-mechanical barrier to prevent the escape of foul air into the building, but in addition the water reservoir can act as a dilution feature and to intercept small accidentally dropped objects.

There are essentially two types of trap; tubular, and bottle. Kitchen sinks and macerators should only be fitted with tubular traps. Kitchen sinks with two or three bowls may be provided with an outlet manifold and a single trap. There should not be more than one trap on the discharge pipework from any appliance. The minimum depth of trap seal for various applications is given in Table 2. Resealing traps and anti-vacuum traps are available where self-siphonage may be a problem; some types are noisy in use.

*Table 2* *Minimum depth of trap seal*

| Use | Seal |
|---|---|
| Baths & showers which discharge to a stack | 50mm |
| Baths & showers located at ground floor level which discharge to a gully having a grating | 38mm |
| Wash basins with spray taps, and no outlet plugs | 50mm |
| Appliances with an outlet bore of 50mm or larger | 50mm |
| All other appliances | 75mm |

## Unventilated branch discharge pipes

The general requirements for unventilated branch discharge pipes are given in Table 3. If the configuration of a discharge pipe from a single appliance does not comply with the requirements for unventilated branches, then there is a risk of self-siphonage of the trap. In which case a resealing trap, anti-vacuum trap, or small air admittance valve should be used. Alternatively, a vent pipe should be provided (see Figure 20 and 21).

## Ventilated branch discharge pipes

The general requirements for ventilated branch discharge pipes are given in Table 4.

## Waste disposal units & macerators

Branch discharge pipes serving waste disposal units and macerators should be connected to a discharge stack, stub stack, or direct to drain; not to a trapped gully. Only tubular traps should be used, and any bends should be swept (not the 'knuckle' type). The minimum bore and gradient of the discharge pipe should be as recommended by the appliance manufacturer, but in any event not less than given in Table 3 and 4.

## Washing machines & dishwashers

Branch discharge pipes serving washing machines and dishwashers should be connected as shown in Figure 8, 9 or 10. The minimum bore and gradient of the discharge pipe should be as recommended by the appliance manufacturer, but in any event not less than given in Table 3 and 4.

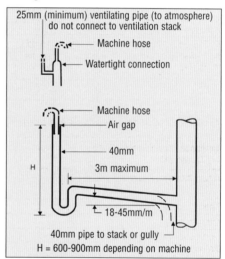

*Figure 8* *Upstand discharge pipe arrangements for washing machines and dishwashers*

*Figure 9* *Discharge pipe arrangements for washing machines and dishwashers with low level outlets*

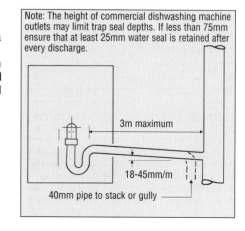

Note: The height of commercial dishwashing machine outlets may limit trap seal depths. If less than 75mm ensure that at least 25mm water seal is retained after every discharge.

*Table 3* *Limitations for unventilated branches*

| Appliance (See Figures 11, 12, 13 and 14) | Diameter (mm) | Max. pipe length (m) | Pipe gradient mm per m run | Max. number of bends | Max. drop (m) vertical pipe |
|---|---|---|---|---|---|
| Wash basin or bidet | 32 | 1.7 | 18 to 22 | None[1] | None |
| | 32 | 1.1 | 18 to 44 | None[1] | None |
| | 32 | 0.7 | 18 to 87 | None[1] | None |
| | 40 | 3.0 | 18 to 44 | 2[1] | None |
| Bath or shower | 40 | 3.0[2] | 18 to 90 | No limit | 1.5 |
| Kitchen sink | 40 | 3.0[2] | 18 to 90 | No limit | 1.5 |
| Domestic washing machine or dishwashing machine | 40 | 3.0 | 18 to 44 | No limit | 1.5 |
| WC with outlet up to 80mm dia. | 75 | No limit | 18 min. | No limit[4] | 1.5 |
| WC with outlet over 80mm dia. | 100 | No limit | 18 min. | No limit[4] | 1.5 |
| Bowl urinal[4] | 40 | 3.0[3] | 18 to 90 | No limit[4] | 1.5 |
| Trough urinal | 50 | 3.0[3] | 18 to 90 | No limit[4] | 1.5 |
| Slab urinal[5] | 65 | 3.0[3] | 18 to 90 | No limit[4] | 1.5 |
| Food waste disposal unit[6] | 40 min. | 3.0[3] | 135 min. | No limit[4] | 1.5 |
| Sanitary towel disposal unit | 40 min. | 3.0[3] | 54 min. | No limit[4] | 1.5 |
| Floor drain | 50 to 100 | 3.0[3] | 18 min. | No limit | 1.5 |
| Branch serving 2 to 4 wash basins | 50 | 4.0 | 18 to 44 0 | None | None |
| Branch serving several bowl urinals[4] | 50 | 3.0[3] | 18 to 90 | No limit[4] | 1.5 |
| Branch serving 2 to 8 WC's | 100 | 15.0 | 9 to 90 2 1.5 | 2 | 1.5 |
| Up to 5 wash basins with spray taps[7] | 32 | 4.5[3] | 18 to 44 | No limit[4] | None |

1. *Excluding the 'connecting bend' fitted directly or close to the trap outlet.*
2. *If longer than 3m, this may result in noisy discharge, and there will be an increased risk of blockage.*
3. *Should ideally be as short as possible to limit deposition problems.*
4. *Swept bends should be used; not 'knuckle' bends.*
5. *For up to 7 people; longer slabs should have more than one outlet.*
6. *Includes small potato-peeling machines*
7. *Wash basins must not be fitted with outlet plugs.*

*Table 4* *Limitations for ventilated branches*

| Appliance (See Figures 12, 13, 14, 20 and 21) | Diameter (mm) | Max. pipe length (m) | Pipe gradient mm per m run | Max. num ber of bends | Max. drop (m) vertical pipe |
|---|---|---|---|---|---|
| Wash basin or bidet | 32 | 3.0 | 18 min. | 2[1] | 3.0 |
| | 40 | 3.0 | 18 min. | No limit | 3.0 |
| Bath or shower | 40 | 3.0[2] | 18 min. | No limit | No limit |
| Kitchen sink | 40 | 3.0[2] | 18 min. | No limit | No limit |
| Domestic washing machine or dishwashing machine | 40 | No limit[3] | 18 min. | No limit | No limit |
| WC with outlet up to 80mm dia. | 75 | No limit | 18 min. | No limit[4] | 1.5 |
| WC with outlet over 80mm dia. | 100 | No limit | 18 min. | No limit[4] | 1.5 |
| Bowl urinal[4] | 40 | 3.0[3] | 18 min. | No limit[4] | 3.0 |
| Trough urinal | 50 | 3.0[3] | 18 min. | No limit[4] | 3.0 |
| Slab urinal[5] | 65 | 3.0[3] | 18 min. | No limit[4] | 3.0 |
| Food waste disposal unit[6] | 40 min. | 3.0[3] | 135 min. | No limit[4] | 3.0 |
| Sanitary towel disposal unit | 40 min. | 3.0[3] | 54 min. | No limit[4] | 3.0 |
| Floor drain | 50 to 100 | 3.0[3] | 18 min. | No limit | No limit |
| Branch serving 2 to 5 wash basins | 50 | 7.0 | 18 to 44 | No limit | None |
| Branch serving 6 to 10 wash basins[8] | 50 | 10.0 | 18 to 44 | No limit | None |
| Branch serving several bowl urinals[4] | 50 | 3.0[3] | 18 min. | No limit[4] | No limit |
| Branch serving 2 or more WC's | 100 | No limit | 9 min. | No limit | No limit |
| Up to 5 wash basins with spray taps[7] | 32 | No limit[3] | 18 to 44 | No limit[4] | None |

1. *Excluding the 'connecting bend' fitted directly or close to the trap outlet.*
2. *If longer than 3m, this may result in noisy discharge, and there will be an increased risk of blockage.*
3. *Should ideally be as short as possible to limit deposition problems.*
4. *Swept bends should be used; not 'knuckle' bends.*
5. *For up to 7 people; longer slabs should have more than one outlet.*
6. *Includes small potato-peeling machines.*
7. *Wash basins must not be fitted with outlet plugs.*
8. *Every basin must be separately ventilated.*

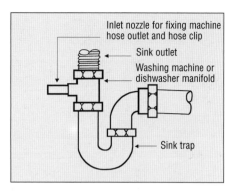

*Figure 10  Sink manifold connection for washing machines and dishwashers*

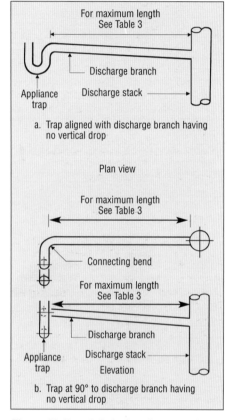

a. Trap aligned with discharge branch having no vertical drop

b. Trap at 90° to discharge branch having no vertical drop

*Figure 11  Branch limitations for unventilated branches where no vertical drop is permitted*

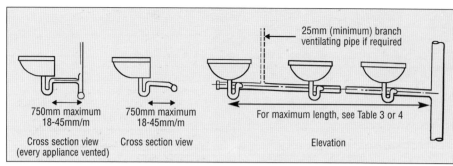

*Figure 12  Combined discharge branch for a group of wash basins (or urinals)*

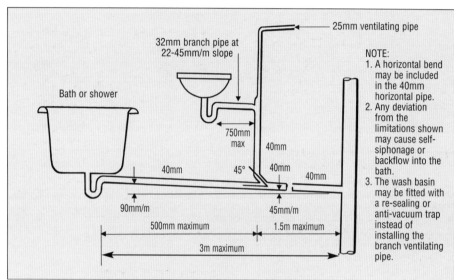

*Figure 13  Combined discharge branch for a bath and wash basin*

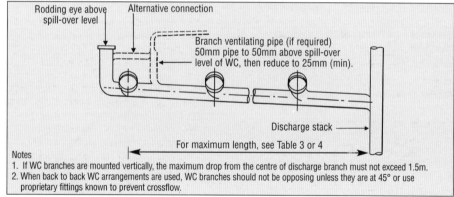

Notes
1. If WC branches are mounted vertically, the maximum drop from the centre of discharge branch must not exceed 1.5m.
2. When back to back WC arrangements are used, WC branches should not be opposing unless they are at 45° or use proprietary fittings known to prevent crossflow.

*Figure 14  Combined discharge branch for a group of WC's*

## Prevention of cross flow – small diameter pipes

Opposed small diameter branch discharge connections to stacks (without swept entries) should be arranged so that risk of the flow from one branch affecting another branch is avoided. See Figures 15 to 18.

## Prevention of cross flow – large diameter pipes

To prevent the discharge from a large branch (e.g. WC) from affecting a smaller opposed discharge branch connection, the latter should not be connected to the stack within a vertical height of 200mm below the larger branch, (see Figure 18). Where this cannot be achieved, a parallel branch can be used, (see Figure 16), or a proprietary 'Collar Boss' could be used, (see Figure 19).

*Figure 15  Example of permitted stack connection for small diameter branch pipes*

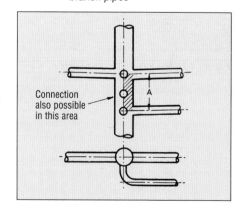

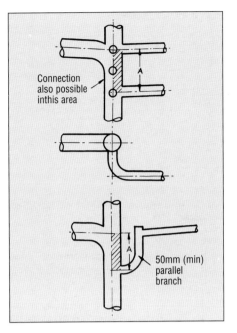

*Figure 16  Example of permitted stack connections for adjacent small & large diameter branch pipes*

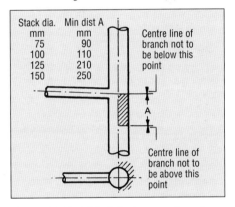

| Stack dia.<br>mm | Min dist A<br>mm |
|---|---|
| 75 | 90 |
| 100 | 110 |
| 125 | 210 |
| 150 | 250 |

Centre line of branch not to be below this point

Centre line of branch not to be above this point

*Figure 17  Restricted stack connections for small diameter branch pipes*

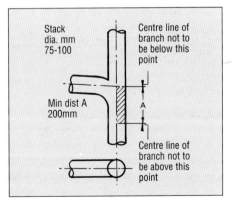

Stack dia. mm 75-100

Centre line of branch not to be below this point

Min dist A 200mm

Centre line of branch not to be above this point

*Figure 18  Restricted stack connections for adjacent small & large diameter branch pipes*

## 'Collar Boss' system

The 'Collar Boss' (see Figure 19) was specifically designed to overcome the installation difficulty imposed by the 200mm restricted zone, and to allow multiple low level discharge pipes to be connected to the stack above floor level. The boss inlets can be adapted for 32, 40 and 50mm connections. Cross-flow is prevented as the annular chamber protects the small diameter connections from the WC discharge, allowing wastewater to flow freely and merge below the critical zone.

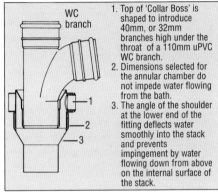

WC branch

1. Top of 'Collar Boss' is shaped to introduce 40mm, or 32mm branches high under the throat of a 110mm uPVC WC branch.
2. Dimensions selected for the annular chamber do not impede water flowing from the bath.
3. The angle of the shoulder at the lower end of the fitting deflects water smoothly into the stack and prevents impingement by water flowing down from above on the internal surface of the stack.

*Figure 19  'Collar Boss' fitting*

## Ventilating pipes

The purpose of ventilating pipes is to maintain equilibrium of pressure within the sanitary discharge system, and thus prevent the depletion of trap seals by siphonage, or compression. They should be connected to the discharge pipe no further than 750mm from the trap, (see Figure 20). They should be provided with a continuous back fall towards the branch discharge connection pipe, in order to prevent any trapped condensation interfering with the free air movement. Alternatively a 'loop vent' arrangement could be used (see Figure 21), and the ventilating pipe sloped downwards towards the ventilating stack.

Except where forming a secondary ventilated system, or used for offset venting, pipes should have a bore of not less than 25mm, but if longer than 15m or include more than 5 bends, the pipe size should be increased to 32mm. To reduce the risk of blockage, vent pipe connections to WC branches should be not less than 50mm, and extend upwards not less than 50mm above the spill over level of the WC pan before reducing in size.

The top end of a ventilating stack may connect to the discharge stack above the spill over level of the highest appliance, fitted with an air admittance valve, or extended outside the building to form a vent terminal.

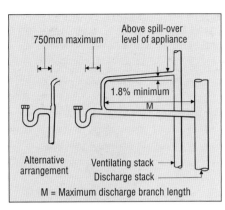

750mm maximum          Above spill-over level of appliance

1.8% minimum

M

Alternative arrangement          Ventilating stack

Discharge stack

M = Maximum discharge branch length

*Figure 20  Branch ventilation*

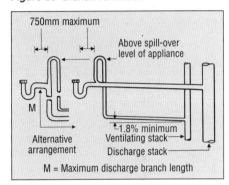

750mm maximum          Above spill-over level of appliance

M          1.8% minimum

Alternative arrangement          Ventilating stack

Discharge stack

M = Maximum discharge branch length

*Figure 21  Branch 'Loop Vent'*

## Capacities of stacks

The maximum capacity of a discharge stack is normally limited to about one quarter full. The purpose of this is to allow space for a core of air within the centre of the stack, whilst the discharge falls downwards around the internal surface of the vertical pipe. The movement of air keeps pressure fluctuations to a minimum. The size of a discharge stack, and decision on whether a secondary ventilation stack is required depends on the peak design flow from the connected appliances.

Table 5 gives the discharge unit values (DU), in litres per second, for common appliances, and is valid for System III. The values for WC's are dependent on the design of the appliance, and the relevant manufacturer should be consulted. Where the type of WC is unknown at the design stage, or likely to change, the maximum rating should be assumed. The first task is to add up all the discharge units applicable to a discharge stack. Where a shower mixer is located over a bath, the shower should be ignored, and only the bath DU should be included in the total. Readers familiar with the 'domestic group unit' included in BS 5572 will notice that this approach has been discontinued. However, for most practical applications the method explained in this Section will yield similar results.

Not all sanitary appliances will be in simultaneous use. The peak design flow can be assessed by applying a frequency of use K factor (see Table 6) to the total sum of the discharge units, and by using the following equation:

$$Q_{ww} = K \sqrt{\sum DU}$$

Where:

$Q_{ww}$ = Wastewater flow rate (l/s)

$K$ = Frequency of use

$\sum DU$ = Sum of discharge units

Before the stack selection can be made, any other continuous or fixed flow must be added to the Qww value. The following equation explains further:

$$Q_{tot} = Q_{ww} + Q_c + Q_p$$

Where:

$Q_{tot}$ = Total flowrate (l/s)

$Q_{ww}$ = Wastewater flowrate (l/s)

$Q_c$ = Continuous flowrate (l/s)

$Q_p$ = Pumped flowrate (l/s)

Once the $Q_{tot}$ value has been obtained, a decision about the stack size, and ventilation principle can be made by referring to Table 7 and 8. The pipe sizes relate to the pipe bores which have traditionally been used in the UK. The theoretical minimum bore for 50, 75, 100 and 150 sizes is 44, 75, 96, and 146mm respectively. Both Table 4 and 5 are based on 'swept entry' equal branches, which are required in the UK.

*Table 5*

| Appliance | DU (L/s) |
|---|---|
| Wash basin or bidet | 0.3 |
| Shower without plug | 0.4 |
| Shower with plug | 1.3 |
| Single urinal with cistern | 0.4 |
| Slab urinal (per person) | 0.2 |
| Bath | 1.3 |
| Kitchen sink | 1.3 |
| Dishwasher (household) | 0.2 |
| Washing machine (6kg) | 0.6 |
| Washing machine (12kg) | 1.2 |
| WC with 6 l cistern | 1.2 – 1.7 |
| WC with 7.5 l cistern | 1.4 – 1.8 |
| WC with 9 l cistern | 1.6 – 2.0 |

*The Water Regulations & Byelaws in the UK do not allow the use of 7.5 or 9 litre WC flushing cisterns on new installations, the information is provided for use in connection with existing systems.*

*Table 6*

| Usage of appliances | K |
|---|---|
| Intermittent use, e.g. dwelling, guesthouse, office | 0.5 |
| Frequent use, e.g. hotel, restaurant, school, hospital | 0.7 |
| Congested use, e.g. toilets and/or showers open to the public | 1.0 |
| Special use, e.g. laboratory | 1.2 |

*Table 7  Maximum capacity of PRIMARY ventilated discharge stacks*

| Min. stack & vent I.D. | Litres/sec |
|---|---|
| 75mm* | 2.6 |
| 100mm | 5.2 |
| 150mm | 12.4 |

*\* No WC's allowed on 75mm stacks*

*Table 8  Maximum capacity of SECONDARY ventilated discharge stacks*

| Min. stack & vent I.D. | | Litres/sec |
|---|---|---|
| Stack & vent | Vent | |
| 75mm* | 50mm | 3.4 |
| 100mm | 50mm | 7.3 |
| 150mm | 50mm | 18.3 |

*\* No WC's allowed on 75mm stacks*

## Example 1

Determine total design flowrate and stack requirements for an 11-storey block of apartments. The each stack will serve one apartment per floor, comprising of bathroom, en-suite shower room and fully fitted kitchen.

DU per flat:
2 WC's × 1.7 =      3.4
2 wash basins × 0.3 =  0.6
1 bath =          1.3
1 shower =         0.4
1 kitchen sink =      1.3
1 washing machine =   0.6
1 dishwasher =       0.2
                7.8

Assume a primary ventilated stack is adequate; therefore the bottom storey must connect separately to drain (see Figure 5).

For 10 storeys, $\sum DU$: 7.8 x 10 = 78

K = 0.5, so $Q_{ww}$ = 0.5 √78 = 4.42l/s

$Q_c$ & $Q_p$ = zero, so $Q_{tot}$ = 4.42l/s

From Table 7, a 100mm primary ventilated stack has a limit of 5.2l/s, so this size is adequate. Secondary ventilation is not required.

## Example 2

Determine total design flowrate and stack requirements for an 11-storey hotel. The stack will serve two en-suite bathrooms on each floor; there will be air conditioning units on the roof with a peak discharge of 0.2L/s, and laundry equipment on the 5th floor with a peak discharge of 0.5l/s.

DU per typical floor:
2 WC's × 1.7 =      3.4
2 wash basins x 0.3 =  0.6
2 baths × 1.3 =      2.6
                6.6

Assume a primary ventilated stack is adequate; therefore the bottom storey must connect separately to drain (see Figure 5).

For 10 storeys, $\sum DU$: 6.6 x 10 = 66

K = 0.7, so $Q_{ww}$ = 0.7 √66 = 5.7l/s

$Q_{tot}$: 5.7 + 0.2 + 0.5 = 6.4l/s

There are two options; a 150mm primary ventilated stack, or a 100mm secondary ventilated stack and 50mm secondary vent. Practical considerations would dictate the best choice, for example a proprietary fitting such as the collar boss (see Figure 19) is only available in the 100mm size.

# Self-sealing waste valves

The recent introduction to the plumbing market of waste valves to replace the water seal trap offers the installer an opportunity to reconsider his system design, often reducing the amount of pipework required, whilst still meeting the mandatory requirement of Building Regulation ADH.1. These valves and their function are described in Figures 22 to 26.

As the name suggests, these valves open to allow the flow of water from the appliance, or to allow air to enter the pipework system in the case of negative pressure, then closes automatically when the flow stops or the pipework system pressure reaches eqilibrium with atmosphere.

This means that a system fitted with valves in place of water seal traps would be self-ventilating.

The valves are designed to open between 3 and 6mb and will remain sealed against 400+mb back pressure.

These valves are particularly useful for situations where water seals would be lost by evaporation – for example, holiday homes, condensate drains from chillers and air conditioning units. (See manufacturers' detailed instructions.)

The valves are available in 32mm (1¼˝) and 40mm (1½˝) body size, together with 87½° knuckle elbow and running adaptor. Universal compression outlets are used for making connections to either push fit BS 5254 or solvent weld BS 5255 waste systems.

## Testing of waste valves

Because these devices do not depend on a water seal in a trap, many of the guidelines related to prevention of seal loss contained in the previous pages need not be applied, typically:

a. Performance testing for retention of water seal on applications fitted with the valve is of course irrelevant.

b. Performance test for WC water seal retention should be carried out.

c. Soundness testing – First flush the appliances to ensure free flow of water through the valves and clearance of possible site debris, then carry out a 38mm (50mm Scotland) water test.

## Standards

As these valves are not covered by British Standards, it is important that they carry performance certification by a third party approvals body acceptable to Building Regulations, eg WIMLAS or BBA.

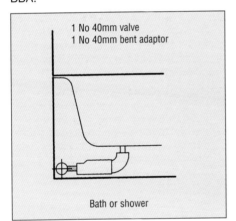

*Figure 22  Bath or shower*

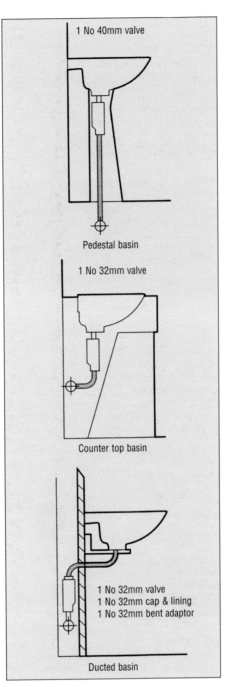

*Figure 24  Single wash basin*

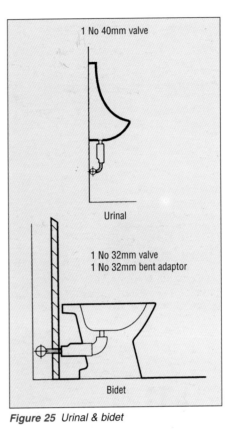

*Figure 25  Urinal & bidet*

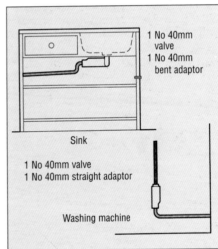

*Figure 26  Sink & washing machine*

*Figure 23  A range of wash basins*

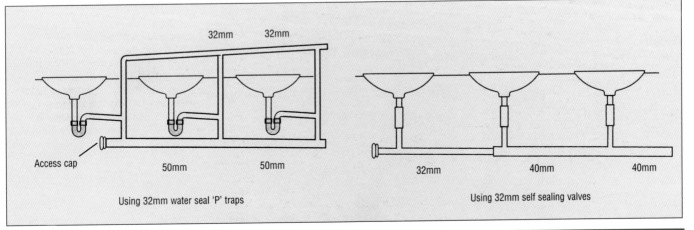

# Kitchen Drainage

## Drainage (above ground)

Kitchens are of necessity, designed to ensure a natural flow of work and seldom permit the grouping of the appliances to give the best conditions of drainage. As it is of primary importance that there should be no loss of water seal in traps on kitchen appliances, an adequate ventilated system of drainage is necessary.

## Materials

Only smooth bore materials should be used for any system of drainage pipework but particular care is required when selecting materials for drainage from restaurant kitchens. It is essential that pipework should be robust and, in appropriate situations, suitable to receive high temperature discharges.

## Backflow problems

Backflow can occur and manifest itself in the kitchen system if a blockage occurs downstream at a point where the kitchen system joins the main system in a large complex or if effluents pass down stacks from floors above and through the kitchen system. It is recommended therefore that kitchen drainage systems should not be closely linked with those of other parts of the building complex and that separate drainage stacks be provided where kitchens are located other than on ground floors.

## Grease separators

The Building Regulations Approved Document H requires that a grease separator is provided for kitchens in commercial hot food premises. The grease separator (or grease trap) should be designed and located to promote cooling, coagulation and retention of the grease within the trap and sized to achieve maximum efficiency.

The temperature and velocity of flow of the wastewater should allow the grease to separate and collect on the surface of the water in the trap reservoir. Consideration should also be given to the general nature of the waste matter to be discharged since the reduced flow velocity through the trap will allow solid waste matter in suspension to settle and collect in the trap reservoir.

Provision should be made to facilitate the hygienic removal and disposal of the grease. Provision should also be made

for the trap to be completely emptied and cleaned periodically to limit the build-up of settled matter which inhibits the effctiveness of the grease trap.

Ideally, grease traps should be located externally and siting of grease traps within kitchens should be avoided if at all possible. In no circumstances should they be sited in food storage or preparation areas.

An hygienic alternative to grease traps is a grease removal unit. These are retention units which maintain the wastewater at sufficient temperatures to allow the grease to rise to the surface and remain liquid. The unit automatically skims off the grease into a container for removal and recycling. Strainer baskets can be included to retain vegetable matter.

## Pumped installations

Where kitchen drainage has to be pumped, it is essential that the pumps and sump are regularly maintained. If an effective grease trap is not installed prior to the sump, provide a chemical drip feed of a grease dissolving type into the sump to prevent grease coagulating.

Similarly, coating of any electrodes or controls with silicone will inhibit adhesion of grease to their surface.

## Branch discharge pipes

In view of the high proportion of solid matter and grease from kitchen appliances, 'flat' gradients should be avoided. Branch discharge pipes from macerators should be as short as practicable and connected directly to a main discharge pipe or stacks. The gradient should be at least $7\frac{1}{2}°$ (135mm/m) to the horizontal although steeper gradients are advisable, and any bends should be of a large radius.

It is an advantage if other appliances can be connected to the discharge pipe upstream of the macerator connection, to assist with the discharge of the waste material. The discharge pipe should connect directly to a drain without an intervening gully trap.

## Traps

Traps up to and including 50mm diameter should be tubular with a 75mm seal and preferably of a two piece type for easy access.

## Access

Access points should be above spill-over level of the appliances at risk and located in positions permitting effective use without nuisance.

## Floor drainage

Floor channels, open gullies and gratings in kitchens, food preparation and wash-up rooms harbour dirt and grease and if not properly fitted can be hazardous to pedestrian traffic. This form of drainage is unhygienic and should be avoided. However, an open top gully with sediment bucket should be provided for discharge from mobile sinks where these are to be used in vegetable preparation areas.

## Specific requirements

a.  Drain-off valves on food containers should be of the full way plug-cock type with quick release bodies for easy cleaning. Thes valves must not be connected to a common waste pipe or drain without an intervening air break.

b.  Sinks and washing up machines must be individually trapped and connected directly to the building drainage/plumbing system.

c.  Vegetable paring machines should be fitted with a waste dilution unit and the waste should be trapped and connected directly to the building drainage/plumbing system.

d.  The pipes from appliances which discharge wastewater containing heavy concentrations of solid matter, e.g. vegetable paring machines and waste disposal macerators, should not be connected to the head of long runs of horizontal waste pipes. They should be connected as close as is practicable to the main drain or discharge stack so as to gain the maximum flushing advantage from appliances with high wastewater discharge rates.

e.  Where practicable, items of kitchen equipment such as steaming ovens, bains marie, boilers and cafe sets should discharge over a drip tray or fixed tundish having a trapped waste pipe connected to the discharge system. In situations where this is impracticable, the waste should discharge over a suitable container which can be emptied as required.

f. Boiling pans should be drained separately over removable tundishes into trapped gullies. The trapped gully should be fitted with a solid hinged flap set flush with the floor and kept closed when not in use.

# Laboratory drainage

## General

At the outset of any design of a laboratory waste system it is imperative to ascertain and receive written confirmation from the client as the type and probable quantities of effluents that will be discharged. It is also important to know whether any allowance for future alterations or extensions is to be made.

## Design of stack layout

There is divided opinion of the relative advantages and disadvantages of either horizontal or vertical stack layout but the latter is to be preferred for discharge systems and will generally permit a large degree of planning flexibility.

Vertical distribution is ideal for laboratory premises with repetitive planning on successive floors and also when dealing with alterations, as their effect is invariably confined to the laboratory concerned.

## Replacement

Due to the nature of discharges from laboratories, despite the fact that the best material for the job should be selected, the life expectancy may well be less than for ordinary discharge systems. The design must therefore take into consideration ease of replacement.

## Dilution

The greater the dilution of laboratory waste obtained, the better, so as to minimise possible damage to final drains and sewers. Dilution may be achieved by individual dilution recovery traps (catchpots), by similar fittings serving groups of appliances or by dilution chambers constructed below ground level as part of the drainage system.

## Incompatible wastes

The designer should always bear in mind that chemical wastes may be incompatible e.g. chemicals each

producing few problems on their own, but which, if combined in a common branch discharge pipe, may have a tendency to gel or produce an undesirable chemical effect and therefore will need to be kept separate until sufficient dilution has occurred in the system.

As a general rule it is preferable for each laboratory to have its own connection(s) to the main stack(s), and not to combine wastes by continuous branch discharge pipes passing through a number of laboratories. Obviously this will be easier where vertical stack layout has been adopted. For most practical purposes, once the wastes discharge into a main stack, sufficient dilution will occur, but each instance must be considered on its own merits.

Sanitary/laboratory appliances should be easy to clean. Discharge pipes must be sealed throughout their run to the sewer which should be as short as possible. The routing of pipes must take into account areas which might be put in hazard by leakage, and should be freely accessible for inspection and repair. A secondary system of containment may be considered necessary.

Radioactive pipe runs must be labelled at points of access.

The designer should consult the user about the pattern of usuage and monitoring procedures. Any small or intermittent radioactive discharges should be well flushed out to main drainage, by other flow and allowed to dry out along the pipe line. The character of any added discharge should however be taken into account, particularly to avoid the risk of blockage; discharges carrying a high proportion of paper or macerated materials should be kept separate. If a holding tank is installed for monitoring purposes, matter likely to turn septic must be excluded.

# Materials for above ground drainage systems

## General

For a well designed above ground drainage system it is essential to have considerable knowledge of the materials that are available and their fixing and jointing techniques.

## Types of materials

a. Cast iron

b. Copper

c. Galvanised steel

d. ABS (Acrylonitrile butadiene styrene)

e. HDPE (High density polyethlene)

f. MUPVC (Modified unplasticized polyvinyl chloride)

g. UPVC (Unplasticized polyvinyl chloride)

h. PP (Polypropylene)

i. Borosilicate glass (primarily for laboratory waste)

j. Heavy duty polyethylene (primarily for laboratory use)

k. Heavy duty polypropylene (primarily for laboratory use).

## Selection

When designing a laboratory drainage system the following factors require consideration:

a. The type, quantity, dilution strength, and temperature of chemicals, also the disposal position

b. Whether the effluent may be conveyed direct to the sewer, or whether treatment is required

c. Whether the pipe material and pipe jointing method can withstand the chemicals and/or temperature involved

d. Whether the pipe jointing process requires any specialist knowledge or equipment

e. Ease of future alteration and repair.

f. Properties of piping, e.g. expansion, flammability, weight, etc.

g. Cost and availability of any non-standard products.

*NOTES:*
*When considering the chemical effects on any piping, it is advisable to seek written confirmation from the manufacturer. For plastics and rubber seal rings, ISO/TR 10358 and ISO/TR 7620 may be consulted respectively.*

# Inspection and testing of discharge pipes

Work should be inspected and tested during installation, care being taken that all work which is to be concealed is tested before it is finally enclosed. Final tests should be applied on completion of the installation both for soundness and performance. Normally, the air test is used for soundness, but if the water test is applied, it should be used only up to the level of the lowest sanitary appliance connected to the system, and then only in new systems.

When testing old systems, it may be necessary to limit the pressure applied because of shallow trap seals; the water test should not be used. Any defects revealed by the test should be made good and the test repeated until a satisfactory result is obtained.

Reference should be made to Local Authority and other enforcing authority requirements, particularly where pipework passes through areas where blockages and leaks cannot be detected. In general, sufficient access should be provided to enable complete systems to be tested.

Access points should be carefully sited to allow the entry of cleaning and testing equipment and consideration also be given to adjacent services. Traps and joints that are easily disconnected can be an advantage so additional access is required only under exceptional circumstances.

The discharge from urinals can give rise to heavy deposits, especially in hard water areas. Regular maintenance is therefore required and access should be provided so that all parts of the stack, branch, discharge pipe and trap can be readily cleaned. Where the vertical discharge pipe has a long connection to a manhole, access should be provided at ground floor near the foot of the stack.

In multi-storey domestic buildings, access should be provided at 3 storey intervals or less. In public and commercial buildings and more complex drainage systems, access should be provided at each floor level.

## Air test

An air test should apply a pressure equal to 3.8mbar (38mm) water gauge and should remain constant for a period of not less than three minutes. The water seals of all sanitary appliances which are installed should be fully charged and a

Table 9 *Number of sanitary appliances to be discharged for performance testing*

| Type of use | Number of appliances of each kind on the stack | Number of appliances to be discharged simultaneously | | |
|---|---|---|---|---|
| | | WC | Wash basin | Kitchen sink |
| Domestic | 1 to 9 | 1 | 1 | 1 |
| | 10 to 24 | 1 | 1 | 2 |
| | 25 to 35 | 1 | 2 | 3 |
| | 36 to 50 | 2 | 2 | 3 |
| | 51 to 65 | 2 | 2 | 4 |
| Commercial or public | 1 to 9 | 1 | 1 | – |
| | 10 to 18 | 1 | 2 | |
| | 19 to 26 | 2 | 2 | |
| | 27 to 32 | 2 | 3 | |
| | 53 to 78 | 3 | 4 | |
| | 70 to 100 | 3 | 5 | |
| Congested | 1 to 4 | 1 | 1 | – |
| | 5 to 9 | 1 | 2 | |
| | 10 to 13 | 2 | 2 | |
| | 14 to 26 | 2 | 3 | |
| | 27 to 39 | 3 | 4 | |
| | 40 to 50 | 3 | 5 | |
| | 51 to 55 | 4 | 5 | |
| | 56 to 7 | 4 | 6 | |
| | 71 to 78 | 4 | 7 | |
| | 79 to 90 | 5 | 7 | |
| | 91 to 100 | 5 | 8 | |

*These figures are based on a criterion of satisfactory service of 99%. In practice, for systems serving mixed appliances, this slightly overestimates the probable hydraulic loading. The flow load from urinals, spray tap basins and showers is usually small in most mixed systems, hence these appliances need not normally be discharged.*

test plug inserted into open ends of the pipework to be tested, each plug being sealed with a small quantity of water. One testing plug should be fitted with a tee-piece, with a valve on each branch, one branch being connected by a flexible tube to a manometer.

To apply the test, air is introduced into the system through the other branch of the tee-piece until the desired pressure is shown on the manometer scale. Alternatively, the pressure may be applied by passing a flexible tube from a tee-piece attached to a manometer through the water seal of the trap of a sanitary appliance, the test then being carried out as previously described.

Defects revealed by an air test may be located by the following:

a. Soap solution can be applied to the pipes and joints, under test, leakage can be detected by the formation of bubbles.

b. A smoke producing machine may be used which will introduce smoke under pressure into the defective pipework. Leakage can be observed as the smoke escapes. Smoke producing equipment should not be used where plastic piping has been installed.

c. A proprietary aerosol leak detection spray. Leakage can be detected by foaming.

## Performance of testing systems

In addition to a test for air or water-tightness, every discharge pipe installation should be tested for stability of the trap seals on the system. When subjected to the appropriate discharge tests, every trap must retain not less than 25mm of water seal. Each test should be repeated three times, traps being recharged before each test and the maximum loss of seal in any one test should be taken as the significant result.

To test for the effect of self siphonage, waste appliances should be filled to over flowing level and discharged in the normal way. The seal remaining in the trap should be measured when the discharge is finished.

To test for the effects of probable maximum simultaneous discharges of sanitary appliances, the number of appliances to be discharged together is given in Table 9. For the purpose of this test, baths are ignored as their use is spread over a period and they do not normally add materially to the peak flow.

Where a stack services baths only, the number to be discharged simultaneously in a test should be the same as for sinks. The worst conditions occur when appliances on the upper floors are discharged. A reasonable test therefore is to discharge up to one WC, one basin and one sink from the top floor of the building with any other appliances to be discharged on the floor immediately below.

# Methods of waste collection

1. Refuse chutes provide an economic solution in multi-storey and similar type buildings. Adequte precautions must be taken to prevent entry of rodents into the bin storage area and also to minimise the entry of flies.

2. Kitchen waste disposal units are a means of disposal of food waste and for commercial and industrial use. It is advisable to consult specialist suppliers.

3. Sanitary towel disposal can be carried out by incineration, maceration or by collecting bins for storing and bulk disposal.

4. Owing to its varied nature, hospital refuse should be disposed of by maceration (near as possible to the disposal source) or by incineration.

5. Compression systems are available which reduce the volume to between 1/3rd to 1/12th.

6. Composting refuse in agricultural areas is considered the most economic method of disposal. Refuse collection and disposal methods used should be determined in consultation with the Local Authority.

# Sanitary accommodation

1. The planning in most instances is performed by the Architect, who should be advised of special requirements and where an alteration to the layout, within structural limitations, can affect economies and performance.

2. Hand drying facilities can either be
   i. disposable paper
   ii. roller towel
   iii. warm air electric.

3. Soap solution dispensers, fed from local reservoirs provide a ready alternative to the provision of bar soap.

4. Hand rinse basins have found a ready use in general toilet accommodation. Operation other than by hand can lead to removal of taps completely from basins and this can lead to a reduction of cross-infection.

5. Spray mixer taps produce savings in water consumption, economies in pipework and fuel costs. However, in some hard water areas the spray nozzles rapidly become blocked with lime scale and in some soft water areas, gelling of soap residues occurs in branch discharge pipes. The additional maintenance costs may outweigh any savings made in water and fuel costs.

6. The use of wall hung or concealed outlet type WC pans makes for easier cleaning.

7. Automatic water flow for hand washing, flushing etc. can be achieved (i) hydraulically (ii) pneumatically (iii) electrically.

Reference should also be made to BS 6465: Part 1.

*Table 10 Dwellings*

| Type of dwelling | Appliances | Number per dwelling | Remarks |
|---|---|---|---|
| Dwellings on one level e.g. bungalows & flats | WC | 1 for up to 5 persons 2 for 6 or more | Except for single persons accommodation, where 1 WC is provided, the WC should be in a separate compartment. Where 2 WC's are provided, 1 may be in the bathroom |
| | Bath/shower | 1 | |
| | Wash basin | 1 | |
| | Sink | 1 | |
| Dwellings on one or more levels e.g. houses and maisonettes | WC | 1 for up to 4 persons 2 for 5 or more | Except for single persons accommodation, where 1 WC is provided, the WC should be in a separate compartment. Where 2 WC's are provided, 1 may be in the bathroom. |
| | Bath/shower | 1 | |
| | Wash basin | 1 | |
| | Sink | 1 | |

*NOTE 1  Where en-suite facilities are provided there should be additional provision of toilets for visitors & staff.*

*Table 11  Accommodation for elderly people and sheltered accommodation*

| Type of accommodation | Appliances | Number per dwelling | Remarks |
|---|---|---|---|
| Self-contained for 1 or 2 elderly persons, or grouped apartments for 2 less-active elderly persons | WC | 1 | An additional WC May be provided in the bathroom. |
| | Bath/shower | 1 | |
| | Wash basin | 1 | |
| | Sink | 1 | |
| Grouped apartments for less-active elderly persons | WC | 1 | |
| | Wash basin | 1 | |
| | Sink | 1 | |
| | Bath/shower | Not less than1 per 4 apartments | Some may be Sitz baths or level access showers |
| Additional provisions for communal facilities | | | |
| Common room for self-contained or grouped | WC | 1 | Minimum number required. Should be available for use by visitors. |
| | Wash basin | 1 | |
| The pan try or kitchen for self-contained or grouped apartments | Sink | 1 | Adjacent to common room |
| Laundry room for grouped apartment schemes | Sink | 1 | |
| | Washing machine | 1 | |
| | Tumble drier | 1 | |
| Cleaner's room | Bucket/cleaner's sink | | 1 in each cleaner's room |

*NOTE 1  Many persons using this type of accommodation may have disabilities therefore the layout of rooms, approaches and accesses should be capable of being used by disabled persons.*

*Table 12  Residential homes and nursing homes for elderly people.  Type of accommodation*

| Type of accommodation | Appliances | Number recommended | Remarks |
|---|---|---|---|
| Residents | WC | 1 per 4 persons | An adjacent wash basin is also required |
| | Bath | 1 per 10 persons[1] | |
| | Wash basin | 1 to each bedsitting room | |
| Staff | WC | At least 2 for non-residential staff[2] | |
| | Wash basin | 1 | In WC compartment |
| Visitors | WC | 1 | |
| | Wash basin | 1 | In WC compartment |
| Kitchen | Sink | As appropriate | |
| Cleaner's room | Bucket/cleaner's sink | 1 | In each cleaner's room |
| Other | Bed pan cleaning/disposal | As appropriate | Service area |
| | Wash basin | 1 | In each medical room, hairdressing, chiropodist, non-residential staff toilets and kitchen areas. |

*NOTE 1  Where en-suite facilities are provided, toilets for visitors and staff should also be provided.*
*NOTE 2  Attention is drawn to the Workplace (health, Safety and Welfare) Regulations.*
*NOTE 3  Attention is drawn to the Department of Health and Social Security Local Authority Building Note No. 2 and the National Assistance Regulations 1962.*

[1] *Sitz baths with hand showers (not fixed overhead) and/or shower units suitable for use by residents in wheelchairs or sani-chairs, may be suitable alternatives. The number may vary in different parts of the country.*
[2] *Where residential accommodation is provided for staff, sanitary appliances should be in accordance with table 11*

**Table 13** Staff toilets in offices, shops, factories and other non-domestic premises used as place of work

Sanitary appliances for any group of staff

| Number of persons at work | Number of WC's | Number of washing stations |
|---|---|---|
| 1 to 5 | 1 | 1 |
| 6 to 25 | 2 | 2 |
| 26 to 50 | 3 | 3 |
| 51 to 75 | 4 | 4 |
| 76 to 100 | 5 | 5 |
| Above 100 | One additional WC and washing station for every unit or fraction of a unit of 25 persons | |

Alternative scale of provision of sanitary appliances for use by male staff only

| Number of men at work | Number of WC's | Number of urinals |
|---|---|---|
| 1 to 15 | 1 | 1 |
| 16 to 30 | 2 | 1 |
| 31 to 45 | 2 | 2 |
| 46 to 60 | 3 | 2 |
| 61 to 75 | 3 | 3 |
| 76 to 90 | 4 | 3 |
| 92 to 100 | 4 | 4 |
| Above 100 | One additional WC for every unit or fraction of a unit of 50 men provided at least an equal number of additional urinals are provided. | |

NOTE 1 Where work activities result in the heavy soiling of hands and forearms washing stations should be provided for staff as follows:
1 per 10 people at work (or fraction of 10) up to 50 people
1 additional washing station for every further 20 people (or fraction of 20)
NOTE 2 For facilities for disabled workers and visitors attention is drawn to the building regulations
NOTE 3 Where sanitary conveniences provided for staff are also used by the public the number of conveniences specified should be increased by at least one, for each sex as necessary to ensure that staff can use the facilities without undue delay
NOTE 4 In certain situations where security necessitates separate provision for visitors, this should be sited in or adjacent to the public area.

**Table 14** Facilities for customers in shops and shopping malls

| Sales area of shop | Appliances | Male | Female |
|---|---|---|---|
| 1000m$^2$ to 2000m$^2$ | WC | 1 | 2 |
| | Urinal | 1 | Nil |
| | Wash basin | 1 | 2 |
| | Toilet for disabled people | | 1 |
| 2001m$^2$ to 4000m$^2$ | WC | 1 | 4 |
| | Urinal | 2 | Nil |
| | Wash basin | 2 | 4 |
| | Toilet for disabled people | | 1 |
| Greater than 4000m$^2$ | In proportion to the size of the net sales area | | |

NOTE 1 This table of recommendation scale of provision for customers applies to shops having a net sales area in excess of 1000m$^2$
NOTE 2 In this table it has been assumed that the customers will be 50% male and 50% female. For different proportions the accommodation levels will have to be adjusted proportionally.
NOTE 3 For shopping malls the sum of the floor areas of the shops should be calculated and used with the above table.

*Table 15  Schools*

| Type of school | Appliances | Number recommended | Remarks |
|---|---|---|---|
| Special | Fittings | 1/10 of the number of pupils rounded up to the next nearest whole number | |
| | WC only | Girls: all fittings | |
| | Urinals and WC | Boys: not more than 2/3 of fittings should be urinals | |
| | Wash basin | As for secondary school | |
| | Shower | Although not required by statute, it is suggested that sufficient showers should be provided for physical education | |
| | Bucket/cleaner's sink/slop hopper | At least one per floor | |
| Primary | Fittings | Aggregate of 1/10 of the number of pupils under 5 years old and 1/20 of the number of others. Not less than 4. Rounded up to the nearest whole number | |
| | WC only | Girls: All fittings | |
| | Urinal and WC | Boys: not more than 2/3 of fittings should be urinals | |
| | Wash basin | As for secondary school | |
| | Shower | Although not required by statute, it is suggested that sufficient showers should be provided for physical education | |
| | Bucket/cleaner's sink/slop hopper | At least one per floor | |
| Secondary | Fittings | 1/20 of the number of pupils. Not less than 4. Rounded up to the nearest whole number | |
| | WC only | Girls: All fittings | |
| | Wash basin | 1 in each washroom. At least 2 basins per 3 fittings | |
| | Shower | As for primary school | |
| | Bucket/cleaner's sink/slop hopper | At least one per floor | |
| Nursery and play | WC | 1 per 10 pupils (not less than 4) | |
| | Wash basins | 1 per WC | |
| | Sink | 1 per 40 pupils | |
| Boarding | WC | 1 per 5 boarding pupils | Where sanitary accommodation for day pupils is accessible to and suitable for the needs of boarders, these requirements may be reduced to such an extent as may be approved in each case. |
| | Wash basin | 1 per 3 pupils for the first 60 boarding pupils: 1 per 4 pupils for the next 40 boarding pupils; 1 for every additional 5 boarding pupils; | |
| | Bath | 1 per 10 boarding pupils | |
| | Shower | May be provided as alternative to not more than ¾ of the minimum number of baths | |

NOTE 1  *For the purpose of this table 'fittings' is the sum of WC's and urinals.*
NOTE 2  *Attention is drawn to the Workplace (Health, Safety and Welfare) Regulations1992.*
NOTE 3  *Attention is drawn to the need for facilities for the disposal of sanitary dressings.*
NOTE 4  *For educational  establishments not mentioned above, advice should be sought for the Department of Education*
NOTE 5  *For Scotland attention is drawn to the School Premises (Scotland) Regulations 1967, 1973 and 1979*
NOTE 6  *For Northern Ireland attention is drawn to the statutory requirements of the Department of Education (Northern Ireland).*
NOTE 7  *Attention is drawn to the Education (School Premises) Regulations, 1981 an 1989, upon which this table is based*
NOTE 8  *Changing accommodation and showers should be provided for staff engaged in PE where pupils have achieved the age of 8 years.*
NOTE 9  *Medical accommodation should be provided centrally in all schools, to include a wash basin sited near to a WC. For boarding schools attention is drawn to the Education  (School Premises) Regulations 1981 and 1989.*
NOTE 10  *For toilets for disabled people attention is drawn to the Department of the Environment Design Note 18 1984 (12)*

*Table 16* *Buildings used for public entertainment*

| Appliances | Males | Females |
|---|---|---|
| WC | In single-screen cinemas, theatres, concert halls and similar premises without licensed bars: 1 for up to 250 males plus 1 for every additional 500 males or part thereof | For single-screen cinemas, theatres, concert halls and similar premises without licensed bars: 2 for up to 40 females 3 for 41 to 70 females 4 for 71 to 100 females plus 1 for every additional 40 females or part thereof |
| Urinal | In single-screen cinemas, theatres, concert halls and similar premises without licensed bars: 2 for up to 100 males plus 1 for every additional 80 males or part thereof | |
| Wash basins | 1 per WC and in addition 1 per 5 urinals or part thereof | 1, plus 1 per 2 WCs or part thereof |
| Bucket/cleaner's sink | Adequate provision should be made for cleaning facilities including at least one cleaner's sink | |

NOTE 1  In the absence or more reliable information it should be assumed that the audience will be 50% male and 50% female
NOTE 2  In cinema-multiplexes and similar premises where the use of facilities will be spread through the opening hours the level of provision should normally be based upon 75% of total capacity and the assumption of equal proportions of male and female customers.  (For single-screen cinema 100% occupancy is assumed).
NOTE 3  Where buildings for public entertainment have licensed bars, facilities should also be provided in accordance with Table 19, based upon the capacity of the bar(s) and assuming equal proportions of male and female customers.
NOTE 4  Attention is drawn to the necessity to provide facilities for the disposal of sanitary dressings.
NOTE 5  Attention is drawn to the Workplace (Health, Safety and Welfare) Regulations 1992.

*Table 17*  *Hotels*

| Type of accommodation | Appliances/facilities | Number required | Remarks |
|---|---|---|---|
| Hotel with en-suite Accommodation | En-suite | 1 per residential guest bedroom | Containing bath/shower, WC and wash basin |
| | Staff bathroom | 1 per 9 residential staff | |
| | Bucket/cleaners' sink | 1 per 30 bedrooms | At least 1 on every floor |
| Hotels and guest houses without en-suite accommodation | WC | 1 per 9 guests | |
| | Wash basin | 1 per bedroom | |
| | Bathroom | 1 per 9 guests | Containing: Bath/shower, wash basin and additional WC |
| | Bucket/cleaners' sink | 1 per floor | |
| Tourist hostels | WC | 1 per 9 guests | |
| | Wash basin | 1 per bedroom or 1 for every 9 guests in a dormitory | |
| | Bathroom | 1 per 9 guests | Containing bath/shower, wash basin and additional WC |
| | Bucket/cleaners' sink | 1 per floor | |

NOTE 1  For staff toilets attention is drawn to the Workplace (Health, Safety and Welfare) Regulations 1992.
NOTE 2  Attention is drawn to the necessity to provide facilities for the disposal of sanitary dressings.
NOTE 3  For provision of facilities associated with buildings used for public entertainment, restaurants and licensed bars see Tables 16, 18 and 19.

*Table 18* Restaurants, cafés, canteens and fast food outlets

| Appliances | For male customers | For female customers |
|---|---|---|
| WC | 1 per 100 up to 400 males. For over 400 males, add at the rate of 1 per 250 males or part thereof | 2 per 50 up to 200 females. For over 200, add at the rate of 1 per 100 females or part thereof |
| Urinal | 1 per 50 males | |
| Wash basins | 1 per WC and in addition 1 per 5 urinals or part thereof | 1 per WC |
| Bucket/cleaner's sink | Adequate provision should be made for cleaning facilities including at least one cleaner's sink | |

NOTE 1  In the absence of more reliable information it should be assumed that the customers will be 50% male and 50% female.
NOTE 2  Attention is drawn to the Workplace (Health, Safety and Welfare) Regulations 1992.
NOTE 3  Attention is drawn to the necessity to provide facilities for the disposal of sanitary dressings.
NOTE 4  For establishments with licensed bars see also Table 19.

*Table 19* Public houses and licensed bars

| Appliances | For male customers | For female customers |
|---|---|---|
| WC | 1 for up to 150 males plus 2 for every additional 150 males or part thereof | 1 for up to 12 females plus 1 for 13 to 30 females plus 1 for every additional 25 females or part thereof |
| Urinal | 2 for up to 75 males plus 1 for every additional 75 males or part thereof | |
| Wash basins | 1 per WC and in addition 1 per 5 urinals or part thereof | 1 per 2 WC's |
| Bucket/cleaner's sink | Adequate provision should be made for cleaning facilities including at least one bucket/cleaner's sink | |

NOTE 1  Occupancy should be calculated at the rate of 4 persons per 3m² of effective drinking area (EDA)
NOTE 2  In public houses a ratio of 75% male customers to 25% female customers may be assumed.  In many other situations a ration of 50% males and 50% females may be appropriate.
NOTE 3  For provision of toilets for employees and staff see table 13
NOTE 4  Public houses with restaurants should provide facilities as for licensed bars but restaurants should have additional separate toilets in accordance with table 18.
NOTE 5  Public houses with public music, singing and dancing licences should be as for licensed bars.  The licensed area for public music, singing and dancing should be separated for calculation of occupancy and the provision of toilets should be in accordance with Table 16.

*Table 20* Swimming pools

| Appliances | For male bathers | For female bathers |
|---|---|---|
| WC | 2 for up to 100 males plus 1 for every additional 100 males or part thereof | 1 per 5 females for up to 50 females plus 1 for every additional 10 females or part thereof |
| Urinal | 1 per 20 males | |
| Wash basins | 1 per WC and in addition 1 per 5 urinals or part thereof | 1, plus 1 per 2 WC's or part thereof |
| Shower | 1 per 10 males | 1 per 10 females |

NOTE 1  Toilets should be provided for staff in accordance with table 13
NOTE 2  Toilets should be provided for spectators in accordance with table 16
NOTE 3  Attention is drawn to the need to provide facilities for the disposal of sanitary dressings
NOTE 4  In this table it has been assumed that the ratio of swimmers using the pool(s) will be 50% male and 50% female.

Tables 10-20 are extracts from BS 6465 Part 1: 1994 reproduced with the kind permission of BSI under licence number 2002SK/0140.

# The design of building drainage systems

The scope of this section is to provide guidance for the design of foul and surface water systems constructed in the ground under and around buildings, together with some general commentary regarding larger drainage systems beyond those directly associated with a building development.

All drainage systems should be designed to be as simple and direct as possible. All vertical stacks should terminate with long radius bends, and changes in direction and gradient should be minimised and as easy as practicable. Access points should be provided only if blockages could not be cleared without them, and drain runs between access points should be laid in straight lines, both in the horizontal and vertical planes. However, where it is unavoidable drains may be laid to slight curves in the horizontal plane, if these can still be cleared of blockages. All changes in gradient should be at an inspection chamber or manhole. The drain soffit should invariably be level, to facilitate ventilation of the system, thus minimising the problems associated with foul smells, gases and the creation of positive and negative pressures.

Historically, installation required that all manhole branch inverts should be joined level with the horizontal centreline of the main stream drain. However, this is not

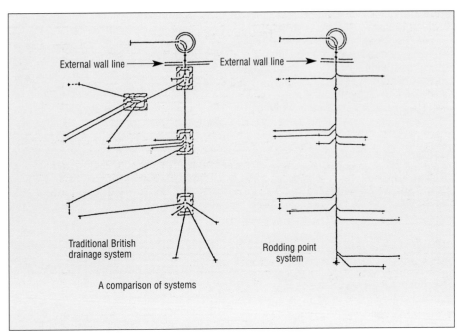

External wall line → | External wall line →

Traditional British drainage system

Rodding point system

A comparison of systems

**Figure 27** Rodding Point

**Table 21** Maximum spacing of access points

| Distance to | From access fitting | | From junction or branch | From inspection | From manhole |
|---|---|---|---|---|---|
| | 1 (m) | 2 (m) | (m) | (m) | (m) |
| Start of external drain | 12 | 12 | - | 22 | 45 |
| Rodding eye | 22 | 22 | 22 | 45 | 45 |
| Access fitting (1) min. | | | | | |
| 150mm x 100mm or 159mm dia | – | – | 12 | 22 | 22 |
| Access fitting (2) min. 225mm x 100mm | – | – | 22 | 45 | 45 |
| Inspection chamber | 22 | 45 | 22 | 45 | 45 |
| Manhole | 22 | 45 | 45 | 45 | 90 |

**Figure 28** Rodding Point Gulley

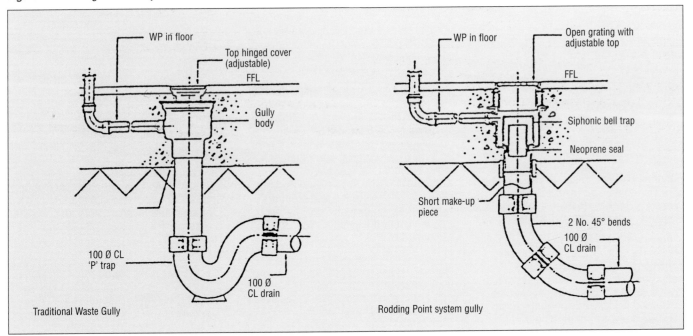

WP in floor

Top hinged cover (adjustable)

FFL

Gully body

100 Ø CL 'P' trap

100 Ø CL drain

Traditional Waste Gully

WP in floor

Open grating with adjustable top

FFL

Siphonic bell trap

Neoprene seal

Short make-up piece

2 No. 45° bends

100 Ø CL drain

Rodding Point system gully

relevant to one-piece chamber branches or chamber bases that are factory formed. Branches from individual gullies and sanitary appliances may be square, but any branch that may run more than a proportional depth of 0.3 (30% full) should be connected into the main stream with a 45 degree baron bend or 3/4 slipper bend, plus a long radius bend where necessary to minimise turbulence.

A relatively new development in the design of UK drainage systems is the adoption of the 'Rodding Point System', which minimises the need for manholes or inspection chambers within a building. Figure 27 shows a 'traditional' UK design, and the same system designed using the rodding point principles. Both systems comply with Building Regulations (approved Document H) and BSEN 752 Parts 1-7, and are designed so that every aspect of the system is roddable. It is imprtant when designing a rodding point system to ensure that the maximum spacings of access points as given in the Building Regulations (Approved Document H) and BSEN 752 Parts 1-7 are observed, and also that a roddable gully is used. Table 21 shows the maximum spacing of access points. Figure 28 shows a rodding point system gully against a traditional UK waste gully, which is not truly roddable. The rodding point system gully, commonly known as a syphon bell gully is becoming more commonly available within the UK from both European and British manufacturers.

All drainage systems should be designed to flow at a constant velocity. Where this cannot be achieved, the method of dealing with the problem will depend upon the capacity of the downstream receiving sewer under flood conditions.

Some sewers have spare capacity, in which case a gradual rise or fall in the system velocity is relatively unimportant. Some sewers surcharge under storm conditions and where this situation occurs, the local authority may require the design and installation of flow restrictors and temporary storage/retention of flood waters.

If it is not possible or economic to achieve sufficient storage of storm water in the drain system, then suitable areas for surface flooding, (for surface water drainage only) such as car parks or flood plains should be considered. For guidance on Sustainable Urban Drainage Systems, refer to CIRIA guidelines.

Wherever possible, steep drain gradients should be avoided. Most difficult site conditions can be overcome with backdrops, allow the horizontal drain to flow at an acceptable velocity and the increased velocity down the backdrop can be attenuated at the bottom of the drop. In hilly districts it is sometimes necessary to use ramp drains.

Under storm conditions, the bottom of the sloping drain may become surcharged causing flood water to issue from low level gullies and manholes.

Here again, flow restrictors and temporary retention of flood water at the top of the ramp/s plus the sealing of low level manholes can be used to prevent or reduce the surface flooding of low lying areas, both for new and existing systems.

All drainage systems should be designed using an appropriate method. For small sites and individual buildings long hand calculations are invariably used. However, larger drainage schemes may be calculated using computer programs and cross checked by a few long hand calculations.

## Pipe gradients

The maximum flow rate in a drain occurs at a proportional depth of 82 to 83%. Any rise in water level above this figure will cause increased frictional resistance, a hydraulic jump and a reduced flow rate, which will tend to maintain the full surcharge condition.

The maximum depth of flow for stormwater in estate drainage generally should not exceed 75%. This will allow for changes in site development, the ingress of ground water, and a margin to allow the free ventilation of the system and spare capacity for infrequent peak storms.

Gradients and velocities should be kept low or reduced over the total length, and this will tend to increase the drain sizes, volume and transitional capacity/storage of the system. However, any continuous velocity should theoretically not be lower than 0.75m/s to maintain self cleansing. There is no practical limit to maximum velocity, but it is widely accepted that 3.6 metres/second should not be exceeded.

The popular myth of a self cleansing velocity in foul drains, was arbitrarily set in the early Victorian era, when the manufacturing standards and quality of materials was much lower than it is today. National standards of workmanship and supervision had not been established and much drainage work was being done for the first time, with limited and less accurate hand calculated hydraulic formula.

Modern drain pipes, manufactured from plastics, vitrified clay and spun iron are made in long straight lengths. All have true and smooth bores, which provide a considerable improvement by comparison to their predecessors, manufactured prior to the 1950's.

This improvement in standards and quality allow drain gradients to be reduced whilst still maintaining an adequate velocity at the calculated depth of flow.

Discharges in branch drains are intermittent and normally start in the form of a short wave, close to the bottom of the stack or appliance, such as from a WC. As the wave travels down the branch drain, the initial vertical discharge energy is lost and the depth of flow flattens out, this attenuation occurs because at all normal gradients, the top of the wave travels faster than the water in contact with the invert, thus leveling out the flow. Unless there is a continuous discharge of water to maintain the hydraulic depth of flow, it is not possible to achieve a constant velocity. As the numbers of discharges from branches and buildings increase, so does the diversity of use. This, together with an extended time of travel, creates the average and peak dry weather flows found in the main public sewers.

Table 22 which is taken from the Approved Document H to the Building Regulations 2002 for England and Wales, shows a very simple way of sizing a scheme for small drainage systems, provided the maximum capacities are not exceeded.

*Table 22* Recommended minimum gradients for foul drains

| Peak flow (litres/sec) | Pipe size (mm) | Minimum gradient (1 in ...) | Maximum capacity (litres/sec) |
|---|---|---|---|
| <1 | 75 | 1:40 | 4.1 |
| | 100 | 1:40 | 9.2 |
| >1 | 75 | 1:80 | 2.8 |
| | 100 | 1:80* | 6.3 |
| | 150 | 1:150§ | 15.0 |

*\* Minimum of 1 WC*
*§ Minimum of 5 WCs*

Drainage systems should be designed to provide constant or gradually changing velocities at the design proportional depth of flow. With the exception of backdrops and ramps, all designs should avoid marked changes in velocity from one section of drain to another.

Branch drains carrying low volume intermittent flows from individual fittings and stacks should be laid to steeper gradients than main drains that carry the discharge from multiple stacks and buildings. The reasoning behind this approach is extended as follows:

1.	Main surface water drains may be laid at a gradient equal to their diameter in millimeters e.g. 100% gradient = 300mm diameter drain laid at a gradient of 1:300.

*Table 23*

| Diameter (mm) | Surface water drains | | Foul drains | |
|---|---|---|---|---|
| | Main drain 100% gradient | Branch drain 50% gradient | Main drain 80% gradient | Branch drain 40% gradient |
| 75 | 1:75 | 1:35 | 1:60 | 1:30 |
| 100 | 1:100 | 1:50 | 1:80 | 1:40 |
| 150 | 1:150 | 1:75 | 1:120 | 1:60 |
| 225 | 1:225 | 1:110 | 1:180 | 1:90 |
| 300 | 1:300 | 1:150 | 1:240 | 1:120 |

2. alternatively, main foul drains may be laid at a gradient equal to 80% of their diameter, e.g. 300mm diameter, drain laid at a gradient of 1:240.

3. Branch drains with low flow rates may be laid at 50% of their respective main drain gradients as follows in Table 23.

The above schedules is an example of what may be applied to a relatively flat site; other percentage values may be usefully applied to suit different site surface slopes.

## Discharge units

The Water Regulations make provision for water savings in the UK particularly with WCs and urinals.

A number of other countries, such as the USA, Germany, Japan, Mexico, Africa, Asia and some Scandinavian counties have for some years, been using 3 and 4 litre low volume designs for matched pans and cisterns. The UK now has a maximum flush volume of 6 litres for any new WC suite. Metered water supplies are also required for all new connections and there is a general move towards compulsory metering for all premises as a result of the water shortages experienced in recent years.

The general trend in the volume of water used by appliances both in the UK and abroad has been downwards and it is now more important not to oversize foul drains.

The new less wasteful low volume flush designs will make it possible to utilise the capacity of existing drainage systems more efficiently and the demand for new sewage treatment works may be reduced. The overall effect should make substantial savings to water supply, treatment and disposal.

## Surface water flows

The method adopted for the assessment of the peak discharge flowrate of surface water from a building development will vary according to the area and type of development. For areas which require a main surface water drain up to 200m in length, a unifrom rate of rainfall intensity may be adopted. A rate of 50mm/h is commonly used for such areas, but higher rates may be applicable in specific circumstances and reference should be made to BS EN 12056 in these cases.

The whole of the rainfall on impervious areas should be assumed to reach the drains. The impervious areas should include the horizontal projection of the roof areas, paved areas connected to the drainage system and half the area of the exposed vertical face of tower buildings. Unpaved areas are generally assumed not to contribute.

For larger areas when a design based on a uniform rate of rainfall intensity is not appropriate, the use of the 'Wallingford Rational' method for the design of storm sewers is recommended and reference should be made to BS EN 752 Parts 1-7 and BS EN 12056-3 for further guidance.

For surface water drains where larger quantities of grit are liable to be carried into the drain or sewer, the minimum velocity of flow should be 0.75m/s as for foul drains and sewers.

However, as a guide for systems where grit is not anticipated to be a problem, then an absolute minimum flow rate of 0.3m/s should be allowed for in order to avoid possible obstruction due to the build up of solid matter not being carried along by the water, particularly at low depths of flow.

## Drainage pipe sizing calculations

In calculating pipe sizes for drainage installations, it is essential to record in a clear and concise manner all factors which determine the selected pipe size for the section of the drainage installation under consideration. The calculations should be recorded in an orderly manner, so that arithmetical checks can be easily made at the completion of the pipe sizing exercise, to enable the implication of subsequent site variations to be assessed, and modifications to the drainage design made where necessary; and finally to provide a source of design information for the designer or the building user, which can be filed for future reference.

Design information which it is necessary to record, includes gradients, maximum and minimum flow rates, velocities and depths of flow together with the invert levels at predetermined points.

## Gravity flow pipe design charts

Charts for the design of circular pipes have been available from various sources for many years and have been used, with varying degrees of success to design pipes running part full under gravity. Graphs can overcome the difficulties encountered with the older style charts, making it possible to read velocity and flow rate directly from a single chart, for all depths of flow.

## Theory

Each chart has has been prepared for a particular combination of pipe diameter (D) and roughness (K) and is composed of two familites of curves (S and Q) superimposed on a pair of orthogonal axes. The intersection of these curves represents the relationship between flow rate (Q), pipe gradient (S), proportional depth of flow (d/D) and flow velocity.

The Colebrook-White equation has been selected to represent gradient (S) curves because of its sound basis in both theory and experimentation.

$$V = -2\sqrt{(2gs\psi D)}\log\left[\frac{K_s}{3.7\psi D} + \frac{\sqrt{2.51\nu}}{\psi D\sqrt{(2gs\psi D)}}\right]$$

where $\nu$ = kinematic viscosity and g = gravitational acceleration

In this form of the equation, D has been modified by a correction factor ($\psi$) to account for depths of flow less than full. This factor is only dependent on the geometry of flow, and is defined in terms of the angle ($\theta$) subtended at the pipe centre by the free water surface.

$$\psi^2\frac{\theta - \sin\theta}{\theta} \text{ where } \theta = 2\cos^{-1}\left(\frac{1-2d}{D}\right)$$

The continuity equation forms the basis of the flow (Q-) curves which, when modified for gravity flow, can be written as:

$$v = \frac{8Q}{\sqrt{\theta}D^2}$$

**Example 1**

It is estimated that a new housing development will produce daily peak foul sewage flow of 52l/sec. Determine the pipe size and minimum gradient required to carry this flow whilst ensuring that a velocity of 0.76m/sec is achieved and that a proportional depth of 0.75 is not exceeded. Site conditions dictate that the maximum grade available is 1:40 and the ground surface falls at 1:240. Confirm that a satisfactory velocity is also achieved before completion of the development when the flow is 10 l/sec.

Assume $K_s$ = 1.5mm

*Step 1*

Select a design chart by choosing:

a. A pipe roughness (e.g. $K_s$ = 1.5mm) relevant to this application

b. A pipe diameter (e.g. D=250mm) which can carry the design flow (Q). Q must lie within the range of flows on the right hand side of the chart.

*Step 2*

Sketch on the limiting factors:

a. Minimum self-cleansing velocity (V) e.g. 0.76m/sec.

b. Maximum proportional depth of flow (d/D) e.g. 0.75

c. Maximum available fall (e.g. 1:40)

d. Minimum available fall (e.g. 1:240).

This will define the allowable gradient 'window' (shown shaded in Graph 5) within which all combinations of flow and gradient satisfy the constraints listed above.

*Step 3*

Locate the actual design flow Q-curve (e.g. 52 l/sec) and verify that it passes through the 'window'. If it does not change the pipe diameter and go to Step (1).

*Step 4*

Read along the Q-curve and:

a. Note the point where it leaves the 'window'

b. Locate the gradient S-curve which intersects it at this point (e.g. 1:110). This value represents the minimum gradient at which the pipe can be laid whilst satisfying the velocity and proportional depth constraints given in Step (2).

Also read-off for this flow and grade:

c. Proportional depth (e.g. 0.75)

d. Velocity (e.g. 1.32m/sec).

*Step 5*

For other flows in a pipe laid at the gradient found in Step (4ii) (e.g. 1:110).

a. Locate and read along the new Q-curve (e.g. 10l/sec) to the intersection with the chosen S-curve

  Read off:

b. Proportional depth (e.g.0.28)

c. Velocity (e.g. 0.89).

*NOTES*
*It is recommended that a value of K = 0.6 is used when designing stormwater drains and K = 1.5 is used for foul drains.*

*For a fuller account of the theory, more examples and a range of forty-four different two colour charts, the reader is referred to the reference below. Graphs 1 to 5 have been reproduced by permission of the authors and publishers; Butler D and Pinkerton B.R.C. 'Gravity flow pipe design charts', Thomas Telford Limited 1987.*

*Graph 1* 100mm diameter pipe – gravity flow ($K_2 = 0.6$)

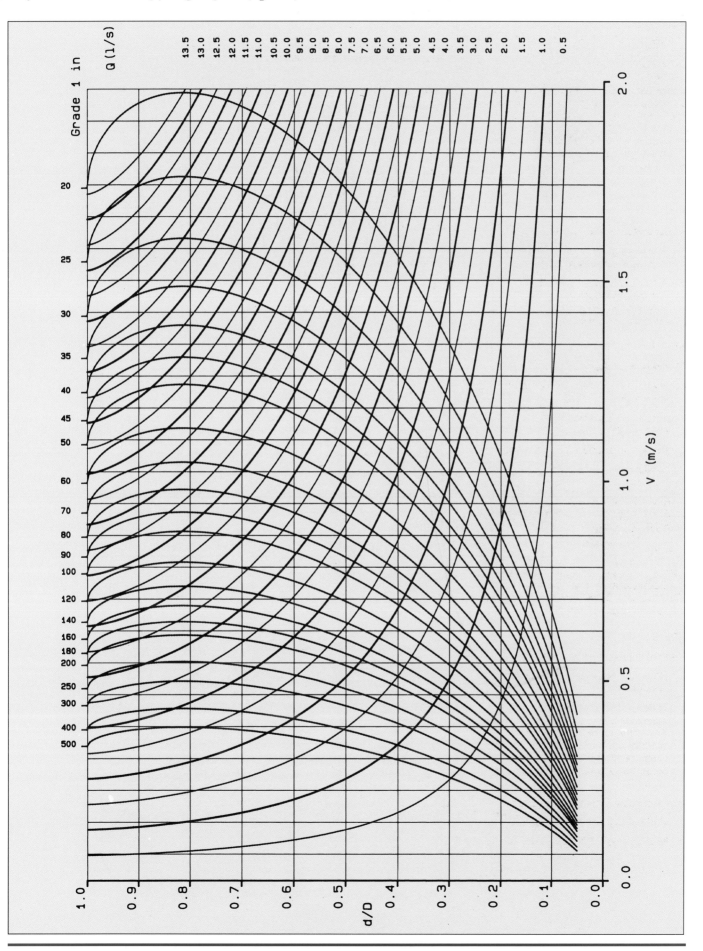

*Graph 2*  *100mm diameter pipe – gravity flow ($K_2 = 1.5$)*

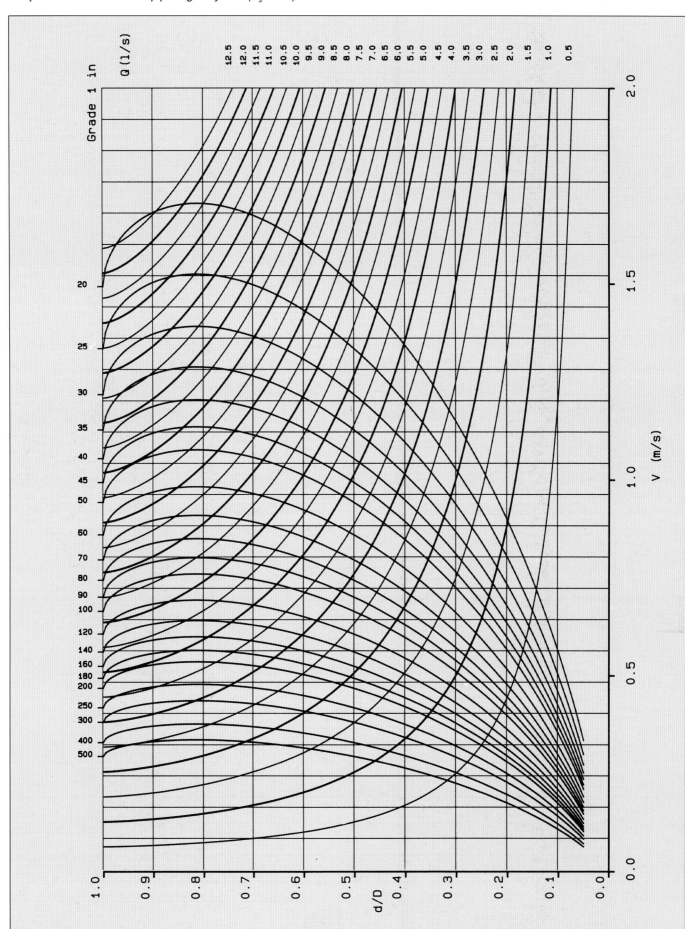

*Graph 3* *150mm diameter pipe – gravity flow (K₂ = 0.6)*

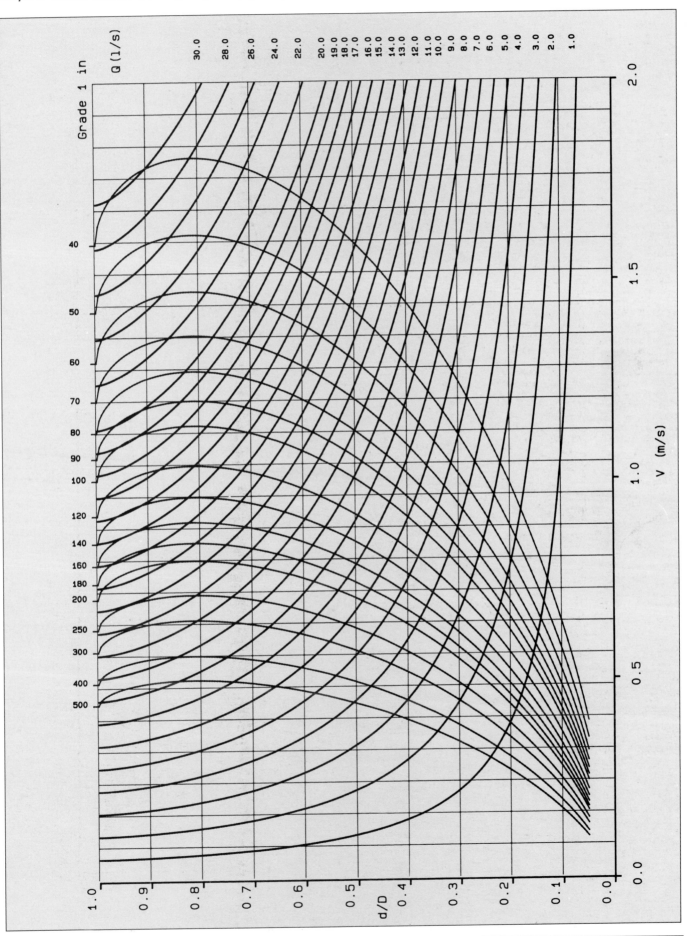

*Graph 4* *150mm diameter pipe – gravity flow (K$_2$ = 1.5)*

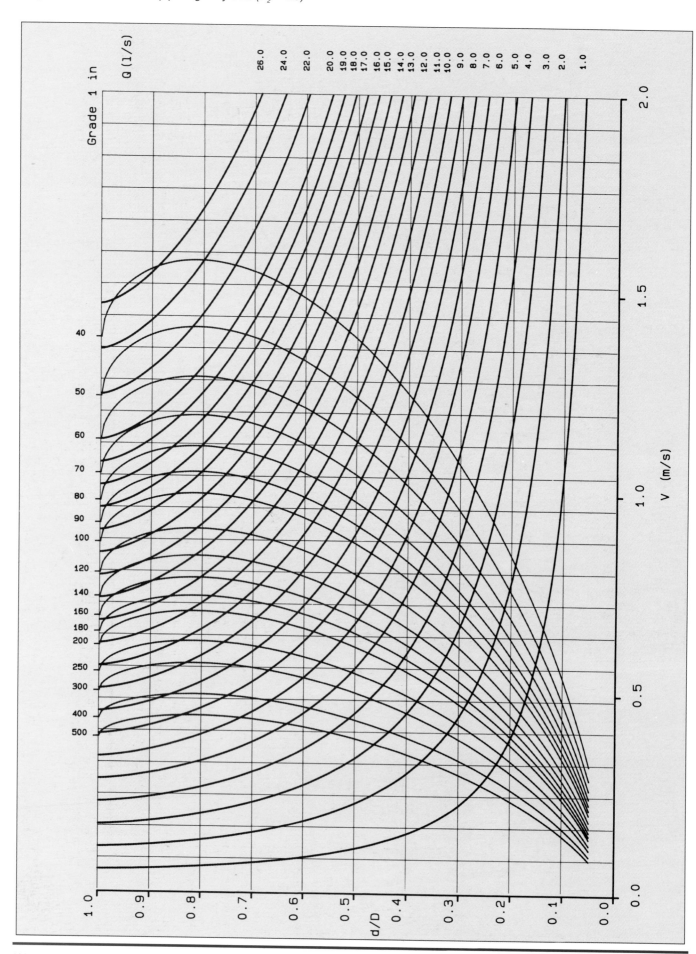

*Graph 5* 250mm diameter pipe – gravity flow ($K_2 = 1.5$)

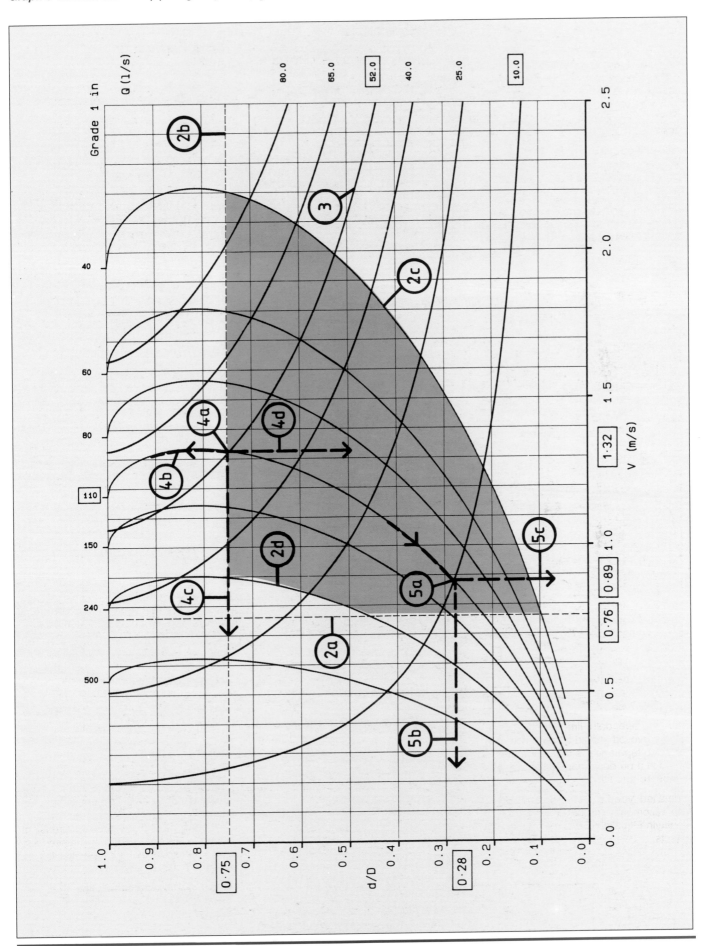

# Below ground drain renovation

The type of renovation will be dependent on the extent of defects, the means of access, usage of the drain and the type of effluent being discharged.

Where a drain has been cracked for some time, the egress of water from the cracked pipe will wash away the bedding material surrounding the drain, creating a void which could lead to the collapse of the pipe.

In order to ascertain the condition of a drain, it will be necessary to carry out a Closed Circuit Television (CCTV) Survey.

## Closed circuit television survey

Although not in itself a method of renovation, the use of CCTV is vital to establish the need for and to monitor all of the renovation works, to ensure, for example, that the pressure jet cleaning and de-scaling has been fully completed and all the debris removed from the drain.

In some operations, such as root cutting and lining, a CCTV camera is used within the drain to monitor the works as they are carried out.

With drains from 100mm to 300mm diameter, the camera is mounted on a stainless steel skid, aligned in the centre of the drain, to produce a clear view of the complete circumference of the pipe. This is then winched through the drain at a rate of approximately 6 metres per minute.

Drains with a larger diameter are surveyed by mounting the camera on a remote controlled electrically operated tractor unit linked to the CCTV camera operator.

Where required, the CCTV survey can be recorded on video tape, which should be in colour VHS format (standard play).

The meterage, date, time and drain being surveyed should be recorded on the video tape and the tape should be stored in a purpose made folder, numbered and titled.

A detailed typed survey report should also accompany the CCTV survey identifying the position and extent of all defects.

# Methods of renovation

## High pressure water jet-cleaning

Water is pumped under pressure through a flexible hose to a steel nozzle, producing a backwards umbrella-shaped jet. This has the effect of pulling the hose through the drain and forcing the flow of water carrying any debris back along the pipe.

Jet cleaning is carried out by feeding the hose into the drain in an upstream direction. The hose is then pulled back in stages and the resulting debris removed.

For pipes between 100mm and 300mm, the high pressure water jetting equipment will be trailer-mounted with a 20mm hose delivering water at pressure. Pressures should be dependent on the type of jet and the material and condition of the sewer.

Larger diameter drains and those that are heavily silted or blocked with solid debris require a larger volume of water. This cannot be provided by a trailer-mounted unit and so a lorry tanker unit is required. The hose would be larger – up to 30mm diameter and would deliver 140 bar – 750 bar with volumes of 0.5-1.5 l/sec.

## De-scaling

In vitrified clay drains, scale can form, particularly at joints, creating a rough surface where blockages can occur.

Cast iron drains develop heavy scale and corrosion, particularly where there are only low flows.

The same equipment and procedures are used in de-scaling as for pressure jet cleaning. However, a different shape jet nozzle is used and lower flow rates are required.

For de-scaling, the nozzle is designed to produce very fine water jets at 90° to the hose.

As the water flows through the jets, the nozzle rotates to allow the water jets to be directed to the complete circumference of the pipe.

The scale is cut away from the walls of the drain by the water pressure.

Following the de-scaling operation, it is then necessary to pressure jet clean the drain to remove the resulting debris.

There is electro mechanical equipment available for de-scaling works. However,

it is not commonly used on below ground drainage pipework.

## Root cutting

A common problem, particularly in older vitrified clay drains with sand and cement joints, is the ingress of plant and tree roots.

The roots can enter the drain through very fine cracks and, once in the drain, can expand and multiply, often blocking the drain completely.

The process and equipment for cutting and removing roots from the drain are as for de-scaling. However, the process can be very time consuming, as the roots are often difficult to clear from the drain and only small sections of drain can be cut and cleared at a time. Once all of the roots have been cut and removed, the drain will require lining to prevent the roots growing back into the drain.

## Trenchless replacement

This method, using a system of 'pipe bursting', can be considered when the condition of a drain is such that it cannot be repaired, but the cost or disruption caused by traditional replacement is not acceptable.

For example, a vitrified clay drain, which has partly collapsed, passing under a busy access way or road.

Because of its condition, the drain could not be internally lined and the cost and disruption associated with traditional excavation and replacement would be prohibitive.

In this situation, the defective drain can be replaced by inserting an expanding mandrill, which forces the existing pipe outwards allowing a new pipe to be threaded into position.

Although termed as being 'trenchless', this system does require an excavation between 1000mm × 800mm and 2500mm × 1500mm, depending on the size of the pipe.

Where there is an available manhole, an excavation is not always required, as the equipment can be located with the manhole.

The steel mandrill is forced into the drain and expanded using compressed air. As the mandrill is moved along the drain, new sections of pipe manufactured from concrete, clay or plastic are pushed into place to follow the line of the existing drain.

Where a drain has connecting branches, these have to be replaced by traditional excavation.

# Lining

There are several types of liner, all of which reduce the bore of the existing drain.

The minor reduction in bore, between 10mm and 25mm depending on the size of the pipe and type of liner, does not adversely affect the flow characteristics, which are greatly improved by the smooth bore of the liner.

Each lining method has advantages and disadvantages, which must be considered for the application at hand.

## Cement lining

This is the oldest form of drain lining and has been used successfully for about 40 years.

Originally used with ordinary Portland cement, applications today are more common using a range of specially produced quick drying resin based cement compounds.

This type of lining is only suitable for rigid drain installations where there is no anticipated movement.

The method of application is by pulling two loose rubber pistons, slightly smaller in diameter than the drain, filled with the mixed cement through the drain. The pressure exterted by the piston at the front pushes the cement in the pipe and leaves a thin lining all around the pipe.

To provide a smooth internal lining with all cracks etc. filled, it is usually necessary to repeat this process 3 or 4 times.

Where there are branches connecting to the drain being lined, these will have to be thoroughly cleaned following this type of lining operation to ensure they are clear of any cement debris.

## Rigid plastic liners

Made from high density polyethylene or polyolefin polymer based materials, with screw and socketed joints.

These liners are winched into the drain, providing a new smooth bore, although of reduced diameter.

In order to pull this type of liner through a drain, a tolerance should be allowed in sizing to ensure that the liner can pass through the drain without becoming stuck on open joints or in a section of slightly non-uniform pipe.

Once in place, the annular space between the new liner and the drain has to be sealed to prevent movement. This is carried out by pumping a weak cement grout.

Where the existing drain is found to be oversized, for example where the use of a building has changed, this type of lining system is very effective and there is a range of liner diameters from 75mm to 600mm.

This type of lining system is ideally suited where flexibility is required and where aggressive discharges are anticipated.

Where there are connecting branches, these have to be excavated and connected to the new liner with a purpose made branch section.

# Grouting

This is the term used for sealing cracks or open joints in a drain with an aqueous compound.

There are a number of different products on the market. However, there are two main types of grout:

## Cement

This is applied in the same way as the cement lining, using larger pistons so that the cracks and gaps are filled, but a lining is not left in the pipe.

Any movement in the pipe will result on the repaired cracks opening up. Therefore, this system should only be considered where no possible movement is anticipated.

This system does have a good resistance to chemical attack. However, branch connections cannot be repaired by this method, as access is required from both ends of the drain.

## Resin

Resin compounds used for grouting in drain renovation works were originally developed for use in stabilising ground in mining and excavations and in controlling the flow of ground water.

The use of these resins has been adapted and they have been in use for drain renovation works for over 20 years.

*Figure 29 Cement and resin grouting*

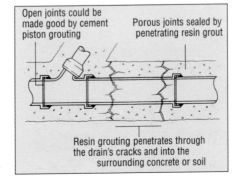

Open joints could be made good by cement piston grouting

Porous joints sealed by penetrating resin grout

Resin grouting penetrates through the drain's cracks and into the surrounding concrete or soil

There is a wide range of products available, each with a slightly different chemical make up.

However, there are two main generic types, both of which have the same qualities are widely used in grouting defective drains.

The resin produced with a mixture of polyphenolic vegetable extract and paraformandehyde or from other organic monomers is delivered to site in a dry powder form.

This is then mixed with water at a concentration of 20-22% depending on the type of product used and the ambient temperature.

The drain to be grouted is thoroughly cleaned and sealed at its lowest point and the aqueous resin grout is pumped into the drain and filled through a standpipe to produce a static head pressure of 1.5m above the highest point.

Under pressure, the aqueous resin grout is forced into any cracks or open joints in the drain.

Due to its viscosity, the resin grout passes through any crack and permeates the surrounding ground.

As the resin grout passes through any cracks, voids in the surrounding bedding material are filled and replaced with the grout.

When the level in the standpipe has stabilised, the grout is left to cure for between 30 minutes and 90 minutes depending on the resin product and the ground temperature.

When fully cured, the resin forms a solid flexible gel, which is impervious to water.

Before the resin becomes fully cured, which takes between 2 and 3 hours, the drain plug should be taken out and the surplus resin within the pipe pumped out and disposed of.

After allowing the remaining resin to cure fully, the drain should then be pressure jet cleaned to remove any surplus resin gel from the walls of the pipe.

Being flexible, the grouted drain is not adversely affected by movement. However, where the drain carries aggressive or chemical waste, the selection of the resin material must be carefully considered.

The life of the resin grout for drainage renovation is not guaranteed beyond 15 years, as tests beyond this period have not yet been carried out.

However, from the research carried out on these resin materials where they have been used to stabilise ground water, no deterioration has been found after periods of 20-30 years.

# Continuous fibre liners

These consist of a felt or polyester sleeve which is impregnated with a hardening resin.

The sleeve, which is sized to suit the diameter of the drain, is winched into the drain and filled with water, pushing the liner out to the wall of the drain.

Some types of liner require the water to be heated to allow the resin to harden. However, this has always been difficult and time consuming and, with the advent of more advanced resin formulae, this system is not as often used.

Once in position and filled with water to a static head of between 3m and 6m, the liner is left to cure for between 1 and 2 hours depending on the weather conditions.

When the liner is set, the ends are trimmed and sealed.

This type of liner provides a smooth solid wall to the drain and reduces the bore by only 10-15mm.

Being completely flexible when installed, the liner can be used in drains that are not true to line or bore.

The liner adheres to the wall of the drain and is very secure. Once fully cured, the drain will remain relatively flexible, with a tolerance of ±2° per metre.

This type of system is resistant to a large range of chemicals. However, a detailed check of the manufacturer's chemical resistance chart for the type of liner considered should be made where the discharge is aggressive or likely to contain high levels of chemical waste.

Although it is possible to use this type of system to line a drain and reduce the bore, great care is required in the installation to avoid undulation of the invert and flotation during grouting.

*Figure 30  Insertion of continuous fibre liner*

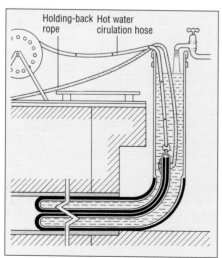

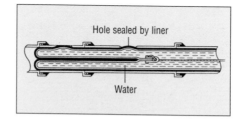

*Figure 31  Typical fibre liner*

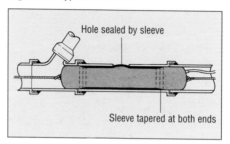

*Figure 32  Continuous fibre liner*

Where this type of liner is used to provide a considerably reduced bore to the drain, the installation should be as before. However, prior to releasing the water, the annular space should be filled by pumping with grout. Due to the high temperatures created by cement based grouting materials due to exothermic reaction, a resin or clay based compound should be used.

Where there are connecting branches, the liner has to be cut internally after curing by a remote controlled tractor unit.

# Sectional fibre liners

These are of the same material as the continuous fibre liners above. However, they are used in short lengths of 300mm to 1500mm to deal with isolated defects in a drain where a continuous liner is not required.

The liner is winched into position on an inflatable carrier tube and its location confirmed by CCTV.

The carrier tube is then inflated, pushing the liner onto the wall of the pipe.

Once cured, the carrier tube is deflated and removed, leaving the liner in place.

To improve the sewers hydraulic gradient, a vitrified channel is bedded onto the existing brick invert and benched both sides would provide a new clean, efficient, self cleansing sewer invert.

Where the general condition of a brick sewer is poor, glass reinforced plastic sewer liners are available for installing into the sewer in one piece sections, up to 6m long.

The annular gap between the new section and existing brickwork is pressure grouted to complete the job.

# Rainwater systems

This section has been produced using charts and tables as an alternative to the British Standards. Although most of the data used is from BS 6367, similar results will be obtained by using BS 12056-3.

The flow chart (See Figure 33) is designed to suggest appropriate routes for the various situtations.

## Method of design

The method of design is based on the following assumptions:

a.  The gutter is normally level

b.  The gutter has a uniform cross-sectional shape

c.  The outlets are large enough to allow the gutter to discharge freely.

An alternative is the Wyly-Eaton equation in BS EN 12056.

## Sources of data

a.  Data and formulae for rainfall intensities are from BS 6367

b.  Formulae used for production of gutter sizing nomograms are from BS 6367

c.  Actual flow rates for grated roof outlets should be obtained from the manufacturers

d.  Flow rates for ungrated outlets are based on Weir formula

e.  The rainwater downpipe sizing chart is based on the formula:

$$q = Kd^{8/3}$$

resulting from work carried out by BRE and the US National Standards Bureau, where:

q = discharge capacity in litres/sec

d = stack diameter in mm

K (1/5 full) = $2.1 \times 10^{-5}$

K (1/4 full) = $3.2 \times 10^{-5}$

K (1/3 full) = $5.2 \times 10^{-5}$

The following two examples are for information purposes only, giving a step-by-step guide through the calculation procedure.

*Figure 33* Flow chart showing calculation procedure

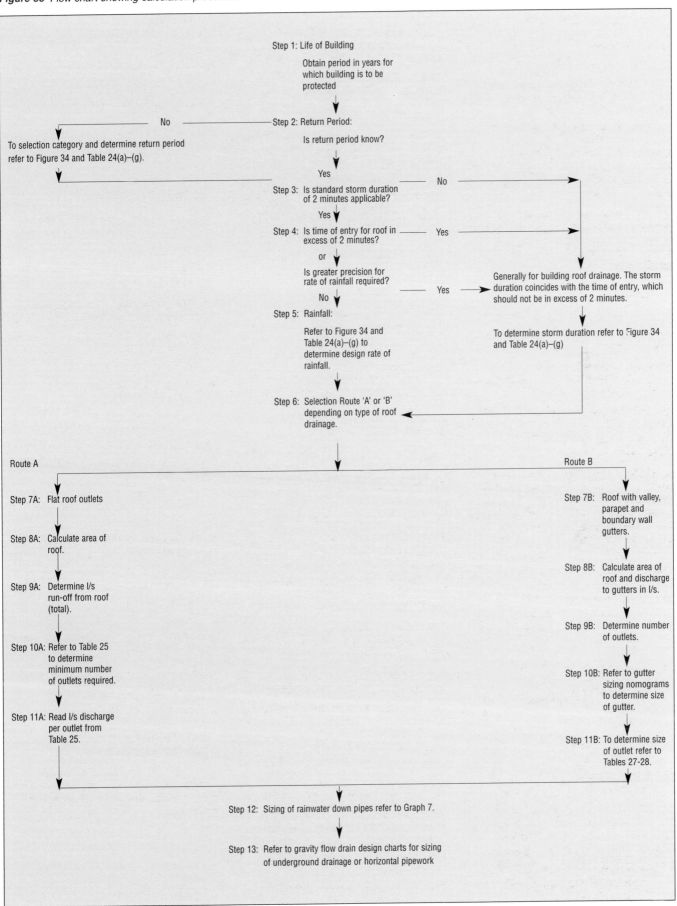

### Example 1: Route A – flat roof

A typical spec office block of approximate plan dimensions of 50m × 20m sited in Newcastle. The expected life of the building is 40 years and it has been decided to allow for a 60 years period.

The Architect has specified a flat roof, asphalt finish with a parapet around the perimeter of the roof.

*Step 1:* Life of building    40 years

*Step 2:* Yes    60 years

*Step 3:* Yes    2 min M5

*Step 4:* No

*Step 5:* Location of building – Newcastle

Design rate of rainfall

By reference to the UK rainfall map. Figure 34, we can see that the site of our building (Newcastle) is adjacent to contour line D.

We now refer to Table 24(d), from which we can determine that, for a 60 year return period with a 2 minute duration rainfall, the required design intensity is 150mm per hour.

*Step 6/7*

In this example we have an upstand flat roof with grated rainwater outlets. Therefore we follow Route 'A' through the guide.

*Step 8A*

Determine area of roof and flow rate in litres per second from the roof. We are assuming in this example that the area of roof to be drained is the same as the plan area. i.e. no overhangs.

Area of roof    A    =    length × width

Therefore    A    =    50m × 20m

    =    1000m²

*Step 9A*

Total run off from roof in litres per second.

Now from Step 5 we know that the design intensity is 150mm/hr (0.15m/hr).

So flow rate    =    Area × intensity

        (in metres)

Therefore,

flow rate    =    1000m² × 0.15m/hr

    =    150m³/hr or 41.66l/sec

*Step 10A*

Select type of outlet

For installation reasons a 100mm diameter vertical grated type outlet Type 17B is selected.

Details of this outlet are to be found in Table 25.

From this Table we can determine the discharge rate in litres per second that the chosen outlet is capable of receiving at a given head. So calculating the number of outlets required to drain the roof of the building:

Number of outlets =

$$\frac{\text{Total run-off in litres per second (from step 9)}}{\text{litres per second discharge per outlet}}$$

An outlet has been chosen, having a head of 30mm over the outlet. The roof is protected with an asphalt upstand which is capable of containing at least 60mm head over the outlet without risk of damage to the building.

Therefore number of outlets = $\dfrac{41.66}{2.92}$ l/sec

Therefore 14 outlets required.

*Step 11A*

Flow rate per outlet is 2.92 litres per second (from Table 25)

*Step 12*

To determine diameter of rainwater pipes. We have assumed for the purpose of this exercise that there is one outlet per rainwater downpipe.

Therefore flow down any one pipe is 2.92 litres per second.

By reference to Graph 8, it can be seen that a 100mm diameter pipe flowing 1/5 full (curve A) is capable of receiving 4.2 litres per second and is therefore satisfactory.

*Step 13*

Horizontal pipework should be sized using underground gravity flow charts.

When using high intensities for roof areas the flow rates should only be carried through to the branch drains immediately outside drainage system.

*NOTE*
*Flow rates for roof outlets should be obtained from manufacturers, as these are usually higher than the BS standard types listed due to their type of design and construction.*

### Example 2: Route B – valley gutter

Design and size roof drainage for a large warehouse with pitched roof and valley gutters.

The warehouse is to be located in Swindon and is to be designed for a 40 year building life, with a high degree of confidence that the building will be protected from rainwater for the duration of its life.

The roof construction is to be steeply pitched roof with valley gutters.

*Step 1*

Life span of building: 40 years

Sensitive warehouse with steeply pitched roof and valley gutter.

*Step 2*

Return period. This is not known and has therefore to be determined. Refer to Table 26.

Return period, T = 'C' factor × life of building

Selecting category 3 from Table 26.

'C' factor is 4.5

Life of building is: 40 years

Therefore T = 4.5 × 40 years

    = 180 years.

*Step 3*

Is standard storm duration of 2 minutes applicable?

*Step 4*

No: storm duration (time of entry) is required to be 1 minute.

*Step 5*

To determine the rainfall design intensity:

Referring to Figure 34, locating the building on the map of UK, Swindon lies on contour F. This corresponds with Table 24(f) and shows that, for a storm duration of 1 minute with a return period of 180 years, the design rainfall intensity is 275mm per hour (0.275m/hr).

*Step 6/7*

Type of roof drainage

Steeply pitched roof with valley gutters, follow Route 'B' (trapezoidal Gutter).

*Step 8B*

Plan area of roof and discharge to gutter.

Plan area of roof draining into each valley gutter = 1000m²

Flow rate in litres per second to the gutter:

= area of roof × design rainfall intensity (Step 3)

= 1000m² × 0.275 m/hr

= 275m³/hr

$$= \frac{275000}{3600} \text{ l/hour}$$

= 76 l/s (run-off per second per length of gutter)

*Step 9B*

Determine number of outlets and discharge in litres per second per outlet:

Number of outlets provisionally determined by potential stack location (one per outlet).

Therefore number selected: 8

Therefore flow rate per outlet

$$= \frac{\text{total flow rate}}{\text{number of outlets}}$$

$$= \frac{76}{8} \text{ l/s}$$

$$= 10 \text{ l/s}$$

approximately (5 l/s from each length of gutter)

*Step 10B*

Determine size of gutter:

Known criteria:

1. Gutter sole to be suitable for foot traffic, therefore minimum width of sole to be 300mm.

2. Drainage (Length of gutter 7.0 metres) (assuming equal outlet centres).

Now refer to respective nomogram; in this exercise we are using trapezoidal gutters with a 1.1 side slope.

Reading from gutter sizing nomogram, Graph 9 where

yc  = 29mm (critical depth)

yuf = 63mm (depth upstream of gutter – high point of water)

Freeboard must be added to yuf; this should be a minimum of 2/5ths of the maximum depth of flow (yuf) subject to a minimum of 25mm.

Therefore freeboard = 25mm (minimum)

So, total depth of gutter is, yuf + freeboard

= 63mm = 25mm

= 88mm

Details of roof construction and weathering might dictate that a greater overall depth of gutter is required.

For added safety overflow pipes or weirs should be installed at either end of the gutter as a minimum, preferably between each pair of outlets.

For the gutter to discharge freely, the outlet should be ungrated and of not less than three quarters of the width of the gutter. It may not be possible to select an outlet to conform with this, therefore we must alternatively construct a box receiver at the outlet. Box receivers should be the width of the gutter and the depth should not less than H + 25mm, where H = head of water over outlet.

*Step 11B*

Size of rainwater outlet (and depth of box receiver). Having selected a circular un-grated outlet refer to Table 28.

Know criteria:

1. Flow rate per outlet
   = approximately 10l/s

2. Head of water cover outlet to be not more than yc or 29mm (from Step 10).

Referring to Table 28, a 250mm diameter outlet requires a head of water H of 45mm over the outlet to receive a flow rate of 10.06l/s. It is not possible to select a stanadard outlet.

A smaller outlet could be chosen by using a box receiver to give a free discharge, as the outlet would then be less than three quarters of the width of the sole of the gutter.

Selecting a 150mm diameter outlet, the head of water over the outlet, H, is 65mm.

65 + 25mm = 90mm (minimum depth of box receiver)

Plan area of Box receiver would be made up as follows:

Width = Not less than the width of flow in the gutter.

Length = the length of the box for a flow of water from one direction should not be less than (0.75 × depth of gutter). If the flow of water is from both directions, the length of the box should be (1.5 × depth of gutter) minimum.

*Step 12*

Sizing of rainwater downpipes.

Refer to Graph 7.

Know criterion:

1. Flow rate = 10 l/s

A 150mm diameter rainwater downpipe flowing 1/5 full is capable of carrying 10 litres per second.

When using high intensitites for roof areas the flow rates should only be carried through to the branch drains immediately outside the building.

Design flow rates should be reassessed based on the sensitivity of the underground drainage system.

## Design rate of rainfall for varying storm durations and return periods

The following tables should be used as follows:

a. Read from Figure 34 the contour reference for the site location.

   The areas between contour lines on Figure 34 (which correspond with Tables 24(a)–(g) should not be read as having a blanket coverage of rainfall, but as two extreme rates of rainfall that coincide with the contour lines, having a constant graduation from one contour to the other, e.g. Derby is situated mid-way between contours E and F, therefore a judgement must be made between Tables 24(e) and (f).

b. Now read off from the selected table the intensity in mm/hr against the required storm duration and return period.

*Figure 34* *Key to rainfall Tables 24(a) to (g)*

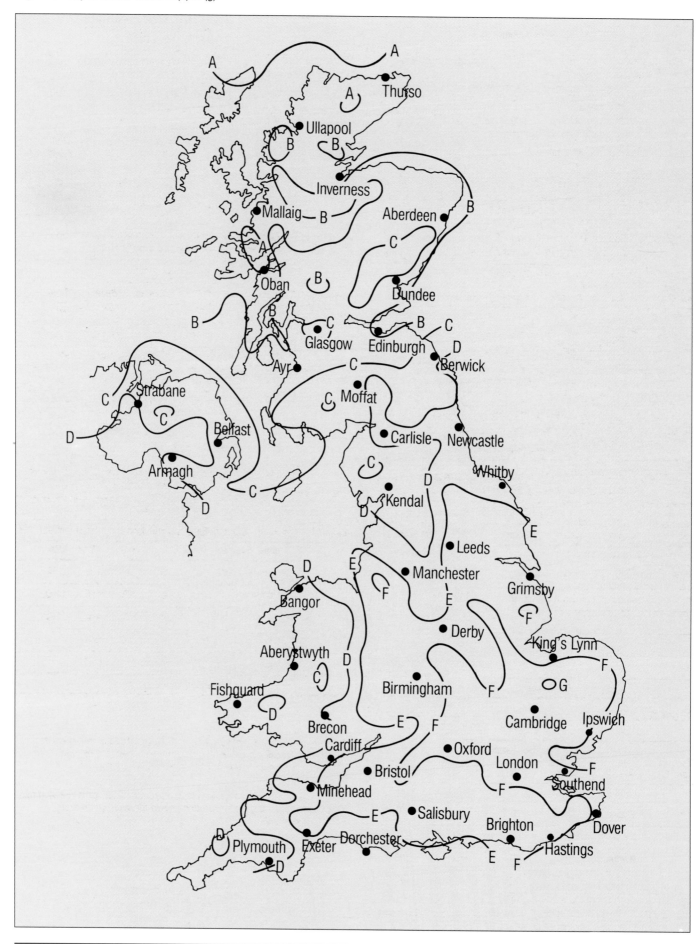

# Series of tables relating rainfall intensity, duration and return period

*Table 24(a)* Rainfall amount 1.5mm in 2 minutes, occuring on average once in 5 years (2 min M5)

| Duration (mins) | Intensity (mm/hr) | | | | |
|---|---|---|---|---|---|
| | 50mm | 75mm | 100mm | 150mm | 225mm |
| 1 | 4.5 | 35 | 185 | 1800 | – |
| 2 | 5.5 | 55 | 300 | 3500 | – |
| 3 | 10 | 175 | 800 | _ | – |
| 4 | 20 | 210 | – | – | – |
| 5 | 40 | 400 | 2000 | – | – |
| 10 | 300 | 300 | – | – | – |
| | Return period (years) | | | | |

*Table 24(b)* Rainfall amount 2mm in 2 minutes, occuring on average once in 5 years (2 min M5)

| Duration (mins) | Intensity (mm/hr) | | | | |
|---|---|---|---|---|---|
| | 50mm | 75mm | 100mm | 150mm | 225mm |
| 1 | 1.75 | 7 | 35 | 325 | 4000 |
| 2 | 2 | 18 | 60 | 850 | – |
| 3 | 4.5 | 35 | 175 | 1800 | – |
| 4 | 7 | 45 | 350 | 3000 | – |
| 5 | 8 | 60 | 750 | 4000 | – |
| 10 | 45 | 450 | 2500 | – | – |
| | Return period (years) | | | | |

*Table 24(c)* Rainfall amount 2.5mm in 2 minutes, occuring on average once in 5 years (2 min M5)

| Duration (mins) | Intensity (mm/hr) | | | | |
|---|---|---|---|---|---|
| | 50mm | 75mm | 100mm | 150mm | 225mm |
| 1 | 7 mths | 3 | 8 | 90 | 1000 |
| 2 | 1.5 | 5 | 20 | 300 | 2500 |
| 3 | 2 | 7.5 | 40 | 500 | – |
| 4 | 3 | 15 | 60 | 800 | – |
| 5 | 4 | 20 | 100 | 1000 | – |
| 10 | 15 | 150 | 700 | – | – |
| | Return period (years) | | | | |

*Table 24(d)* Rainfall amount 3.0mm in 2 minutes, occuring on average once in 5 years (2 min M5)

| Duration (mins) | Intensity (mm/hr) | | | | |
|---|---|---|---|---|---|
| | 50mm | 75mm | 100mm | 150mm | 225mm |
| 1 | 6 mths | 3 | 8 | 35 | 400 |
| 2 | 7 mths | 5 | 20 | 60 | 750 |
| 3 | 8 mths | 7.5 | 40 | 190 | 2000 |
| 4 | 9 mths | 15 | 60 | 350 | 3000 |
| 5 | 2 yrs | 20 | 100 | – | – |
| 10 | 7 yrs | 150 | 700 | – | – |
| | Return period (years) | | | | |

*Table 24(e)* Rainfall amount 3.5mm in 2 minutes, occuring on average once in 5 years (2 min M5)

| Duration (mins) | Intensity (mm/hr) | | | | |
|---|---|---|---|---|---|
| | 50mm | 75mm | 100mm | 150mm | 225mm |
| 1 | 5 mths | 1 | 2 | 20 | 180 |
| 2 | 6 mths | 1.75 | 4.5 | 35 | 320 |
| 3 | 7 mths | 2 | 10 | 60 | 700 |
| 4 | 9 mths | 4 | 12 | 100 | 800 |
| 5 | 10 mths | 4.5 | 18 | 185 | 1800 |
| 10 | 4 yrs | 20 | 95 | 750 | – |
| | Return period (years) | | | | |

*Table 24(f)* Rainfall amount 4mm in 2 minutes, occuring on average once in 5 years (2 min M5)

| Duration (mins) | Intensity (mm/hr) | | | | | |
|---|---|---|---|---|---|---|
| | 50mm | 75mm | 100mm | 150mm | 225mm | 275mm |
| 1 | 4 mths | 17 mths | 1.5 | 7 | 50 | 180 |
| 2 | 5 mths | 8 mths | 2 | 18 | 110 | 450 |
| 3 | 5 mths | 1.75 | 4 | 35 | 250 | 700 |
| 4 | 6 mths | 1.75 | 6 | 40 | 350 | 1000 |
| 5 | 7 mths | 2 | 7.5 | 50 | 650 | – |
| 10 | 2 yrs | 7.5 | 40 | 300 | 3500 | – |
| | Return period (years) | | | | | |

*Table 24(g)* Rainfall amount 4.5mm in 2 minutes, occuring on average once in 5 years (2 min M5)

| Duration (mins) | Intensity (mm/hr) | | | | | | |
|---|---|---|---|---|---|---|---|
| | 50mm | 75mm | 100mm | 150mm | 225mm | 275mm | 300mm |
| 1 | 3 mths | 5 mths | 2 | 7 | 55 | 190 | 350 |
| 2 | 3 mths | 6 mths | 2 | 7 | 55 | 190 | 750 |
| 3 | 4 mths | 1 | 3 | 18 | 120 | 350 | 1100 |
| 4 | 6 mths | 1.5 | 4.5 | 20 | 200 | 450 | 1600 |
| 5 | 6 mths | 2 | 5 | 38 | 250 | 650 | – |
| 10 | 1 yr | 6 | 50 | 200 | 1800 | 1900 | – |
| | Return period (years) | | | | | | |

*For intensities of 225mm per hour and above, alternative means of protecting the building other than increasing the size of rainwater pipes etc. should be considered, such as the provision of overflows or additional freeboard.*

*The average roof should have a duration/run off time not exceeding two minutes. Periods of greater duration shown for information and completeness only.*

*Table 25  Estimated capacities of outlet for flat roofs*

| Outlet type | Table in BS416: 1973 | Outlet size (mm) | Area drained at rainfall intensity of 75mm/h at depth of water above outlet: | | | | | |
|---|---|---|---|---|---|---|---|---|
| | | | 5mm (m²) | 10mm (m²) | 15mm (m²) | 20mm (m²) | 25mm (m²) | 30mm (m²) |
| Square flat grating | 17A | 100 | 17 | 49 | 90 | 135 | 190 | 250 |
| Circular flat grating | 17B | 50, 75 | 4.5 | 12 | 23 | 36 | 51 | 67 |
| | 17B | 75, 90, 100 | 9.6 | 27 | 50 | 77 | 105 | 140 |
| 'D'-shaped flat grating | 17C | 65 | 5.2 | 14 | 27 | 42 | 58 | 77 |
| | 17C | 75 | 5.4 | 15 | 28 | 43 | 61 | 80 |
| | 17C | 90, 100 | 7.6 | 21 | 39 | 60 | 85 | 110 |
| Circular flat grating with | 17D | 50 | 4.5 | 12 | 23 | 36 | 51 | 67 |
| | 17D | 75, 100 | 7.1 | 20 | 37 | 57 | 80 | 105 |
| | | | (l/s) | (l/s) | (l/s) | (l/s) | (l/s) | (l/s) |
| Square flat grating | 17A | 100 | 0.354 | 1.021 | 1.875 | 2.812 | 3.958 | 5.208 |
| Circular flat grating | 17B | 50.65 | 0.093 | 0.250 | 0.479 | 0.750 | 1.062 | 1.396 |
| Circular flat grating | 17B | 75, 90,100 | 0.200 | 0.562 | 1.040 | 1.604 | 2.187 | 2.920 |
| D shaped flat grating | 17C | 65 | 0.108 | 0.292 | 0.562 | 0.875 | 1.208 | 1.604 |
| D-shaped flat grating | 17C | 75 | 0.112 | 0.312 | 0.583 | 0.896 | 1.270 | 1.667 |
| D-shaped flat grating | 17C | 90, 100 | 0.158 | 0.437 | 0.812 | 1.250 | 1.771 | 2.292 |
| Circular flat grating | 17D | 50 | 0.093 | 0.250 | 0.479 | 0.750 | 1.062 | 1.396 |
| Circular flat grating | 17D | 75,100 | 0.148 | 0.417 | 0.771 | 1.187 | 1.667 | 2.187 |

## Procedure

i.   Determine type of outlet required.

ii.  Refer to the Table for cast iron roof outlets as BS 416.

Actual flow rates for grated roof outlets should be obtained from the manufacturers.

Rainwater downpipes should be sized separately using
Graph 7 if vertical, or drain sizing data if horizontal.

*Table 26*

| Type of Roof | Category | C Factor |
|---|---|---|
| Pitched roof with external eaves, gutters and flat roofs | 1 | 1 |
| Valley and parapet gutters | 2 | 4.5 |
| Valley gutters with higher security | 3 | 1.5 |
| Highest possible security | 4 | See BS EN 12056-3 |

The C factor is used when calculating the return period i.e. Return period, T = C factor × life of building.

## Use of gutter sizing charts

The charts provide a unique method of selecting gutter sizes and produce results similar to BS 6367 and BS EN 12056-3.

A series of four charts cover four basic gutter profiles.

British Standard gutters are manufactured in a limited range of shapes and sizes, but with the aid of the charts it is possible to select a gutter to suit any application.

### Procedure

i.   Calculate the flow of water (Q)

ii.  Select the breadth (Bs) and length (Lg) to read off depth of water at point of discharge (Yc) and the upstream depth (yuf) to which a suitable freeboard depth must be added 2/5ths of yuf subject to a minimum of 25mm.

### Example

Roof size: 20 × 19.2 m  = 384m2
(Refer to Graph 6)

Rainfall intensity  = 75mm/hr

100% run off  = 8 l/s

*Graph 6* Gutting sizing nomogram showing worked example

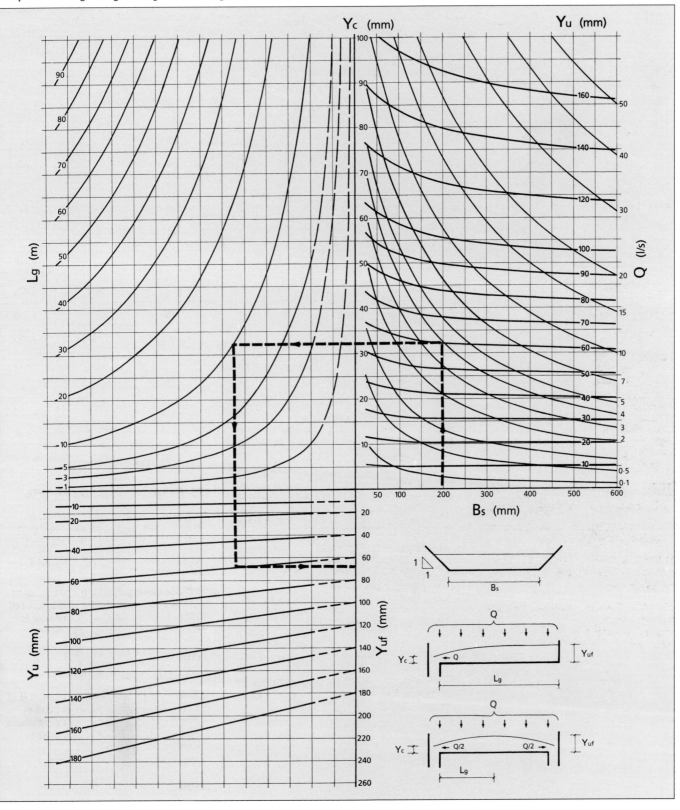

The gutter runs off full length (20m) of the building and has one outlet at each end. Half of the water will discharge in each direction; ie. 4.0 l/s into 10m length of gutter. Select the appropriate nomogram for gutter profile required and range of sizes.

Starting at the bottom right-hand side of the chart select a gutter breadth (B), say 200mm, follow vertically up the nomogram to the flow rate curve of 4.00 l/s. Read off and note value of yu, 60mm.

Read across to the centre axis noting the depth (yc) at the outlet 0f 32mm. Continue to the left to the curve representing the

gutter length (10m) and drop into the bottom left-hand section of the nomogram to the value of the depth (yu) of 60m previously established.

Follow right (horizontally) to the intercept with the yuf axis and read off the value at yuf. Add freeboard to yuf.

*Table 27*  *Flow rates, square/rectangular ungrated gutter outlets (litres per second)*

| Head of water over outlet in mm H | Size of rainwater outlets in mm | | | | | | |
|---|---|---|---|---|---|---|---|
| | 75 × 75 | 100 × 75 | 100 × 100 | 150 × 100 | 150 × 150 | 200 × 150 | 200 × 200 |
| 5 | 0.14 | 0.16 | 0.19 | 0.23 | 0.28 | 0.33 | 0.37 |
| 10 | 0.40 | 0.46 | 0.53 | 0.66 | 0.79 | 0.92 | 1.05 |
| 15 | 0.73 | 0.85 | 0.97 | 1.21 | 1.45 | 1.69 | 1.94 |
| 20 | 1.12 | 1.30 | 1.49 | 1.86 | 2.24 | 2.61 | 2.98 |
| 25 | 1.56 | 1.82 | 2.08 | 2.60 | 3.13 | 3.65 | 4.17 |
| 30 | 2.05 | 2.40 | 2.74 | 3.42 | 4.11 | 4.79 | 5.48 |
| 35 | 2.59 | 3.02 | 3.45 | 4.31 | 5.18 | 6.04 | 6.90 |
| 40 | 2.96 | 3.69 | 4.22 | 5.27 | 6.32 | 7.38 | 8.43 |
| 45 | 3.14 | 4.19 | 5.03 | 6.29 | 7.55 | 8.80 | 10.06 |
| 50 | 3.31 | 4.42 | 5.89 | 7.37 | 8.84 | 10.31 | 11.79 |
| 55 | 3.48 | 4.64 | 6.18 | 8.50 | 10.20 | 11.90 | 13.60 |
| 60 | 3.63 | 4.84 | 6.45 | 9.68 | 11.62 | 13.56 | 15.49 |
| 65 | 3.78 | 5.04 | 6.72 | 10.08 | 13.10 | 15.28 | 17.47 |
| 70 | 3.92 | 5.23 | 6.97 | 10.46 | 14.64 | 17.08 | 19.52 |
| 80 | 4.19 | 5.59 | 7.45 | 11.18 | 16.77 | 20.87 | 23.85 |
| 85 | 4.32 | 5.76 | 7.68 | 11.52 | 17.29 | 22.86 | 26.12 |
| 90 | 4.45 | 5.93 | 7.91 | 11.86 | 17.79 | 23.72 | 28.46 |
| 95 | 4.57 | 6.09 | 8.12 | 12.18 | 18.28 | 24.37 | 30.86 |

## Gutter outlets

(Use of Tables 27 and 28)

Having determined the depth of water at the downstream end of the gutter (yc). The depth (yc) is for a free flowing gutter and a depth not less than this must be used to size the gutter outlet from the Figures.

### Procedure

Select Table 27 or 28 for type of outlet required, i.e. square/rectangular or circular, and read outlet size from table against depth of water over outlet.

*NOTE*

1.  *It is recommended that a box receiver is constructed at the outlet to be full width of gutter, and depth no less than H + 25 mm. The gutter will not otherwise act as a free outlet, which would invalidate previous data.*

2.  *Diameter of outlet to be a minimum of 3/4 the width of gutter to ensure free discharge where a sump is not used.*

3.  *Bs (mm)  = Sole width of gutter*

    *Lg (m)   = Length of gutter*

    *Q (l/sec) = Discharge of flow in gutter*

    *yc (mm)  = Depth of flow at downstream end of gutter discharging freely*

    *yu (mm)  = Depth of flow at upstream end of gutter*

    *yuf (mm) = Depth of flow at upstream end of gutter taking into account the affect of frictional resistance*

    *yg (mm)  = Overall depth of gutter*

    *yg x 1.5 = Length of sump*

*Table 28* Flow rates, circular ungrated gutter outlets (litres per second)

| Head of water over outlet in mm H | Size of rainwater outlets in mm | | | | |
|---|---|---|---|---|---|
| | 75 | 100 | 150 | 200 | 250 |
| 5 | 0.11 | 0.15 | 0.22 | 0.30 | 0.37 |
| 10 | 0.32 | 0.42 | 0.63 | 0.84 | 1.05 |
| 15 | 0.58 | 0.77 | 1.16 | 1.55 | 1.94 |
| 20 | 0.89 | 1.19 | 1.79 | 2.39 | 2.98 |
| 25 | 1.25 | 1.67 | 2.50 | 3.33 | 4.17 |
| 30 | 1.64 | 2.19 | 3.29 | 4.38 | 5.48 |
| 35 | 2.07 | 2.76 | 4.14 | 5.52 | 6.90 |
| 40 | 2.37 | 3.37 | 5.06 | 6.75 | 8.43 |
| 45 | 2.52 | 4.02 | 6.04 | 8.05 | 10.06 |
| 50 | 2.65 | 4.71 | 7.07 | 9.43 | 11.79 |
| 55 | 2.78 | 4.94 | 8.16 | 10.88 | 13.60 |
| 60 | 2.90 | 5.16 | 9.30 | 12.39 | 15.49 |
| 65 | 3.02 | 5.37 | 10.48 | 13.97 | 17.47 |
| 70 | 3.14 | 5.58 | 11.71 | 15.62 | 19.52 |
| 75 | 3.25 | 5.77 | 12.99 | 17.32 | 21.65 |
| 80 | 3.35 | 5.96 | 13.42 | 19.08 | 23.85 |
| 85 | 3.46 | 6.15 | 13.83 | 20.90 | 26.12 |
| 90 | 3.56 | 6.32 | 14.23 | 22.77 | 28.46 |
| 95 | 3.66 | 6.50 | 14.62 | 24.69 | 30.86 |

*Graph 7* *Vertical rainwater pipe sizing chart*

An alternative to this Graph is Table 8 from BS EN 12056

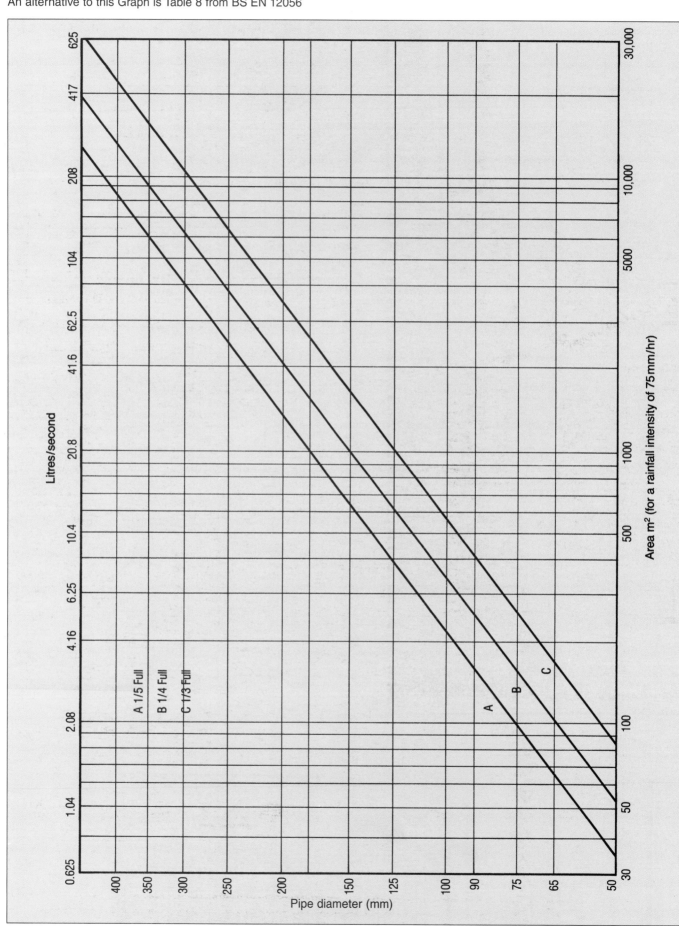

**Graph 8** *Rectangular Box Gutter*

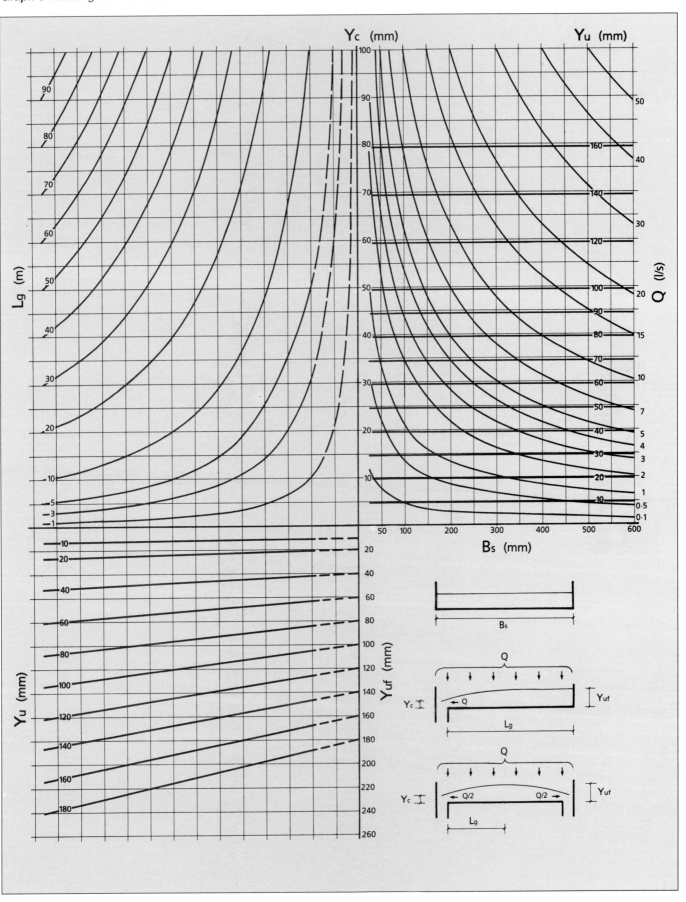

*Graph 9* Trapezoidal gutter with 1 to 1 side slope

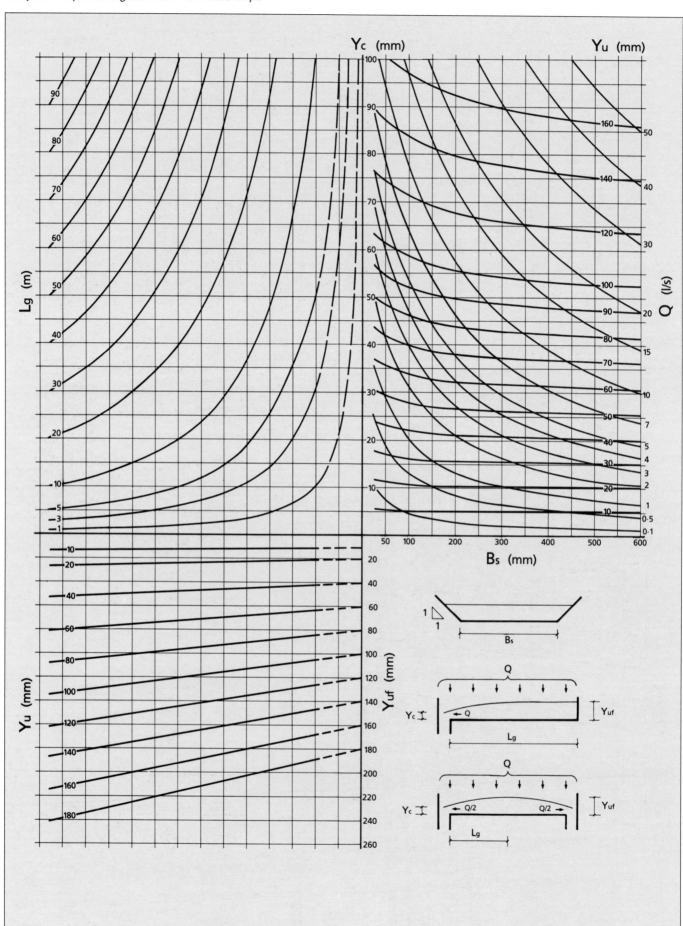

*Graph 10* Trapezoidal gutter with 1 to 1.5 side slope

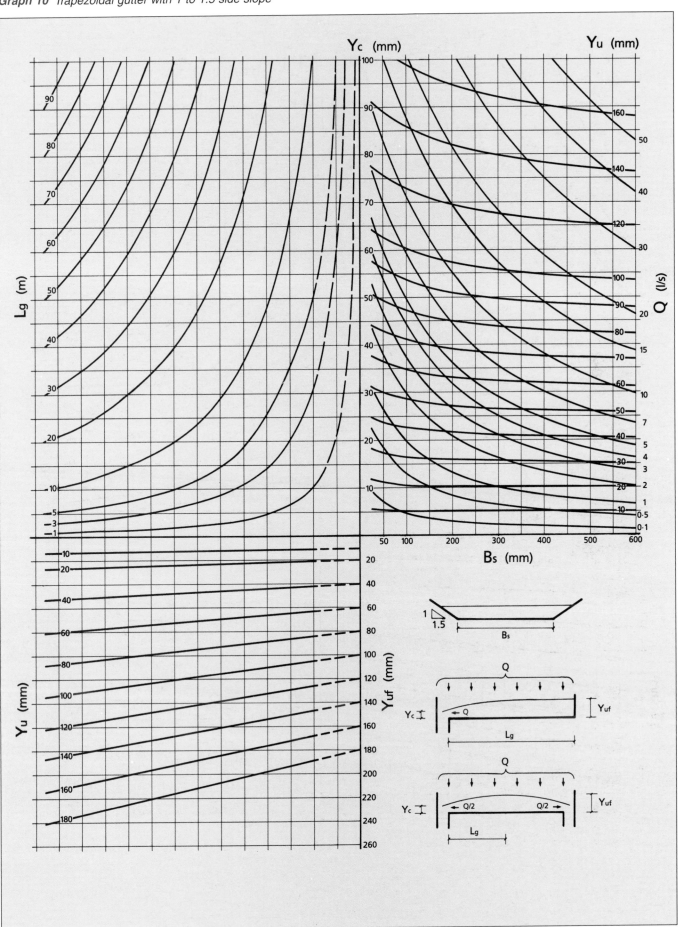

*Graph 11* Trapezoidal gutter with 1 to 2 side slope

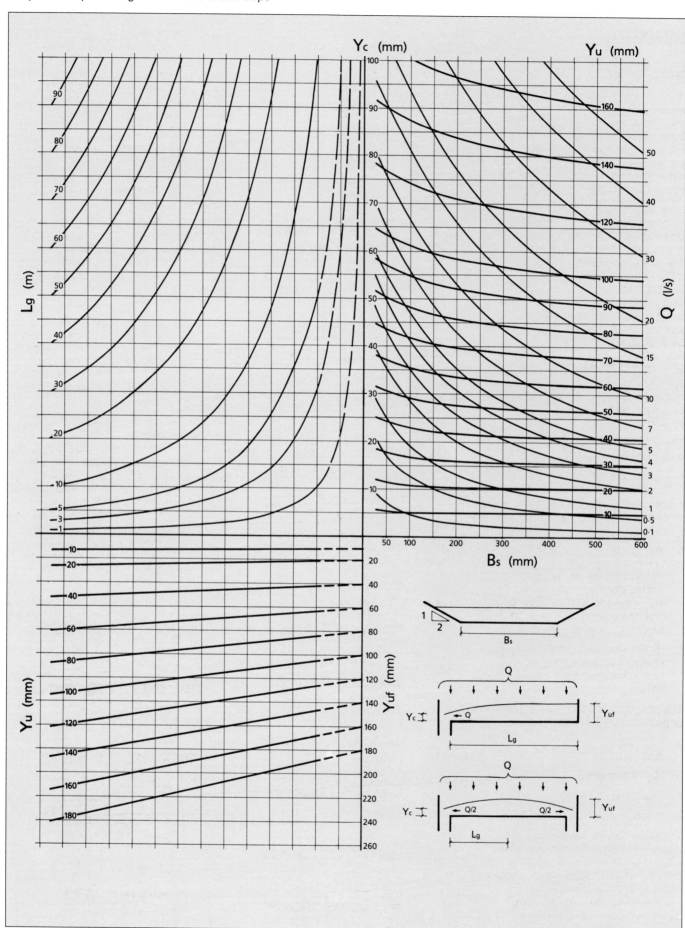

# Siphonic rainwater systems

## Introduction

A siphonic rainwater system is not truly siphonic according to the dictionary definition and should be seen as a full bore system. The capacity of a full bore system is dependent upon the size of the pipework and the available head from the water level over the outlet to the 'velocity break' at the bottom of the system.

Specially deisgned roof outlets restrict air from entering the system allowing the pipework to be balanced using hydraulic principles. This allows the pipework to flow full bore under a head at the design rainfall intensity. Roof outlet manufacturers provide validated test data which indicate the minimum head of water required over outlets, to prevent air entrainment at given flow rates. It must be appreciated that this head requirement is to prevent air entrainment at the stated flow rate and not to force the water into the outlet as with a gravity system. The driving force in a siphonic system is the available head in the total system.

There are several space and cost advantages with a siphonic system:

a. Pipework is smaller in diameter than a comparative gravity system and can be run level, occupying less space in ceiling voids making co-ordination of services easier.

b. Vertical discharge pipes can be kept to a minimum reducing the number of connections to the underground stormwater drainage system. This minimises the amount of associated ground works to be implemented on site.

c. Higher velocities generated in the pipework produce a self cleaning flow, eliminating the need for rodding points.

The design must be carefully considered or problems will be encountered due to:

a. High negative pressures and possible cavitation

b. High noise levels

c. Excessive vibration

d. Potential surcharging of gutters.

The rainwater pipework must not be designed in isolation, but must form an integral design with the roof/gutter and the external drainage. The final balancing of the system head losses is critical and extremely sensitive to any variation in pipe lengths and fitting changes. For this reason several balance checks may have to be made during installation if variations occur on site.

## Design criteria and considerations

The roof area to be drained and the rainfall design intensity should be calculated as described elsewhere in this Guide.

Design of the system considers the building roof area to be drained together with the rainfall design intensity peculiar to the project location and building protection, in accordance with BS EN 12056-3. Where long term protection is required, the high rainfall intensity and consequent long return period, may conflict with the need to operate the siphonic system at full bore flow regularly to flush it through. In this situation consideration should be given to storing the higher intensity flows at roof level for a few minutes with the siphonic outlets operating as regulating valves. The additional head over the outlets will not noticeably increase the flow into the pipes. Due allowance must of course be made for the additional depth of water to build up without penetrating the waterproofing details.

Alternatively, provision must be made to discharge the water resulting from storms above the design intensity. The incorporation of weir or piped overflows at the end of long valley gutters is inadequate as they do not control the depth of water between outlets in the centre portion of the gutter. The use of a separate overflow system with overflows located between each outlet is necessary. Alternatively a system comprising siphonic outlets positioned at suitable intervals and heights along the gutter and connected to separate overflow siphonic pipework is another solution. The required hydraulic gradient and freeboard must of course be calculated from these higher outlets and added to the gutter depth. Such a system is not easy to detail or install and the additional depth of gutter is likely to make it impractical.

In order to maintain self cleansing flows a minimum discharge capacity for individual outlets should not be less than 1 litre/sec, unless otherwise specified by the outlet manufacturer.

The roof outlets are specially designed to control the pattern of discharge from the roof. This is achieved by the use of a baffle which when submerged prevents air entrainment and the formation of a vortex.

The full design discharge will not occur instantaneously, sufficient rainwater is required to enter the pipework to prime the system. During this period a number of flow patterns occur with increasing flows until the flow rate to the outlet is exceeded and air enters the system. (Figure 35.)

Figures 35 and 36 illustrate the development of rainfall and roof drainage with approximate limits for the different flow patterns. It can be seen that with flows less than the design intensity the system will drain and a wavy/pulsating flow occurs. As the water to air ratio increases then a plug flow occurs which leads to a bubble flow. The bubble flow can occur with flows as low as 50% water volume. Full bore flow occurs as the water volume increases and if the

**Figure 35** *Flow patterns*

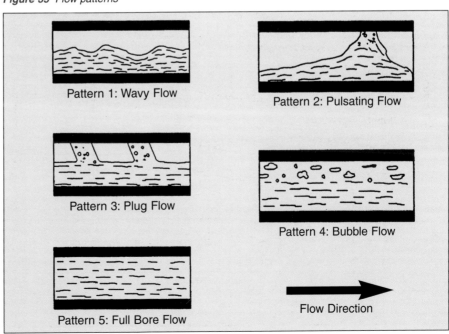

Pattern 1: Wavy Flow

Pattern 2: Pulsating Flow

Pattern 3: Plug Flow

Pattern 4: Bubble Flow

Pattern 5: Full Bore Flow

Flow Direction

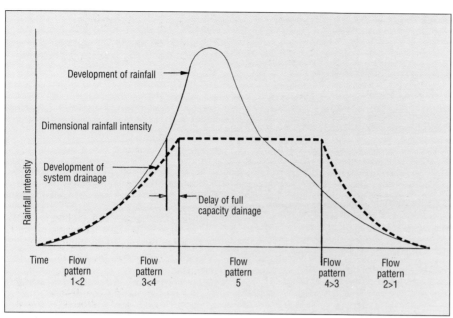

**Figure 36** *Typical storm flows*

system is correctly balanced. If the system has an imbalance then wavy/pulsating flow may occur more often resulting in a less effective discharge from the roof. Extensive pipe systems may take considerably longer to fill if not designed correctly.

The system will start to discharge under 'siphonic conditions' with water volumes of 50-60% and improve its discharge capacity as water volumes approach 100% of the design rainfall intensity.

Roof outlets currently available tend to cater for nominal flows of 6 l/sec and 12 l/sec. These flow rates are not fixed and are dependent on the working head in the system and the head over the outlet. For exceptional storm intensities such as found in Asia, outlets with a capacity of up to 80 litres/sec are available.

It is important to ensure the free flow of water to all sides of the outlets, on flat roofs they should be located at a minimum distance of 0.5m from vertical walls and not less than 1.5m from intersecting walls or the end of a gutter.

A check of the required free standing head of water over the outlet is necessary to achieve the maximum discharge capacity as this can vary between different manufcturers.

As with conventional design, it will be necessary to provide an overflow system designed to function when the water retained on the roof or in a gutter reaches an unacceptable level. This is very important with a siphonic system as unlike a conventional system there is practically no spare capacity above the design flow. For example a gravity system typically running approximately

one third full when subjected to an additional 40mm over its design head, could have an increased carrying capacity of up to 20%. This is due to the head of water over the outlet being the driving force in the system.

With a siphonic system the driving force is the difference in height from the water level over the outlet to the 'siphonic break', normally at ground level. Increasing this height by 40mm is insignificant and would typically result in an increased capacity of less than 1%. It will therefore often be necessary to provide deeper gutters to store the additional rainfall above the design figure.

The design of the system must take into account the negative pressures that are created within the pipework. If the maximum permitted negative pressure is exceeded there is a risk of cavitation and collapse of plastic pipes. The maximum permitted negative pressure for a system can be calculated as follows:

Vapour pressure – atmospheric pressure = permitted max. negative pressure

*Atmospheric pressure at different elevations above sea level*

| Elevation above sea level (m) | 0 | 500 | 1000 | 1500 | 2000 | 2500 |
|---|---|---|---|---|---|---|
| $p_a/\varrho(.g)$ (m) | 10.09 | 9.50 | 8.95 | 8.45 | 7.95 | 7.45 |

*Vapour pressure at different temperatures*

| Temperature °C | 0 | 5 | 10 | 15 | 20 | 25 | 30 |
|---|---|---|---|---|---|---|---|
| $p_a/\varrho(.g)$ (m) | 0.06 | 0.09 | 0.13 | 0.17 | 0.22 | 0.32 | 0.43 |

## Example

If a system is designed on a building 500m above sea level and the temperature of the rainwater is taken as 10°C, then the permitted negative pressure is 0.13 – 9.50 = –9.37m.

The maximum negative pressure must be considered when selecting the working pressure of pipework. Whilst the systems operate well within the pressure range of copper, steel and cast iron, care must be taken when specifying plastics. Manufacturers do not generally publish negative ratings as pipes are normally used for positive applications and therefore the grade of material will have to be confirmed with the manufacturer.

The 'velocity break' is where the full bore system converts to a conventional gravity system and is an integral part of the design. The receiving pipe must be sized to accept the flow rate (by gravity) that is discharging from the siphonic system. If the velocity of the discharge is high then it may be necessary to introduce an initial collection chamber, to allow the velocity to be reduced before discharging to the sewer via conventional sized drain pipework. Typical velocity breaks are illustrated in Figures 37 and 38.

The positioning of the siphon or velocity break is important and it must be maintained at all times or the calculations will be invalidated. If the siphon break is surcharged during a storm and the working head increased there could be a significant effect upon the system. Connecting directly from full bore rainwater pipework to full flowing drains extends the working head which increases the negative pressure in the upper part of the system. If the negative pressure exceeds the designed value the possibility of cavitation increases and under extreme conditions the pipework can implode. Conversely, connections to a surcharging drain will result in backing up in the rainwater pipework and cause the system to overload.

The siphon break will not always be at the bottom of the building as it only needs to be at a height to generate the required working head, ie to overcome the system resistances. This may only be one or two storeys down the building. The system sections must be designed within a head loss balance of typically 400mm between each section to ensure all outlets achieve their design flows within acceptable limits. A section in a system is the run of pipework from each outlet to the velocity break. (Figure 39.)

If this balance is not achieved the system will not function effectively due to increased air entrainment, a reduced discharge capacity and irregular flow. A minimum design velocity of 1m/s is required to enable the system to be self

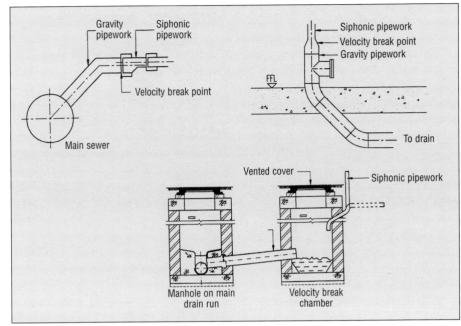

*Figure 37  Typical ground level velocity breaks*

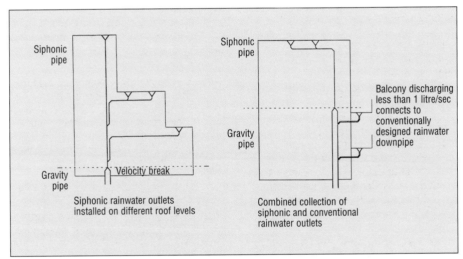

*Figure 38  Typical velocity breaks above ground*

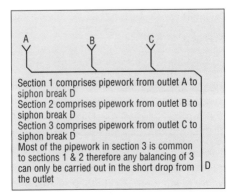

*Figure 39  System sections*

cleaning, however, during maximum discharge, flow velocities of 6-7m/s are often achieved.

Consideration should be given to pipe fixing, in particular at changes in direction, as movement and vibration can occur due to the high flow velocities.

Changes of direction should be achieved using 45° bends and branches, both to assist the flow of water and to reduce the resistance.

The high velocity combined with slugs of air during certain flow patterns can generate higher noise levels than would be experienced with a gravity system. Where horizontal pipework is routed above office space or other quiet areas sound insulation should be considered. The outlets themselves generate noise at the point immediately before and after the full bore flow state. This is caused by air being drawn into the outlet at high velocities.

Joints occurring along the collection pipework should not allow the ingress of air into the system, therefore, during installation there must be the necessary supervision and pressure testing to ensure the system is airtight.

# Pipework materials

At present the following materials are being utilised for the installation of siphonic systems:

Steel

Copper

Cast Iron

Polyethylene

When choosing the material to be used, consideration should be given to the following:

a. Will the material and jointing method withstand the negative pressure that the system has been designed to, plus a safety margin.

b. Due to the reduction of vertical pipes longer horizontal runs may be required, provision should be made to accommodate thermal expansion and or contraction (in particular, with the use of plastics).

# System design

### Procedure

i. Calculate area of roof to be drained (m²)

ii. Calculate the flow of rainwater to be discharged (l/s)

iii. Has client given any specific design requirements, if not confirm basis of design

iv. Note the head. Clearly identify the height from the roof outlet to the velocity break

v. Fix the position of the roof outlets and hence the area drained, note the individual discharges

vi. Design the pipework layout, an isometric is useful to mark up the information prior to calculating

vii. Note the individual pipe lengths and heights within the system

viii. Calculate the system to achieve the required balance. Note the velocity and negative pressure developed.

This is where a computer program or spreadsheet are essential. The calculations are simple in that for given flow rates and pipe sizes the engineer calculates the head loss in each length of pipe and totals the losses for each section. The losses for each section are then compared to establish the system balance. At this point there invariably follows many recalculations as the losses in the sections are balanced and pipe diameters changed to achieve this. In some cases in order to fine tune the head loss a length of pipe between two fittings will comprise two different diameters. This is quite valid as the calculation is about balancing head losses and velocity variations are secondary.

The designer should aim to use all of the available working head in each section leaving as near as practical zero head on the last pipe. In reality this will be a small negative or positive figure but with a maximum difference of 400mm between the lowest and highest section.

These calculations are possible by hand but they are very time consuming and a simple spreadsheet will save many design hours. Alternatively some of the specialist designer installers and outlet manufacturers are now releasing their design software to consultants.

Where outlets are located in a common gutter any small differential in system pressure will result in load sharing between outlets. This is a valid adjustment to a calculation but can only be carried out by trial and error. When the flow rates have been adjusted to achieve a pressure balance the resulting hydraulic gradient and increase in flow depth must be checked to ensure the gutter has adequate depth. This method of balancing should only be used when a balance cannot be achieved with the available pipe lengths. It must not be used for outlets in separate roof areas. Alternatively, some proprietary software will size orifice plates for insertion in the outlets to fine tune a system. This can be a useful method of adjusting a system on site where for instance the intended pipe lengths or numbers of fittings have not been achieved resulting in an imbalance.

When balancing a system the engineer will often find the need for additional short lengths of pipe in order to fine tune the head losses. For this reason when numbering a system prior to calculating always break the system down into more than one length between each fitting. A short length upstream of each junction is often useful when balancing. Also with a run of pipe serving a series of outlets in a gutter, it can be beneficial to run the branches parallel to the main run for a short distance before connecting. This will allow more flexibility in pipe lengths and sizes when balancing.

Balancing a system is simply a matter of achieving the same head loss in each section. This inevitably means that with a typical run of pipework serving outlets in a gutter and dropping at one end, the branches closest to the drop will be smaller in diameter. This is due to the need to create additional head loss in these branches. Failure to achieve this will allow outlets on these branches to over perform and introduce air into the system, breaking the siphonic effect. The

upper part of the system will then operate as an undersized gravity system.

The section of pipework from the last branch to the siphon break will often comprise more than one diameter in order to use up all of the working head. Where this happens the smaller diameter pipes should be at the downstream end of the system. This will allow the system to fill more rapidly and therefore run full bore sooner. The system will be equally balanced if the larger pipes are positioned downstream but it will be difficult or impossible to fill them with water during the early stages of a storm. A system must be fully primed before it will operate at its design capacity and the sooner this is achieved the better.

Having designed a few systems, the engineer will see a common theme to the calculations and will soon get a feel for a systems balance by observing the system losses.

Taking a typical run of pipework say 0.5m below a gutter with a drop at one end. The system will start with a small positive head over the outlet. This will be lost through the outlet and the losses will build up progressively along the horizontal run leading to the greatest negative approaching the top of the vertical drop. Moving down the vertical pipe the system head will overcome the previous losses until at the bottom of the system zero is indicated.

If this can be repeated from each outlet to the siphon break a perfectly balanced system will be achieved.

In the above example all pressures are negative along the horizontal pipe run. It is a common misconception that water is pulled through the system by the action of water dropping down the final vertical pipe and that therefore all pressures along the horizontal pipe must be negative. In a situation where the horizontal run is midway down the building and drops from the outlets are of sufficient height to overcome losses in that branch (probably in excess of 1.5m), positive pressures will appear. If the branches are of sufficient height most of the horizontal pipework could be positive. This is perfectly valid as the working head is the total height of the system not just the final vertical section of pipework.

The design of a siphonic system is closer to a cold water down service than a gravity drainage system. If the system is thought of as a cold water down service served by several water cisterns supplying one outlet, then it can be easier to grasp the concept. The level of water in the cistern (above the outlets) is minimised by the use of vortex inhibitors in the outlets. Now all that has to be done is to size the pipes to achieve identical head losses from each cistern to the outlet.

# Vacuum rainwater systems within buildings

## Introduction

Rainwater systems within buildings have traditionally relied on gravity to function. This has been due to the overwhelming reliability of gravity systems and the traditional form of buildings over the millenia.

As architects and engineers explore new forms of construction the Plumbing Services Design Engineer has to respond and provide systems that work in harmony with the architectural form of the buildings.

This in recent years has led to the incorporation of siphonic rainwater systems within developments which allow smaller pipework to be incorporated but still essentially rely on gravity to function.

More recently vacuum has been seen as way of providing rainwater drainage within buildings with advantages such as being able to route pipework upwards over obstructing beams or in fact over long distances with no or minimal fall.

Vacuum drainage isn't the answer to all rainwater drainage problems; several fundamental questions have to be answered before it is considered by the designer for use on a project to ensure that it is suitable. Vacuum systems require maintenance and rely on there being a reliable electrical power source.

The following section identifies the major components within systems and discusses their operation.

## Fundamentals

### Intensity

As with any rainwater system the designer must review the parameters to which he is going to design. This obviously starts with the question of what rainfall intensity is to be used. Many methods exist for obtaining the point rainfall intensities to be designed for linked to the level of risk and the security required for the building.

These methods suggest an intensity for design based on a gravity system where only limited possibilities of failure exist such as blockages. A mechanical system by its nature incorporates a greater number of possibilities for failure and for this reason the engineer must also consider this against whether a vacuum system is suitable for a particular building.

For instance it may be an acceptable risk to incorporate a vacuum system within an office development but not in an art gallery where the consequence of failure is greater. Each building should be considered on it's own merits and the pros and cons considered before any system is selected for use. Even then the designer should consider the form of the roof, a flat roof with internal parapet gutters is less secure than a pitched roof with eaves gutter that would purely shed water over the side at times of failure.

## Components

Vacuum systems used for draining water from roofs and other similar areas incorporate similar items of equipment to foul drainage systems, including vacuum pumps, vacuum pipework, vacuum vessels, discharge pumps, actuators and interface valves.

## Interface valves and actuators

The interface valves are located within the box receivers designed as part of the gutter system. It is important that some form of box receiver or sump is used in order to ensure that the interface valve, when called upon to function, will have a reasonable quantity of water to discharge. The system will, for lower rates of runoff, remove water from the sumps intermittently as they fill up and stop once the sumps are empty. The actuators which should be located remotely from the interface valves in a position to aid maintenance, sense the rise in water level within the sump/box receiver and open the interface valve for a predetermined time, sufficient to ensure the sump unit/receiver is emptied.

## Vacuum pipework

The vacuum pipework consists of a network of pipes which are routed back to the main collecting vessels. These pipes are constantly maintained at vacuum, the level of which is dependant on the lift required of the system. If a system is required to lift rainwater through 2m vertically then the vacuum the system generates must be in excess of the 2m lift required.

## Vacuum vessels

The vacuum vessels within a surface water system serve two functions. Initially they act as vacuum buffers that enable the system to function and for the vacuum pumps to operate. The buffer allows the vacuum pumps when called upon to operate to do a reasonable amount of work replenishing the vacuum in the buffers before they need to turn off.

Systems with low volumes would require the pumps to constantly be switching on and off in response to valves opening.

Their second function is to act as a holding tank prior to discharge to the sewer/discharge system. This is necessary as vacuum systems need to be pumped to waste, it is not possible to simply open a valve on the vessels and allow them to empty by gravity. Vacuum, and therefore the operational status of the system, must be maintained at all times and the opening of a valve on a vessel would result in vacuum being lost. The provision of vacuum tanks gives the designer the opportunity to provide attenuation within the system. This is where the allowable discharge to the sewer is less than the expected runoff from the roofs. As local authority sewers become more congested the requirements for attenuating of discharge become more and more likely. Many projects within built up areas now require some form of attenuation. The attenuated runoff is stored within the vessels whilst the discharge is arranged to release water to the sewer at a controlled rate, the excess being the volume required to be stored within the vessels.

If the required attenuation storage is high a separate storage vessel should be provided to receive the pumped discharge from the vacuum vessel.

Local authorities will need to be consulted as to what their limits of discharge are likely to be and what level of protection is required. This will be specified as an allowable discharge in l/s and a return period critical storm to be protected against. The return period will be given by the local authority and could be for example 10 years. The duration of the storm that gives the critical (maximum) volume of storage will then have to be calculated. The actual stored volume is dependent on the areas drained, the limit set by the local authority and the allowable flow to the sewer. These calculations balance the inflow with the outflow and give a resultant volume required to be stored throughout the storm. If allowable discharges are relatively high then short sharp flash storms can result in peak storage volumes whilst longer storms require peak storage when allowable discharges are small.

The calculations required for this type of analysis are complex and require input hydrographs for storm profiles relevant to the location of the site and for the duration of storms likely to yield the critical volume, usually between 30 minutes and 2 hours duration. These are most easily assessed using proprietary software.

## Vacuum pumps

The vacuum pumps are required to generate the vacuum within the system. These should be arranged as duty, assist and standby. Their duty cycle should be rotated after each operation to yield even wear on the pumps. The pumps are connected via a header to the vacuum vessels and operate on pressure switches to maintain the vacuum in the system.

The vacuum pumps draw the air contained within the vessels above the water surface to maintain a vacuum and this needs to be expelled to outside. Although relatively clean water is contained in the vessels it may contain leaf debris which over time will rot and cause odours. The discharge from the vacuum pumps should therefore be directed to discharge in a location so as not to cause nuisance. Location in accordance with the building regulations for vent pipes would be appropriate for such a termination but it should be remembered that the discharge is forced by the vacuum pumps and could be moisture laden, so siting next to surfaces where it could readily condense such as metal cladding systems may cause staining.

Any moist air within the vent will have a tendency to condense and run to the bottom of the vent during times when the vacuum pumps are not operating. To remove condensation from the discharge line a small suction line is connected into the discharge at its lowest point to suck the condensate back into the vessels by opening a solenoid valve on the small bleed line before the vacuum pumps operate.

## Discharge pumps

Having been filled with the surface water from the roofs, the discharge pumps empty the contents of the vessels ino the drainage system or sewer. Vacuum pumps used for the discharge of water from a vacuum must be designed specifically for this use. Conventional pumps are designed to draw water under flooded suction yielding a positive suction head. Pumps used on vacuum systems need to draw water from a vessel that is at a negative head and raise its pressure sufficient to overcome the negative head plus any lift involved. It is important when specifying duties for systems that it is clear exactly what the pumps need to achieve, to avoid confusion it is worth stating both the lift the pump is required to perform as well as the negative head the pumps are to overcome.

On start up of the discharge pumps they must overcome the maintained level of vacuum in the vessels. In order to allow the pumps to discharge efficiently certain other components within the system need to operate. If the discharge pumps were to start pumping out the contents of the vessels then as the water level drops within the vessels the air above its surface will become more rarefied and the vacuum in the vessels will increase to a point where the discharge pumps may not pass any more water. To ensure the level of vacuum in the system does not increase due to the discharge pumps functioning the increased vacuum must be released. This can be done by opening a small solenoid valve on the top of the vessel so as to admit air into the vessels to replace the volume of water being removed. The opening of the solenoid can also help in priming the pumps by ensuring the water in the suction headers is not drawn away from the impeller by the vacuum in the vessels.

Some manufacturers achieve this by having a balance line connected to the discharge side of the pump linking back into the vessels which ensures even pressure either side of the pump at all times until it operates. When this happens the balance line is shut with a solenoid valve ensuring the pumps discharge to waste and not back into the vessels.

### Vessel operating cycle

On initial start up the vessel is empty and the system is at atmospheric pressure. The pressure within the vessels is registered by the pressure switch and starts the vacuum pump to expel air from the vessels and system. Upon reaching the design level of vacuum the pressure switch shuts the vacuum pumps down, the system will sit in this static mode until the pressure drops in the system once again whereby the vacuum pumps will start to replenish the vacuum. See table 28.

A drop in vacuum can be caused by either a leak within the pipework and system or by the admittance of water into the system. It is important to ensure the system does not incorporate any leaks as this, even if small, will cause the system to cycle the vacuum pumps which will increase wear on them leading to premature failure.

Water entering the system will be pushed along towards the collecting vessels each time the interface valve, within the box receiver or sump, operates. The water will therefore move along the pipework system in pockets, each containing the volume drawn into the system at each operation of the interface valve. The heavier it rains the closer together these pockets of water become. In order to assist in the transport of the water, reforming points

**Table 28** *Typical control sequence*

| Condition | System function |
|---|---|
| System charged with vacuum whilst it is rarely not raining | System remains static. Vacuum pumps cut in to maintain vacuum and to exercise pumps. |
| Rain starts | Gutters convey water to the box receivers. Water levels in receivers rise. Sensors detect the rise. At the set level the interface valve will open and allow the pipework to draw water into it, emptying the box receiver. When empty the interface valve will close. The entry of water into the system will lower the vacuum level in the pipework and vessels. |
| Interface valves open allowing slugs of water to enter the system. Vacuum levels within the system drop to below lower set point. | At lower set point the vacuum pumps will start to replenish vacuum. Prior to vacuum pumps starting the vacuum pump discharge line will be purged of condensation via a link back to the receiver vessels. This is achieved by a solenoid valve opening and closing prior to the pumps starting. |
| Repeated opening of discharge valves and transport of rainwater to the vessels causes them to become full and need emptying. | High level float, or sensor, will initiate the discharge pump. |
| Water level in tanks drop during pump out to the lower level float or probe. | Discharge pumps are stopped and system returns to normal, awaiting next cycle of operation. |

are fitted in the system. These take the form of a trap in the pipework, which allows the water pockets to reform across the diameter of the pipe ensuring they get transported along the system the next time a valve opens. Without reforming pockets it is possible for the water within the pipework to pond at the base of the pipe and for the air within the system to rush past when the interface valves open and for the water not to be transported along the pipe efficiently.

The water moves along the system until it arrives at the vacuum vessels. The vessels fill and upon reaching a high level float switch or sensor the discharge pumps will empty the vessels. The pumps are arranged to shut off once a low level cut-out switch or sensor has been reached.

As all rainwater systems are designed to function for a finite rainfall intensity and it is likely that it will rain at an intensity greater than this at some point in the life of the system certain safeguards need to be incorpororated.

In order to ensure the system does not overfill and flood the vacuum pumps a means of shutting the vacuum lines need to be incorporated into the system. This is often achieved by the introduction of a motorised valve in the vacuum line and a high level flooding float/sensor introduced into the vessels.

The high level flooding float/sensor will isolate the vacuum pumps from the vessel in the event of a high water level in the vessels ensuring that water cannot enter the vacuum pumps.

## Design hints

a. Allow freeboard at the top and bottom of the vessels for dead water and freeboard. The operating band of the vessels between high water level and low water level is the actual holding capacity of the tanks. This is the actual volume required for retention. The vessel volume must be greater than this to allow for freeboard and dead water.

b. Operate the system at as low a vacuum as possible. This will reduce the tendency for leaks and reduce the noise from the interface valves.

c. Fix the pipework adequately. The velocity of water slugs is high and can cause vibration at changes of direction and if not properly braced.

d. Ensure the discharge pumps discharge into an adequately sized/vented drain.

e. Discharge lines should rise to high level and loop in to the top of the drain in order to eliminate siphonage assisting the discharge pumps and greater volumetric flows entering the drainage system than the design discharge.

f. Locate interface valves in easily accessible locations. It is not necessary for them to be immediately adjacent to box receivers.

g. Consider acoustically treating pipework in sensitive areas.

h. Provide duplicate interface valves in gutters to provide backup in the event of one becoming stuck.

i. Hold adequate supplies of spares on site to assist in the routine maintenance of the plant.

# Vacuum drainage systems

## Introduction

Vacuum systems for the transportation of waste water can be divided into two basic systems; within buildings and outside buildings. European Standards, adopted as British Standards, have been written for these two systems. The Standards contain the design, installation and performance requirements for vacuum drainage and vacuum sewerage systems. However, such systems are currently manufactured by a few international companies that fiercely safeguard their system design details. Hence, although the Standards specify the requirements for systems and set out the design principles, the actual design process depends upon the performance of the individual components and the design philosophy of the manufacturer. The main manufacturers of vacuum systems use different design philosophies and this results in their use of different pipe sizes, pipework configurations and interface valve sizes. It would be wrong for this book to recommend one manufacturer's system, as each prospective installation usually requires a unique design. Unlike a conventional gravity drainage or sewerage system, a vacuum system should be considered as a complete machine and not a simple hydraulic network. Engineers often want to be able to design a vacuum system in the same way that they would design conventional systems. However, currently the information they require, such as the performance characteristics of the interface valves, is not in the public domain. Hence, designers, specifiers and clients are only able to use the Standards, and information such as this section, to help them decide if a vacuum system is applicable for the project they have in mind, and agree an informed specification for any system.

## Background

Generally, the modern vacuum drainage system is believed to have been started by the development of the vacuum toilet by Mr Joel Liljendhal in the mid 1950s. The concept of his system was to separate the heavily polluted waste and the lightly polluted water (black and grey water) for separate treatment. The vacuum toilets used only about 1 litre of water per flush improving the efficiency of the system and making treatment easier. This two-pipe system, although environmentally friendly, met with quite a lot of resistance because houses needed to be re-plumbed and the vacuum toilet required more maintenance than a conventional toilet. This led to the development of the single pipe vacuum drainage system generally employed today.

Whilst the original systems were developed for domestic wastewater transportation, the systems evolved in two different areas; transportation and land-based systems. The majority of work has been in the transportation sector, and the marine industry continues to be the major user of the system, where the need to conserve wholesome water, and the problems of confined pipework runs and sewage disposal are paramount. For the same reasons this technology was adopted by the other forms of mass transport, ie airlines and railways. Today some 5,000 ships, from yachts to cargo vessels to ocean-going cruise liners, 50 major airline companies, and over 100 train installations use vacuum drainage systems.

The buiding sector has been slow to adopt this new technology, but with the restrictions placed on new projects such as small conduit, ceiling voids and service ducts, and the growing awareness of the need to limit water consumption, the system is finding a place in the building sector.

## Applications

Particular consideration should be given to the use of vacuum drainage in the following circumstances:

a. Water shortage or other reasons for reducing water consumption

b. Limited sewerage capacity

c. Where separation of black and grey water is desired, eg where grey water is reused

d. Where separation of wastewaters is desired, eg for different treatments

e. In hospitals, hotels, office buildings or other areas where congested usage occurs

f. When flexibility in pipe routing is required to drain appliances or where frequent pipe layout changes are expected

g. Building refurbishment

h. Where drainage by gravity becomes impractical

i. In complex building structures and

j. In penal installations where isolation and control of the appliances is necessary to prevent concealment of weapons and drugs.

### Black and grey water

The collection arrangements and small bore pipework of vacuum drainage systems provide the possibility of easily separating grey and black water. This was one of the original aims of the invention by Mr Liljendhal. This would be of particular advantage if sewerage capacity was at a premium as the grey water could be run to a water course after preliminary treatment. Also, it would be of advantage if there was a requirement to use the grey water for reuse or irrigation.

### Retrofit and newbuild flexibility

When conventional gravity drainage systems are extended as in refurbishment work, the existing gravity drainage system can be fed into the vacuum drainage system. This may be achieved by the use of a sump into which the wastewater from the gravity system drains. When sufficient water has accumulated in the sump, an interface valve will open allowing the wastewater to enter the vacuum drainage system. This arrangement can also be used to collect rainwater or as an interface between a building with conventional drainage and a vacuum sewer.

## System descriptions

### Definitions of terminology

A selection of the fundamental definitions that are required to understand the terminology of vacuum drainage systems are listed below. A complete set of definitions is contained within the European Standard EN 12109.

*Buffer volume:* The storage volume of the interface unit which balances the incoming flow of wastewater to the output capacity of the discharge valve.

*Controller:* The device which, when activated by its level sensor, opens the interface valve and, after the passage of wastewater and normally air, closes the valve.

*Interface valve:* A valve which admits the

flow of wastewater only or wastewater and air into the vacuum drainage system pipeline.

*Lift:* Section of vacuum pipeline with an increase in invert level in the direction of flow.

*Reforming Pocket:* A low point in the piping profile installed intentionally to produce a controlled slug flow.

*Service Connection:* The section of vacuum pipeline connecting an individual interface unit to the vacuum main.

*Slug:* An isolated quantity of wastewater flowing full bore through the vacuum pipeline.

*Vacuum:* Any pressure below atmospheric.

*Vacuum Station:* An installation comprising vacuum generator(s), a means of discharge, and control equipment and which may also incorporate vacuum vessel/holding tank(s).

## The vacuum transport process

An understanding of the vacuum transport process is helpful to the system designer. As long as no interface unit is operating, little wastewater transport takes place. All wastewater remaining in the vacuum pipework will drain, by gravity, into the reforming pockets when all upstream interface valves are closed. When an interface valve opens, the differential pressure between the vacuum in the system and atmosphere, forces the wastewater into the vacuum pipework. Whilst accelerating, the wastewater is transformed into foam and soon occupies only part of the vacuum pipe cross section so that the momentum transfer from air to water takes place largely through the action of shear stresses. The magnitude of the propulsive forces starts to decline noticeably when the interface valve closes but remain important as the admitted air continues to expand. Eventually, friction and gravity bring to rest the wastewater at the low points of the pipework system; such as reforming pockets and at the bottom of pipeline lifts.

The vacuum drainage system transports wastewater by means of atmospheric pressure acting against vacuum.

When designing systems greater than 100m in length (from the valve to the vacuum station), a series of reforming pockets must be used. These minimise the break-up of the wastewater slug and reform that portion of the slug that remains in the piping between interface

valve discharges. The reformed slug is then propelled by the air admitted during the next discharge.

Once the interface valves have operated, the discharge travels to the vacuum station, normally located at ground or basement level. Air is discharged to atmosphere only from the vacuum station. From the vacuum station, the wastewater is pumped automatically to the building outfall connection, to discharge into the external drainage system by gravity.

To design a reliable and economic vacuum drainage system, it is necessary to generate sequentially high acceleration and self-cleansing velocities with the least amount of energy.

*NOTE:*
*A vacuum drainage system is NOT a reversed pressure system where all the water would be accelerated simultaneously.*

## Basic components

A vacuum drainage system may be considered as comprising four elements:

a.　The automatic interface units (AIU)

b.　The vacuum toilets

c.　The pipework

d.　The vacuum station.

### Interface units

The valves that form the interface between the vacuum drainage lines and the appliances can be used directly with some appliances and with buffer volumes for others. When used with buffer volumes, level sensors and controllers, the valves are termed interface units (AIUs). Although AIUs are operated by air, non-automatic units may use electricity to control their operation.

They are of various sizes of interface valve up to about 100mm bore. The larger valves are used in vacuum sewerage systems.

Typically a complete interface unit is composed of a buffer volume of varying size, a sensor to sense the wastewater level in the buffer volume, a controller which operates a pilot valve to open and close a vacuum supply line to the interface valve. In many designs of interface unit, level sensors and controllers are combined into one device.

### Vacuum toilets

A vacuum toilet uses air instead of water to remove the contents of the bowl, and is a form of interface valve. Usually, it includes a flushing rim and the toilet's controller may have a memory function

so that it will operate as soon as there is sufficient vacuum available.

Typically, when operating a flush button, pressurised water is introduced into the bowl through a water valve and a flushing ring with holes to clean the bowl. Simultaneously the interface valve opens and the pressure differential in the piping forces the contents through the valve. Before the interface valve closes, air is drawn into the pipe. The flush water valve stays open for about two seconds to re-establish the water pool in the bowl. The typical water consumption for this timing sequence would be 0.8-1.5 litre per flush. Vacuum toilets may be re-flushed in less than a quarter of the time taken for a conventional WC to refill, on average, a vacuum toilet will take 3 seconds to complete a flush cycle.

### Ejector unit

Ejector units are used on small systems, which require approximately 40m$^3$ of air an hour at peak flow. They have the advantage of having a lower capital cost, being small in physical size and with fewer working parts than vacuum pumps, and are easy to maintain and operate. However, they are less power efficient than a conventional vacuum station and, therefore, are more expensive to run. The control of this kind of vacuum station is similar to a conventional pumping station. These units can also receive discharges from gravity drainage systems directly into the tank. However, wastewater containing high levels of detergents may cause foaming problems.

### Vacuum station

A vacuum station has three functions:

i.　Generate vacuum

ii.　Receive and forward the wastewater and

iii.　Control and monitor the system.

Although vacuum stations may be used with similar systems as the ejector unit, they are used mainly for larger systems, ie greater than 40m$^3$ of air. They are large units with a higher capital cost but typically are cheaper to run than ejectors.

The machinery installed is similar to that of a conventional wastewater pumping station or lift station, and consists of a collection tank, wastewater forwarding pumps, vacuum pumps, controls and alarms, and where required a standby generator.

The vacuum receiver tank size and/or number of tanks depends on the number of appliances connected to the system and the expected frequency of discharge. Each tank incorporates level switches that control the discharge pumps automatically, vacuum regulator switches which control the vacuum pumps and level alarms which can be audible or connected to the building management system.

### Vacuum generating and forwarding pumps

*Vacuum generating pumps*

Vacuum pumps of the liquid ring and sliding vane types are both suitable for use in vacuum drainage systems. Vane type vacuum pumps are recommended for most projects since they are more efficient, ie they have a greater throughput of air and are less temperature sensitive than similarly powerful liquid ring pumps.

The maximum vacuum provided by a liquid ring pump often will not exceed −0.8 bar gauge, whilst the maximum vacuum of a vane pump will typically be closer to −1 bar gauge. This will affect the choice of pumps where vacuum levels of a greater magnitude than the normal −0.5 to −0.7 bar gauge operating range will be required, or for projects at high elevations where atmospheric pressure is lower.

A vacuum switch attached to the pipework and adjustable timer are used to control the vacuum pumps. A second vacuum switch may control a low vacuum control alarm signal. These switches are fitted with stainless steel bellows to protect against corrosion from any gases evolving from the wastewater.

### Forwarding pumps

Forwarding pumps are required to discharge the collected wastewater to the external gravity sewerage system. These pumps are designed to operate with a large pressure differential across them with their inlets under vacuum. The size of the forwarding pump is a function of the following: design peak flow, volume to be discharged, and the permissible discharge rate for the receiving sewer.

To enable some forwarding pumps to work, a vacuum balance line may be required down stream of the discharge pump to reduce the pressure differences across the pump (a balance line is not required with an ejector system). To prevent loss of vacuum when the pump is not discharging, a check valve is required in the discharge pipework downstream of the connection of the balance line.

## Controls

### System controls

The vacuum drainage system control panel contains the main power switch and the pump operating system which includes: magnetic starters, overload protection, control circuitry and hours run meters for each vacuum and forwarding pump. A data recorder may be built into this panel, as well as the collection tank level control relays. Alarm and telemetry systems may also be included if required.

### Pump controls

The controls should be designed so that, where stand-by pumps and collection tanks are installed, both the vacuum and forwarding pumps alternate their use and are interconnected and controlled to allow them to be used with either tank automatically. The pump controls will include logic controllers that will be connected to the various level and vacuum sensors. The signal to start the discharge comes from the high level switch in the collection tank, the stop function is either controlled by a low level switch or timer. For example, when the high level sensor indicates to the logic control that water has risen to the high level, this sequence of operation will commence:

i.   The controller will close automatic valve in balance line, where fitted, and start the forwarding pump

ii.  If level does not fall within the pre-set time, a second pump will be started or an alarm generated

iii. If level reaches the high level alarm sensor, then an alarm is given and the vacuum system is shut down

iv.  When the water level has fallen to a low level sensor or after a pre-set time period, the controller will stop the forwarding pump(s) and open the automatic balance line valve, if fitted.

In systems where only black water is being collected it is prudent to use the second forwarding pump as a circulation pump. This circulates sewage within the collection tank and breaks up any solids which may have formed on the surface of the wastewater. This operation should be programmed into the logic system as the first step in the discharge cycle.

### Collection tank level controls

Level detectors are available in various forms, some are float switches, others are fixed probes that may be conductive, inductive or capacitative. Where a lot of condensate is being collected, for example in supermarkets with chiller cabinets, the mineral content of the water may affect the operation of the system

and conduction probes may need to be used.

Level detectors, of some form, are fitted to all collection tanks. The signals from the six common detectors control the discharge pumps and alarms as follows, in accending order of height from the base of the tank:

i.   Earthing probe, or sensor float switch or similar

ii.  Both forwarding pumps stop

iii. Lead forwarding pump start

iv.  Assist forwarding pump start

v.   High level alarm

vi.  High level cut-off – stop vacuum pumps.

## Vacuum gauges

It is important that all vacuum gauges be specified to indicate gauge pressure and have stainless steel bourdon tube and socket.

Vacuum gauges should be provided at the following locations in positions that can be viewed easily:

a.  the side of the vacuum moisture removal tank (where fitted)

b.  the collection tank

c.  one gauge on each incoming vacuum main or header.

It is important that these gauges are located above the incoming pipes and in a position that is easily viewed from the operating position of the isolation valves.

## Combined vacuum generator and forwarding pump

A combined vacuum generator and forwarding pump or 'vacuumarator' is a screw vacuum pump with liquid ring seal with a macerator for breaking up any solids passing through it. The macerator consists of one rotating knife fixed to the shaft and one stationary knife fixed to the suction chamber.

The combined vacuum generator and forwarding pump;

a.  generates vacuum

b.  macerates solids

c.  pumps wastewater in the same operation.

A combined vacuum generator and forwarding pump can generate vacuum directly on the pipeline to an appliance and discharge to a gravity system in the same operation. Vacuum tanks or collecting tanks are not required normally. Combined vacuum generators and forwarding pumps can be used for all size of systems. The size and number of combined vacuum generator and forwarding pumps to be used depends upon the required capacity. Combined vacuum generators and forwarding pumps have a small footprint compared to conventional vacuum stations and can be located in small ducts. A combined vacuum generator and forwarding pump is more power efficient than an ejector system, but a large number of combined vacuum generator and forwarding pumps would be more expensive to purchase and run than a comparable vacuum station based system.

## Check and isolation valves

A check valve is installed in each vacuum pump suction line to maintain the vacuum in the system. Check valves are also fitted on the discharge from a vacuum discharge pump, and often are fitted on the service connection from an appliance.

Isolation valves are fitted to all forwarding and vacuum pumps to allow their removal without disrupting the system. Also they are fitted in strategic locations to enable sections of a system to be isolated for service. Isolation valves should be suitable for vacuum use and may be of the eccentric plug type or resilient face gate type and have a clean opening of not less than the nominal diameter of the pipe. Both check and isolation valves must be capable of withstanding 0.8 bar gauge vacuum, when open, and a differential pressure of 0.8 bar, when closed on a functioning system.

## Pipework

Usually stainless steel and thermoplastic (ABS, HDPE, PVCu or MDPE) pipes are utilised for the construction of the vacuum pipelines, the selection of pipeline material is dependent upon its location and the characteristics of the waste water. All pipes used should be suitable for vacuum, and the minimum pressure rating for thermoplastics should be 10 bar but higher ratings shall be used if the pipe has an initial ovality; if progressive deformation or long term loss of strength due to high temperature is likely to occur. The velocities of water within the pipework and the resulting percussive effects at changes of direction lead to the requirement for such pressure rated pipe. Standard manufactured fittings are used where available; Y junctions for incoming branches should be 45° and reducers be concentric.

Generally, joints should be smooth and protrusion free to ensure full flow conditions.

Not all rubber ring pipe joints are suitable for vacuum systems, the manufacturer should supply a guarantee along with the test certification that the products are appropriate for vacuum drainage applications.

## Design

### Design requirements

The system should be designed to accept discharges from all appliances planned to be connected to the system. The designer should take into consideration any known possible future additions or modifications to the system to avoid future installation and operating constraints.

### Design criteria

In order to design a vacuum drainage system the following basic parameters should be determined and obtained:

i.  Service life expectancy

ii. Type of building

iii. Number of people the system is to serve

iv. Types, number and location of appliances to be connected

v.  Wastewater temperature range (high temperature grey water discharges shall be specified concerning temperature, flow, batch volume and frequency)

vi. Ambient temperature range within which the system shall operate

vii. Minimum vacuum level required to operate the interface units and vacuum toilets

viii. Air to water ratios required for the interface units

ix. Air consumption of vacuum toilets

x.  Permissible leakage factors.

The following parameters are required to calculate the pipe sizes and system layout. They should be determined by the designer and equipment supplier for each system:

i.  Total wastewater flow

ii. Vacuum toilet flush frequency

iii. Dynamic losses between the vacuum station and the furthest appliance on each pipeline

iv. Static losses between the vacuum station and the furthest appliance on each pipeline

v.  Required operational level of vacuum

vi. Required vacuum generator capacity

vii. Required forwarding pump capacity, if utilised

viii. Required collecting tank capacity, if utilised

ix. Pipe sizes

x.  Vacuum recovery time.

### Pipework design

Vacuum systems are designed to operate on two-phase air to liquid flows. The air in the pipework is not, as in a conventional horizontal gravity system, flowing above the wastewater but is entrained into the wastewater where its expansion propels the wastewater and lowers its bulk density. These factors enable the wastewater to behave more like a gas than a liquid and in particular flow uphill.

The strength of thermoplastics is affected by temperature. In industrial installations where high wastewater temperatures are anticipated, care must be taken in the selection of pipe materials. Wastewater temperatures greater than 70°C should be notified to the designer, so that the design can limit, by pipework design and buffer volume sizing, possible boiling due to pressures lower than atmosphere.

The pipes are installed in a near horizontal profile, without backfall (0.2-0.5% fall) to a suitably located vertical pipe. Once the vertical pipe (stack) is installed, all horizontal pipes may be connected at each level in the building in the void between floor and ceiling, subject to lift height restrictions. All service connections from the interface units could either be lifted to the pipeline in the ceiling above or dropped through the floor to the pipeline below. This makes installation one floor at a time possible which is particularly valuable in building refurbishment.

Preferably, connections to horizontal pipelines should be arrange so that the branch pipe enters from the top by way of a Y-fitting. As a minimum it shall connect into the top sector of the vacuum main pipeline contained within the angle of ±60° about the vertical axis. Vertical lift piping connecting to horizontal pipelines should enter from the top by way of a Y-fitting. Precautions should be taken, eg the use of a check valve suitable for vacuum drainage, to prevent filling the rise with wastewater by back surges. Horizontal piping connecting to vertical stacks should enter by way of single Y-branches. Multiple connections should be at staggered levels where practical.

For a larger building it is customary to divide the system into smaller sub-systems, possibly with a crossover, if not cost prohibitive, so that, in the event of failure of part of the system, each sub-system could operate as a standby for the other. The crossover pipework would be located between the vacuum station and pipework manifold of each sub-system. An isolation valve, the crossover valve, located within the crossover pipework would, for normal operation, be closed.

## Maintainability

System maintainability affects not only maintenance costs but also availability. The following aspects are the minimum that should be addressed as part of system design:

i.   Fault finding procedures

ii.  Access to all interface units, isolation valves, cleaning eyes, check valves and other items that need inspection and/or service

iii. Procedures for removal of interface units and their temporary effect on system performance, if any

iv.  Maintenance schedules for interface units in relation to cycle frequency and endurance

v.   Estimated repair or replacement times of interface units

vi.  Maintenance schedule for vacuum station equipment

vii. Procedures for removal or repair of vacuum station equipment and their temporary effects on system performance, if any

viii. Estimated repair or replacement times for vacuum station equipment

ix.  Precaution routines if system performance is temporarily lost or reduced

x.   Training of maintenance personnel

xi.  Recommended stocking of spare parts

xii. Estimated cost of maintenance per year.

## References

The Environment Protection Agency (EPA) in USA.

Internet sites, and manufacturer's literature.

IoP/BRE/CIBSE Vacuum Drainage Systems Guidance (book and video).

# Pumps and pumping

# Definitions and descriptions

## Absolute pressure

The gauge pressure, plus the pressure of the atmosphere. (When a pressure is referred to without 'gauge' or 'absolute' being stated, it is normally understood to be the gauge pressure).

## Atmospheric pressure

Normal atmospheric pressure at sea level is 1.00 bar = 10.20m head. Atmospheric pressure varies with the altitude above sea level and with the weather conditions.

## Pressure

All pipework, pipe fittings, radiators, etc. will create a resistance to the flow of water through them. The more or faster you try to circulate water through them, the more resistance they will create to this flow.

Water, like electricity, will always try to take the least line of resistance. To overcome this resistance, a force must be put into the water. That force will overcome resistance and circulate the water. This force is pressure.

## Gravity circulation

When heating systems were first developed, they worked on gravity circulation.

You probably now know the principle of gravity circulation. The lighter hot water was forced upwards by the cooler, heavier water dropping. The difference in weight between the light hot water and the heavier cool water created a pressure. If circulating pipes were located higher above the boiler, more pressure was created. This was called circulating head.

## Positive and negative pressure

The increase in pressure on the outlet is called positive pressure. It is shown by a plus sign (+).

The decrease in pressure on the inlet side is called negative pressure shown by a negative sign (−).

The water within the system is being circulated from boiler to radiators and

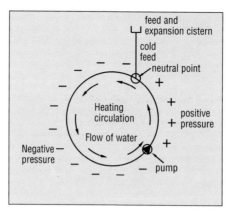

*Figure 1 Neutral point*

back to boiler. Its motion is like a circle, as you can see from figure 1.

## Neutral point

The pump creates a negative and positive pressure within the circle (figure 1).

Somewhere it must change from positive to negative. This is called the neutral point.

The neutral point is where the cold feed enters the system.

The increase or decrease in pressure will be at its greatest close to the pump. Moving away from the pump, the increase or decrease in pressure will reduce. This is because pressure is being used to overcome the resistance of the pipes etc. If the cold feed is the neutral point, the system will have an increase or a decrease in pressure corresponding to how far from the pump it is, whether more (increase) or less (decrease). Figure 1 illustrates this point.

## Capacity

The volumetric flow rate delivered by a pump, normally expressed in cubic metres per hour (m³/h), or litres per second (l/s).

## Cavitation

Cavitation is defined as the formation of cavities beneath the back surface of an impeller vane and the liquid normally in contact with it.

It can be caused in a centrifugal pump:

a.  by the impeller vane travelling faster, at higher rpm, than the liquid can keep up with it

b.  by a restricted function (therefore never throttle the suction of a centrifugal pump)

c.  when the required NPSH is equal or greater than the available NPSH

d.  when the specific speed is too high for optimum design parameters

e.  when the temperature of the liquid is too high for suction conditions.

The cavity consists of a partial vacuum, gradually being filled with vapour as the liquid at the interface boils at the reduced pressure in the cavity. As the cavity moves along the underside of the vane towards the outer circumference of the impeller, the pressure in the surrounding liquid increases and the cavity collapses against the impeller vane with considerable force, it produces a kind of water-hammer effect. This means that on very small areas of the metal extremely high pressures are momentarily developed and, although each individual hammer-blow may be minute, if the blows are repeated often enough and for a sufficiently long period, the said metal may be damaged or even destroyed.

Some of the consequences are:

a.  Erosion of metallic surfaces, which often gives a characteristic appearance to the damaged material, suggesting that it has been gnawed by rodents. The rate of erosion may be accentuated if the liquid itself already has corrosive tendencies, e.g. water with large amounts of dissolved oxygen, or acids.

b.  Audible rattling or cracking sounds may be heard which can reach the pitch of dangerous vibration.

c.  Reduction in the efficiency of the pump.

### How to avoid cavitation

i.   To ensure cavitation free running, the Net Positive Suction Head required by the pump must be matched by the Net Positive Suction Head from the system.

ii.  Wherever possible, suction lines should be kept as short as possible and suction velocities should not exceed 1.5 m/s. Bends (which should be large radius) and 'T' pieces should be kept to a minimum and should not be positioned so near to the pump suction that local effects are still present as the liquid enters the pump.

iii. Ensure that all valves which are fitted in the suction line are essential. If so then check that these are of the gate type. The latter type of valve has an appreciable pressure drop, even when fully open.

iv. Special care should be taken with installations where two or more pumps are fed from a common heater.

v. Care should also be taken to avoid places where gas pockets can occur. See Figure 1 which illustrates good and bad practices in suction pipework layout.

vi. When a by-pass is fitted to a pump and this has to go back into the suction line at some point, a check must be made to ensure that the resultant temperature rises (at any point) do not reduce the Net Positive Suction Head available to a point where cavitation occurs.

## Efficiency

Efficiency of a pump is its ability to perform with the least energy input.

## Friction head

The head is necessary to overcome resistance to motion in pipes and fittings. It is of great importance as it may exceed the static head.

## Gauge pressure

The intensity of pressure exerted by a pump, recorded by gauge, calibrated above atmospheric pressure.

## Net positive suction head (NPSH)

The method of specifying suction performance under critical suction conditions including altitude, high temperature and high vapour pressure and the limitations of the pump itself.

## NPSH available

The absolute pressure of the liquid at the pump entry, less its vapour pressure at the pumping temperature. It is an expression of the installation conditions.

## NPSH required

The minimum absolute pressure necessary at the pump entry to maintain the required flow without cavitation.

*NOTE:*
*The NPSH required must always be less than the NPSH available.*

## Power

The total amount of energy required to drive a pump or a pumping set.

## Power and efficiency

$$\text{Power of a pump} = \frac{\text{work done}}{\text{time (seconds)}}$$

$$= \frac{\text{Newton} \times \text{metres}}{\text{seconds}}$$

$$= \frac{\text{force} \times \text{total head}}{\text{seconds}}$$

$$= \frac{\text{kg} \times 9.81 \times \text{head}}{\text{seconds}}$$

$$= \frac{9.81 \times \text{litres} \times \text{head}}{\text{seconds}}$$

Pump power $= 9.81 \times \text{l/sec} \times \text{m}$

Watts $= \dfrac{\text{Nm}}{\text{S}}$

*NOTE:*

*1 kg/s = 1 l/sec*

*1 Newton = 1kg × m/sec² = force*

*1 Newton = 1kg × 9.81*

The total pump head must include the measured pump head, plus all pipe and fitting resistances plus the velocity head.

Total head $= L + Lf + \frac{1}{2}MV^2$

The efficiency of a pump is the ratio of the input power to the brake power. The brake power is the power absorbed by the pump output.

Efficiency % $= \dfrac{\text{output} \times 100}{\text{Input}}$

Input or power to be provided.

Input in kW $= \dfrac{\text{output in kW}}{\text{Efficiency: \%}}$

Owing to the combined effectiveness of the pump and motor, overall efficiencies of about 50% are quite normal for coupled sets.

## Self-priming

When a pump is operating under suction lift (negative) conditions, self-priming is the characteristic which enables the pump to evacuate air from the suction line, thus creating a vacuum which allows the atmospheric pressure to push the liquid through the suction pipe into the pump.

## Static delivery head

The vertical distance between the centre-line of the pump and the free surface of the discharged liquid.

## Static head

The pressure exerted by a liquid at rest, to the surface, expressed in terms of vertical head of the liquid.

## Suction head (positive)

This exists if the source of liquid is above the pump, a condition generally known as 'flooded suction,' and is the vertical distance from the centre-line of the pump up to the free surface of the liquid.

## Suction lift (negative)

This exists if the source of the liquid is below the pump and is the vertical distance from the centre-line of the pump up to the free surface of the liquid.

When a fluid (liquid or air) is sucked into a pump, it is pushed in by the pressure of the atmosphere as a result of the pressure of the fluid in the pump being reduced. The pressure of the atmosphere and hence the depth from which a pump will 'suck', varies with the altitude above sea-level and with the state of the weather (see definition of Atmospheric Pressure).

The suction lift for which a pump is listed is, unless otherwise stated, the total suction lift of which the pump is capable at the listed speed, assuming normal temperature at normal atmospheric pressure, deductions being made for high altitude and for high temperature and vapour pressure. The suction lift of a pump is also affected by the viscosity of the liquid, but this should be covered by the manufacturers' ratings at stated viscosities.

The effect of vapour pressure or permissible suction lift is important, particularly with volatile liquids such as gasoline, aromatic solvents and most liquids at elevated temperatures and where suction lift is necessary, full details of the installation should preferably be referred to the supplier for consideration.

Where the suction conditions are liable to be critical it will be necessary to calculate NPSH values to ensure correct pump selection.

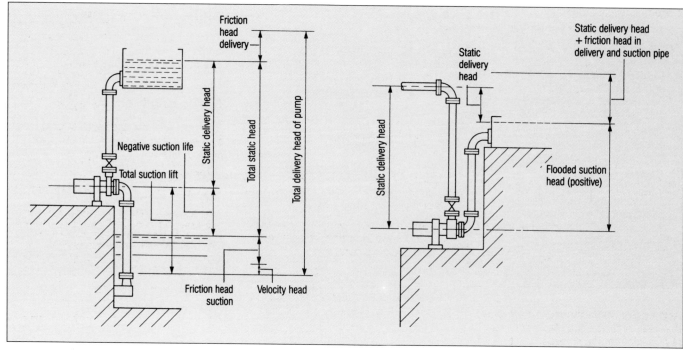

**Figure 2** *Pumping definitions*

## Total delivery head

The static delivery head, plus the velocity head and the friction head in the inlet pipe system.

## Total head on the pump

The static delivery head, plus the velocity head and the friction head in the entire pipe system, plus the static suction lift, or minus the static suction head (positive), as the case may be. (See Figure 2, which illustrates various head conditions on a pump).

## Total suction head (positive)

The static suction lift, minus the velocity head and friction head in the inlet pipe system.

## Total suction lift (negative)

The static suction lift, plus the velocity head and friction head in the suction pipe system.

## Vacuum

A space in a pump system from which, some or all of the air has been removed and the pressure is below atmospheric pressure.

Vacuum is normally measured in millimetres head of mercury, indicating the degree of partial vacuum in a pipe or vessel. A complete or perfect vacuum is impossible to attain.

## Vapour pressure

Is the minimum pressure necessary to prevent evaporation of a liquid at a given temperature. All liquids evaporate spontaneously unless prevented by external pressure. Vapour pressure increases rapidly by a rise in temperature. The vapour pressure of water is 0 at freezing point but reaches normal atmospheric pressure, bar at 100°C, which is the boiling point of water at sea-level.

## Velocity head

This is the pressure required to set a liquid in motion and is generally of practical importance only in the case of pumps of large capacity or where the suction lift is near the limit.

Velocity head $= 0.5 \times M \times V^2$

where $M = kg$

$V$ = velocity in m/second

# Pump types

The two main pump classifications are centrifugal and positive displacement, there being many different types within each category. However, the main characteristics referred to below can be regarded as generally applicable.

## Centrifugal

A centrifugal pump in its simplest form consists of an impeller and a volute casing which has to be filled completely with liquid when the pump is in operation, the impeller 'throwing' the pump liquid to the outside of the volute, thus imparting kinetic energy. In this way a centrifugal pump is capable of generating a certain head which varies according to the pump speed and the accepted method of expressing the relationship between capacity and head is by means of a 'characteristic curve,' often referred to as the Q/H curve where Q is the quantity (flow rate) and H is the head.

Typical characteristic curves for a simple centrifugal pump including power and efficiency are illustrated in Graph 1.

*Graph1* *Typical characteristic curves*

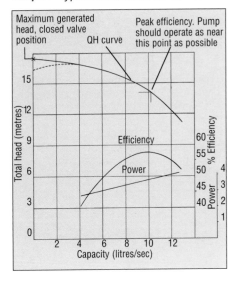

At the point where the curve intersects the head ordinate, the generated head is at a maximum and corresponds to a no-flow condition. This is often referred to as the 'closed valve pressure' and a centrifugal pump should not be left operating in this condition for any length of time as it will rapidly over-heat due to the horse power at this point being turned effectively into heat energy.

The main characteristics of centrifugal pumps can broadly be summarised as follows:

a. Capacity varies with head (see Q/H curve)

b. Capacity proportional to pump speed

c. Head proportional to the square of the pump speed

d. Non-self-priming

e. Suitable for low-viscosity liquids.

## Positive displacement

Positive pumps usually consist of a casing containing gears, vanes, pistons, lobes, screws, sliding-shoes etc. operating with minimum clearance, the liquid being positively transferred from suction to discharge port. Due to fine clearances involved, most positive pumps are self-priming and some will handle entrained gas or air. Neglecting leakage, they deliver almost constant capacity irrespective of variations in head so that the usual Q/H curve when drawn for a typical positive-displacement pump is an almost vertical straight line. For this reason it is not usual to provide Q/H curves for positive pumps.

Their main characteristics are as follows:

a. Capacity substantially independent of head

b. Capacity proportional to speed

c. Self-priming

d. Suitable for viscous liquids (reduced speeds usually necessary for high viscosities).

# Applications

Pumped systems or a booster set will be required where any one or number of the following conditions prevail.

1. Where there is no piped public water supply and the only available water is at or below ground level.

2. Where the pressure from the public supply main is insufficient to reach the highest or most distant draw-off point for the whole or part of the day.

3. Where the available pressure is sufficient for normal domestic and culinary purposes but is too low for other equipment or fittings to the building, e.g. hose reels, fire hydrants, wash down points, showers, process equipment etc.

4. Where the pressure is adequate for all the building's requirements but the Water Supply Undertaker is not prepared to guarantee the pressure in the foreseeable future.

# Systems

## Packaged systems

Most pump manufacturers supply equipment that is prefabricated using all the components necessary to provide a system that is factory tested to a proven performance. Package systems reduce the amount of site work and ensure that the arrangement of all components can be adequately maintained.

It is usual for package units to be positioned on a prepared base; only final connections to the suction and discharge pipework and connection of the electricity supply to the pre-wired integral control panel is required on site.

## Unpackaged component systems

It is sometimes necessary to design and install separate items of pumping equipment and controls to form a system on site. The collection of items are all

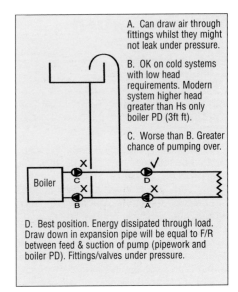

D. Best position. Energy dissipated through load. Draw down in expansion pipe will be equal to F/R between feed & suction of pump (pipework and boiler PD). Fittings/valves under pressure.

*Figure 3* *Pump positioning*

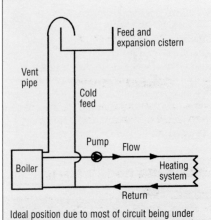

Ideal position due to most of circuit being under positive pressure to prevent ingress of air into the system, causing subsequent damage. Pump over will not occur due to position of open vent and cold feed making the neutral point on the same side of the pump.

*Figure 4* *Ideal position*

supplied separately and the installer is required to connect the pumps, vessels, valves and control equipment into an operational system.

Although satisfactory systems can be arranged, there are a number of disadvantages. When properly costed, it is often found that this method of providing a pumping system is expensive and the responsibility for resolving problems is impossible to apportion between the pump manufacturer, ancillary equipment supplier and the installer. There may also be over design of some systems due to the 'ad hoc' selection of various components.

# Pump selection

Between 90 and 95 per cent of the world's pumping is carried out using centrifugal pumps and wherever the conditions are suitable, a centrifugal pump is normally the simplest and most economical type available.

For installations operating under flooded suction conditions, i.e. with a positive suction head, or where large volumes of water have to be moved at relatively low heads, then the centrifugal pump is the natural choice. Many special types have been developed, including multi-stage designs in which a number of impellers are assembled from a common shaft with the pumped liquid being delivered to each impeller. Multi-stage pumps may be of horizontal or vertical design, the latter having the advantage of requiring appreciably less floor space.

For water boosting services where relatively small capacities are required at fairly high heads, vertical multi-stage centrifugal pumps have been developed. These have small diameter impellers having a low tip velocity, one of the factors contributing to the quiet operation which is so often essential for this class of application, particularly in residential premises and hospitals. Where viscous liquids are to be pumped or where self-priming with good suction function performance is essential, a positive-displacement pump would be the first choice. With some applications however, it is necessary for the pump to operate for periods with a completely dry suction and one specialised type, the sliding shoe design, is capable of handling this condition for reasonable periods without harm. Such a dry suction condition could arise with recirculation systems where the suction source may be starved for periods due to cyclical or abnormal operating conditions, with sump pumps emptying engine-room bilges aboard ship and similar duties.

With the growing interest in pollution control, there is an increasing interest in pumps suitable for handling oily water without excessive emulsification so that the liquid can be handled efficiently by conventional oil/water separators and the sliding-shoe design, for example, operating at reduced speed, has proved very suitable for this application.

Centrifugal pumps are generally considered unsuitable as they churn the liquid excessively and the oil/water separators are unable to handle the resultant emulsification.

Although these notes on pump types have referred briefly to the main characteristics of centrifugal and positive displacement pumps, the past few years have seen a rapid growth in the number of specialised designs available for particular applications. It is therefore advisable for pump manufacturers to be approached during the early stages of installation layout and design for their recommendations.

# Noise

Noise can be very simply defined as unwanted sound. It is generally accepted as an irritant which can affect our mental and physical state and its effect can be particularly significant in the relatively quiet environment of the office, domestic and hospital buildings.

Noise transmission associated with pumping systems falls into three main categories, airborne noise, water borne noise and noise transmitted through the actual structure of a building. Careful selection of equipment is most important to ensure that noise generation is kept to an absolute minimum.

Airborne noise is not normally a particularly serious problem with pumping equipment and its effects can be minimised by careful siting of the plant room in relation to working or living areas and by the use of sound insulating materials on the walls and ceiling of the plant room.

Water borne noise may be more of a problem as it carries through the pipework to any part of the building and the most effective way of dealing with it therefore is to prevent it at source as far as possible, rather than to suppress it. Particular attention should be paid to pipe sizing and layout to keep water velocities low and avoid turbulence and pipework should be securely anchored to prevent vibration. Where risers pass through floors they should not be grouted in but supported by soft packing materials and where pipework is clipped to walls, ceilings etc. pipe clips should preferably be insulated with rubber, felt or similar absorbent material. While it is generally considered that 1440rpm pumps are inherently quieter than 2900rpm pumps, modern vertical multi-stage pumps with small diameter impellers having a low top speed operating at 2900rpm have proved to be extremely quiet in operation.

Noise can be transmitted to the structure of the building through the foundations of the pump and in certain instances it may be desirable to mount the pump sets on resilient mats or anti-vibration mountings in which case it is essential that flexible connections are fitted to the suction and discharge flanges of the pump set to minimise the possibility of vibrations being transmitted to the structure through the pipework and to prevent undue strain on the flanges.

These simple precautions are normally sufficient to produce satisfactory results but where exceptionally quiet operation is essential for a very specialised application it may be necessary to take additional precautions and such cases should be referred to companies who specialise in noise suppression.

# Pump installation

It is most important that pumps are correctly installed and the following notes are intended as a general guide.

## Location

The pump should be in an accessible location and there must be room for dismantling and maintenance. It is normally advisable to raise the pump above floor level so that it is more accessible and can be easily drained.

## Piping

The size and suction of delivery pipes should be carefully calculated and should in any case not be smaller than the pump connections. For long runs of piping or when handling viscous liquid they should generally be larger than the pump connection. For other than very simple runs, the actual pipe losses should be calculated so as to check the total head on the pump. It is quite common for the friction head to exceed the static liquid.

Piping should be accurately cut and fitted so that it can be bolted up to the pump branches without putting any strain on the pump or pipe joints. Easy bends should be used and sharp elbows and tees avoided. Particular care must be taken that all joints in the suction line are absolutely tight to avoid loss of capacity or difficulty in priming due to airleaks. In the case of non-self priming centrifugal pumps, the suction pipe should slope up towards the pump suction to avoid the possibility of trapping air in the top of the suction piping.

## Suction strainer

For most industrial applications or where solids may be present, a suction strainer should be fitted to protect the pump. The total area of the holes in the strainer should never be less than twice the cross-sectional area of the suction pipe, preferably three times as a general rule and four times or more if there is likelihood of frequent clogging.

## Foot valve

With most pumps operating under suction lift conditions a foot valve at the end of the suction pipe is desirable to keep the suction pipe full at all times and eliminate the need for priming after a shutdown. Depending upon the application, the foot valve may be combined with the suction strainer.

## Discharge non-return valve

If there is any appreciable head or length of delivery pipe, a non-return valve should be fitted, both to make it possible to open up the pump without draining the pipe and to prevent the head of water from driving in reverse after stopping.

## Relief valve

Positive displacement pumps will develop excessively high pressures if run with the discharge shut-off or throttled and a spring-loaded relief valve should be fitted to the pump.

A relief valve is designed to give temporary protection against an abnormal condition and, should the valve operate, the cause should be ascertained and rectified.

## Electric motors

Squirrel-cage AC motors are the normal choice wherever possible and can usually be started direct-on-line. Under these conditions the average motor takes four to six times full load current on starting and where local regulations or conditions prohibit direct-on-line starting, the use of slip-ring motors or other reduced-current starting methods should be considered. The type of enclosure, e.g. drip proof or totally enclosed, should be considered with reference to conditions under which the pump will be working.

## Switch gear

It is not possible to protect a motor adequately by means of fuses only as a fuse that will carry the normal starting current is too heavy to give protection against ordinary overloads. Pumps should be controlled by starters with suitable overload releases, set in accordance with the manufacturer's recommendations.

# A guide to sewage submersible pump selection

## Pump options

There are a considerable number of pump variations available for an even larger range of applications.

## Liquids

Sewage may consist of mainly water with a wide range of other matter. Human waste is mainly 1% approximately solids. Soaps, cooking oil, bleach and a lot more are usually diluted, however sand and grit can cause damage to the pumps.

Storm water, has grit, sand and plastic items in suspension against which care has to be taken in selection of a pump.

Water features, fish ponds and fountains, again have sand and grit in the water and are the main problems that cause a pump to fail. The conditions are very harsh, pump selection is therefore very important.

## Sewage

Pumping Sewage for a building complex to a mains pipeline or process station has its options of pump available, the impeller types include, vortex, single channel and chopper.

First there is the fully packaged unit, this consists of a GRP tank with one or two pumps fitted inside. Size is the limiting factor for transporting to site and the cost. The advantage of this type of unit is the site work is kept to a minimum, simply set the tank into the desired hole, connect the incoming pipe(s) and the discharge pipe, the electrical connection to the starter box and the job is almost complete.

Larger collection sumps may be constructed from concrete. The pumps are often slid into place down guide rails fixed to the side of the tank. When required the pumps can be raised for cleaning or repair. Some times the pumps are free – standing secured by a chain and the delivery pipe is a flexible hose.

When the sump type and size has been selected, it is necessary to select the pump impeller but perhaps more importantly the shaft seal arrangement.

## Impeller types

### Vortex impeller

This type of Impeller is ideal for solids in suspension and depending on the pump inlet size will pass solids clear through the pump with little risk of damage to the pump.

### Mono channel

A single non clogging impeller, this type is ideal for the higher more viscose liquids, for example sludges. The impeller is good for producing higher heads.

### Chopper

The chopper type impeller is designed to condition the solids in the liquid. String, small plastic items etc., can be cut up prior to entering the pump. The main advantage is the risk of blocking the pipe work with large solids is reduced. The main problem can be the blades can be damaged by stones or metal objects. As a result the repair costs can be high and frequent.

## Mechanical shaft seals

There are a number of combinations of seal arrangement available, by far the best option is a double mechanical hard faced seal. Silicon and tungsten carbide faces are ideal for the demanding conditions, both are expensive but give a long working life and so work out cheaper to run over a long period, well worth the investment.

The best combination of double mechanical seal is one of them being hard faced or a standard carbon faced seal with back up lip seal. Or the less expensive option, a double lip seal with an 'O' ring for a seal. Beware, the latter will not last long, repairs and down time will be frequent.

## Double mechanical shaft seal

A quality seal arrangement in a submersible pump will have a hard faced seal that is in contact with the liquid being pumped. A second seal say 25mm higher up the shaft can be either hard faced or a carbon faced seal. The second seal is to give added protection to the Electric motor to prevent water ingress should the first seal fail. Between the seals is a small reservoir that is filled with a non conductive oil, the oil serves to lubricate the seal faces, should water get past the first seal a probe that is built into this area short circuits. (12-24 volts). The probe is connected to a warning device light or buzzer in the control panel. As soon as practical the pump can be removed a new seal and oil installed and returned to work. The advantages are minimum down time with minimum parts required.

## Calculations

Most of the calculations related to pumps have been covered in other parts of this guide and they apply to submersibles just the same. However viscosity and solids content are of major importance to our pump selection.

Heavy sludge may be some 3% solids in suspension, this will increase the specific gravity of the liquid and so must be allowed for. Viscosity will vary depending upon the nature of the liquid.

Domestic sewage is 1% approximately solids. Use of a chopper or vortex impeller type pump is your choice.

When pumping the solids (1-2%) through horizontal pipework there is a need to keep the liquid velocity to at least 1.5 metres per second or more, failure to do so will allow the solids to settle out in the pipe and may cause a blockage after a period of time. Similarly to pump the liquid vertically the velocity should be increased to 2.5 metres per second, failure to do so will result in solids falling back down the pipe, with a blockage shortly to follow.

The following question check list should be answered before selecting a pumping system:

1. What is the liquid to be pumped? Sewage, storm water, dirty water.

2. What is the quantity to be pumped in what time?

3. What static head height is the liquid to be pumped to?

4. Where is the liquid to be pumped from – to? Distance?

5. What is the solids content, nature of the liquid?

6. What is the most efficient impeller we can use for the task? Vortex, chopper, single channel?

7. What power is there available? 415-3-50 240-1-50 UK?

8. What is the best installation GRP tank or concrete sump?

9. Is a duty and standby pump(s) required?

# Fire protection services

# Principle causes of fires in buildings

The three basic essentials required before any fire can start are:

a. Fuel, i.e. something to burn
b. Air, i.e. oxygen to sustain combustion
c. Heat.

The process of combustion or burning can be likened to a triangle as shown in Figure 1.

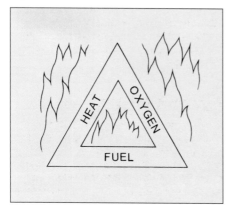

*Figure 1* Fire triangle

Removal of any one of the sides of that triangle will result in extinguishment of the fire and this is the principle on which all forms of fire extinguishment are based.

# Classification of fire risks

Fires are divided into three categories, A, B and C. Details of these together with the methods of extinguishment and extinguishing agents are shown in Table 1.

*Table 1* Classification of fire risks

| Class | Risk involved | Method of extinguishant | Extinguishing agent |
|---|---|---|---|
| A | Wood<br>Textiles<br>Paper<br>All goods manufactured from above | Cooling | Water |
| B | Inflammable liquids | Smothering | Dry powder<br>$CO_2$ gas<br>Foam |
| C | Electrial equipment | Smothering with a non-conductive agent | Dry powder<br>$CO_2$ gas |

# Residential/ domestic fire sprinkler systems

A residential fire sprinkler system for life safety purposes is designed to fight fires at an early stage in their development, thus controlling the fire and enabling occupants to reach safety. The sprinkler system will consist of pipework that is constantly charged with water, connected to a suitable water supply, with a number of sprinkler heads that discharge water. In the event of a fire it is the heat generated which will cause a sprinkler head to operate. Thus the closest sprinkler head to the fire is most likely to operate, and may be the only head to operate. Once a flow of water is detected in the pipework an alarm is triggered which operates a visual and audible alarm.

Sprinkler protection for residential and domestic properties are described in DD251, a Draft for Development published in 2000, issued by BSI. DD251 gives recommendations for the water supplies, system components such as the sprinkler heads and valves, and for the design, installation, commissioning, and maintenance of the system. The Draft for Development is open to public comment and changes to the recommendations contained within it may be made during the documents lifetime. The public comment period will usually last for 2 – 3 years after which time BSI will consider whether a full British Standard is required.

It is recommended that installers of residential/domestic systems be familiar with the content of DD251. Installation of residential sprinkler systems should only be undertaken by certificated sprinkler contractors, i.e. those contractors who have undertaken and passed a recognised course of training specific to sprinkler system installation.

The properties covered by DD251 include 'Residential occupancies', such as: apartments, residential homes, HMOs, blocks of flats, boarding houses, aged persons homes, nursing homes, residential rehabilitation accommodation and dormitories, and 'Domestic occupancies', such as individual dwelling houses, individual flats, maisonettes and transportable homes.

Where a sprinkler system is being considered it is necessary to consult the fire authority, the water supplier, the building control body and the insurer(s) of the dwelling and dwelling contents.

# Feasibility

Before installation work can begin the service pipe water supply should be tested to ensure that, when at its lowest hydraulic characteristic, the required flow rate and pressure requirement can be achieved. If the required pressure and flow rate is not achieved the installation should not proceed and the designer of the system should be consulted.

The installation requirements of BS 6700 (Specification for design, installation, testing and maintenance of services supplying water for domestic use within buildings and their curtilages) and the Water Regulations apply.

# Water supplies

Sprinkler systems should ideally be connected to a town main but may also be connected to one of the following water supplies:

a. Pressure tank or vessel

b. Automatic pump drawing from a stored water facility

c. Automatic booster pump drawing water from a town main or an elevated storage tank

d. Gravity fed stored water system.

The majority of installations will be mains connected with either a dedicated sprinkler supply or a demand valve to divert all available incoming water to the sprinkler system. Where the water supply is shared with the domestic services and there is no priority demand valve an additional flow rate is required in all calculations, reference should be made to DD251.

# Components

## Sprinkler heads

A sprinkler head is a device that allows water to discharge in a predetermined pattern; different types of sprinkler head produce different patterns. The sprinkler head is operated by temperature, i.e. when a critical temperature is reached the water will flow through the sprinkler.

This critical temperature is known as the 'temperature rating' of the sprinkler and for normal conditions in the United Kingdom will be 57°C or 68°C. In any case the temperature rating of the sprinklers should be the closest to but at least 30°C greater than the highest anticipated ambient temperature of the location. If sprinklers are installed under glazed roofs the sprinkler temperature rating should be within the range of 79°C to 100°C.

Sprinklers should be installed in accordance with their approval listing specification and supplier/manufacturer's instructions. Only new equipment should be used. Any sprinkler head removed from a system should be discarded. Sprinkler heads should only be fitted by qualified installers.

When using residential/domestic sprinkler heads the system should be capable of providing flow rates in accordance with the manufacturer's recommendations, based on the result of the component performance test, or the flow rates required for conventional sprinkler heads, see DD251.

If conventional sprinkler heads are to be used the flow rate at the sprinkler head should be not less than 60 l/min for single head operation and 42 l/min for each of two heads operating simultaneously in domestic properties and for each of four heads operating simultaneously in residential properties.

Sprinklers should be positioned such that they are not more than 4m apart nor are they more than 2m from any wall or partition. The distance between sprinklers within a room should not be less than 2m. DD251 recommends that the maximum area protected by a single sprinkler be 15m².

Sprinklers should be positioned so that:

a. They are in accordance with the manufacturer's instructions identified in the approval listing.

b. Their sensitivity and discharge pattern are not adversely affected by obstructions such as constructional beams or light fittings or other sprinkler heads.

c. The potential for a shielded fire to develop is taken into account.

d. The heat sensitive elements are within 25 to 100mm below the ceiling for ceiling mounted sprinklers.

e. The heat sensitive elements are within 100 to 150mm below the ceiling for wall mounted sprinklers.

f. The whole of the floor area and the walls from the floor up to 0.7m below the ceiling are wetted when the sprinklers are operated.

*NOTE concealed sprinklers may be considered with the approval of the authority having jurisdiction.*

The minimum operating pressure at any sprinkler should not be less than 0.5 bar.

Sprinklers should be threaded suitable for use with fittings threaded in accordance with ISO 7-1: 1982 and ISO 65: 1981 and BS 21.

The nominal size of sprinklers should be one of those shown in Table 2.

*Table 2  Sprinkler head orifice and pipe thread sizes*

| Nominal diameter of orifice (mm) | Nominal pipe thread size (inch) |
|---|---|
| 10 | $\frac{3}{8}$ |
| 15 and 20 | $\frac{1}{2}$ |
| 20 | $\frac{3}{4}$ |

## Valves and alarm devices

Valves and alarm devices suitable for residential and domestic systems should be installed in accordance with manufacturers' instructions and should be manufactured to the appropriate British Standards, where applicable.

The sprinkler system should have:

a. A backflow prevention valve to prevent mains water contamination.

b. A stop valve, of the full bore lever type to isolate sprinkler pipework from mains water supply. The valve should be locked in the open position to prevent accidental interruption of the water supply to the sprinkler system.

c. And, where appropriate, a priority demand valve.

d. An alarm test valve; a test facility should be provided at the end of the hydraulically most remote range pipe on the system consisting of not less than a 22mm nominal diameter pipe and quick acting test valve with an outlet nozzle equivalent in size to the smallest sprinkler in the system.

e. A drain and test valve should be fitted at the lowest point of the sprinkler pipework to allow testing and the complete draining of the sprinkler system, consisting of not less than a 22mm nominal diameter pipe and quick acting test valve with an outlet nozzle equivalent in size to the smallest sprinkler in the system.

f. An air bleed valve fitted to the highest point/s of the sprinkler system to allow the purging of air from the system.

g. A water flow alarm for detecting water flow into the system and sounding an alarm.

h. A mechanically driven alarm or an electrically operated flow switch which, when triggered by the flow of water in the sprinkler system, will operate an audio-visual alarm.

# Pipework installation

## Pipework

All pipework should be installed in the same way as other water services, as described in BS 6700.

Pipes and fittings should either comply with the appropriate standards of Table 3 or for plastic and other pipe and fittings suitable for residential and domestic sprinkler systems, be installed in accordance with the manufacturers' instructions and the approval and listing requirements of an independent third party certification body.

## Pipework support

Only metallic pipe fixings should be used. Batons and lock type clips should be fitted in close proximity to the sprinkler heads to ensure no movement is allowed which may recoil heads into the ceiling or loft voids. Sprinkler system pipework should be supported at the intervals given in Tables 4, 5, and 6.

## Pipe sizing (Hydraulic calculations)

All pipework downstream of the alarm valve should be sized by hydraulic calculation; calculation of pressure losses throughout the system.

The difference in static pressure between two connected points in a sprinkler system is given by the following formula:

Static pressure difference, $p = 0.1h$ (bar) where $h$ is the vertical distance between the two points (in m).

The pressure loss due to pipe friction should be calculated from the Hazen-Williams formula.

$$p = \frac{6.05 \times 10^5}{C^{1.85} \times d^{4.87}} \times L \times Q^{1.85}$$

where $p$ = pressure loss in pipe (bar)

$Q$ = flow rate through pipe (litres/min)

$d$ = mean bore of pipe (mm)

$L$ = equivalent length of straight pipe, bends and fittings (m)

$C$ = a constant for pipe material (see Table 7)

For flow rates of 60 l/min the following tables give the appropriate pressure losses per metre of pipe.

*Table 3* *Pipe and pipe fittings specifications*

| Location | Pipe | Fittings |
|---|---|---|
| Below ground | BS EN 1057 NOTE 1<br>BS 1387<br>BS 3505<br>BS 3506<br>BS 6572 | BS EN 1254 Part 2 NOTE 1<br>BS 1740 Part 1<br>BS 4346<br>BS 4346<br>BS EN 1254 Part 3 |
| Above ground | BS EN 1057<br>BS 1387<br>BS 7291 Part 4 | BS EN 1254 Part 1 NOTE 2<br>BS 1740 Part 1<br>BS 7291 Part 4 |

1. Copper tube to BS EN 1057 used in underground locations should be R220 (annealed), thick walled, factory plastic coated tube. In this case, fittings should be manipulative Type B. Brass fittings in underground locations should be immune to de-zincification.

2. Capillary fittings to be jointed by soldering or brazing with alloys with a melting point of not less than 230°C as specified in BS EN 29453.

*Table 4* *Maximum spacing of fixings for copper and stainless steel pipework*

| Nominal diameter (mm) | Horizontal run (m) | Vertical run (m) |
|---|---|---|
| 22 | 1.8 | 2.4 |
| 28 | 1.8 | 2.4 |
| 35 | 2.4 | 3.0 |
| 42 | 2.4 | 3.0 |
| 54 | 2.7 | 3.0 |

*Table 5* *Maximum spacing of fixings for steel pipework*

| Nominal diameter (mm) | Horizontal run (m) | Vertical run (m) |
|---|---|---|
| 15 | 1.8 | 2.4 |
| 20 | 2.4 | 3.0 |
| 25 | 2.4 | 3.0 |
| 32 | 2.7 | 3.0 |
| 40 | 3.0 | 3.6 |
| 50 | 3.0 | 3.6 |

*Table 6* *Maximum spacing of fixings for CPVC pipework*

| Nominal diameter (mm) | Horizontal run (m) | Vertical run (m) |
|---|---|---|
| 12 (⅜″) | 0.6 | 1.2 |
| 15 (½″) | 0.8 | 1.6 |
| 22 (¾″) | 0.8 | 1.6 |
| 28 (1″) | 0.9 | 1.8 |
| 32 (1¼″) | 1.0 | 2.0 |
| 40 (1½″) | 1.05 | 2.1 |
| 50 (2″) | 1.2 | 2.4 |

*Table 7* *Values of C for steel, copper and CPVC*

| Material | C |
|---|---|
| Steel | 120 |
| Copper | 140 |
| CPVC | 150 |

*Table 8* *Pressure loss in 1m of copper pipe for a water flow rate of 60 litres/min*

| Tube size (mm) | Mean size (mm) | Pressure loss (bar) |
|---|---|---|
| 22 | 20.2 | 0.0554 |
| 28 | 26.2 | 0.0156 |
| 35 | 32.6 | 0.0054 |
| 42 | 39.6 | 0.0021 |
| 54 | 51.6 | 0.0006 |

*Table 9* *Pressure loss in 1m of CPVC pipe for a water flow rate of 60 litres/min*

| Tube size (mm) | Mean size (mm) | Pressure loss (bar) |
|---|---|---|
| 20 | 20 | 0.0512 |
| 25 | 25 | 0.0173 |
| 32 | 32 | 0.0052 |
| 40 | 40 | 0.0018 |
| 50 | 50 | 0.0006 |

*Table 10* *Pressure loss in 1m of steel pipe for a water flow rate of 60 litres/min*

| Tube size (mm) | Mean size (mm) | Pressure loss (bar) |
|---|---|---|
| 20 | 21.63 | 0.0529 |
| 25 | 27.31 | 0.0170 |
| 32 | 35.97 | 0.0044 |
| 40 | 41.86 | 0.0021 |
| 50 | 52.98 | 0.0007 |

## Equivalent lengths of pipe for pulled bends in copper tube (in m of pipe)

Frictional pressure loss in copper pipework bends where the direction of water flow is changed through 45° or more should be calculated using the following equation.

Equivalent length

$$= 7.65 \times 10^{-3} \, Q^{0.15} \, d^{0.87}$$

where  Q = the water flow rate (litres/min)

d = the tube bore (mm)

The equivalent length of pipe for the pressure loss due to the bend for a water flow rate of 60 litres/min is as given in Table 11.

*Table 11* *The equivalent length of copper pipe for the pressure loss due to the bend for a water flow rate of 60 litres/min*

| Tube size (mm) | Mean size (mm) | Equivalent length (m) |
|---|---|---|
| 22 | 20.2 | 0.1932 |
| 28 | 26.2 | 0.2423 |
| 35 | 32.6 | 0.2930 |
| 42 | 39.6 | 0.3470 |
| 54 | 51.6 | 0.4369 |

## Frost protection

It is essential that any water filled pipework which may be subjected to low temperatures should be protected against freezing at all times. Note: the use of electrical trace heating and/or lagging or antifreeze solutions, or subsidiary alternate systems may be considered.

## Extent of sprinkler protection

Sprinkler protection should be provided in all habitable parts of the dwelling. There are a number of areas that can be exempt from protection including:

a. Bathrooms with a floor area of less than 5m²

b. Cupboards and pantries with floor areas of less than 2m² and where the least dimension does not exceed 1m and the walls and ceilings are covered with non-combustible or limited-combustible materials

c. And crawl spaces.

Non-communicating parts of the property e.g. attached garages, boiler houses, etc., can also be exempted if the separation from the habitable areas has a 30 minute fire resistance.

**Table 12** *Copper - equivalent lengths of pipe for fittings (in m of pipe)*

| Fitting | Nominal diameter (mm) | | | | |
|---|---|---|---|---|---|
| | 22 | 28 | 35 | 42 | 54 |
| Tee run | 0.068 | 0.10 | 0.13 | 0.16 | 0.22 |
| Tee branch | 1.00 | 1.40 | 1.80 | 2.30 | 3.10 |
| 90° capillary elbow | 0.49 | 0.68 | 0.91 | 1.10 | 1.70 |
| 90° compression elbow | 0.74 | 1.00 | 1.30 | 1.50 | 2.10 |

**Table 13** *Steel - equivalent lengths of pipe for fittings (in m of pipe)*

| Fitting | Nominal diameter (mm) | | | | | |
|---|---|---|---|---|---|---|
| | 20 | 25 | 32 | 40 | 50 | 65 |
| 90° screwed elbow | 0.63 | 0.77 | 1.04 | 1.22 | 1.46 | 1.89 |
| 90° welded elbow | 0.30 | 0.36 | 0.49 | 0.56 | 0.69 | 0.88 |
| 45° screwed elbow | 0.34 | 0.40 | 0.55 | 0.66 | 0.76 | 1.02 |
| Standard screwed tee or cross | 1.25 | 1.54 | 2.13 | 2.44 | 2.91 | 3.81 |

**Table 14** *CPVC - equivalent lengths of pipe for fittings (in m of pipe)*

| Fitting | Nominal diameter (mm) | | | | | | |
|---|---|---|---|---|---|---|---|
| | 20 | 25 | 32 | 40 | 50 | 65 | 80 |
| Tee run | 0.30 | 0.30 | 0.30 | 0.30 | 0.30 | 0.60 | 0.60 |
| Tee branch | 0.90 | 1.50 | 1.80 | 2.40 | 3.00 | 3.60 | 4.50 |
| 90° elbow | 2.10 | 2.10 | 2.40 | 2.70 | 3.30 | 3.60 | 3.90 |
| 45° elbow | 0.30 | 0.30 | 0.60 | 0.60 | 0.60 | 0.90 | 1.20 |
| Coupling | 0.30 | 0.30 | 0.30 | 0.30 | 0.30 | 0.60 | 0.60 |

# Commissioning

On completion of the installation the pipework needs to be tested; leakage and hydraulic tests need to be carried out. A small quantity of air should be left in the system at the end of the purging process.

With the pipework filled with water at the normal working pressure for the system any leaks should be found and repaired. The water supply to the system should then be isolated and the system should be tested to a minimum of 1.5 times working pressure for one hour. If the system fails to maintain pressure the leak should be found and corrected and this test repeated.

The sprinkler system should be tested to ensure that at least the required flow rate can be achieved at the required pressure at the alarm test valve. If this flow rate at the required pressure cannot be achieved, the system should not be approved for use until the system has been corrected and the test specified in this clause has been passed. The installer and the designer should be responsible for correcting the system.

The alarm (and/or repeaters) should be heard in all habitable rooms in the premises protected by sprinklers coupled to the alarm device being tested. The stated audibility should be achieved when there is a water flow of not more than 60 litres/minute through the alarm device under test.

When all the commissioning tests have been passed the installer should sign a Certificate to indicate that the system has been designed and installed following the guidance set out in DD251.

# Documentation

For new and extended systems all drawings and documents should bear:

a. The address and location of the premises

b. The name and address of the installer

c. The name of the designer

d. The date of installation.

On completion of the installation, the installer should provide the following information to the owner or occupier:

a. Details of the authorities consulted and any response to consultation.

b. A general specification of the system and a statement of compliance with the guidance given in DD251.

c. A layout of the sprinklered premises showing the extent of the installation.

d. Details of the water supplies which, if a town main, should include pressure/flow rate data at a specified location for the commissioned installation, with the time and date of the test.

e. An inspection and routine checking program for the system. The program should include instructions on the actions to be taken in respect of operation of the system, faults, etc.

f. A list of components used, identifying manufacturer's name and parts reference number.

g. A 24 hour emergency telephone number which can be used to obtain assistance.

h. A Log Book containing inspection, checking and maintenance documents, detailing a regular program to be undertaken by an approved contractor.

i. Essential information for the user e.g. 'do not paint, cover or in any way impede the operation of a sprinkler head'.

It is recommended that a number of spare sprinkler heads be left at the site of the installation to replace activated, or damaged, sprinkler heads. Heads should only be replaced by qualified installers.

# Logbook

A logbook should be handed over on completion of the system commissioning. This logbook should give details of:

a. The date of inspection

b. Details of all tests conducted and their results

c. Details of any remedial action taken

d. Confirmation or otherwise of the sprinkler systems operational status

e. Confirmation or otherwise of the alarm systems operational status

f. Details of any recommendations or comments.

# Maintenance

It is the property owner's responsibility to ensure that a regular inspection and testing program is in place. The person carrying out the inspection should complete and sign the logbook accordingly.

The sprinkler system should be subject to an annual inspection and test by a qualified installer to ensure that the sprinklers' heat sensing capacity and their spray pattern is not impeded; the minimum flow rates are achieved at the drain and test valve; the alarm is effective and that the system has not been modified, unless by a qualified designer/installer.

The person carrying out the inspection should test the system by visually inspecting for leaks wherever possible.

Should a leak be suspected the pipework should be pressure tested to 1.5 times working pressure for 1 hour. The alarms should be activated so that their satisfactory operation can be audibly verified. The sprinkler system should be flow tested for 1 minute at the drain and test valve, or the highest test point of the installation pipework, to ensure that the system flow rate requirements are met. Stop valves should be exercised to ensure free movement. Where trace heating is installed, its effective operation should be checked.

# Hose reel installations

A hose reel consists basically of a steel drum or reel on which is rolled a length of suitable rubber hose with a shut-off nozzle at the end; the whole unit being connected to a suitable water supply. They are installed to provide the occupants of a building with first aid means of fighting a fire whilst awaiting the arrival of the local fire brigade. The fire service personnel do not normally use them unless the fire happens to be a small localised one, as the amount of water discharged by each reel, approximately 23 litres/min is not sufficient to extinguish a large fire.

## Positioning of hose reels

As hose reels are intended for use by the building occupants, it is of vital importance that they are placed in readily accessible positions so that they can be used without exposing the personnel to danger. This means that they must as a general rule be fixed along escape routes or adjacent to fire exits so that personnel escaping from an outbreak of fire will pass them on their way to safety and can thus use them without having their means of escape cut off.

In office blocks especially the multi-storey type, the hose reels must be fitted inside the actual office accommodation which as a general rule means that they are fitted adjacent to the fire exit doors into the lift or stair lobbies. This enables the hose reel to be used without opening the smoke stop doors thus preventing the lobby from being filled with smoke. In industrial premises, it is not always possible to site hose reels adjacent to the fire exits owing to the fact that the width of the building would prevent the hose from reaching a fire in the centre. In these circumstances it is necessary to position the hose reels in the centre of

the building usually on the columns or stanchions but care must be taken to ensure that they can be used safely in the event of fire.

## Types of hose reel

There are two basic types of hose reel, fixed or swinging. The fixed type of reel should normally have its centre line at least 1.5m above the floor. A swinging type hose reel can be swung through 180° and be mounted at any convenient height, the average being 900mm to 1.05m above the floor.

Hose reels are normally fitted with 20mm diameter reinforced non-kink rubber hose but hose reels fitted with 25mm dia. are available if required. The usual lengths of hose are 23m, 30m, 36m and 45m.

Each reel is also fitted with a 5mm lever operated shut off nozzle at the end of the hose.

In determining the length of hose to be used the critical factor is the requirement that all areas of the building must be covered and no part must be more than 6m from the hose reel nozzle when the hose is uncoiled.

Manually operated hose reels are fitted with a wheel head type isolating valve on the inlet to the reel which is closed when the reel is not in use to prevent the hose from being continuously subject to water pressure. Before running out the hose, it is necessary to turn on the isolating valve and a warning notice to this effect must be positioned adjacent to the reel.

Automatic hose reels are fitted with a valve which is opened or closed by the revolving action of the reel when the hose is pulled out or rewound and with this type it is only necessary to pull out the hose and open the shut off nozzle at the end to allow water to be discharged. It is however, normal practice to fit a lock shield type isolating valve on the feed pipe so that individual reels can be shut down for maintenance purposes without isolating the whole system.

**Discharge from jets**

Quantity　　= Velocity × area

$$q = Cd \times V \times A \times 1000$$

Putting $C_d$ = 0.96 – co-efficient of discharge

H in m

d in mm

V in m/s = $\sqrt{2gH}$

q in litres/sec

$$q = 0.96 \times \sqrt{2gH} \times \frac{\pi}{4} \times \frac{d^2}{10^6} \times 10^3$$

This reduces the formula:

$$q = \frac{3.35d^2}{1000} \times \sqrt{H}$$

**Example**

when d = 8mm

H = 9m

$$q = \frac{3.35 \times 8^2 \times \sqrt{9}}{1000}$$

$$= \frac{3.35 \times 64 \times 3}{1000}$$

$$= \frac{10.05 \times 6.4}{1000}$$

q = 0.64 l/sec

## Pipework

Hose reel systems are classed by the water authorities as domestic cold water services owing to the fact that water can be freely drawn off through the reels.

All hose reels must be fitted with a union between the isolating stop valve on the feed pipe and the inlet to the reel. This enables individual reels to be shut off and dismantled for maintenance and overhaul without shutting down the entire system.

The drop pipe to the hose reel from the distribution main is normally 25mm

*Table 15  Height of jet (max) in metres*

| Head on jet in metres | Diameter of orifice in millimetres | | | | | | |
|---|---|---|---|---|---|---|---|
| | 3.2 | 6.3 | 9.5 | 12.7 | 16.8 | 19.0 | 25.4 |
| 3.0 | 2.67 | 2.86 | 2.93 | 2.97 | 2.99 | 3.00 | |
| 6.0 | 4.57 | 5.33 | 5.59 | 5.72 | 5.79 | 5.85 | 5.91 |
| 9.0 | 5.79 | 7.44 | 8.00 | 8.29 | 8.46 | 8.63 | 8.72 |
| 12.0 | 6.10 | 9.14 | 10.15 | 10.67 | 10.97 | 11.28 | 11.43 |
| 15.2 | – | 10.49 | 12.07 | 12.86 | 13.41 | 13.72 | 14.05 |
| 18.3 | – | 11.43 | 13.72 | 14.84 | 15.54 | 15.83 | 16.50 |
| 21.3 | – | 12.19 | 16.15 | 18.29 | 19.51 | 20.42 | 21.34 |
| 24.4 | – | 12.19 | 16.15 | 18.29 | 19.51 | 20.42 | 21.34 |
| 27.4 | – | – | 17.07 | 19.81 | 21.34 | 22.25 | 23.47 |
| 30.4 | – | – | 17.68 | 21.03 | 23.86 | 24.08 | 25.60 |

*Table 16 Discharge from jets in litres per second*

| Head on jet in metres | Diameter of orifice in millimetres | | | | | | | | | | |
|---|---|---|---|---|---|---|---|---|---|---|---|
| | 3.2 | 4.8 | 6.3 | 8.0 | 9.5 | 11.5 | 12.7 | 16.8 | 19.0 | 22.0 | 25.4 |
| 1.5 | 0.04 | 0.09 | 0.16 | 0.25 | 0.36 | 0.49 | 0.65 | 1.00 | 1.46 | 1.99 | 2.60 |
| 3.0 | 0.06 | 0.12 | 0.23 | 0.36 | 0.52 | 0.70 | 0.92 | 1.43 | 2.07 | 2.81 | 3.67 |
| 4.5 | 0.07 | 0.16 | 0.28 | 0.44 | 0.63 | 0.86 | 1.12 | 1.76 | 2.53 | 3.45 | 4.50 |
| 6.0 | 0.08 | 0.18 | 0.32 | 0.51 | 0.73 | 0.98 | 1.30 | 2.03 | 2.70 | 3.99 | 5.20 |
| 7.6 | 0.09 | 0.20 | 0.36 | 0.57 | 0.82 | 1.11 | 1.45 | 2.27 | 3.27 | 4.46 | 5.82 |
| 9.0 | 0.10 | 0.22 | 0.40 | 0.62 | 0.89 | 1.22 | 1.59 | 2.44 | 3.58 | 4.88 | 6.37 |
| 10.6 | 0.11 | 0.24 | 0.43 | 0.67 | 0.97 | 1.32 | 1.72 | 2.69 | 3.87 | 5.27 | 6.89 |
| 12.0 | 0.12 | 0.26 | 0.46 | 0.72 | 1.03 | 1.41 | 1.87 | 2.87 | 4.14 | 5.63 | 7.36 |
| 13.7 | 0.125 | 0.27 | 0.49 | 0.77 | 1.10 | 1.53 | 1.95 | 3.05 | 4.39 | 6.11 | 7.80 |
| 15.2 | 0.13 | 0.29 | 0.51 | 0.80 | 1.15 | 1.61 | 2.05 | 3.21 | 4.63 | 6.43 | 8.26 |
| 18.3 | 0.14 | 0.31 | 0.56 | 0.88 | 1.27 | 1.73 | 2.25 | 3.52 | 5.07 | 6.90 | 9.02 |
| 21.3 | 0.15 | 0.34 | 0.60 | 0.95 | 1.37 | 1.86 | 2.43 | 3.80 | 5.48 | 7.46 | 9.77 |
| 24.4 | 0.16 | 0.36 | 0.65 | 1.02 | 1.46 | 1.99 | 2.60 | 4.06 | 5.85 | 7.96 | 10.38 |
| 27.4 | 0.17 | 0.39 | 0.69 | 1.08 | 1.55 | 2.05 | 2.76 | 4.24 | 6.21 | 8.41 | 10.99 |
| 30.4 | 0.18 | 0.40 | 0.73 | 1.14 | 1.64 | 2.23 | 2.91 | 4.55 | 6.55 | 8.86 | 11.59 |

diameter with a 25mm by 20mm reducing elbow at the bottom, the feed pipe to the reel being 20mm diameter.

Care should be exercised in positioning hose reels on drinking water systems that a sufficient flow of water passes along the pipework (oversized to meet the hose reel requirements) to ensure fresh wholesome water at all drinking and culinary terminal fittings.

## Water supplies

The following water systems are acceptable for hose reel installations and are the ones most commonly used.

a. Direct connection from town's main (or mains)

b. Connection from sprinkler installation trunk main

c. Pump supply (usually with suction break tank)

d. Connection from boosted domestic water service

e. Connection from hydrant main or wet fire riser.

A normal requirement for a hose reel system water supply is that it should be capable of providing a flow rate of at least 2.27 l/s at a running pressure of 2 bar at the level of the top hose reel in the system.

With a pressure drop of approximately 0.5 bar through the reel this is sufficient to produce a 6m jet of water to comply with requirements. The flow rate of 2.27 l/s will permit up to six reels to operate efficiently (0.38 l/s per reel), although if a fire has reached a size requiring this number of hose reels to be brought into action, it is unlikely to be extinguished solely by their use.

## Special provision in respect of pump supplies

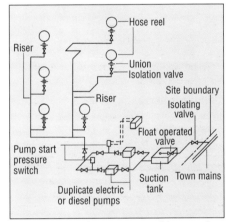

*Figure 2 Typical arrangement of hose reel system.*

A typical pump supply is shown in Figure 2.

As most water companies do not permit direct connections from their mains to be boosted, it is often necessary to provide a suction break tank supplied from the town's main via a suitable float operated valve. The required capacity of the break tank varies. As a general guide a capacity of 1250 litres or 1.2m³ is a common requirement, but the local water company should be contacted to establish their requirements.

## Duplicate pumps

Duplicate pumps are normally provided and these may be controlled as follows:

### As automatic 'On' and manual 'Off'

This system of control is identical to that used for sprinkler system pumps in that the pump is started automatically by a pressure switch and stopped manually by a stop/reset push button on the starter. In

addition, an electrical alarm bell is provided to run all the time the pump is running and thus provide a remote warning of system operation.

### Automatic 'On' and 'Off'

With this system the pumps are started by a pressure switch but a flow switch is also provided in the pump delivery line to ensure that the pump continues to run all the time there is a flow of water through the system.

## Testing and approval

Completed installations are normally required to be tested in the presence and to the satisfaction of the local fire authority and to be approved by both the local fire authority and water company.

# Wet risers

*Figure 3 Typical arrangement of wet riser*

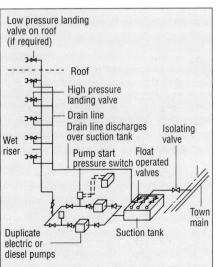

## Statutory regulations

There are no insurance requirements relating to wet risers. Also as they are only installed in buildings exceeding 61m in height and as there are very few standard requirements, it is advisable to obtain the local authority requirements in each instance.

## Size and positioning

A wet rising main should be positioned either in the ventilated lobby approach staircase or within the stair enclosure itself.

The riser should be 100mm diameter normally with outlets on all floors. Normally only one outlet per floor would be required, but where two are necessary the second riser should be provided at the opposite end of the building.

## Water supplies

Generally, a wet riser supply system should be capable of maintaining a minimum running pressure at the top outlet at roof level of 4 bar at a flow rate of 22.7 l/s. The maximum running pressure permitted with only one outlet in operation is 5 bar.

To maintain the above pressure and flow rates it is necessary to employ pumping equipment, usually duplicate electric and diesel fire pumps. In view of the very high pressures involved (up to 16.5 bar at the pump delivery) direct boosting of the town's mains is not permitted and therefore it is necessary for the pumps to be supplied from a suction break tank which must have a minimum actual capacity of 45.45m³. An automatic inflow from a town's main having a flow rate of at least 7.6 l/s must be provided to refill the tank.

## Outlets

Wet riser outlets are 65mm diameter high pressure landing valves with flanged inlets and female instantaneous outlets fitted with plugs secured by short chains. They should be mounted with their centre lines between 910mm and 1.06m above finished floor level and one outlet should be provided for every 929m² of floor area.

In order to reduce the running pressure in the canvas hose line, high pressure landing valves are fitted with an adjustable butterfly valve in the inlet which acts in a similar manner to an orifice plate and reduces the pressure under flow conditions when the valve is open between 4 bar and 5 bar. The

butterfly can be adjusted by means of a nut on the outside of the landing valve body and by use of a special test pipe and gauge, can be altered to give the correct running pressure when the landing valve is fitted in position.

It is also necessary to limit the static pressure in the canvas hose to a maximum of 6.6 bar if water is shut off by closing the branch pipe nozzle at the end of the hose. This is achieved by means of a spring loaded pressure relief valve incorporated in the outlet from the landing valve. The discharge from the relief valve is piped via a 50mm dia. connection into a 100mm dia. drain pipe running vertically down the building alongside the main riser and discharging over the suction tank. In early wet riser installations a lot of trouble was experienced through inadequate drainage facilities and it is important to ensure that the drain pipework is short and direct with the minimum number of bends.

## Pumping equipment

The arrangement of the duplicate electric and diesel fire pumps, starters and suction tank is identical to that used for sprinkler installations with the exception of the method of control. In a similar way to hose reel systems, the electric pump can be either 'Auto On' and 'Manual Off' or 'Auto On' and 'Auto Off' but in both cases the diesel pump (which is on standby) is 'Auto On' and 'Manual Off'. The 'Auto Off' facility is provided by incorporating a flow switch in the electric pump delivery line.

## Installation

The requirements for installation during construction of a building are the same as from a dry riser. If when the riser is initially installed it is impossible to commission the pumping equipment, then it must be fitted out as temporary dry riser with a temporary breaching inlet in a suitable position at ground level.

It is necessary to efficiently earth wet risers to prevent damage from lightning.

## Testing and approval

Completed installations are normally required to be tested in the presence, and to the satisfaction, of the Local Fire Authority and be approved by both the Local Fire Authorities and Water Companies.

# Dry risers

A dry riser consists of an empty or dry pipe rising vertically up a building with hydrant valve outlets on each floor and at roof level. An inlet (Breeching Piece) is provided at ground level in an external wall to enable the Fire Brigade to pump water into the riser from the nearest suitable hydrant.

Dry risers are provided solely for use by the Fire Brigade personnel and they are not intended as first aid fire fighting equipment for use by the building occupants in the same way as a hose reel system. Use of a dry riser in the event of fire avoids the necessity of running long lengths of canvas hose up the staircase of a building and thus enables the Fire Brigade to tackle the blaze much more effectively and in the case of very tall buildings much more quickly (see Figure 4).

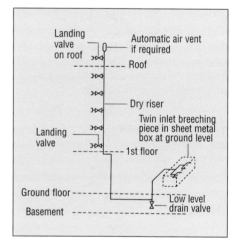

*Figure 4* *Typical arrangement of dry riser.*

## Statutory regulations

Dry risers are normally installed when they are a requirement of the Local Water Company. Most local Fire Brigades publish a standard for dry risers installed in their area. They are normally only installed in buildings up to 61m high; wet risers being required in buildings exceeding this height.

## Size and positioning of risers

Risers should be 100mm diameter where only one hydrant valve outlet is provided on each floor. When two outlets are provided on a floor fed from the same riser then the diameter should be 150mm.

Dry risers should normally be positioned in the ventilated lobby approach staircase or within a staircase enclosure. This enables Fire Service personnel to couple up their hose to the riser outlet in a smoke-free area and it is not necessary to open the smoke stop doors until the last moment when the water is turned on.

## Inlets

A 100mm riser should be fitted with twin inlets and a 150mm riser should have four inlets. Each inlet consists of a 65mm diameter male instantaneous coupling to BS 336 with a non-return valve and a blank cap secured with a short length of chain. The inlets are normally grouped together in a single casting called a "breeching pipe" or "inlet breeching" which has a single flanged or screwed outlet. The "inlet breeching" must be mounted in an external wall with its centre line not more than 762mm above pavement level. When positioning inlets due regard must be paid to accessibility, the positions of adjacent street hydrants and danger from falling glass, etc, in the event of a fire.

Inlet breechings are normally contained in sheet metal inlet boxes with wired glass doors in accordance with BS 3980. The doors are secured with spring locks so that they can be opened from inside by smashing the glass and releasing the catch on the lock.

## Outlets

Dry riser outlets are 65mm diameter gunmetal gate pattern landing valves with flanged inlets and female instantaneous outlets fitted with plugs secured by short chains. They should be mounted with their centre lines between 910mm and 1.06m above finished floor level.

Outlets should be provided for every 929m$^2$ of floor area on every floor from first floor level to the roof. An exception to this requirement is made in the case of blocks of flats where outlets are normally only required on every other floor from first floor to roof.

Automatic Air Relief Vents are sometimes required by the Local Fire Authority to be fitted at the top of the riser.

Owing to the fact that dry risers project above the roof level of buildings it is necessary for them to be efficiently earthed to prevent damage from lightning.

## Installation

Dry risers should be installed progressively as a building is constructed in order to provide protection during the building operations. In buildings over 30.48m in height the riser must be installed when the building exceeds 18.28m in height.

## Testing and approval

Completed installations are normally required to be tested in the presence, and to the satisfaction, of the Local Fire Authority and be approved by both the Local Fire and Water Companies.

# Foam systems

Foam is a frothy product, similar in appearance to soap suds and it is so light that it will float on the surface of a liquid. The properties desired in foam are that it should be tough, tenacious, long lasting and flow freely. It should also resist heat, wind and rain, and retain its water content for a long time.

Foam has three constituents; foam, water and air, and its production takes place in two stages. First the liquid foam compound is induced into the water stream and the aeration takes place. The two stages (induction and aeration) are sometimes carried out in one apparatus but often separate units are employed, in which case the mixture of foam compound and water is pumped through a pipe or hose to the foam maker (sometimes known as an aerator box or aspirator box).

## Application

Foam may be used for extinguishing fires of oils, spirits, paints, molten fats and similar liquids. Foam may also be used for items of plant or complete buildings.

To appreciate the value of foam when used to fight fires involving liquids, it must be remembered that the liquid itself does not burn. It is the mixture of air and the vapour given off from the liquid that burns. Combustion does not occur actually at the surface of the liquid because the proportion of vapour to air is too great to form a combustible mixture. The fire occurs slightly above the surface of the liquid.

Liquid stored in open or closed tanks is dealt with by applying foam to the surface of the liquid, in such quantities as to cover the entire surface of the burning liquid. This blanket of foam excludes air and prevents the formation and possible re-ignition of further vapour.

Foam should not be used on live electrical equipment because it is a conductor of electricity.

# Types of system

## Portable extinguishers

Extinguishers generally have a nominal capacity of up to approximately 17kg and should be capable of expelling a continuous discharge of foam in the form of a jet until the whole of the contents have been discharged.

## Mobile foam units

MFU-s may be used in situations where the quantity of foam likely to be required is greater than could be provided by portable extinguishers, foam trailers, tenders or engines. These units have the disadvantage in that they are always ready for immediate use, but as they cannot be refilled quickly, their use is limited to the time taken to discharge the original contents.

## Fixed foam installations

Where large quantities of foam are required such as oil storage tanks, boiler houses, etc, it is normal practice to install a system of pipework to deliver the foam to the particular risk.

The oil storage tank is a risk commonly protected by the application of foam and the installation would be designed to provide a blanket of foam to the burning oil surface within the storage tank. Assuming an adequate supply of water at the required pressure is available from an underground main, a typical installation would comprise a valid connection from the water main via an induction unit or venturi to the oil storage tank.

## Foam branch pipes

These are generally carried on Fire Brigade appliances and comprise a specially designed branch pipe for use with a 65mm hose. A small tank of foam compound (sometimes in the form of a knapsack) is connected by a flexible pipe to the branch pipe. The flow of water through the branch pipe induces the foam compound into the water stream, aeration takes place within the branch pipe and a jet of foam capable of a range of 9m from water pressure of 3.3 bar up to 30m from water pressure 8 bar.

## Foam inlets

Rooms which contain oil fired boilers, oil storage tanks, oil filled electrical equipment or other materials or apparatus for which foam is a suitable extinguishing medium may be fitted with pourers so placed that a foam blanket can be formed over the equipment and floor of the room. Pipework from the pourers would be connected back to a convenient point in the open (generally in an outside wall), the fire brigade can then connect a foam making branch pipe by means of an adapter and pump foam into the room or basement area to deal with the fire.

## Design data

Minimum recommendations for foam systems have been established by the National Fire Protection Association (NFPA). Application rates higher than these will be beneficial and reduce extinguishing time but as a general rule the NFPA standard is accepted as a good basis for design purposes.

## High expansion foam

Foam has an expansion ratio of between 6 and 8 to 1. High expansion foam has an expansion rate of between 600 and 1000 to 1. The method of generating high expansion foam differs from the method employed with ordinary foam systems in that a fan is incorporated to provide the large quantity of air necessary for making high expansion foam.

High expansion foam units may be installed as a permanent system with manual operation, automatic operation or both. They may also be carried as part of a fire brigade's equipment.

# Steam and condensate

# Introduction

Steam is water which has taken in heat and passed through to the complete vaporization stage.

At atmospheric pressure, boiling water and steam have the same temperature, ie 100°C.

As in practice, a differential pressure is required to cause steam to flow along a pipe, steam is normally supplied at a pressure, some way above atmospheric pressure. Above atmospheric pressure the steam temperature rises; this temperature gradient makes the steam more useful as a heating agent.

There are three quantities of heat in steam:

1. Specific enthalpy of water (sensible heat) – this is the heat which is added to the water up to the point at which it is converted into steam.

2. Specific enthalpy of evaporation (latent heat) – which must be added to the water at the vapour change state to convert all the water into steam at the same temperature.

3. Specific enthalpy of steam – this is the sum of 1 and 2.

# Steam tables

Owing to somewhat complex effects which occur at various steam pressures, the actual quantity of heat to be supplied or available in steam can only be determined from steam tables.

The steam table, Table 1, indicates the specific enthalpy of water, evaporation and steam available in steam at pressures up to 27 bar (1 bar = 14.5lb/in$^2$).

# Design considerations

There are two methods of sizing pipework both of which have an unknown factor which must be assumed:

1. Pressure drop

2. Velocitiy.

## Method 1 – Pressure drop

Steam will only flow along a pipeline when there is a sufficient pressure differential between the point of supply and the outlet. The first consideration therefore is distribution pressure. Per unit of weight, low pressure steam is a better heat carrier than high pressure steam and is easy to control. However, low pressure systems require larger diameter pipes than high pressure systems. High pressure systems utilising smaller distribution pipework with pressure reductions at the equipment inlet are generally preferred.

When undertaking the sizing of steam mains, a differential principle is expressed in the formula:

$$F = \frac{(P_1 - P_2)}{L}$$

and equates the necessary final pressure required.
where:

$P_1$ = a factor based on the initial pressure

$P_2$ = a factor based on a final pressure

$L$ = an effective length of service pipe which is inclusive of frictional allowance for fittings

$F$ = pressure drop factor determined by above formula

Table 2 indicates the relationship between pressure factors and the working gauge pressure expressed in bar.

Required flow rates of steam over a wide range of pressures can be evaluated from Table 3. The pressure factors applicable to design can be determined from the following worked example:

### Example 1

A steam main, after allowing for all resistances has an effective length of 165 metres. The initial gauge pressure ($P_1$) is 7 bar and the final outlet pressure ($P_2$) after due allowance for radiation loss, is 6.6 bar.

Using Table 2, we can calculate a suitable pipe diameter for a steam demand of 270kg per hour required by the unit above.

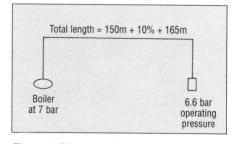

*Figure 1* Diagrammatic steam main

$P_1$ at 7.0 bar has a pressure of 56.38

$P_2$ at 6.6 bar has a pressure of 51.05

$$F = \frac{(P_1 - P_2)}{L}$$

$$F = \frac{56.38 - 51.05}{165}$$

$$= 0.0323$$

At 0.0323 the steam flow rate from a 50mm (2in) diameter pipe read from Table 3 is 501.00kg/h.
Checking that the supply available in 40mm (1½in) diameter pipe is below our needs, a 50mm (2in) diameter is the correct size and allows for a working margin.

## Method 2 – Velocity

If a velocity is assumed then calculations are based on the specific volume of steam being carried, in relation to the cross sectional area of the pipe.

Practical experience shows that reasonable velocities for dry saturated steam mains are 25-35m/s. These velocities should be regarded as maximum values above which noise and erosion will take place, particularly if the steam is wet.

However, to avoid high pressure drops a steam velocity of no more than 15m/s should be used on long lengths of pipework.

Reading the specific volume of steam from the steam tables, pipe size can be determined from the following formula:

$$Wkg/h = 0.002827 \times \frac{D^2 V}{U}$$

Where D = pipe diameter in mm

V = velocity, m/s

U = specific volume m$^3$/kg

Selection of a pipe size can be simplified by reference to Table 4 which has been compiled to give easy and convenient selection without the need to use the calculation method.

The method is clearly easy and convenient but it provides no guarantee of pressure at the using end.

*Table 1* *Steam tables*

| Pressure (bar) | Pressure (kPa) | Temperature (°C) | Specific enthalpy: Water ($h_1$) (kJ/kg) | Specific enthalpy: Evaporation ($h_{lg}$) (kJ/kg) | Specific enthalpy: Steam ($h_g$) (kJ/kg) | Specific volume of steam ($m^3/kg$) |
|---|---|---|---|---|---|---|
| absolute | | | | | | |
| 0.30 | 30.0 | 69.10 | 289.23 | 2336.1 | 2625.3 | 5.229 |
| 0.50 | 50.0 | 81.33 | 340.49 | 2305.4 | 2645.9 | 3.240 |
| 0.75 | 75.0 | 91.78 | 384.39 | 2278.6 | 2663.0 | 2.217 |
| 0.95 | 95.0 | 98.20 | 411.43 | 2261.8 | 2673.2 | 1.777 |
| gauge | | | | | | |
| 0 | 0 | 100.00 | 419.04 | 2257.0 | 2676.0 | 1.673 |
| 0.10 | 10.0 | 102.66 | 430.2 | 2250.2 | 2680.4 | 1.533 |
| 0.20 | 20.0 | 105.10 | 440.8 | 2243.4 | 2684.2 | 1.414 |
| 0.30 | 30.0 | 107.39 | 450.4 | 2237.2 | 2687.6 | 1.312 |
| 0.40 | 40.0 | 109.55 | 459.7 | 2231.3 | 2691.0 | 1.225 |
| 0.50 | 50.0 | 111.61 | 468.3 | 2225.6 | 2693.9 | 1.149 |
| 0.60 | 60.0 | 113.56 | 476.4 | 2220.4 | 2696.8 | 1.083 |
| 0.70 | 70.0 | 115.40 | 484.1 | 2215.4 | 2699.5 | 1.024 |
| 0.80 | 80.0 | 117.14 | 491.6 | 2210.5 | 2702.1 | 0.971 |
| 0.90 | 90.0 | 118.80 | 498.9 | 2205.6 | 2704.5 | 0.923 |
| 1.00 | 100.0 | 120.42 | 505.6 | 2201.1 | 2706.7 | 0.881 |
| 1.10 | 110.0 | 121.96 | 512.2 | 2197.0 | 2709.2 | 0.841 |
| 1.20 | 120.0 | 123.46 | 518.7 | 2192.8 | 2711.5 | 0.806 |
| 1.30 | 130.0 | 124.90 | 524.6 | 2188.7 | 2713.3 | 0.773 |
| 1.40 | 140.0 | 126.28 | 530.5 | 2184.8 | 2715.3 | 0.743 |
| 1.50 | 150.0 | 127.62 | 536.1 | 2181.0 | 2717.1 | 0.714 |
| 1.60 | 160.0 | 128.89 | 541.6 | 2177.3 | 2718.9 | 0.689 |
| 1.70 | 170.0 | 130.13 | 547.1 | 2173.7 | 2720.8 | 0.665 |
| 1.80 | 180.0 | 131.37 | 552.3 | 2170.1 | 2722.4 | 0.643 |
| 1.90 | 190.0 | 132.54 | 557.3 | 2166.7 | 2724.0 | 0.622 |
| 2.00 | 200.0 | 133.69 | 562.2 | 2163.3 | 2725.5 | 0.603 |
| 2.20 | 220.0 | 135.88 | 571.7 | 2156.9 | 2728.6 | 0.568 |
| 2.40 | 240.0 | 138.01 | 580.7 | 2150.7 | 2731.4 | 0.536 |
| 2.60 | 260.0 | 140.00 | 589.2 | 2144.7 | 2733.9 | 0.509 |
| 2.80 | 280.0 | 141.92 | 597.4 | 2139.0 | 2736.4 | 0.483 |
| 3.00 | 300.0 | 143.75 | 605.3 | 2133.4 | 2738.7 | 0.461 |
| 3.20 | 320.0 | 145.46 | 612.9 | 2128.1 | 2741.0 | 0.440 |
| 3.40 | 340.0 | 147.20 | 620.0 | 2122.9 | 2742.9 | 0.422 |
| 3.60 | 360.0 | 148.84 | 627.1 | 2117.8 | 2744.9 | 0.405 |
| 3.80 | 380.0 | 150.44 | 634.0 | 2112.9 | 2746.9 | 0.389 |
| 4.00 | 400.0 | 151.96 | 640.7 | 2108.1 | 2748.8 | 0.374 |
| 4.50 | 450.0 | 155.55 | 656.3 | 2096.7 | 2753.0 | 0.342 |
| 5.00 | 500.0 | 158.92 | 670.9 | 2086.0 | 2756.9 | 0.315 |
| 5.50 | 550.0 | 162.08 | 684.6 | 2075.7 | 2760.3 | 0.292 |
| 6.00 | 600.0 | 165.04 | 697.5 | 2066.0 | 2763.5 | 0.272 |
| 6.50 | 650.0 | 167.83 | 709.7 | 2056.8 | 2766.5 | 0.255 |
| 7.00 | 700.0 | 170.50 | 721.4 | 2047.7 | 2769.1 | 0.240 |
| 7.50 | 750.0 | 173.02 | 732.5 | 2039.2 | 2771.7 | 0.227 |
| 8.00 | 800.0 | 175.43 | 743.1 | 2030.9 | 2774.0 | 0.215 |
| 8.50 | 850.0 | 177.75 | 753.3 | 2022.9 | 2776.2 | 0.204 |
| 9.00 | 900.0 | 179.97 | 763.0 | 2015.1 | 2778.1 | 0.194 |
| 9.50 | 950.0 | 182.10 | 772.5 | 2007.5 | 2780.0 | 0.185 |
| 10.00 | 1000.0 | 184.13 | 781.6 | 2000.1 | 2781.7 | 0.177 |
| 10.50 | 1050.0 | 186.05 | 790.1 | 1993.0 | 2783.3 | 0.171 |
| 11.00 | 1100.0 | 188.02 | 798.8 | 1986.0 | 2784.8 | 0.163 |
| 11.50 | 1150.0 | 189.82 | 807.1 | 1979.1 | 2786.3 | 0.157 |
| 12.00 | 1200.0 | 191.68 | 815.1 | 1972.5 | 2787.6 | 0.151 |
| 12.50 | 1250.0 | 193.43 | 822.9 | 1965.4 | 2788.8 | 0.148 |
| 13.00 | 1300.0 | 195.10 | 830.4 | 1959.6 | 2790.0 | 0.141 |
| 13.50 | 1350.0 | 196.62 | 837.9 | 1953.2 | 2791.1 | 0.136 |
| 14.00 | 1400.0 | 198.35 | 845.1 | 1947.1 | 2792.2 | 0.132 |
| 14.50 | 1450.0 | 199.92 | 852.1 | 1941.0 | 2793.1 | 0.128 |
| 15.00 | 1500.0 | 201.45 | 859.0 | 1935.0 | 2794.0 | 0.124 |
| 15.50 | 1550.0 | 202.92 | 865.7 | 1928.8 | 2794.9 | 0.119 |
| 16.00 | 1600.0 | 204.38 | 872.3 | 1923.4 | 2795.7 | 0.117 |
| 17.00 | 1700.0 | 207.17 | 885.0 | 1912.1 | 2797.1 | 0.110 |
| 18.00 | 1800.0 | 209.90 | 897.2 | 1901.3 | 2798.5 | 0.105 |
| 19.00 | 1900.0 | 212.47 | 909.0 | 1890.5 | 2799.5 | 0.100 |
| 20.00 | 2000.0 | 214.96 | 920.3 | 1880.2 | 2800.5 | 0.0949 |
| 21.00 | 2100.0 | 217.35 | 931.3 | 1870.1 | 2801.4 | 0.0906 |
| 22.00 | 2200.0 | 219.65 | 941.9 | 1860.1 | 2802.0 | 0.0868 |
| 23.00 | 2300.0 | 221.85 | 952.2 | 1850.4 | 2802.6 | 0.0832 |
| 24.00 | 2400.0 | 224.02 | 962.2 | 1840.9 | 2803.1 | 0.0797 |
| 25.00 | 2500.0 | 226.12 | 972.1 | 1831.4 | 2803.5 | 0.0768 |
| 26.00 | 2600.0 | 228.15 | 981.6 | 1822.2 | 2803.8 | 0.0740 |
| 27.00 | 2700.0 | 230.14 | 990.7 | 1813.3 | 2804.0 | 0.0714 |

*Table 2* *Pressure factors for pipe sizing*

| Pressure (bar abs) | Volume (m/kg) | Pressure factor | Pressure (bar abs) | Volume (m/kg) | Pressure factor | Pressure (bar abs) | Volume (m/kg) | Pressure factor |
|---|---|---|---|---|---|---|---|---|
| 0.05 | 28.192 | 0.0301 | 2.15 | 0.576 | 9.309 | 7.70 | 0.222 | 66.31 |
| 0.10 | 14.674 | 0.0115 | 2.20 | 0.568 | 9.597 | 7.80 | 0.219 | 67.79 |
| 0.15 | 10.022 | 0.0253 | 2.25 | 0.560 | 9.888 | 7.90 | 0.217 | 69.29 |
| 0.20 | 7.649 | 0.0442 | 2.30 | 0.552 | 10.18 | 8.00 | 0.215 | 70.80 |
| 0.25 | 6.204 | 0.0681 | 2.35 | 0.544 | 10.48 | 8.10 | 0.212 | 72.33 |
| 0.30 | 5.229 | 0.0970 | 2.40 | 0.536 | 10.79 | 8.20 | 0.210 | 73.88 |
| 0.35 | 4.530 | 0.1308 | 2.45 | 0.529 | 11.10 | 8.30 | 0.208 | 75.44 |
| 0.40 | 3.993 | 0.1694 | 2.50 | 0.522 | 11.41 | 8.40 | 0.206 | 77.02 |
| 0.45 | 3.580 | 0.2128 | 2.55 | 0.515 | 11.72 | 8.50 | 0.204 | 78.61 |
| 0.50 | 3.240 | 0.2610 | 2.60 | 0.509 | 12.05 | 8.60 | 0.202 | 80.22 |
| 0.55 | 2.964 | 0.3140 | 2.65 | 0.502 | 12.37 | 8.70 | 0.200 | 81.84 |
| 0.60 | 2.732 | 0.3716 | 2.70 | 0.496 | 12.70 | 8.80 | 0.198 | 83.49 |
| 0.65 | 2.535 | 0.4340 | 2.75 | 0.489 | 13.03 | 8.90 | 0.196 | 85.14 |
| 0.70 | 2.365 | 0.5010 | 2.80 | 0.483 | 13.37 | 9.00 | 0.194 | 86.81 |
| 0.75 | 2.217 | 0.5727 | 2.85 | 0.477 | 13.71 | 9.10 | 0.192 | 88.50 |
| 0.80 | 2.087 | 0.6489 | 2.90 | 0.471 | 14.06 | 9.20 | 0.191 | 90.20 |
| 0.85 | 1.972 | 0.7298 | 2.95 | 0.466 | 14.41 | 9.30 | 0.189 | 91.92 |
| 0.90 | 1.869 | 0.8153 | 3.00 | 0.461 | 14.76 | 9.40 | 0.187 | 93.66 |
| 0.95 | 1.777 | 0.9053 | 3.10 | 0.451 | 15.48 | 9.50 | 0.185 | 95.41 |
| 1.013 | 1.673 | 1.025 | 3.20 | 0.440 | 16.22 | 9.60 | 0.184 | 97.18 |
| **bar gauge** | | | 3.30 | 0.431 | 16.98 | 9.70 | 0.182 | 98.96 |
| 0 | 1.673 | 1.025 | 3.40 | 0.422 | 17.75 | 9.80 | 0.181 | 100.75 |
| 0.05 | 1.601 | 1.126 | 3.50 | 0.413 | 18.54 | 9.90 | 0.179 | 102.57 |
| 0.10 | 1.533 | 1.230 | 3.60 | 0.405 | 19.34 | 10.00 | 0.177 | 104.40 |
| 0.15 | 1.471 | 1.339 | 3.70 | 0.396 | 20.16 | 10.20 | 0.174 | 108.10 |
| 0.20 | 1.414 | 1.453 | 3.80 | 0.389 | 21.00 | 10.40 | 0.172 | 111.87 |
| 0.25 | 1.361 | 1.572 | 3.90 | 0.381 | 21.85 | 10.60 | 0.169 | 115.70 |
| 0.30 | 1.312 | 1.694 | 4.00 | 0.374 | 22.72 | 10.80 | 0.166 | 119.59 |
| 0.35 | 1.268 | 1.822 | 4.10 | 0.367 | 23.61 | 11.00 | 0.163 | 123.54 |
| 0.40 | 1.225 | 1.953 | 4.20 | 0.361 | 24.51 | 11.20 | 0.161 | 127.56 |
| 0.45 | 1.186 | 2.090 | 4.30 | 0.355 | 25.43 | 11.40 | 0.158 | 131.64 |
| 0.50 | 1.149 | 2.230 | 4.40 | 0.348 | 26.36 | 11.60 | 0.156 | 135.78 |
| 0.55 | 1.115 | 2.375 | 4.50 | 0.342 | 27.32 | 11.80 | 0.153 | 139.98 |
| 0.60 | 1.083 | 2.525 | 4.60 | 0.336 | 28.28 | 12.00 | 0.151 | 144.25 |
| 0.65 | 1.051 | 2.679 | 4.70 | 0.330 | 29.27 | 12.20 | 0.149 | 148.57 |
| 0.70 | 1.024 | 2.837 | 4.80 | 0.325 | 30.27 | 12.40 | 0.147 | 152.96 |
| 0.75 | 0.997 | 2.999 | 4.90 | 0.320 | 31.29 | 12.60 | 0.145 | 157.41 |
| 0.80 | 0.971 | 3.166 | 5.00 | 0.315 | 32.32 | 12.80 | 0.143 | 161.92 |
| 0.85 | 0.946 | 3.338 | 5.10 | 0.310 | 33.37 | 13.00 | 0.141 | 166.50 |
| 0.90 | 0.923 | 3.514 | 5.20 | 0.305 | 34.44 | 13.20 | 0.139 | 171.13 |
| 0.95 | 0.901 | 3.694 | 5.30 | 0.301 | 35.52 | 13.40 | 0.135 | 175.83 |
| 1.00 | 0.881 | 3.878 | 5.40 | 0.296 | 36.62 | 13.60 | 0.133 | 180.58 |
| 1.05 | 0.860 | 4.067 | 5.50 | 0.292 | 37.73 | 13.80 | 0.132 | 185.40 |
| 1.10 | 0.841 | 4.260 | 5.60 | 0.288 | 38.86 | 14.00 | 0.130 | 190.29 |
| 1.15 | 0.823 | 4.458 | 5.70 | 0.284 | 40.01 | 14.20 | 0.128 | 195.23 |
| 1.20 | 0.806 | 4.660 | 5.80 | 0.280 | 41.17 | 14.40 | 0.127 | 200.23 |
| 1.25 | 0.788 | 4.866 | 5.90 | 0.276 | 42.35 | 14.60 | 0.125 | 205.30 |
| 1.30 | 0.733 | 5.076 | 6.00 | 0.272 | 43.54 | 14.80 | 0.124 | 210.42 |
| 1.35 | 0.757 | 5.291 | 6.10 | 0.269 | 44.76 | 15.00 | 0.122 | 215.61 |
| 1.40 | 0.743 | 5.510 | 6.20 | 0.265 | 45.98 | 15.20 | 0.121 | 220.86 |
| 1.45 | 0.728 | 5.734 | 6.30 | 0.261 | 47.23 | 15.40 | 0.119 | 226.17 |
| 1.50 | 0.714 | 5.961 | 6.40 | 0.258 | 48.48 | 15.60 | 0.118 | 231.54 |
| 1.55 | 0.701 | 6.193 | 6.50 | 0.255 | 49.76 | 15.80 | 0.117 | 236.97 |
| 1.60 | 0.689 | 6.429 | 6.60 | 0.252 | 51.05 | 16.00 | 0.115 | 242.46 |
| 1.65 | 0.677 | 6.670 | 6.70 | 0.249 | 52.36 | 16.20 | 0.114 | 248.01 |
| 1.70 | 0.665 | 6.915 | 6.80 | 0.246 | 53.68 | 16.40 | 0.113 | 253.62 |
| 1.75 | 0.654 | 7.164 | 6.90 | 0.243 | 55.02 | 16.60 | 0.111 | 259.30 |
| 1.80 | 0.643 | 7.417 | 7.00 | 0.240 | 56.38 | 16.80 | 0.110 | 265.03 |
| 1.85 | 0.632 | 7.675 | 7.10 | 0.237 | 57.75 | 17.00 | 0.109 | 270.83 |
| 1.90 | 0.622 | 7.937 | 7.20 | 0.235 | 59.13 | 17.20 | 0.108 | 276.69 |
| 1.95 | 0.612 | 8.203 | 7.30 | 0.232 | 60.54 | 17.40 | 0.107 | 282.60 |
| 2.00 | 0.603 | 8.473 | 7.40 | 0.229 | 61.96 | 17.60 | 0.106 | 288.58 |
| 2.05 | 0.594 | 8.748 | 7.50 | 0.227 | 63.39 | 17.80 | 0.105 | 294.62 |
| 2.10 | 0.585 | 9.026 | 7.60 | 0.224 | 64.84 | 18.00 | 0.104 | 300.72 |

*Table 3* Pipeline capacity and pressure drop factors

| F | | 15mm ½" | 20mm ¾" | 25mm 1" | 32mm 1¼" | 40mm 1½" | 50mm 2" | 65mm 2½" | 80mm 3" | 100mm 4" | 125mm 5" | 150mm 6" | 175mm 7" | 200mm 8" | 225mm 9" | 250mm 10" | 300mm 12" |
|---|---|---|---|---|---|---|---|---|---|---|---|---|---|---|---|---|---|
| 0.00016 | a | | | | | | 30.40 | 55.41 | 90.72 | 199.1 | 360.4 | 598.2 | 890.0 | 1275 | 1755 | 2329 | 3800 |
| | v | | | | | | 4.30 | 4.86 | 5.55 | 6.82 | 7.90 | 9.16 | 10.05 | 10.94 | 11.94 | 12.77 | 14.54 |
| 0.00020 | a | | | | | 16.18 | 34.32 | 62.77 | 103.0 | 225.6 | 407.0 | 662.0 | 1005 | 1437 | 1966 | 2623 | 4276 |
| | v | | | | | 3.96 | 4.85 | 5.51 | 6.31 | 7.72 | 8.92 | 10.13 | 11.34 | 12.33 | 13.37 | 14.38 | 16.36 |
| 0.00025 | a | | | | 10.84 | 17.92 | 38.19 | 69.31 | 113.2 | 249.9 | 450.3 | 735.5 | 1008 | 1678 | 2183 | 2904 | 4715 |
| | v | | | | 3.74 | 4.39 | 5.40 | 6.08 | 6.92 | 8.56 | 9.87 | 11.26 | 12.5 | 14.40 | 14.85 | 15.92 | 18.04 |
| 0.00030 | a | | | | 11.95 | 19.31 | 41.83 | 75.85 | 124.1 | 271.2 | 491.9 | 804.5 | 1209 | 1733 | 2390 | 3172 | 5149 |
| | v | | | | 4.13 | 4.73 | 5.92 | 6.65 | 7.60 | 9.29 | 10.79 | 12.31 | 13.65 | 14.87 | 16.26 | 17.39 | 19.7 |
| 0.00035 | a | | | 6.86 | 12.44 | 20.59 | 43.76 | 80.24 | 130.0 | 285.3 | 519.2 | 845.3 | 1279 | 1823 | 2497 | 3346 | 5406 |
| | v | | | 3.88 | 4.30 | 5.04 | 6.21 | 7.04 | 7.96 | 9.77 | 11.38 | 12.94 | 14.44 | 15.64 | 17.00 | 18.34 | 20.69 |
| 0.00045 | a | | 3.62 | 7.94 | 14.56 | 23.39 | 50.75 | 92.68 | 150.9 | 333.2 | 604.6 | 979.7 | 1478 | 2118 | 2913 | 3884 | 6267 |
| | v | | 3.54 | 4.49 | 5.03 | 5.73 | 7.18 | 8.13 | 9.24 | 11.42 | 13.26 | 15.00 | 16.68 | 18.18 | 19.82 | 21.29 | 23.99 |
| 0.00055 | a | | 4.04 | 8.99 | 16.18 | 26.52 | 57.09 | 103.8 | 170.8 | 337.1 | 674.2 | 1101 | 1663 | 2382 | 3281 | 4338 | 7057 |
| | v | | 3.96 | 5.09 | 5.59 | 6.49 | 8.08 | 9.10 | 10.46 | 12.78 | 14.78 | 16.85 | 18.22 | 20.44 | 22.32 | 23.78 | 27.01 |
| 0.00065 | a | | 4.46 | 9.56 | 17.76 | 29.14 | 62.38 | 113.8 | 186.7 | 409.8 | 739.9 | 1207 | 1823 | 2595 | 3597 | 4781 | 7741 |
| | v | | 4.37 | 5.41 | 6.13 | 7.14 | 8.82 | 9.98 | 11.43 | 14.04 | 16.22 | 18.48 | 20.58 | 22.27 | 24.47 | 26.21 | 29.62 |
| 0.00075 | a | | 4.87 | 10.57 | 19.31 | 31.72 | 68.04 | 124.1 | 203.2 | 445.9 | 804.5 | 1315 | 1977 | 2836 | 3908 | 5172 | 8367 |
| | v | | 4.77 | 5.98 | 6.67 | 7.77 | 9.62 | 10.88 | 12.44 | 15.28 | 17.64 | 20.13 | 22.32 | 24.34 | 26.59 | 28.35 | 32.02 |
| 0.00085 | a | | 5.52 | 11.98 | 21.88 | 35.95 | 77.11 | 104.7 | 230.2 | 505.4 | 911.8 | 1490 | 2240 | 3215 | 4429 | 5861 | 9482 |
| | v | | 5.41 | 6.78 | 7.56 | 8.80 | 10.91 | 12.34 | 14.09 | 17.32 | 19.99 | 22.81 | 25.29 | 27.59 | 30.13 | 32.13 | 36.29 |
| 0.00100 | a | 1.96 | 5.84 | 12.75 | 23.50 | 38.25 | 81.89 | 148.6 | 245.2 | 539.4 | 968.5 | 1579 | 2403 | 3383 | 4707 | 6228 | 10052 |
| | v | 4.10 | 5.72 | 7.21 | 8.12 | 9.37 | 11.58 | 13.03 | 15.01 | 18.48 | 21.24 | 24.17 | 27.13 | 29.03 | 32.02 | 34.14 | 38.47 |
| 0.00125 | a | 2.10 | 6.26 | 13.57 | 24.96 | 40.72 | 87.57 | 159.8 | 261.8 | 577.9 | 1038 | 1699 | 2544 | 3634 | 5035 | 6655 | 10639 |
| | v | 4.39 | 6.13 | 7.68 | 8.62 | 9.97 | 12.39 | 14.02 | 16.03 | 19.80 | 22.76 | 26.01 | 28.72 | 31.19 | 34.26 | 36.48 | 40.71 |
| 0.00150 | a | 2.39 | 7.35 | 15.17 | 28.04 | 45.97 | 98.84 | 179.3 | 295.1 | 652.8 | 1172 | 1908 | 2896 | 4091 | 5631 | 7493 | 11999 |
| | v | 5.00 | 7.20 | 8.58 | 9.68 | 11.26 | 13.98 | 15.72 | 18.07 | 22.37 | 25.70 | 29.21 | 32.69 | 35.11 | 38.31 | 41.08 | 45.92 |
| 0.00175 | a | 2.48 | 7.51 | 16.30 | 29.61 | 49.34 | 103.4 | 188.8 | 311.1 | 686.5 | 1270 | 2017 | 3046 | 4291 | 5921 | 7852 | 13087 |
| | v | 5.19 | 7.36 | 9.22 | 10.23 | 12.08 | 14.63 | 16.56 | 19.05 | 23.52 | 27.85 | 30.88 | 34.39 | 36.83 | 40.28 | 43.04 | 50.08 |
| 0.0020 | a | 2.84 | 8.58 | 18.63 | 33.83 | 56.39 | 118.2 | 215.8 | 355.5 | 784.6 | 1451. | 2305 | 3482 | 4904 | 6767 | 8974 | 14956 |
| | v | 5.94 | 8.40 | 10.54 | 11.68 | 13.81 | 16.72 | 18.93 | 21.77 | 26.88 | 31.82 | 35.28 | 39.31 | 42.09 | 46.04 | 49.19 | 57.24 |
| 0.0025 | a | 3.16 | 9.48 | 20.75 | 37.25 | 61.30 | 132.0 | 240.5 | 391.3 | 881.7 | 1556 | 2546 | 3819 | 5422 | 7544 | 10090 | 16503 |
| | v | 6.61 | 9.29 | 11.74 | 12.86 | 15.01 | 18.67 | 21.09 | 23.96 | 30.21 | 34.12 | 38.97 | 43.11 | 46.53 | 51.33 | 55.31 | 63.16 |
| 0.0030 | a | 3.44 | 10.34 | 22.5 | 40.45 | 66.66 | 143.4 | 262.0 | 429.8 | 942.4 | 1701 | 2767 | 4183 | 6068 | 8275 | 11033 | 18021 |
| | v | 7.20 | 10.13 | 12.73 | 13.97 | 16.33 | 20.29 | 22.98 | 26.32 | 32.29 | 37.30 | 42.36 | 47.22 | 52.08 | 56.30 | 60.48 | 68.97 |
| 0.0040 | a | 4.17 | 12.50 | 26.97 | 48.55 | 80.91 | 173.1 | 313.8 | 514.9 | 1128 | 2040 | 3330 | 5051 | 7208 | 9905 | 13240 | 21625 |
| | v | 8.73 | 12.25 | 15.26 | 16.77 | 19.82 | 24.49 | 27.52 | 31.53 | 38.65 | 44.73 | 50.67 | 57.02 | 61.86 | 67.39 | 72.58 | 82.76 |
| 0.0050 | a | 4.71 | 14.12 | 30.40 | 54.92 | 90.23 | 196.1 | 354 | 578.6 | 1275 | 2305 | 3727 | 5737 | 8189 | 11278 | 14858 | 24469 |
| | v | 9.86 | 13.83 | 17.20 | 18.97 | 20.10 | 27.74 | 31.05 | 35.43 | 43.68 | 50.54 | 57.05 | 64.76 | 70.28 | 76.73 | 81.45 | 93.64 |
| 0.0060 | a | 5.25 | 15.69 | 35.80 | 60.31 | 99.05 | 215.8 | 392.3 | 647.3 | 1412 | 2550 | 4148 | 6277 | 9072 | 12406 | 16476 | 26970 |
| | v | 10.99 | 15.37 | 20.26 | 20.83 | 24.26 | 30.53 | 34.41 | 39.63 | 48.38 | 55.92 | 63.50 | 70.86 | 77.86 | 84.40 | 90.32 | 103.21 |
| 0.0080 | a | 6.08 | 18.34 | 39.23 | 70.12 | 116.2 | 251.5 | 456.0 | 750.3 | 1648 | 2976 | 4879 | 7355 | 10543 | 14417 | 19173 | 31384 |
| | v | 12.72 | 17.97 | 22.20 | 24.22 | 28.46 | 35.58 | 40.00 | 45.95 | 56.46 | 65.26 | 74.69 | 83.03 | 90.48 | 98.09 | 105.1 | 120.1 |
| 0.0100 | a | 6.86 | 20.64 | 44.13 | 79.44 | 130.4 | 283.9 | 514.9 | 845.9 | 1863 | 3334 | 5492 | 8336 | 11867 | 16280 | 21576 | 35307 |
| | v | 14.36 | 20.22 | 24.97 | 27.44 | 31.94 | 40.16 | 45.16 | 51.80 | 63.83 | 73.11 | 84.07 | 94.11 | 101.8 | 110.8 | 118.28 | 135.1 |
| 0.0125 | a | 7.35 | 22.20 | 47.28 | 81.00 | 140.1 | 302.1 | 547.3 | 901.9 | 1983 | 3589 | 5867 | 8844 | 12697 | 17426 | 23074 | 37785 |
| | v | 15.38 | 21.75 | 26.75 | 27.98 | 34.31 | 42.74 | 48.00 | 55.22 | 67.94 | 78.70 | 89.81 | 99.84 | 109.0 | 118.5 | 126.5 | 144.6 |
| 0.0150 | a | 8.27 | 25.00 | 53.33 | 95.62 | 157.2 | 342.0 | 620.6 | 1020 | 2230 | 4045 | 6620 | 10022 | 4251 | 19584 | 25974 | 42616 |
| | v | 17.31 | 24.49 | 30.18 | 33.03 | 38.50 | 48.38 | 54.43 | 62.46 | 76.40 | 88.70 | 101.3 | 113.1 | 22.3 | 133.2 | 142.4 | 163.09 |
| 0.0175 | a | 8.58 | 26.39 | 55.78 | 100.4 | 165.6 | 360.4 | 665.1 | 1073 | 2360 | 4291 | 6994 | 10512 | 5017 | 20595 | 27461 | 44194 |
| | v | 17.95 | 25.85 | 31.56 | 34.68 | 40.65 | 50.99 | 58.34 | 65.70 | 80.52 | 94.09 | 107.1 | 118.7 | 128.9 | 140.1 | 150.5 | 169.1 |
| 0.020 | a | 9.80 | 30.16 | 63.75 | 114.7 | 189.3 | 411.9 | 760.1 | 1226 | 2697 | 4904 | 7993 | 12014 | 7163 | 23538 | 31384 | 50508 |
| | v | 20.51 | 29.55 | 36.07 | 39.62 | 46.36 | 58.27 | 66.67 | 75.01 | 92.41 | 107.5 | 122.3 | 135.6 | 147.3 | 160.1 | 172.0 | 193.3 |
| 0.025 | a | 10.99 | 33.48 | 70.73 | 127.3 | 209.8 | 459.7 | 834.6 | 1367 | 2970 | 5422 | 8817 | 13296 | 9332 | 26357 | 34750 | 56581 |
| | v | 23.00 | 32.80 | 40.02 | 43.97 | 51.39 | 65.03 | 73.20 | 83.70 | 101.7 | 118.9 | 135.0 | 150.1 | 65.9 | 179.3 | 190.5 | 216.5 |
| 0.030 | a | 12.00 | 36.78 | 77.23 | 137.9 | 229.9 | 501.1 | 919.4 | 1480 | 3264 | 5884 | 9792 | 14481 | 20917 | 28595 | 37697 | 62522 |
| | v | 25.11 | 36.03 | 43.70 | 47.63 | 56.31 | 70.89 | 80.64 | 90.42 | 111.8 | 129.0 | 149.9 | 163.5 | 179.5 | 194.5 | 206.6 | 239.3 |
| 0.040 | a | 14.46 | 44.13 | 93.17 | 169.2 | 279.5 | 600.7 | 1093 | 1790 | 3923 | 7110 | 11622 | 17457 | 25254 | 34571 | 45604 | 75026 |
| | v | 30.26 | 43.23 | 52.72 | 58.44 | 68.44 | 84.98 | 95.87 | 109.6 | 134.4 | 155.9 | 177.9 | 197.2 | 216.7 | 235.2 | 250.0 | 287.1 |
| 0.050 | a | 16.43 | 49.53 | 104.4 | 191.2 | 313.8 | 676.7 | 1231 | 2020 | 4413 | 8042 | 13044 | 19370 | 23441 | 39229 | 51489 | 85324 |
| | v | 34.38 | 48.52 | 59.08 | 66.04 | 76.86 | 95.73 | 108.0 | 123.7 | 151.2 | 176.3 | 199.7 | 218.7 | 244.1 | 266.9 | 282.3 | 326.5 |
| 0.06 | a | 18.14 | 52.96 | 115.7 | 210.8 | 343.2 | 750.3 | 1373 | 2231 | 4855 | 8827 | 14368 | 21282 | 31384 | 43152 | 57373 | |
| | v | 37.96 | 51.88 | 65.47 | 72.81 | 84.06 | 106.1 | 120.4 | 136.6 | 166.3 | 193.5 | 219.9 | 240.2 | 269.3 | 293.6 | 314.5 | |
| 0.08 | a | 21.08 | 62.28 | 134.8 | 245.2 | 402.1 | 872.8 | 1594 | 2599 | 5688 | 10249 | 16672 | 24518 | 36532 | | | |
| | v | 44.11 | 61.02 | 76.28 | 86.69 | 98.49 | 123.5 | 139.5 | 159.1 | 194.9 | 224.7 | 255.2 | 276.8 | 313.5 | | | |
| 0.10 | a | 24.03 | 70.12 | 152.0 | 277.0 | 456.0 | 980.7 | 1804 | 2942 | 6424 | 11524 | 18879 | 27461 | | | | |
| | v | 50.29 | 68.70 | 86.01 | 95.67 | 111.7 | 138.7 | 158.2 | 180.1 | 220.1 | 252.7 | 289.0 | 310.0 | | | | |
| 0.12 | a | 25.99 | 77.48 | 167.7 | 306.5 | 500.2 | 1079 | 1986 | 3236 | 7110 | 12700 | 20841 | | | | | |
| | v | 54.39 | 75.91 | 94.90 | 105.9 | 122.5 | 152.6 | 174.2 | 198.1 | 243.6 | 278.5 | 319.0 | | | | | |
| 0.15 | a | 28.50 | 84.13 | 183.9 | 334.2 | 551.7 | 1195 | 2161 | 3494 | 7769 | | | | | | | |
| | v | 59.64 | 82.42 | 104.1 | 115.4 | 135.1 | 169.0 | 189.5 | 213.9 | 266.2 | | | | | | | |
| 0.20 | a | 34.32 | 102.0 | 220.7 | 402.1 | 662.0 | 1427 | 2599 | 4217 | 9317 | | | | | | | |
| | v | 71.82 | 99.93 | 124.9 | 138.9 | 162.1 | 201.9 | 228.0 | 258.2 | 319.2 | | | | | | | |
| 0.25 | a | 37.72 | 112.7 | 245.2 | 447.9 | 735.5 | 1565 | 2876 | 4668 | | | | | | | | |
| | v | 78.94 | 110.4 | 138.7 | 154.7 | 180.1 | 221.4 | 252.3 | 285.8 | | | | | | | | |
| 0.30 | a | 41.37 | 122.7 | 266.6 | 487.3 | 804.5 | 1710 | 3126 | 5057 | | | | | | | | |
| | v | 86.58 | 120.2 | 150.9 | 168.3 | 197.0 | 241.9 | 274.2 | 309.6 | | | | | | | | |
| 0.35 | a | 43.34 | 128.7 | 283.2 | 514.9 | 841.0 | 1802 | 3261 | | | | | | | | | |
| | v | 90.70 | 126.1 | 160.2 | 177.8 | 206.0 | 254.9 | 286.0 | | | | | | | | | |
| 0.40 | a | 49.93 | 147.1 | 323.6 | 588.4 | 961.1 | 2059 | 3727 | | | | | | | | | |
| | v | 104.5 | 144.1 | 183.1 | 203.2 | 235.4 | 291.3 | 326.9 | | | | | | | | | |
| 0.45 | a | 50.31 | 150.0 | 326.6 | 600.2 | 979.7 | 2083 | | | | | | | | | | |
| | v | 105.3 | 146.9 | 184.8 | 207.3 | 239.9 | 294.7 | | | | | | | | | | |
| 0.50 | a | 55.90 | 166.7 | 362.9 | 666.9 | 1089 | 2314 | | | | | | | | | | |
| | v | 117.0 | 163.3 | 205.3 | 230.3 | 266.7 | 327.4 | | | | | | | | | | |
| 0.6 | a | 62.28 | 185.3 | 402.1 | 735.5 | 1201 | | | | | | | | | | | |
| | v | 130.3 | 181.5 | 227.5 | 254.0 | 294.1 | | | | | | | | | | | |
| 0.7 | a | 63.07 | 188.8 | 407.6 | 750.9 | | | | | | | | | | | | |
| | v | 132.0 | 185.0 | 230.6 | 259.3 | | | | | | | | | | | | |
| 0.8 | a | 72.08 | 215.8 | 465.8 | 858.1 | | | | | | | | | | | | |
| | v | 150.8 | 211.4 | 263.6 | 296.4 | | | | | | | | | | | | |
| 0.9 | a | 73.28 | 218.4 | 476.6 | | | | | | | | | | | | | |
| | v | 153.3 | 214.0 | 269.7 | | | | | | | | | | | | | |

a = kg/h capacity    v = m/s velocity with a volume of 1 m³/kg

*Table 4* Pipeline capacities at specific velocities

| Pressure (bar) | Velocity (m/s) | kg/h | | | | | | | | | | |
|---|---|---|---|---|---|---|---|---|---|---|---|---|
| | | 15mm | 20mm | 25mm | 32mm | 40mm | 50mm | 65mm | 80mm | 100mm | 125mm | 150mm |
| 0.4 | 15 | 7 | 14 | 24 | 37 | 52 | 99 | 145 | 213 | 394 | 648 | 917 |
| | 25 | 10 | 25 | 40 | 62 | 92 | 162 | 265 | 384 | 675 | 972 | 1457 |
| | 40 | 17 | 35 | 64 | 102 | 142 | 265 | 403 | 576 | 1037 | 1670 | 2303 |
| 0.7 | 15 | 7 | 16 | 25 | 40 | 59 | 109 | 166 | 250 | 431 | 680 | 1006 |
| | 25 | 12 | 25 | 45 | 72 | 100 | 182 | 287 | 430 | 716 | 1145 | 1575 |
| | 40 | 18 | 37 | 68 | 106 | 167 | 298 | 428 | 630 | 1108 | 1712 | 2417 |
| 1.0 | 15 | 8 | 17 | 29 | 43 | 65 | 112 | 182 | 260 | 470 | 694 | 1020 |
| | 25 | 12 | 26 | 48 | 72 | 100 | 193 | 300 | 445 | 730 | 1160 | 1660 |
| | 40 | 19 | 39 | 71 | 112 | 172 | 311 | 465 | 640 | 1150 | 1800 | 2500 |
| 2.0 | 15 | 12 | 25 | 45 | 70 | 100 | 182 | 280 | 410 | 715 | 1125 | 1580 |
| | 25 | 19 | 43 | 70 | 112 | 162 | 295 | 428 | 656 | 1215 | 1755 | 2520 |
| | 40 | 30 | 64 | 115 | 178 | 275 | 475 | 745 | 1010 | 1895 | 2925 | 4175 |
| 3.0 | 15 | 16 | 37 | 60 | 93 | 127 | 245 | 385 | 535 | 925 | 1505 | 2040 |
| | 25 | 26 | 56 | 100 | 152 | 225 | 425 | 632 | 910 | 1580 | 2480 | 3440 |
| | 40 | 41 | 87 | 157 | 250 | 357 | 595 | 1025 | 1460 | 2540 | 4050 | 5940 |
| 4.0 | 15 | 19 | 42 | 70 | 108 | 156 | 281 | 432 | 635 | 1166 | 1685 | 2460 |
| | 25 | 30 | 63 | 115 | 180 | 270 | 450 | 742 | 1080 | 1980 | 2925 | 4225 |
| | 40 | 49 | 116 | 197 | 295 | 456 | 796 | 1247 | 1825 | 3120 | 4940 | 7050 |
| 5.0 | 15 | 22 | 49 | 87 | 128 | 187 | 352 | 526 | 770 | 1295 | 2105 | 2835 |
| | 25 | 36 | 81 | 135 | 211 | 308 | 548 | 885 | 1265 | 2110 | 3540 | 5150 |
| | 40 | 59 | 131 | 225 | 338 | 495 | 855 | 1350 | 1890 | 3510 | 5400 | 7870 |
| 6.0 | 15 | 26 | 59 | 105 | 153 | 225 | 425 | 632 | 925 | 1555 | 2525 | 3400 |
| | 25 | 43 | 97 | 162 | 253 | 370 | 658 | 1065 | 1520 | 2530 | 4250 | 6175 |
| | 40 | 71 | 157 | 270 | 405 | 595 | 1025 | 1620 | 2270 | 4210 | 6475 | 9445 |
| 7.0 | 15 | 29 | 63 | 110 | 165 | 260 | 445 | 705 | 952 | 1815 | 2765 | 3990 |
| | 25 | 49 | 114 | 190 | 288 | 450 | 785 | 1205 | 1750 | 3025 | 4815 | 6900 |
| | 40 | 76 | 117 | 303 | 455 | 690 | 1210 | 1865 | 2520 | 4585 | 7560 | 10880 |
| 8.0 | 15 | 32 | 70 | 126 | 190 | 285 | 475 | 800 | 1125 | 1990 | 3025 | 4540 |
| | 25 | 54 | 122 | 205 | 320 | 465 | 810 | 1260 | 1870 | 3240 | 5220 | 7120 |
| | 40 | 84 | 192 | 327 | 510 | 730 | 1370 | 2065 | 3120 | 5135 | 8395 | 12470 |
| 10.0 | 15 | 41 | 95 | 155 | 250 | 372 | 626 | 1012 | 1465 | 2495 | 3995 | 5860 |
| | 25 | 66 | 145 | 257 | 405 | 562 | 990 | 1530 | 2205 | 3825 | 6295 | 8995 |
| | 40 | 104 | 216 | 408 | 615 | 910 | 1635 | 2545 | 3600 | 6230 | 9880 | 14390 |
| 14.0 | 15 | 50 | 121 | 205 | 310 | 465 | 810 | 1270 | 1870 | 3220 | 5215 | 7390 |
| | 25 | 85 | 195 | 331 | 520 | 740 | 1375 | 2080 | 3120 | 5200 | 8500 | 12560 |
| | 40 | 126 | 305 | 555 | 825 | 1210 | 2195 | 3425 | 4735 | 8510 | 13050 | 18630 |

*Table 5* Flow of water in heavy grade steel pipes

| Pa per m | mbar per m | 15mm | 20mm | 25mm | 32mm | 40mm | 50mm | 65mm | 80mm | 100mm |
|---|---|---|---|---|---|---|---|---|---|---|
| | | | | | | kg/h | | | | |
| 28 | 0.28 | 90 | 209 | 380 | 865 | 1320 | 2554 | 5194 | 8079 | 16511 |
| 29 | 0.29 | 92 | 214 | 400 | 878 | 1340 | 2590 | 5271 | 8196 | 16756 |
| 30 | 0.30 | 93 | 218 | 403 | 890 | 1361 | 2631 | 5348 | 8314 | 17000 |
| 33 | 0.33 | 97 | 226 | 414 | 930 | 1420 | 2744 | 5579 | 8677 | 17736 |
| 39 | 0.39 | 107 | 249 | 469 | 1028 | 1565 | 3025 | 6142 | 9526 | 19514 |
| 40 | 0.40 | 108 | 253 | 476 | 1040 | 1583 | 3062 | 6214 | 9639 | 19736 |
| 43 | 0.43 | 113 | 263 | 496 | 1079 | 1646 | 3180 | 6454 | 10024 | 20457 |
| 45 | 0.45 | 116 | 270 | 508 | 1107 | 1687 | 3261 | 6618 | 10297 | 21002 |
| 47 | 0.47 | 119 | 277 | 521 | 1134 | 1728 | 3338 | 6777 | 10523 | 21500 |
| 50 | 0.50 | 123 | 286 | 538 | 1172 | 1787 | 3447 | 6949 | 10859 | 22154 |
| 53 | 0.53 | 127 | 296 | 557 | 1211 | 1846 | 3565 | 7235 | 11249 | 22907 |
| 55 | 0.55 | 130 | 302 | 569 | 1238 | 1887 | 3638 | 7380 | 11476 | 23360 |
| 57 | 0.57 | 133 | 308 | 580 | 1261 | 1923 | 3710 | 7525 | 11703 | 23814 |
| 59 | 0.59 | 135 | 314 | 591 | 1288 | 1959 | 3783 | 7666 | 11884 | 24268 |
| 61 | 0.61 | 138 | 320 | 602 | 1311 | 1996 | 3851 | 7806 | 12111 | 24721 |
| 64 | 0.64 | 141 | 327 | 615 | 1338 | 2041 | 3933 | 7970 | 12383 | 25220 |
| 67 | 0.67 | 146 | 337 | 634 | 1379 | 2100 | 4051 | 8210 | 12746 | 25991 |
| 69 | 0.69 | 148 | 343 | 645 | 1402 | 2136 | 4119 | 8342 | 12973 | 26400 |
| 70 | 0.70 | 149 | 345 | 649 | 1411 | 2150 | 4146 | 8432 | 13041 | 26563 |
| 71 | 0.71 | 150 | 348 | 655 | 1424 | 2168 | 4182 | 8473 | 13154 | 26808 |
| 73 | 0.73 | 152 | 354 | 665 | 1447 | 2200 | 4246 | 8600 | 13336 | 27216 |
| 75 | 0.75 | 154 | 358 | 673 | 1458 | 2227 | 4291 | 8695 | 13517 | 27506 |
| 76 | 0.76 | 155 | 359 | 675 | 1465 | 2236 | 4305 | 8723 | 13563 | 27579 |
| 77 | 0.77 | 157 | 365 | 685 | 1488 | 2268 | 4368 | 8850 | 13744 | 27987 |
| 78 | 0.78 | 158 | 366 | 689 | 1497 | 2282 | 4390 | 8900 | 13812 | 28132 |
| 80 | 0.80 | 160 | 370 | 695 | 1510 | 2300 | 4427 | 8972 | 13925 | 28350 |
| 82 | 0.82 | 162 | 375 | 704 | 1529 | 2331 | 4491 | 9072 | 14407 | 28758 |
| 88 | 0.88 | 168 | 391 | 733 | 1590 | 2427 | 4536 | 9453 | 14651 | 29865 |
| 90 | 0.90 | 170 | 395 | 740 | 1606 | 2449 | 4717 | 9548 | 14787 | 30142 |
| 98 | 0.98 | 179 | 414 | 777 | 1696 | 2567 | 4944 | 10025 | 15513 | 31616 |
| 100 | 1.00 | 180 | 418 | 785 | 1701 | 2590 | 4990 | 10115 | 15649 | 31879 |
| 114 | 1.14 | 194 | 450 | 845 | 1832 | 2790 | 5366 | 10841 | 16828 | 34247 |
| 118 | 1.18 | 198 | 457 | 857 | 1860 | 2830 | 5443 | 11022 | 17055 | 34746 |
| 120 | 1.20 | 199 | 462 | 867 | 1880 | 2860 | 5502 | 11113 | 17282 | 35120 |
| 131 | 1.31 | 209 | 484 | 907 | 1996 | 2994 | 5761 | 11657 | 18053 | 36742 |
| 137 | 1.37 | 215 | 497 | 931 | 2018 | 3071 | 5906 | 11948 | 18507 | 37667 |
| 140 | 1.40 | 216 | 502 | 939 | 2037 | 3103 | 5965 | 12066 | 18688 | 38012 |
| 147 | 1.47 | 224 | 516 | 966 | 2096 | 3189 | 6128 | 12383 | 19187 | 39055 |
| 157 | 1.57 | 231 | 534 | 1002 | 2168 | 3298 | 6337 | 12814 | 19822 | 40361 |
| 160 | 1.60 | 234 | 541 | 1011 | 2195 | 3334 | 6409 | 12973 | 20049 | 40797 |
| 163 | 1.63 | 237 | 546 | 1025 | 2218 | 3370 | 6477 | 13109 | 20278 | 41232 |
| 176 | 1.76 | 246 | 570 | 1066 | 2309 | 3511 | 6740 | 13608 | 21092 | 42938 |
| 180 | 1.80 | 249 | 576 | 1075 | 2331 | 3547 | 6808 | 13744 | 21319 | 43364 |
| 196 | 1.96 | 261 | 603 | 1129 | 2440 | 3710 | 7130 | 14379 | 22317 | 45360 |
| 200 | 2.00 | 265 | 611 | 1143 | 2472 | 3760 | 7221 | 14560 | 22589 | 45931 |
| 212 | 2.12 | 273 | 629 | 1179 | 2549 | 3874 | 7434 | 15014 | 23270 | 47265 |
| 216 | 2.16 | 275 | 634 | 1188 | 2567 | 3905 | 7493 | 15132 | 23451 | 47637 |
| 220 | 2.20 | 278 | 641 | 1200 | 2595 | 3942 | 7570 | 15277 | 23678 | 48014 |
| 229 | 2.29 | 284 | 655 | 1225 | 2649 | 4028 | 7729 | 15604 | 24177 | 49125 |
| 235 | 2.35 | 288 | 664 | 1243 | 2689 | 4086 | 7843 | 15840 | 24522 | 49832 |
| 240 | 2.40 | 292 | 672 | 1256 | 2719 | 4129 | 7927 | 16017 | 24780 | 50363 |
| 245 | 2.45 | 295 | 679 | 1270 | 2749 | 4173 | 8010 | 16193 | 25039 | 50894 |
| 255 | 2.55 | 301 | 694 | 1297 | 2806 | 4260 | 8176 | 16520 | 25556 | 51928 |
| 260 | 2.60 | 304 | 701 | 1311 | 2834 | 4304 | 8260 | 16683 | 25814 | 52445 |
| 261 | 2.61 | 305 | 703 | 1315 | 2844 | 4318 | 8287 | 16738 | 25900 | 52618 |
| 274 | 2.74 | 313 | 721 | 1348 | 2917 | 4331 | 8501 | 17173 | 26554 | 54069 |
| 277 | 2.77 | 315 | 727 | 1356 | 2935 | 4459 | 8555 | 17282 | 26717 | 54432 |
| 280 | 2.80 | 317 | 730 | 1363 | 2948 | 4479 | 8593 | 17357 | 26839 | 54636 |
| 294 | 2.94 | 325 | 749 | 1402 | 3025 | 4595 | 8813 | 17781 | 27533 | 55793 |
| 300 | 3.00 | 328 | 757 | 1414 | 3055 | 4641 | 8900 | 17956 | 27803 | 56428 |
| 310 | 3.10 | 335 | 771 | 1438 | 3112 | 4726 | 9063 | 18280 | 28308 | 57507 |
| 314 | 3.14 | 336 | 775 | 1446 | 3129 | 4752 | 9074 | 18380 | 28459 | 57879 |
| 320 | 3.20 | 340 | 784 | 1462 | 3163 | 4825 | 9204 | 18579 | 28767 | 58424 |
| 327 | 3.27 | 344 | 792 | 1479 | 3198 | 4853 | 9299 | 18776 | 29076 | 58968 |
| 333 | 3.33 | 348 | 801 | 1495 | 3230 | 4904 | 9408 | 18979 | 29366 | 59612 |
| 340 | 3.40 | 351 | 809 | 1511 | 3263 | 4955 | 9516 | 19178 | 29656 | 60057 |
| 343 | 3.43 | 353 | 813 | 1520 | 3279 | 4980 | 9571 | 19278 | 29801 | 60329 |
| 353 | 3.53 | 358 | 825 | 1541 | 3328 | 5054 | 9707 | 19550 | 30237 | 61236 |
| 359 | 3.59 | 362 | 834 | 1556 | 3361 | 5103 | 9798 | 19732 | 30522 | 62143 |
| 360 | 3.60 | 363 | 835 | 1558 | 3365 | 5109 | 9809 | 19754 | 30564 | 62211 |

# Alignment and drainage

Problems associated with a steam distribution system can be minimised if the correct consideration is given to the alignment and drainage of the pipework. Steam leaving a boiler is often much wetter than is appreciated, it starts to condense as heat losses take place from the pipework. The rate of condensation is heavy at plant start-up when the system is cold. During normal running, the rate is reduced but remains as small but finite amounts, however well insulated the pipework may be.

The condensate forms droplets on the inside of the pipe walls, these droplets can merge into a film as they are swept along by the steam flow. This film will gravitate to the bottom of the pipe so the water film will be greatest there.

Unless the condensed water is removed as quickly as possible, slugs of water will collect. These slugs of water carried down the pipework by the steam, build up considerable amounts of kinetic energy which reappear as pressure energy when the water is stopped at any obstruction.

The resultant shock waves created, cause water hammer, which in turn can damage both pipework and fittings.

If a few simple rules are observed, proper alignment and drainage will do much to ensure a trouble free system.

Pipework should be arranged with a fall in the direction of flow, a fall of around 40mm in 10m (1 in 250) in the direction of flow is considered adequate. The fall in the pipework ensures the condensate is carried by the steam to drain points located in the system.

Saturated steam pipework should be drained at regular intervals. The distance between drain points will depend on line size, location and the frequency of start-up, intervals of 30 to 50m between points is usual, any low point where condensate can collect should be drained.

Changes of direction on pipework are effective locations for drain points.

Due to the falls required on pipework, long horizontal lengths of pipe should have relay points, these points allow for the pipework to be raised to a higher level and fall again. Relay points are ideal drain points as the change in level helps to separate out entrained water droplets.

Drain points on long straight lengths of pipework should be as large as possible, full bore pockets are ideal on pipelines up to 100mm, above this size pockets can be one or more sizes smaller than the pipe, effectively.

Branch connections should always be taken from the top of any main to ensure the driest possible steam is supplied.

Branch connections from the side and particularly from the bottom of mains should be avoided, such branches would in effect become drain pockets, the result would be very wet steam reaching equipment.

Low points occur in branch pipework and drop legs to low level equipment with isolating or control valves are the most common occurrence. Condensate will build up in front of a closed valve, therefore a drain point with steam trap set is required as indicated in Figure 3.

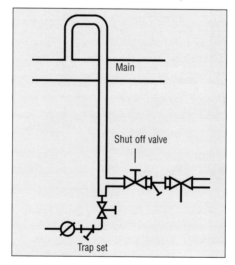

*Figure 3* Recommended take-off from main with branch drainage

*Figure 2* Condensate removal from distribution main

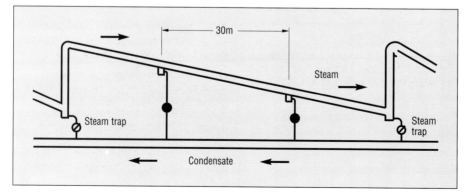

# Steam and condensate traps

The steam traps used to drain steam mains must be suitable for use at the maximum steam pressure within the main, they should have sufficient capacity to pass the amounts of condensate reaching them with the pressure differentials which are present at the time.

A steam trap is an essential piece of equipment which must be fitted to the condense outlet of the steam heated equipment before discharging into the condensate return. The basic function of the steam trap is to release condensate and to hold back steam in the equipment.

There are three basic designs of steam trap which are most widely used:

## Thermostatic traps (Figure 4)

These traps are bi-metallic devices or liquid-filled bellows which, because of their construction, are able to 'sense' the difference in temperature between condensate and steam. When condensate is flowing, the trap remains open but when the higher temperature steam enters the trap, it closes and will not allow the steam to pass through. When the steam condenses and loses temperature, the sensing element allows the trap valve to open and the cycle is repeated. Therefore these traps will cause a certain amount of water logging and allowance must be made for this.

## Mechanical traps (Figures 5 & 6)

This type of trap relies for its principle of action on the difference in density between steam and water acting on a ball float which rises in the presence of condensate and thus opens the valve which then permits condensate to pass through the trap. The inverted bucket in this type of trap floats when steam is admitted to the trap and thus this action closes the trap valve.

## Thermodynamic traps (Figure 7)

Some traps rely on the fact that when condensate at near steam temperature is reduced in pressure at an orifice, flash steam is produced. The most common trap of this type is the thermodynamic trap which uses the increased velocity of the flash steam to close a disc against a seat. The trap opens on a cyclic

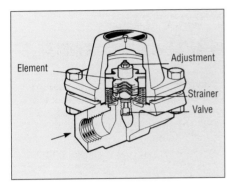

*Figure 4   Operation of bi-metal steam trap*

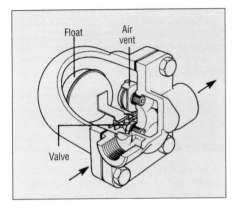

*Figure 5   Float trap with thermostatic air vent*

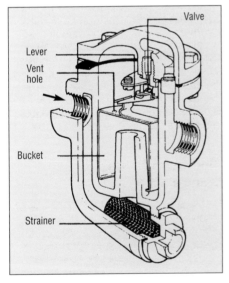

*Figure 6   Inverted bucket trap*

basis when steam pressure in the control chamber is dissipated due to radiation. These traps discharge condensate as soon as it is formed and are therefore ideal for most trapping applications.

There are a number of other more complex designs of steam trap which can be used in special circumstances. These traps and their special functions lie within the realms of the specialist steam applications engineer.

Figures 4, 5, 6 and 7 indicate the working principles of the steam traps described.

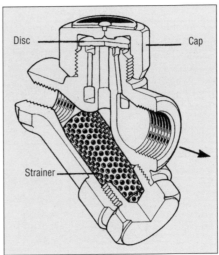

*Figure 7   Thermodynamic trap*

# Steam separators

Although drain points are adequate to deal with condensate on pipeline walls, they cannot remove moisture form the steam itself. This is achieved by a series of simple baffle plates and are arranged to force the steam to change direction and are formed in an item of equipment called a separator. Dry steam passes through with little difficulty but allows the water droplets to drop to the bottom of the unit to a drain outlet and run to a drain point and a steam trap, thus providing better steam for power and process.

# Strainers

The internal passageway of the pipework is continually confronted with deposits that cause blockages. These may take the form of rust, carbonate deposits in hard water districts and any general debris entering during installation. These deposits can easily block pipework and control equipment, jam open valves as well as scoring the face of valves and equipment due to the high velocity at which steam operates.

The most common practice is to provide and install a pipeline strainer upstream to any equipment, steam trap and valve set.

# Steam trap checking

Even when adequately protected by a strainer, a steam trap may fail to operate for a number of reasons. Failure in the closed position would mean rapid reduction of plant output and remedial action must be taken. Conversely, if the trap fails in the open position or partially open position, output may not be affected but live steam could be passed to waste. The traditional method of checking for failure is the installation of a sight glass downstream of each trap to enable viewing of the flow discharge.

A recent development in trap checking is the advent of an electronic device which uses the electrical conductivity of the condensate to sense the conditions within the trap. The test points of a number of traps can be fitted remotely from their sensor chambers by suitable wiring, this is particularly advantageous where access is difficult.

# Air venting

Whem steam is first admitted to the pipework on start-up or after a period of shut-down, the pipework is full of air. Further amounts of air and non-condensable gases are already mixed with the steam, and the air and gases must be removed from the system. This is achieved by the introduction of automatic air vents.

Balanced pressure air vents should be installed at the end of steam pipelines and large branch connections above the level of any condensate.

The discharge from the air vent should be piped to a safe place.

# Reduction of heat losses

Reduction of heat losses within the steam distribution system is an important factor in the efficiency of the system.

Heat losses should be kept to an acceptable minimum so as much of the pipework and fittings within the distribution system as possible should be insulated. The thickness of insulation applied can vary significantly and the designer must make the most economical judgement on the thickness used.

*Table 6* Heat emission from pipes

| Temp. diff. steam to air °C | Pipe size | | | | | | | | | |
|---|---|---|---|---|---|---|---|---|---|---|
| | **15mm** | **20mm** | **25mm** | **32mm** | **40mm** | **50mm** | **65mm** | **80mm** | **100mm** | **150mm** |
| | W/m | | | | | | | | | |
| 56 | 54 | 65 | 79 | 103 | 108 | 132 | 155 | 188 | 233 | 324 |
| 67 | 68 | 82 | 100 | 122 | 136 | 168 | 198 | 236 | 296 | 410 |
| 78 | 83 | 100 | 122 | 149 | 166 | 203 | 241 | 298 | 360 | 500 |
| 89 | 99 | 120 | 146 | 179 | 205 | 246 | 289 | 346 | 434 | 601 |
| 100 | 116 | 140 | 169 | 208 | 234 | 285 | 337 | 400 | 501 | 696 |
| 111 | 134 | 164 | 198 | 241 | 271 | 334 | 392 | 469 | 598 | 816 |
| 125 | 159 | 191 | 233 | 285 | 321 | 394 | 464 | 555 | 698 | 969 |
| 139 | 184 | 224 | 272 | 333 | 373 | 458 | 540 | 622 | 815 | 1133 |
| 153 | 210 | 255 | 312 | 382 | 429 | 528 | 623 | 747 | 939 | 1305 |
| 167 | 241 | 292 | 357 | 437 | 489 | 602 | 713 | 838 | 1093 | 1492 |
| 180 | 274 | 329 | 408 | 494 | 556 | 676 | 808 | 959 | 1190 | 1660 |
| 194 | 309 | 372 | 461 | 566 | 634 | 758 | 909 | 1080 | 1303 | 1852 |

*Table 7* Expansion of steel pipes

| Final temperature (°C) | Expansion per 30m (mm) |
|---|---|
| 66 | 19 |
| 93 | 29 |
| 121 | 41 |
| 177 | 61 |
| 204 | 74 |
| 232 | 84 |
| 260 | 97 |

Expansion (mm) =
$1.25 \times 10^{-5} \times °C \text{ (diff)} \times 1000/m$

External installations require weatherproofing as the heat losses of water saturated insulation, can be up to 50 times greater than from the same pipework in still air conditions.

# Allowance for expansion

Allowance for expansion within the steam distribution system is required to give the necessary flexibility, as the system heats up to ensure no undue stresses are set up. Table 7 shows the approximate expansion of steel pipework installed at a temperature of 16°C, through a range of heat-up temperatures.

The distribution pipework where possible should be installed in reasonable lengths with sufficient bends, ie. changes of direction to allow the expansion to be taken up 'freely'.

Where 'free' movement is not possible other means of achieving the flexibility should be incorporated into the system.

Where practicable the expansion of the steam pipework and any expansion devices incorporated into it should be reduced by the inclusion of 'cold draw' or

'cold stressing' as it is alternatively known. Expansion in long lengths of pipework can be taken up by non-mechanical means by the use of loops in the pipework.

## Full loop

The full loop is achieved by one complete turn of the pipe, the ends being flanged for incorporation into the pipework system, the downstream side passes below the upstream side and should be fitted horizontally or a trapping set would be required to drain the build-up of condensate that would occur.

This type of loop has a tendency to unwind and can exert a force on the connecting flanges.

## Horse shoe or lyre loop

The horse shoe or lyre loop is commonly used. It has a tendency for the ends of the loop to straighten slightly but this does not cause any misalignment of the connecting flanges.

Expansion loops can be fabricated from straight lengths of pipes and bends, long radius bends should be used, as short radius bends restrict flexibility.

## Sliding joint

Sliding joint expansion devices take up little space, however unless they are rigidly anchored they can develop problems of separating, any misalignment in pipework will cause the sleeve to bend, the joints also need regular maintenance, care should be taken in their use.

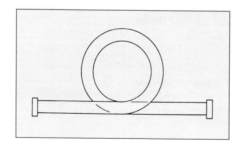

*Figure 8* The full loop

*Figure 9* The horse or lyre loop

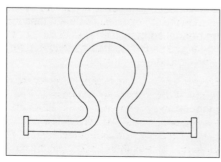

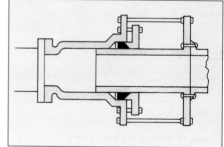

*Figure 10* Sliding joint

*Figure 11* Bellows joint

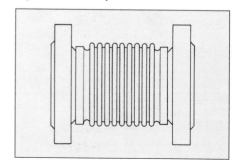

*Table 8 Flow of water in steel pipes (kg/h)*

| Tube diameter (mm) | 0.3 (30Pa) | 0.5 (50Pa) | 0.6 (60Pa) | 0.8 (80Pa) | 1.0 (100Pa) | 1.4 (140Pa) |
|---|---|---|---|---|---|---|
| 15 | 95 | 130 | 140 | 160 | 180 | 220 |
| 20 | 220 | 290 | 320 | 370 | 420 | 500 |
| 25 | 410 | 540 | 600 | 690 | 790 | 940 |
| 32 | 890 | 1180 | 1300 | 1500 | 1700 | 2040 |
| 40 | 1360 | 1790 | 2000 | 2290 | 2590 | 3100 |
| 50 | 2630 | 3450 | 3810 | 4390 | 4990 | 6000 |
| 65 | 5350 | 6950 | 7730 | 8900 | 10150 | 12100 |
| 80 | 8320 | 10900 | 12000 | 13800 | 15650 | 18700 |
| 100 | 17000 | 22200 | 24500 | 28200 | 31900 | 38000 |

Starting load ie running load $\times$ 2
Approx. frictional resistance (mbar per m of travel)
Heavy grade steel tube

## Bellows

Bellows type devices are also in-line fittings but unlike the 'sliding joint' type require no packings, however pressure within the fitting can extend them, adequate anchoring and guiding is essential.

## Articulated bellows

Articulated bellows are capable of absorbing the axial movement in the pipework and some of the lateral and angular displacement and have a number of advantages over other devices particularly at changes of direction. Anchoring and guiding are important with this type of device.

Heavy quality steel pipes have a linear coefficient of expansion of $1.25 \times 10^{-5}°C$ per unit length. Table 7 gives the expansion in steel pipes.

## Example 2

Assume a steam main 30 metres long has a temperature rise from 16°C to 260°C. Calculate the linear expansion to be taken up by an expansion unit.

*Figure 12 Articulated arrangement*

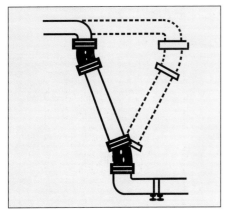

Expansion (mm) = $1.25 \times 10^{-5} \times 30 \times$
$(260 - 16) \times 1000$
= $1.25 \times 30 \times 2.44$
= 91.5mm

The heat emission from bare horizontal pipes with ambient temperatures between 10°C and 21°C in still air conditions are shown in Table 8.

# Condensate return

Design of the condensate return system is important. It should not impose any undue back pressure on the steam traps in the system.

The system should be adequately sized to carry maximum flow and be arranged with a fall to overcome the system resistance and flow under gravity conditions.

It is however rarely possible to return all the condensate produced in the distribution system all the way back to the boiler hotwell by gravity, some lifting will almost certainly be required.

It is therefore usual to direct the condensate to collecting receivers from which it can be pumped back to the boilerhouse.

At start up the plant is cold. Steam will condense rapidly and the steam consumption may be two or three times the normal running rate. Under these conditions, the condensate pipework will be required to pass two or three times the normal condensate rate. As the plant warms up, so the amount of condensate reduces to the running load.

Experience has shown that pipes sized for the above conditions will have an adequate capacity to handle the normal running conditions. For this kind of exercise the start-up load should be taken as not less than twice the running load. This provision will be sufficient for

steam pressures up to 10 bar. Above this pressure range, some additional capacity in the condense lines may however be desirable.

The flow rates and pressure drops given in Tables 5 and 8 may be found convenient for pipe sizing condensate lines.

## Example 3

A plant having a normal running load of 1000kg/h and a starting load of 2000kg/h is to be adopted for condensate line sizing. Assuming a steam trap is fitted not more than 3m from the condensate receiver tank, determine a suitable diameter of pipe for the condensate pipeline.

Referring to Table 8, it will be seen that a 32mm pipe can handle 2040kg/h at a pressure drop of 1.40KPa (mbar) per metre of travel.

The overall pressure drop is therefore $1.40 \times 3 = 4.20$mbar and this small amount of back pressure would be acceptable. If, on the other hand, the condensate has to travel over a distance of say 500m, then the back pressure will be $500 \times 1.4$ = 700mbar and allowing for additional resistance, would impose a total back pressure in the region of 800mbar, to which must be added the back pressure caused by any lift in a line.

Condensate should run away from the trap by gravity but there are occasions when it is necessary to 'lift' it. This is achieved by the pressure available at the trap outlet and therefore, no steam trap will actually 'lift' the condensate.

It is handy to remember in initial design that for each 0.11mbar (11KPa) pressure at the trap, the condensate can be lifted 1 metre. It should be remembered when selecting steam traps that water hammer and attendant noise with the risk of mechanical damage are inevitable when lifting condensate.

Pumped condensate return pipe lines are generally flooded when running, these pipelines often follow the routing of the steam mains. Care should be taken not to connect the pipework from the traps draining the steam main to the flooded pumped condensate returns. Introducing condensate at higher pressure and temperature into flooded condensate pipework will cause re-evaporation where some of the condensate will flash-off into steam again, these steam bubbles will soon collapse in the cooler condensate causing severe water hammer.

# Handling condensate

The receivers that collect condensate are usually at lower level than the boiler 'Hotwell' back at the boilerhouse, it will therefore be necessary to pump the condensate to higher levels than the collection receivers.

There are generally two accepted types of pump for condensate, one is positive displacement and the other uses electronically operated pumps.

## Positive displacement pump

The positive displacement pump generally uses steam as the operating medium, compressed air can be used as an alternative, but due to aeration can have a corrosive effect.

In this type of set, a vented condensate receiver is located above the pump, the receiver ensures a constant head when the pump body is filling by gravity, whilst acting as a reservoir during the discharge stroke of the pump which ensures the flow of condensate from the plant to the receiver is not interrupted.

The advantages of this type of pump are that there is no cavitation and they can pump condensate at boiling point if required. Also because there are no electrics or motors they can continue to operate in damp or moisture laden conditions, they could continue to operate even if submerged in water.

Coupling two or more units together will increase the volume of condensate that can be handled.

## Electronically operated pump

The electronically operated pump set has a much larger receiver, one or more motor driven pumps evacuate the condensate from the receiver back to the main plant Hotwell in the boilerhouse.

These sets can develop problems when dealing with hot condensate, at high temperatures it can flash to steam. This will severely reduce the efficiency of the unit and can also cause damage to the pump impellers.

Units that operate with low nett positive suction head cope with these conditions and will generally run trouble free.

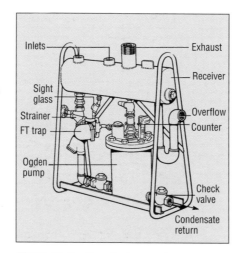

**Figure 13**  *Positive displacement pump*

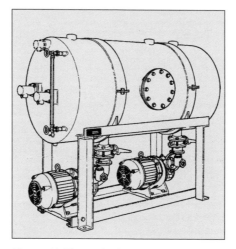

**Figure 14**  *Electronically operated condensate pump*

It should be remembered that both types of condensate sets do not discharge condensate on a continuous basis, therefore the discharge pipework should be sized to take account of this.

Due to the different operating design of the two sets, a good rule of thumb guide to sizing the discharge pipework is to allow three times the rated capacity of the positive displacement set and one and a half times for the electrically operated set.

Care should also be taken to reduce the amount of back pressure imposed on the units due to the frictional resistance in the pipework.

The design of the pipework is important, long horizontal runs should be avoided.

The most suitable arrangement is to have a vertical riser from the set followed by a gravity fall back to the boiler Hotwell. A long horizontal run followed by a final vertical lift would result in fully flooded return lines.

# Pipework expansion

# Consideration for design and installation

All pipework will expand and contract longitudinally and around the circumference when subjected to temperature variations.

The temperature variations can occur as a result of fluids within the pipework being heated or cooled, or from the effects of external heat sources, such as the surrounding air temperatures, solar heat, etc.

The temperature variations can range from gradual, such as the increase and decrease in room air temperatures, to almost instantaneous, such as when hot water is discharged from a sanitary fitting, or when heated water is suddenly circulated through the pipework.

Generally the change in diameter of pipework used for Building Services Engineering will not require detailed consideration, other than to ensure that adequate clearances are maintained between pipes, pipe supports, joists, building structures, etc, to allow free movement of the pipework.

The expansion and contraction along the length of pipework can however be very significant, particularly for steam, condensate, heating, domestic hot water and certain waste pipework installations. Expansion and contraction within cold water pipework systems is minimal and generally does not require any special consideration.

It should be noted that the rate of expansion and contraction varies as a result of the type of material, as well as the temperature variation. PVC pipework, for instance, will expand at over three times that of copper, for the same temperature rise.

Damage and failure from stress and strain can occur to pipework systems, pipework support systems and building structures unless careful consideration is given to the change in pipework length due to temperature change and the direction in which the expansion and contraction will take place.

# Calculation of expansion and contraction

The change in length of pipework, for both expansion and contraction, due to temperature variation can be calculated using the following formula:

**Formula 1**

$$\Delta l = l \times \alpha \times \Delta t$$

where:

$\Delta l$ = The change in length of the pipe due to temperature change.

$l$ = The original length of the pipe.

$\alpha$ = The coefficient of linear expansion (mm/K).

$\Delta t$ = The change in temperature to which the pipe is subjected (K).

*NOTE*
*'K' denotes degrees Kelvin. This is the same as a temperature rise measured in Celsius. 'l' can be any metric unit of measurement. $\Delta l$ will be calculated in the same unit of measurement as that used for 'l'. Generally units of either metres (m) or millimetres (mm) will be used.*

*Table 1   Typical coefficients of linear expansion for various materials*

| Material | Coefficient (mmK × 10$^{-6}$) |
|---|---|
| ABS | 60 to 110.2 |
| Aluminium | 25.6 |
| Brass | 19 |
| Bronze | 18 |
| Cast iron | 12 |
| Chromium | 7 |
| Copper | 16.9 |
| Duralumin | 23 |
| Lead | 29 |
| Mild Steel | 11.3 |
| Nylon | 80 |
| Polyethylene High Density | 140.2 |
| Polyethylene Low Density | 225 |
| PVC unplasticised | 60 to 100 |
| Tin | 21 |
| Zinc | 30 |

*NOTE*
*$10^{-6}$ indicates that the decimal point of the value being considered should be moved six places to the left, eg: $10.2 \times 10^{-6}$ equates to 0.0000102.*

## Example 1

What would be the increase in length and the final length of a straight copper pipe 15 metres long when subjected to a temperature increase from 20°C to 80°C.

From Table 1, the coefficient of linear expansion for copper is $16.9 \times 10^{-6}$mm/K.

From Formula 1

$$\begin{aligned} \Delta l &= l \times \alpha \times \Delta t \\ &= 15 \times 16.9 \times 10^{-6} \times (80 - 20) \\ &= 0.0152m \ (15.2mm) \end{aligned}$$

Therefore the pipe would expand 0.0152m and the final length of the pipe would be:

$$=15m + 0.0152m = 15.0152m.$$

Upon cooling down the pipe will return to its original length, unless it has been heated excessively to such a point where a loss in form has occurred.

# Controlled pipework movement

## Freedom of movement

Consideration must be given during the design and installation of all pipework systems to ensure that they are free to expand and contract. The following important points should be considered:

a. Pipework passing through structures should be provided with sleeves or installed through neatly formed holes, to enable unrestricted movement. This includes walls, floors, ceilings, floorboards, floor joists, etc. It must be ensured that the pipework will not come into contact with the sleeve or wall of the hole. Any mastic or other material used to fill the gap must permit movement of the pipe.

b. Felt pads, or similar, should be provided between pipework and notched joists, and between adjacent pipes which may come into close contact with each other.

c. Pipe clips, supports and guides must not restrict the movement of the pipe, particularly on long pipe runs.

d. Where it is necessary to bury the pipework in the screed, provision must be incorporated to prevent damage to the pipework and screed. This could take the form of a proprietary plastic coated pipe wrapped in fibreglass and the whole surrounded with expanded metal or similar.

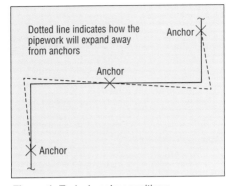

*Figure 1* *Typical anchor positions*

e. Ensure that any branches connected to expanding pipework (eg: connections to radiators), are of adequate length to provide natural flexibility to prevent the connection shearing.

f. Ensure that expanding pipework will not clash with structures.

g. The direction of pipework expansion must always be controlled using suitable anchors, guides and clips. Standard pipework clips may be adequate for short pipework lengths of small bore copper and plastic.

h. Open type pipe clips must not be used where there is a possibility of the pipe springing away from the clip.

The above requirements are also essential to ensure that excessive frictional noises do not occur as a result of expansion and contraction.

## Anchors

Where expansion is excessive, pipe movement must be controlled by installing anchors. Anchors restrain the pipework ensuring that any movement due to expansion occurs in a direction away from the anchor.

Anchors are usually fixed to the middle of the pipe to enable the pipe to move in two directions, therefore effectively halving the maximum change of pipework length in any given direction. Sometimes however, it is desirable to provide an anchor at one end of a pipe run, for instance, to prevent a pipe from coming into contact with an adjacent wall.

When anchors are installed to control expansion, forces will be exerted on the anchor. It is therefore essential to ensure that:

a. The anchor is adequately secured to the pipe

b. The anchor itself is structurally adequate

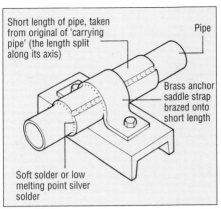

*Figure 2* *Typical anchor for copper pipework*

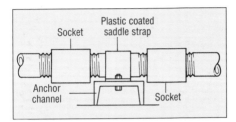

*Figure 3* *Typical anchor for steel pipework (light load)*

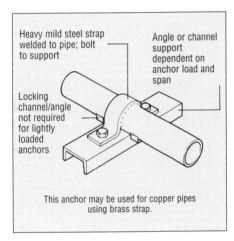

*Figure 4* *Typical light to medium load anchor*

c. The anchor fixings to the building structure are adequate

d. The building structure itself, to which the anchor is fixed, is adequate to accept the forces.

Where necessary, the advice of a structural engineer should be obtained to ensure the anchor and support arrangements are adequate for the anticipated forces which may be exerted.

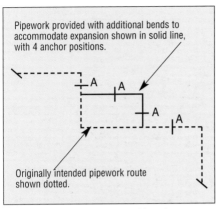

*Figure 5* *Providing additional bends to accommodate pipework expansion*

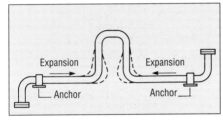

*Figure 6* *Expansion loop/horseshoe section*

## Pipework expansion devices

If expansion and contraction of pipework cannot be controlled with the use of anchors alone, then consideration must be given to providing additional devices to enable movement to take place. These include:

a. Routing pipework with additional bends or offsets

b. Providing purpose designed loop/horseshoe sections in the pipework

c. Installing expansion bellows or compensators

d. Providing expansion couplings for soil and waste pipework systems.

The provision of additional bends, offsets or loop/horseshoe pipework systems must provide adequate natural flexibility to accommodate the pipework expansion.

Expansion bellows or compensators are proprietary manufactured devices, designed to accommodate or absorb expansion and contraction. Various different types of these devices are available. It is essential that the manufacturer be consulted for their particular recommendations regarding the most suitable type for the situation and for their requirements for anchors and guides.

The following points should be noted when using expansion bellows or compensators:

a. Axial type bellows must not be used where the pipe is hung or suspended freely. The pipe supports must guide the pipe and allow only axial movement along the entire length of the pipe.

b. It is essential to ensure that the pipe is guided carefully on each side of the bellows. The guides must allow only axial movement onto the bellows.

c. It is essential to ensure that the pipe is guided carefully at the necessary intervals along the whole pipe run.

d. Only the bellows unit should be installed between two pipe anchors.

e. The line between two anchors should be straight, in plan and in elevation, with no sets or bends.

f. Pipe anchors must be of adequate strength.

g. Bellows must be stretched by half the total expansion movement (cold-draw). This does not apply to special applications or 'pre-cold drawn' units.

h. Screwed end units must be held firm when installing to prevent twisting of the bellows.

The most common method of providing the facility for expansion and contraction in plastic soil and waste pipe systems is the use of proprietary expansion couplings incorporating socket and spigot joints having rubber sealing rings. The couplings should be of the same manufacture as the pipework system.

The expansion couplings should be introduced at 1.8 metre intervals or as recommended by the manufacturer, to connect pipes together.

Plastic pipework should be anchored and supported in accordance with the manufacturer's recommendations. This will depend on the system employed.

## Supports and pipe guides

The purpose of a support is to transfer the load of the pipe and the contents within the pipe safely to a structure. The pipe support should reduce deflection of bending of the pipe.

The purpose of a pipe guide is to control the direction in which a pipe will move when it expands. A pipe guide is any form of constraint which allows the pipe true axial movement along its length but prevents offset movement whether horizontal or vertical. Pipe guides can, however, be designed to also provide a support facility. Some typical pipe guides are indicated in Figures 7 to 11.

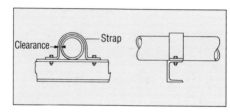

*Figure 7  Strap-type guide*

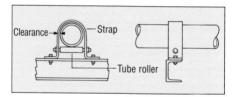

*Figure 8  Strap-type guide with tube roller*

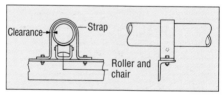

*Figure 9  Strap-type guide with roller and chair*

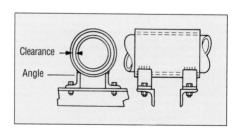

*Figure 10  Tube-type Guide*

*Figure 11  Slip-on Flange Type Guide*

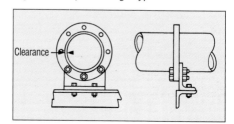

For guides nearest the bellows, the clearances between the outside pipe and inside guide walls should not be greater than 1.6mm for pipe diameter up to 100mm and not greater than 3.2mm for larger pipes. For the guides along the pipe run, maximum clearances of 3.2mm and 6.4mm respectively should be used.

## Guides nearest the bellows

The function of guides closest to the bellows is to ensure true axial movement on to the bellows. This can be achieved by using a tubular type guide (as Figure 10) of such length that the necessary clearances to permit axial movement do not allow appreciable offset movement. Generally a tubular guide having a length to diameter ratio of 6:1 will be adequate.

Tubular guides are generally only fitted to small pipes. For larger sizes (50mm and over), proprietary straps and roller guides are normally employed. Straps and roller guides are short and individually cannot control angular movement of the pipe. To ensure alignment of the pipe onto the bellows, an additional set of guides is required as follows.

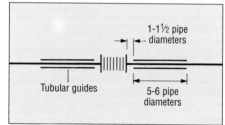

*Figure 12  Guide near bellows*

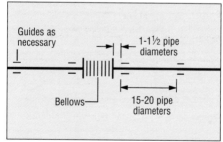

*Figure 13  Installation of additional strap and roller guides*

*Figure 14  Pipework failure may occur without pipe guides*

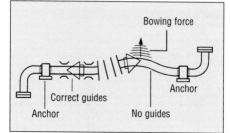

It is essential to ensure that the complete pipe run is adequately guided and not just local to the bellows. If this is not carried out, the pipework may bow outwards as a result of the compressive forces imposed on it.

It is essential that all support arrangements, except for purpose designed anchors, enable controlled pipework movement. If the pipework is incorrectly restrained, damage to the pipe supports or structure may result, due to excessive friction or forces.

# Cold draw of bellows

It is normal for bellows to be 'cold drawn' (eg. stretched) by half the total calculated expansion when installed into a pipe. The bellows will then absorb the total expansion, half in tension and half in compression from the neutral position. This keeps the stress in the bellows material to a minimum for a given expansion and provides maximum bellows life.

In steam and high temperature heating applications, it is not necessary to allow for ambient temperature variation (day/night, summer/winter) when installing the bellows, since this variation is very small compared with the working temperature range. However, on low temperature applications, allowances must be made when calculating cold draw. Where very small movements, vibration or subsidence are to be absorbed, the bellows manufacturers often recommend that cold draw is not used.

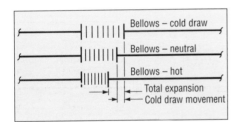

*Figure 15* Cold draw in expansion bellows

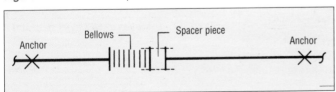

*Figure 16* Taking up cold draw on flanged bellows

*Figure 17* Taking up cold draw on welded end bellows

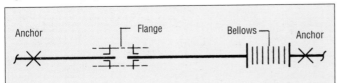

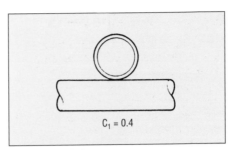

*Figure 18a* Point contact

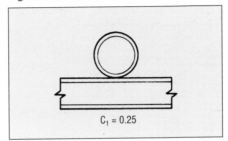

*Figure 18c* Line contact

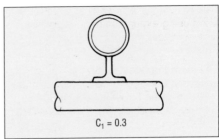

*Figure 18b* Line contact

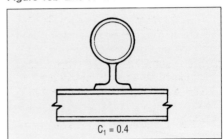

*Figure 18d* Face-to-face contact

Cold draw can be achieved by:

a. for flanged bellows:
Leaving a gap internally between the bellows and pipe flange at one end of the unit and then tightening up the flange using over-sized flange bolts.

b. for screwed bellows:
Under-cutting the length of an adjacent pipe section and allowing the thread of a connecting union to expand the bellows. Care must be taken that the bellow is not twisted during the tightening process.

c. for welded end bellows:
Installing a pair of flanges in the pipework adjacent to the bellows with a gap initially between the flange faces and then tightening up the flange using over-sized flange bolts.

d. for all bellows:
By purchasing pre-cold drawn bellows.

# Calculating forces on anchors

The following main factors have to be taken into consideration when determining forces on anchors:

a. The effect of test pressure on the cross-sectional area of any bellows installed within the pipework system.

b. The elasticity force to stretch and compress bellows installed through the working movement.

c. Frictional forces between the pipe and pipe supports, acting against the direction of movement.

d. The slope of the pipe, affecting the lower anchor (vitally important if the pipe is vertical).

e. Fluid pulsation and flow effects in the pipe.

f. Differential forces due to changes in pipe diameter.

Quoted friction coefficients between pipework and supports vary considerably but the values shown in Figures 18(a), (b), (c), and (d) may be used as a general guide for steel on steel.

The frictional resistance (kg) = dead load at point of support (kg) × coefficient of friction.

*Figure 19*

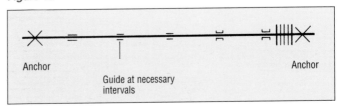

This resistance acts against the direction of movement e.g. it can act either way, depending on whether the pipe is warming up or cooling down.

Should the above figures give unacceptably high forces consideration could be given to using special PTFE support pads which gives figures as low as 0.02.

## Example 2

The following example illustrates the calculation to determine the force imposed on an anchor under normal working and test conditions on a pipework installation indicated in Figure 19, which incorporates axial type bellows.

The designer must obtain the relevant data from the bellows manufacturer.

| | |
|---|---|
| Pipe weight | = 22kg/m |
| Water weight | = 19.5kg/m |
| Lagging weight | = 6kg/m |
| Effective area of bellows | = 0.023m² |

Thrust to compress or extend bellows through full movement from manufacturer's data = 6700N (Newtons)

Coefficient of friction between pipe and supports = 0.3
System working pressure = 550kPa ($550 \times 10^3$Pa)

System test pressure = 830kPa
Length of pipe = 42.5

## Pipework system under normal working conditions

Thrust due to internal pressure on bellows

= working pressure × effective area

= $550 \times 10^3 \times 0.023$N

= 12650N pushing outwards on anchors

Force due to bellows stiffness (bellows compressed in working platform)

= 6700N pushing outwards on anchors.

Frictional resistance to pipe movement over its supports:

= coefficient of friction × (total weight of pipe + water + lagging)

= 0.3 × [(22 × 42.5) + (19.5 × 42.5) + (6 × 42.5)]kg

= Converted to Newtons (1kg = 9.807N)

= 0.3 × [(22 × 42.5 + (19.5 × 42.5) + (6 × 42.5)] × 9.807N

= approximately 6000N against the direction of movement, eg. pushing outwards on anchors.

Total Thrust on Anchor

= 12650 + 6700 + 6000

= 25350N (Newtons) pushing outwards on anchors.

## Pipework system under test conditions

Thrust due to internal pressure on bellow

= test pressure × effective area

= $830 \times 10^3 \times 0.023$N

= 19090N pushing outwards on anchors

Force due to bellows stiffness (bellows stretched in cold-draw position)

= 6700N pulling inwards on anchors

Frictional resistance

= NIL as pipe only moves under temperature effect

Total thrust on anchor

= 19090 − 6700

= 12390N pushing outwards on anchors.

It can be seen in this instance that the greatest force acting on the anchor is under normal working conditions, this however is not always the case.

The following important points should be considered when installing bellows:

i.  When a fitting such as a bend, valve or distance piece is installed into a pipe and subjected to internal pressure. The fitting will act just like a pipe itself, holding the internal pressure, but not pushing or pulling on the pipe.

ii  When an axial bellows is fitted into a pipe and subjected to internal pressure, it reacts to the internal pressure by trying to open out lengthways. An outward pressure is therefore exerted by the bellows.

iii. When a pipe restrained by an anchor at one end, but otherwise free to move longitudinally, is subjected to heat, it will expand away from the anchor position, exerting an outward force away from the anchor.

iv. When a pipe anchored at two points and provided with a bellows between the anchor points is subjected to heat, pressure is exerted by both pipework sections towards the bellows. Meanwhile the pressurised bellows is exerting pressure outwards towards the two anchor points.

v.  When the pipe gets hot, it expands towards the bellows and tries to compress it. Meanwhile, the pressurised bellows is trying to open out lengthways. The expanding pipe therefore has to overcome this pressure force as well as the stiffness of the bellows and the friction of the pipe supports. Hence the need for firm anchors at each end of the pipe run, and careful guiding not only on each side of the bellows but also along the pipe run.

vi. The pipe between bellows and anchors is frequently in compression and unless the pipe is guided carefully, and runs accurately in a straight line from anchor to anchor, the pipe may bow out sideways. This will pull the bellows with it and may cause failure.

vii. Never use axial bellows in pipework systems incorporating suspended hanger supports or any other support systems which can readily swing.

viii. Confirmation should always be obtained from the bellows manufacturer regarding any special requirements they may have regarding the position of anchors and guides.

# Mechanical ventilation

# Measurements of airflow

Air flow can be measured in terms of:

1. Volumetric flow
2. Mass airflow

Units of volumetric airflow rates are generally expressed in:

1. Litres per seond (l/s)
2. Cubic metres per second (m$^3$/s)
3. Litres per hour (l/h)
4. Cubic metres per hour (m$^3$/h).

*NOTE: 1000 litres = 1m$^3$.*

Mass airflow rates are frequently used for air conditioning calculations, but are rarely used for general mechanical ventilation calculations.

Mass airflow rates are generally expressed in kilograms per second (kg/s).

Where a mass airflow rate is used, it can be converted to volumetric airflow by multiplying the value, by the density of the air being considered. For general ventilation calculations, the density of air can be assumed at 1.2m$^3$/kg.

The airflow rate into a room space, for general mechanical supply and extract systems, is usually expressed in:

1. Air changes per hour
2. An airflow rate per person
3. An airflow rate per unit floor area.

Air changes per hour (Ach/h) is the most frequently used basis for calculating the required airflow. Air changes per hour are the number of times in one hour an equivalent room volume of air will be introduced into, or extracted from, the room space.

Airflow rates per person are generally expressed as litres per person (l/p), and are usually used only where fresh air ventilation is required within occupied spaces.

Airflow rates per unit floor area are similar in effect to air changes per hour except that the height of the room is not taken into consideration.

# Calculating room ventilation rates using air changes per hour

## Formula 1

The formula for calculating the ventilation rate is:

$$Q = v \times n$$

Where Q is the ventilation rate in m$^3$/h
v is the volume of the room in m$^3$
n is the air change rate (Ach/h)

## Example 1

Calculate the ventilation rate within a toilet 2.2m long × 1.9m wide × 2.7m high, to provide 6 air changes per hour:

$$\begin{aligned} Q &= v \times n \\ &= 2.2 \times 1.9 \times 2.7 \times 6 \\ &= 67.72 \text{m}^3/\text{h} \end{aligned}$$

# Calculating room ventilation rates using airflow per person

## Formula 2

$$Q = q \times n$$

Where Q is the ventilation rate in l/s
q is the ventilation rate per person in l/s per person
n is the number of people in the room.

## Example 2

Calculate the fresh air ventilation rate required within an office which is designed to accommodate 5 people. The fresh airflow rate required is 12 litres per second, per person.

$$\begin{aligned} Q &= q \times n \\ &= 5 \times 12 \\ &= 60 \text{ l/s} \end{aligned}$$

# Calculating room ventilation rates using airflow per unit floor area

## Formula 3

The formula for calculating the ventilation rate is:

$$Q = q \times a$$

Where Q is the ventilation rate in m$^3$/h
q is the airflow rate in m$^3$/h per m$^2$ of floor area
a is the room floor area in m$^2$

## Example 3

Calculate the ventilation rate within a restaurant 8.5m long × 5.7m wide to provide an airflow of 40m$^3$/h per m$^2$ of floor area.

$$\begin{aligned} Q &= q \times a \\ &= 40 \times 8.5 \times 5.7 \\ &= 1938 \text{m}^3/\text{h} \end{aligned}$$

# Extract air ventilation rates – domestic properties

## Building Regulations requirements

| Room Air | Change Rate |
|---|---|
| Toilets | 3Ach/h* |
| Bathrooms/ shower rooms | 15 l/s** |
| Kitchens | 60 l/s or 30 l/s if incorporated within a cooker hood** <br> *Plus* <br> System capable of operating continuously at 1Ach/h*** |

\* Fan may operate intermittently but must have a 15 minute over-run. Mechanical ventilation is not required if natural ventilation is provided having at least 1/20th of the floor area, some of which must be at least 1.75 metres above floor level.

\*\* May be operated intermittently.

\*\*\* Requirements for continuous operation unnecessary if controllable and secure ventilation openings are provided having a free area not less than 4000mm$^2$, located so as to avoid draughts, eg: a trickle ventilator.

# Extract air ventilation rates – commercial properties

| Room Air | Change Rate |
|----------|-------------|
| Toilets | 3 – 6Ach/h minimum or 6 l/s per WC pan |
| Public toilets | 6 – 12Ach/h |
| Kitchens | 20 – 30Ach/h, 0.35m/s minimum air velocity over hood openings. |
| Offices | 4 – 6Ach/h |
| Meeting rooms/ board rooms | 6 – 10Ach/h |
| Restaurants | 8 – 15Ach/h |
| Laundries | 10 – 15Ach/h |
| Bathrooms/ shower rooms | 3 – 8Ach/h |
| Classrooms | 3 – 6Ach/h |
| Shops | 8 – 12Ach/h |

# Fresh air ventilation rates

No smoking areas         8 l/s per person

Some smoking             16 l/s per person

Heavy smoking            24 l/s per person

Very heavy smoking   32 l/s per person

# Mechanical ventilation heating load

Mechanical ventilation systems, whether they be supply or extract systems, will have an effect on the heating load within the building they serve.

For example, with small supply air systems, the fresh air drawn from outside can be discharged into the unheated room space. The air introduced will then form part of the room heat load in a similar way to fresh air infiltration. Care must be exercised to ensure that the cold air being discharged will not cause draughts or discomfort.

For larger systems, it is necessary to pre-heat the air before it is discharged into the room space. This is to avoid draughts and also the possibility of condensation as the warm moist air

within the room comes into contact with the cold surfaces of the supply air system.

It is normal practice to pre-heat the air to at least room temperature. When heated to room temperature, the supply air will not have any effect on the room heat load. If the supply air is heated to a temperature in excess of the room design temperature, the result will be that useful heat is introduced into the space which can be deducted from the room heating requirements.

The supply air discharge temperature can be generally selected to provide all heating requirements within the room space if required. It must be ensured that the temperature and location of the air being discharged will not cause discomfort. Generally the supply air discharge temperature should not be more than 10°C above room temperature, where the ceiling height is less than 2.7m.

If the supply air is below room temperature, then the balance to heat the air to room temperature must be added to the room heat load.

Pre-heating of the air can be achieved by a water heating coil, an electric heater battery or a heat reclaim device.

Various proprietary heat reclaim devices are available which transfer heat from the warm air within extract systems to heat the incoming cold supply air.

The following should be considered when selecting a heat reclaim device:

1. The device will not be 100% efficient and therefore the supply air will always be at a lower temperature than the extract.

2. Heat reclaim is not required during warm weather. It is therefore necessary to switch off the supply or extract fan, arrange for both fans to be operated in the supply or extract mode simultaneously, or to provide an air by-pass arrangement around the heat reclaim device.

## Formula 4

The formula for the heat load of air passing through a ventilation system or being introduced into or extracted from a room space is:

$$Q = mCp\Delta t$$

Where   Q = The heating load in kW
m = The mass airflow rate of air in kg/s

Cp= The specific heat capacity of air in kJ/kg°C

Δt  = The temperature differential of the air under consideration (°C)

The volume airflow rate is converted to mass airflow by multiplying by the density of the air. For general applications this can be taken as 1.2m³/kg.

The specific heat capacity of air can be taken as 1.01kJ/kg°C.

Therefore the formula can be written as:

$$Q = q \times 1.2 \times 1.01 \times \Delta t$$

Where q = The airflow rate in m³/s.

## Example 4

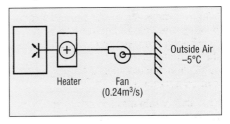

*Design fabric and infiltration heat loss from room = 3.7kW. Room temperature 21°C.*

A fresh air mechanical ventilation system supplies 0.24m³/s into a small office. Calculate:

1. The ventilation system heat load to be added to the room heat loss, if a heater is not provided in the system.

2. The required discharge air temperature into the room and the duct heater output if the system is to provide for the design room heat loss of 3.7kW.

### Ventilation system heat load

From Formula 4

$$Q = q \times 1.2 \times 1.01 \times \Delta t$$
$$= 0.24 \times 1.2 \times 1.01 \times [21 - (-5)]$$
$$= 7.563kW$$

*Table 1 Maximum air velocity and pressure drops in ductwork*

| | Recommended velocity (m/s) | Maximum velocity (m/s) | Recommended pressure drop (Pa/m) | Maximum pressure drop (Pa/m) |
|---|---|---|---|---|
| Main ducts | 5 | 7 | 1.2 | 2 |
| Branch ducts | 3.5 | 5 | 1.0 | 1.5 |
| Louvres | 2.5 | 3 | – | – |
| | (through free airways) | (through free airways) | | |

If the supply air is not pre-heated an additional 7.563kW will need to be added to the room heat loss of 3.7kW.

### Discharge air temperature ($T_s$) to provide 3.7kW heating within room

$$Q = q \times 1.2 \times 1.01 \times \Delta t$$

$$3.7 = 0.24 \times 1.2 \times 1.01 \times (T_s - 21)$$

$$T_s = \frac{3.7}{0.24 \times 1.2 \times 1.01} + 21$$

$$= 33.72°C$$

### Duct heater output

$$Q = 0.24 \times 1.2 \times 1.01 \times [33.72 - (-5)]$$

$$= 11.26kW$$

# Effect of mechanical ventilation on heat producing appliances

It is essential to ensure that any extract system installed does not cause spillage of flue gases from open flued boilers, fires, cooking appliances, etc.

The Building Regulations stipulate that an internal room provided with extract ventilation alone must not contain open flued appliances. If mechanical supply air ventilation is provided to such a room, it must be electrically interlocked with the extract fan(s) and provided with an interlocked supply air flow proving switch to ensure:

1. The supply air system is activated whenever the extract system is operating.

2. The extract fan(s) will not be activated until supply airflow has been proved.

3. The open flued appliances will not operate until supply airflow has been proved.

4. The extract fan(s) and open flued appliances will immediately shut down should the supply airflow proving switch determine that the supply air system has failed.

The Building Regulations also stipulate that a mechanical extract system must not be installed in any room containing a solid fuel burning appliance.

Open flued appliances must be able to operate correctly whether or not the fan(s) is (are) running where natural ventilation and mechanical extract ventilation are provided to the same room space.

**Table 2** *Ductwork fitting K factors (Velocity pressure loss factors). Percentages for branches are based on the change in air velocity of the air stream under consideration.*

| Circular ducts | | Rectangular ducts | |
|---|---|---|---|
| **Fitting** | **K** | **Fitting** | **K** |
| *Bends 90°* (Radius to inside edge of bend) | | *Bends 90° radius $\frac{1}{2} \times D$* (Radius to inside edge of bend) | |
| Radius $\frac{1}{2} \times D$ | 0.34 | Height/width ratio | |
| Radius $1 \times D$ | 0.24 | 0.2 | 0.48 |
| Radius $1\frac{1}{2} \times D$ | 0.23 | 0.4 | 0.37 |
| | | 0.6 | 0.28 |
| | | 0.8 | 0.25 |
| | | 1.0 | 0.23 |
| Conical branch with airflow to branch ($V_C$ to $V_B$). Use velocity pressure in $V_B$ | | Shoe branch with airflow to branch ($V_C$ to $V_B$). Use velocity pressure in $V_B$ | |
| 50% | 3.0 | 50% | 2.5 |
| 60% | 2.0 | 60% | 1.7 |
| 70% | 1.5 | 70% | 1.3 |
| 80% | 1.2 | 80% | 0.8 |
| 90% | 1.0 | 90% | 0.7 |
| Conical branch with through airflow ($V_C$ to $V_D$). Use velocity pressure in $V_D$ | | Shoe branch with through airflow ($V_C$ to $V_D$). Use velocity pressure in $V_D$ | |
| 50% | 0.09 | 50% | 1.0 |
| 60% | 0.06 | 60% | 0.45 |
| 70% | 0.03 | 70% | 0.3 |
| 80% | 0 | 80% | 0.1 |
| 90% | 0 | 90% | 0.07 |
| Conical branch with airflow from branch ($V_B$ to $V_D$). Use velocity pressure in $v_D$ | | Shoe branch with airflow from branch ($V_B$ to $V_D$). Use velocity pressure in $v_D$ | |
| 50% | 0.5 | 50% | 0.5 |
| 60% | 0.52 | 60% | 0.52 |
| 70% | 0.53 | 70% | 0.53 |
| 80% | 0.54 | 80% | 0.54 |
| 90% | 0.55 | 90% | 0.55 |
| Conical branch with through airflow ($V_C$ to $V_D$). Use velocity pressure in $V_D$ | | Shoe branch with through airflow ($V_C$ to $V_D$). Use velocity pressure in $V_D$ | |
| 50% | 0.09 | 50% | 0.09 |
| 60% | 0.06 | 60% | 0.06 |
| 70% | 0.03 | 70% | 0.03 |
| 80% | 0 | 80% | 0 |
| 90% | 0 | 90% | 0 |
| *Concentric reducer* (Use velocity pressure at reduction) | | *Concentric reducer* (Use velocity pressure at reduction) | |
| 30° Angle | 0.02 | 30° Angle | 0.02 |
| 45° Angle | 0.04 | 45° Angle | 0.04 |
| *Aerofoil damper* | 0.2 | *Aerofoil damper* | 0.2 |

*Flexible spiral reinforced duct* $\quad 0.05 \times \dfrac{\text{Length (mm)}}{\text{Diameter (mm)}}$

*Graph 1:* Sizing charts for circular ducts

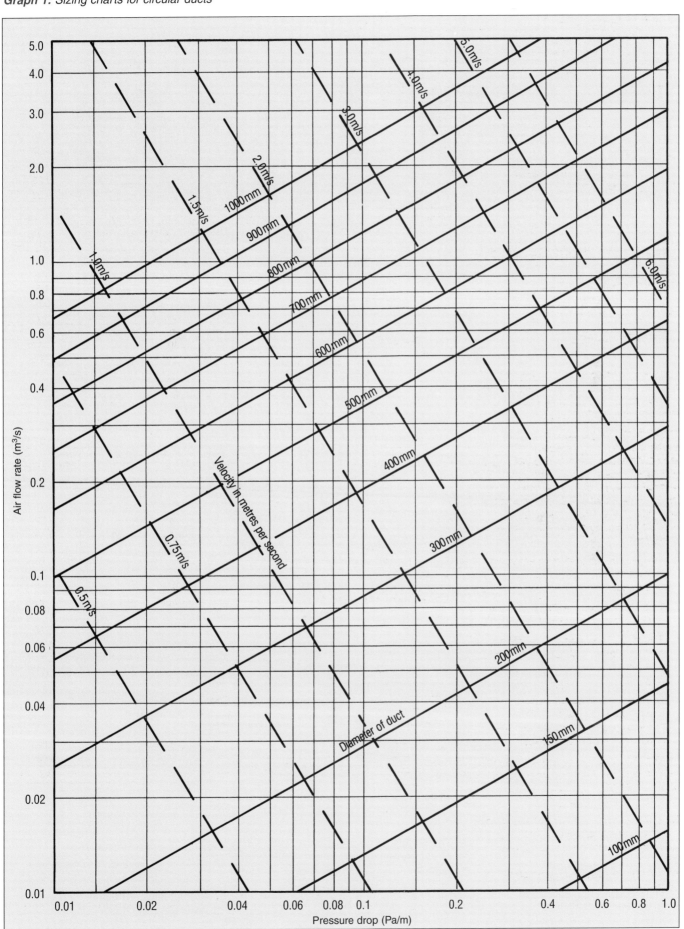

**Graph 2:** *Relationship between rectangular and circular ducts (equal volume flow rate and unit pressure drop)*

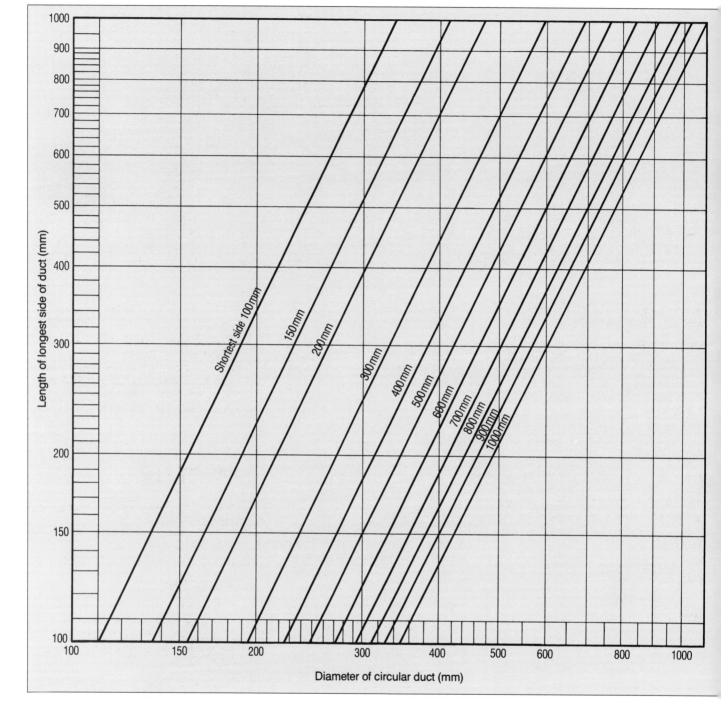

# Ductwork sizing

Ductwork sizing is determined primarily by the following two factors:

1. The air velocity through the duct

2. The resultant resistance to airflow as a result of friction between the airflow and the duct walls.

As the air velocity through the ductwork system increases, the noise generated and the frictional resistance (pressure drop) to airflow will also increase. It is therefore necessary to limit air velocity to ensure that the system is not excessively noisy and that an economical fan selection can be made. It is also necessary to ensure that the velocity is not too low or ducts will be oversized.

Table 1 indicates recommended maximum duct velocities and pressure drops.

The velocity of air through ductwork can be readily calculated using the following formula:

**Formula 5**

$$v = \frac{q}{a}$$

Where  $v$ = The air velocity in metres per second (m/s)

$q$ = The airflow through the duct in cubic metres per second (m³/s)

$a$ = The duct cross sectional area in square metres (m²).

The unit pressure drop through a ductwork system depends to a certain

*Table 3* *Velocity pressure (Pa) against velocity*

| Velocity (m/s) | 0.0 | 0.1 | 0.2 | 0.3 | 0.4 | 0.5 | 0.6 | 0.7 | 0.8 | 0.9 |
|---|---|---|---|---|---|---|---|---|---|---|
| 0 | 0.00 | 0.01 | 0.02 | 0.05 | 0.10 | 0.15 | 0.22 | 0.29 | 0.38 | 0.49 |
| 1 | 0.60 | 0.73 | 0.86 | 1.01 | 1.18 | 1.35 | 1.54 | 1.73 | 1.94 | 2.17 |
| 2 | 2.40 | 2.65 | 2.90 | 3.17 | 3.46 | 3.75 | 4.06 | 4.37 | 4.70 | 5.05 |
| 3 | 5.40 | 5.77 | 6.14 | 6.53 | 6.94 | 7.35 | 7.78 | 8.21 | 8.66 | 9.13 |
| 4 | 9.60 | 10.09 | 10.58 | 11.09 | 11.62 | 12.15 | 12.70 | 13.25 | 13.82 | 14.41 |
| 5 | 15.00 | 15.61 | 16.22 | 16.85 | 17.50 | 18.15 | 18.82 | 19.49 | 20.18 | 20.89 |
| 6 | 21.60 | 22.33 | 23.06 | 23.81 | 24.58 | 25.35 | 26.14 | 26.93 | 27.74 | 28.57 |
| 7 | 29.40 | 30.25 | 31.10 | 31.97 | 32.86 | 33.75 | 34.66 | 35.57 | 36.50 | 37.45 |
| 8 | 38.40 | 39.37 | 40.34 | 41.33 | 42.34 | 43.35 | 44.38 | 45.41 | 46.46 | 47.53 |
| 9 | 48.60 | 49.69 | 50.78 | 51.89 | 53.02 | 54.15 | 55.30 | 56.45 | 57.62 | 58.81 |
| 10 | 60.00 | 61.21 | 62.42 | 63.65 | 64.90 | 66.15 | 67.42 | 68.69 | 69.98 | 71.29 |
| 11 | 72.60 | 73.93 | 75.26 | 76.61 | 77.98 | 79.35 | 80.74 | 82.13 | 83.54 | 84.97 |
| 12 | 86.40 | 87.85 | 89.30 | 90.77 | 92.26 | 93.75 | 95.26 | 96.77 | 98.30 | 99.85 |
| 13 | 101.40 | 102.97 | 104.54 | 106.13 | 107.74 | 109.35 | 110.98 | 112.61 | 114.26 | 115.93 |
| 14 | 117.60 | 119.29 | 120.98 | 122.69 | 124.42 | 126.15 | 127.90 | 129.65 | 131.42 | 133.21 |
| 15 | 135.00 | 136.81 | 138.62 | 140.45 | 142.30 | 144.15 | 146.02 | 147.89 | 149.78 | 151.69 |

extent, on the type of duct material and method of construction.

Graph 1 provides the relationship between airflow, unit pressure drop and air velocity through straight circular ductwork, typical for use in small ductwork systems constructed from PVCu or steel.

The rectangular equivalent of the circular duct section used can be determined from Graph 2.

Pressure loss through ductwork fittings can be calculated by multiplying the fitting K factor listed by Table 2, with the air velocity pressure in the duct.

### Formula 6

The air velocity pressure can be calculated using the formula:

$$P_v = 1/2 \times \varphi \times v^2$$

Where  $P_v$ = The Velocity Pressure in Pascals (Pa)

$\varphi$ = The density of air in kg/m³

$v$ = The air velocity in m/s

For general ventilation systems the density of air can be taken as 1.2kg/m³.

Therefore the formula can be simplified to:

$$P_v = 0.6 \times v^2$$

The velocity pressure against velocity is tabulated in Table 3.

Pressure loss through grilles, air terminals and louvres should be obtained from the manufacturer.

The individual pressure loss through each element of the ductwork system has to be added together to arrive at the required fan pressure. Where branches are provided within the system, it is necessary to determine which route

would be the index run (eg: the run with the highest pressure loss).

It is usual practice when selecting a fan to add a percentage (between 10 and 20%) to the required airflow for ductwork leakage.

## Noise control

Consideration must be given to ensure that vibration and airborne noise generated by a fan will not cause damage or a nuisance.

Vibration transmission can be reduced by providing a sound isolating material between the fan, support structure and connecting ductwork.

This can take the form of:

1. Proprietary anti-vibration mountings constructed from neoprene, metal or plastic springs or similar

2. Neoprene or similar inserts between the fan and fixings

3. Flexible ductwork connections to the fan unit.

It should be ensured that the fan and ductwork system are not fixed to, or in close proximity of any materials which could readily flex and vibrate.

Airborne noise can be reduced, in the first instance, by selecting a fan which has a low sound power level. Tabulated sound power levels in decibels (dB) against frequency (Hz) can be obtained from the fan manufacturer. It should be noted that the published figures can take various forms and it is therefore necessary to ensure that like for like comparisons are made. Also note that

there is a difference between 'sound power' and 'sound pressure' noise levels.

Attenuators (silencers) can be installed within the ductwork to reduce the airborne noise transmission from a fan. Advice regarding attenuator selection should be sought from the fan manufacturers or a specialist.

## Fan types

There are four main types of fans used in ventilation systems:

1. Centrifugal

2. Axial Flow

3. Mixed Flow

4. Propeller.

These four types of fans are further divided into various types, primarily associated with the type of fan blades which they contain.

Generally the type of fan selected will be governed by the fan duty required (airflow and pressure), and the type of application. The following general characteristics of each fan type should be noted:

### Centrifugal fans

a. High airflow

b. High pressure

c. Main sound power generation in lower frequencies, which are more readily controlled by attenuation

d.  Un-cased units require a change in ductwork direction from intake to discharge

e.  Larger fans are readily available with belt drive motors which can facilitate a future change in fan speed and thus fan duty

f.  Backward curved type impellers available which have non-overloading (non-stall) characteristics.

## Axial flow fans

a.  High airflow

b.  High pressure

c.  Fans can be installed in series to increase pressure available

d.  Compact design

e.  Fan installed in-line, in direction of airflow

f.  Fan will stall if ductwork pressure loss is outside fan characteristic

g.  Low cost.

## Mixed flow fan

a.  High airflow

b.  High pressure

c .  High efficiency

d.  Low noise

e.  Low energy consumption.

## Propeller fan

a.  High airflow

b.  Low pressure

c.  Low cost

d.  Low efficiency

e.  Can be noisy.

# Designing for the disabled

# Introduction

The following information provides designers with guidelines for designing plumbing services for the disabled community. It includes information on access to buildings which apply whether the building is large or merely a small toilet. More specifically it gives details of measurements required for WC compartments.

In the case of the compartment, passage ways and door sizes, the figures given are the minimum size required. Additional space is recommended wherever possible.

# Approaches to buildings

Facilities for the disabled should be marked with the internationally agreed disabled sign.

*Figure 1  Disabled sign*

## Parking spaces

Parking spaces should be close to an accessible entrance and preferably on the same level (ramps are permissible but may be tiring for wheelchair or zimmer users). If possible, they should be under cover with covered access to the building and there should be adequate extra space for the transfer from car to wheelchair.

## Dropped kerbs

These should be 1400mm wide with a gradient of at least 1 in 12 and should be placed where there is a merging of roadway and pavement.

## Stepped access

This is not permissible under current government requirements.

## Level/ramped access

Should be provided at one entrance from the adjacent street and car parking spaces with access to the toilet facilities. Ramps should be a minimum width of 1200mm with a maximum gradient of 1 in 12 and having an unobstructed platform of 1200 square millimetres. Resting places should be provided at intervals if the approach ramps are longer than 3 metres and near the maximum gradient of 1 in 12.

## Handrails

Handrails should be provided on both sides of a ramp, or in the centre if its width exceeds 2000mm, and/or where the gradient exceeds 1 in 15. They should be easy to grip firmly with a circular diameter of 45-50mm.

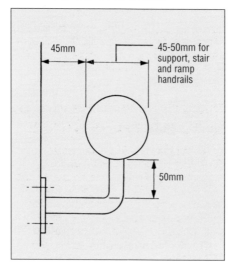

45mm

45-50mm for support, stair and ramp handrails

50mm

*Figure 2  Handrail dimensions*

## Entrance doors

These should have a clear opening not less than 980mm wide and an auxiliary side hung door the same width should be provided if they are revolving. The doors should be easily swung and any spring or hydraulic damper provided must allow easy access for the wheelchair user.

## Automatic entrance doors

These are preferable in certain circumstances but they should have a minimum clear distance of 2100mm between sets for sliding doors and 2500mm for swing types.

# Inside buildings

## Double swing doors

These are preferred in circulation areas.

## Glass doors and other glass areas

Should be made easily identifiable to those with defective vision.

They should never be used in areas/institutions where wheelchair users are prominent.

## Sliding doors

May be necessary in bathrooms and WC compartments. They should not be less than 900mm wide. They can however have disadvantages as adjacent wall space is rendered useless, there is poor acoustic insulation and the typical sliding gear used with low cost doors does not easily withstand disabled usage and may be pulled across the line of the operating track. People in wheelchairs prefer swing doors to sliding doors.

## Internal doors

These should have a clear opening of not less than 900mm. On the leading face of side hung doors there should be a clear wall space or panel equivalent of 300mm.

## Kick plates

These are not essential but are recommended to be fixed to the trailing face of side hung doors as they can help to minimize damage to the building finishes. The plates located at low level to a height above the wheelchair user's foot rest level together with another plate at centre of side wheel level to prevent the wheels from damaging finishes.

## Thresholds

Thresholds must be flush without steps or upstands to comply with statutory requirements.

## Spring closers

These should be avoided but delayed action types are preferred if they are essential. Their spring should be of released tension to allow use by a disabled person.

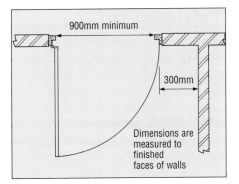

**Figure 3** *Dimensions – internal doors and adjacent areas*

## Door handles

Door handles should be approximately 1040mm above floor level and of the lever type, robust, sufficiently large diameter in size to grip and easy to use.

## Switches

Switches for lights should align with the door handles and be no higher than 1200mm above the floor level. For lifts, touch light controls are preferable, with embossed digits to enable identification by blind people.

## Internal circulation areas

There should be a wheelchair access at the same level as an accessible entrance door, or at the same level as a lift. Changes in level by ramps are permissible. Ramps no greater than 1:15 slope.

## Passage ways

Passage ways should not be less than 1200mm wide.

## Floors

Floors should have a slip resistant surface (wet or dry). There should be no simulation of steps in the patterning.

## Hazards

Hazards such as level variations and projections or obstructions such as floor drainage gullies and upstanding access and manhole covers must be avoided.

## Level changes

Level changes should be easily identifiable by lighting and colour texture contrasts.

# WC compartments in public buildings

At least one unisex public lavatory accommodation should be provided in:

## Entertainment facilities

Concert halls, theatres, cinemas, recreational buildings, leisure and sport facilities.

## Travel facilities

Transport buildings, principal railway stations, road service stations, air terminals.

## Commercial buildings

Shopping centres and large department stores. At least one unisex staff lavatory accommodaiton should be provided in large office buildings and buildings related to other types of employment.

In addition to the above unisex facilities where one assistant can aid the disabled person, supplementary facilities should be provided in large buildings.

## Points to consider for WCs in the Disabled Persons home

a.  If the upstairs WC is inaccessible, a stairlift should be considered if it enables other rooms to be used. Also, if there is sufficient space in the WC the door could be re-hung; a sliding door should not be fitted. If the WC is in an adjacent room, an additional WC could be incorporated into the bathroom.

b.  If the only WC is external to the building, considerations should be given to either covered access to it or a one sided protected walkway installation. Grant help may be available through the Environmental Health Department (for private housing) or the Local Authority (for council housing).

c.  Strict building regulations apply if a new WC is installed and these must be checked with the Environmental Health Department. Utilizing space downstairs may necessitate the fitting of extra doors, additional ventilation and special consideration for understairs installation.

d.  Where there is no suitable downstairs space available, consider installing a ground floor bathroom or shower room extension incorporating a WC suite. All work must comply with the Building Regulations. Allowances must be made for the specific needs or future needs of the disabled person, such as level access, manoeuvring space, attendance helper, etc.

e.  When installing a new WC installation check that the seat height is suitable for the user, securing it on a raised plinth as necessary. Check with the disabled person first to find out what their needs are before finally installing the sanitary fitting.

f.  A wall-hung WC pan must be fitted with a spacer box. This type of pan allows for complete floor cleaning.

g.  A low-level cistern affords some back support and may be useful for those with poor balance but can impede others who have stiff hips. It is very difficult and often impossible for disabled people to flush a low level cistern using a handle behind their seated position.

h.  A slim-line cistern provides more space for those with stiff hips or for a helper assisting with body cleansing.

i.  The WC appliance with a warm water douche and warm air drying facility can provide independence in personal cleansing for some severly disabled users. The installation of this appliance requires Building Control approval.

## Access to WC compartments

All recommendations for passage width, floor types, etc. are detailed in the preceding paragraphs. It is most important that a route is available to the toilet area having suitably sized doors and openings of minimum clearance of 900mm wide along which the disabled person travels to the compartments. Remember no steps, ridges or steep changing floor levels.

The WC compartment should be provided with access to allow wheelchair approach to all the facilities which should include the WC, flushing unit, hand basins with taps, towel dispensers (or hand dryers), sanitary towel disposal units and mirrors.

## Access through lobbies and openings

This is not recommended but where it is essential, room should be allowed for a wheelchair to manoeuvre. Standard

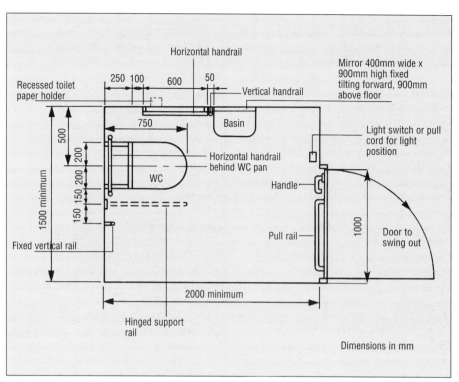

*Figure 4 Dimension of WC compartments and facilities*

wheelchairs need 1800 by 1400mm to turn 180°. Note should be made that wheelchair lengths vary between 945mm and 1150mm with the width between 550mm and 675mm. It must also be remembered that the disabled person's feet extend in front of the wheelchair and their arms and especially their fingers to operate the wheelchair.

## Dimensions

The WC compartment should not be less than 2000mm by 1500mm.

## Door

This should be 1000mm clear wide, open outwards (so that the doorway is not blocked if a person inside falls), have a pull rail and handle, or it should slide. It should only open inwards if there is 1100mm by 700mm of unobstructed space inside it to allow a free door swing with the wheelchair, which has to be manoeuvred backwards at the same time as pulling the door open.

The door must be unlockable from the outside in the event of emergency and assistance needed by an attendant.

## Support rails

50mm minimum diameter support rails should be provided on all sidewalls adjacent to the WC with a hinged horizontal rail of 300mm minimum length on the exposed side. If the design is for

an individual disabled person the rails may be placed according to their specific requirements.

The mirror can equally be positioned above the basin to save movement within the cubicle. The basin can also be used to support make-up and toiletry items.

## Toilets

These should be placed with the seat of the WC at 450-475mm above floor level to top of seat to allow easy transfer from wheelchairs. Preferably the WC should be placed to allow a lateral transfer from the wheelchair, which is placed to one side, or possibly a frontal transfer, in which case a pedestal unit should recede towards floor level to ease transfer. Side transfer should be designed in preference to front.

The flushing device must be easy to operate and must not be higher than 1200mm above floor level. It may be possible to place the flushing device on a side wall within easy reach.

It is poor practice to design the flushing operating device/handle behind the disabled person.

If users are likely to be too severely handicapped to be able to clean themselves, an installation of a proprietary WC/bidet (closomat or medic-loo type of unit) should be considered. These have a warm douche and warm air for drying. These units need a relaxation from the Water Company and Building Control before installation.

## Toilet paper holder

Place on the side closest to the WC seat within easy reach. It is advisable to design the holder to accommodate two rolls of paper.

## Hand rinse basin

Where practical, this should be placed so that it is usable whilst seated on the WC pan. If it is not within reach the individual has to transfer back into the chair before washing their hands and so fouls the chair's arm rests and wheel runs used for propulsion. The basin should be at a height of 750mm.

Do not install shallow basins with pedestals. Vanity units can be suitable for wheelchair users with built into the wall types most useful and practicable. It is possible to get an adjustable height basin, such as the 'Zoom' basin, or items which tip at the front, such as the 'Ifo tilting' wash basin.

## Hand dryers

These are preferable to other less hygienic methods of drying the hands, such as paper towels or roller towels. They should be set at a temperature of not more than 35°C and have a cut-out switch when this is exceeded. There are a number of automatic dryers on the market that work by remote sensor; there is also a selection of less recommended models operated by 'soft touch'.

## Mirrors

The lower edge should not be higher than 900mm above floor level. Mirrors should be tilted to an angle to enable the wheelchair user to use it together with a standing person. Flat on wall mirrors are not suitable.

## WC seats

These should be of a robust material and must not deform when sat on. The seats should be manufactured to British Standards Specification and kitemarked. The 'flimsy' type of WC seat which deforms and moves when sat on must not be used as it could cause accidents during transfer operations. Also accidents can occur during use, resulting in personal injuries, including cuts which result in the disabled person having pressure ulcers.

A raised seat should be adjusted carefully to fit the WC securely and the user or a helper should check frequently that the fittings are secure.

## Restricted space

In a building whose size makes it impractical for a unisex compartment to be installed, the recommended minimum dimensions should be not less than 2000mm by 1500mm. This can result in a limited manoeuvring space, however lateral transfer can be accommodated.

## Additional facilities

Where there is already a unisex toilet compartment and wheelchair users require additional toilet accommodation it is recommended that a WC compartment 2000mm by 1500mm minimum dimensions be installed.

## Macerating WC boxes and WC pans

These electrical mechanical units cannot dispose of sanitary towels or incontinence towels and must not be fitted to WC pans used by the disabled community, unless strict disposal management control is imposed.

## WC facilities for ambulant disabled

Supplementary facilities for ambulant disabled should be provided in large buildings as for the wheelchair disabled users.

# Washbasin fittings

Taps may be paired, with cross-tops, levers, short (or long), quarter turn levers, single lever mixer types or electronic taps.

Electronically operated taps are operated by the user placing their hands under the spout which activates a remote sensor. The remote sensor should be adjusted to suit the application. Combined mixer, separate hot tap, bidets and all other hot water application temperatures should be set at not more than 35°C by the use of a thermostatic valve to maintain an even safe temperature to prevent scalding. Some disabled people are not sufficiently sensitive to temperature to realise when the water is too hot and for such applications, the advice should be sought from the disabled person's medical professional as to the maximum temperature the mixed water should be set to.

Mixer fittings with swivel arms can be moved to the side to leave the sink bowl area free.

Taps can be wall-mounted, which necessitates reaching forward, set into the basin or into the surround. Controls can be fitted to the front of a vanity unit to allow remote control of the tap outlets.

High-necked fittings provide more space when hand-washing and can facilitate cleaning.

In a domestic facility, choose taps which are suitable for the individual, carefully assessing the action required to operate each type.

Long-handled lever taps require less power to operate but need a wider arc of movement than short-handled levers.

Pressure handles vary in the pressure needed and must be held in position to operate. The springs must be reduced in tension for the disabled.

Mixer taps may be dangerous if heat sensation is impaired or if the person is confused.

Foot-operated pressure pads may be useful for some with upper limb diabilities, but they require good balance to use. They are not suitable for wheelchair users.

Knee-action valves are available for those who cannot manage taps and these can be operated from wheelchairs.

Tap turners are a cheaper alternative to fitting new taps for general home use and can be useful when away from home.

Basin plugs with short chains tangle least and may be easier for the disabled user to reach than the longer type.

Central column fitting plugs can be operated with a push and pull movement. Control knobs are easier to handle than a chain but are smaller than most tap handles which cause arthritic disabled people severe problems.

# WC levels in private facilities

## Considerations

The required overall height should be checked for the individual user.

The comfort of the seat for the individual user should be checked.

Wooden seats may be preferred for comfort by some users and may be more stable than plastic seats for some types of transfer.

Most raised seats can be removed for normal use of the WC by able bodied and for cleaning.

Check that the seat fittings are easy to clean.

Some users may require carefully positioned grabrails or a WC support frame to help them transfer on and off the seat.

A padded WC seat may be of help to those with sensitive skins and those prone to pressure sores. Regular dusting with talcum powder helps to prevent the seat from becoming hot and sticky. A raised seat with one cut-out side may be suitable for a person with a stiff hip.

A person with two stiff lower limbs or extremely weak upper limbs may be helped by a self-lifting seat or angled seat fixed to a frame support. Both should be adjusted carefully to the individual and are suitable for those with poor balance.

## Selection of raised toilet seats

The seat should preferably be fixed to the WC pan by brackets: in certain situations removable seats are useful, however seats that are not securely fixed can be dangerous.

The method of fixing should be easy to carry out.

The fixing brackets should not damage the WC Pan.

The seat height must be assessed for each individual and a seat should be supplied which, when placed on the WC pan, provides this height. Some disabled people require a seat height of between 475-550mm.

A convex seat rim is more comfortable than a concave one.

The surface finish of the seat should not adhere to the skin even after prolonged sitting.

To allow easy access for personal cleansing the aperture length should preferably be 300mm.

# Facilities for private use and nursing homes

## Bathroom layout

The layout will depend on various factors including the severity of the disability and the amount of assistance necessary, the size and type of house and the potential space, the financial assistance available, the needs of the family, the method of transfer and the type of hoist and other appliances.

The height of the fittings may not be ideal for the disabled user but a compromise may be necessary to reconcile their needs with those of other members of the family.

Because of the longer time taken by the disabled member to carry out their toilet needs, separate WC and washing facilities are recommended.

Grants may be available for major adaptations and applications should be made to the Local Authority's Environmental Health Department for private housing and to the local council's Housing Department for council housing.

## Spacing

Doors may need repositioning to provide quick, direct access from the bedroom or living room to the WC compartment without negotiating corners and landings.

An ambulant person usually prefers the security of a relatively confined space with carefully positioned and easily reached grabrails.

A wheelchair user will require space for manoeuvring and it may be necessary to remove non-loadbearing walls between the bathroom and WC.

Space will be needed to manoeuvre a portable hoist and the bath panel may be removed to accommodate the hoist legs. Where space is inadequate, a floor-fixed base plate into which the hoist mast can be fitted, could be suitable.

The ceiling joists will need strengthening before an overhead hoist track is fitted.

A straight track from the bedroom to the bathroom spanning the bed, WC and bath may be ideal for a severely disabled person.

The electricity supplier should be consulted before the installation of an electric hoist.

An electric hoist must operate from 24 volts voltage supplied through an approved double-wound isolating transformer. The transformer must be installed outside the bathroom, properly enclosed with a permanently wired connection to the electricity supply.

Space will be necessary to hang towels and clothes.

## Doors

Depending on the space available doors may open inwards or outwards. All doors should have emergency release fittings.

Sliding doors are not recommended however they may be suitable alternatives where space is limited.

All locking doors must be fitted with a lever-operated indicator bolt with an external emergency release.

Door openings must be a minimum of 900mm clear opening width to accommodate the wheelchair user.

## Flooring

Anti-slip flooring such as vinyl sheeting incorporating abrasive grains of aluminium oxide or anti-slip surface tiles are suitable. Carpets designed for bathroom use may be appropriate in some cases.

A damp-proof membrane should be laid beneath the flooring and extended 80mm up the wall to prevent water seepage.

In shower areas, either covered tiles or PVC covering at walls with upstands should be fitted.

Mats should be removed as they are a hazard for an ambulant person together with being an obstruction to a wheelchair.

## Fittings

Sanitaryware must be appropriate for the user and correctly positioned for their use.

An emergency call system may be necessary.

Users with disabled hands should be provided with pull-ring fittings to pull cords for switches. Alternatively provide personal sensors activating the lights.

Shaver points and mirrors should be 1200mm above the floor level and accessible for the user.

Suitable soap holders and twin toilet roll holders must be accessible and at the correct height for the user.

A storage area for toilet accessories must be provided.

## Grabrails

Grabrails will be needed alongside the WC, bath, shower and the basin. A front rail at the basin may be needed to prevent the basin rim being used as a support.

Rails must be positioned for the individual and placed so that accidental misuse of the heated towel rail is avoided as this could be potentially dangerous.

## Heating

The bathroom temperature should be maintained at a higher level than the rest of the home for the disabled person's comfort (see reference to heating for the disabled in this section).

Only heaters approved for bathroom use should be used. They should be fixed above head height to avoid the risk of burns, especially to those with impaired temperature sensation.

## Extractor fan

This should be provided to remove condensation together with toilet smells. There needs to be a permanent fresh air supply passing under the door into the room with undercut space or permanent open low level inlet with privacy grilles. This is in addition to the statutory requirements. The permanent fresh air inlets must be as required by the extractor fan manufacturer's installation requirements.

The extractor fan should be fitted with humidity control stat to operate the fan together with wired-in timer control to over-run for at least 20 minutes.

## Bathing

### Points to consider before alteration

Investigate all possible alternatives before altering bath or shower facilities. An adaption of a preferred arrangement will often be more acceptable than a totally new one, especially to the elderly.

If access to an upstairs bathroom is a problem, consider a stairlift or through-floor lift especially if the person is able to use other rooms upstairs. This is often more economical than building an extension and a lift can be re-sited if the person moves premises.

The bathroom door can be re-hung to open outwards if equipment is bulky or if wheelchair manoeuvring space is needed.

Alternatives should be considered carefully. A bath with a low side may make getting in easier but provides insufficient support when getting out.

The bathroom floor should be checked carefully for suitability if a special bath is being considered.

Fitting a non-slip mat in the bath and teaching the person to turn on their hands and knees after draining the bath water may enable them to get out without further aids.

A combination of bathrails, bathboard, bath seat and non-slip mat may assist many people who have difficulty getting into and out of the bath.

It is recommended that quarter turn lever taps may be the most suitable.

Ensure water pressure is reduced for safety.

Corner taps may be practical for some but if fitted on the outer side, may impede getting into and out of the bath. They are unsuitable if a plastic insert is used.

The tap closest to the bath edge must be the cold tap to help the blind and for the safety of children.

A walk-in bath may suit those who are liable to fall or are afraid of falling. It is particularly practical for institutional use and may prevent the attendants hurting their backs.

The bath can be used as a sit-in bath or as a shower cubicle. The user must be able to sit in the normal position. A water thermostat must be fitted to the taps.

The sensation of rising water may be frightening to some elderly or confused people.

An adjustable height bath is intended for use in hospital or in residential accommodation. It saves the attendant from unnecessary bending and may help prevent back strain.

An ambulant person can step into the bath at its lowest level and be raised to a convenient height for the helper bathing him.

A person who is unable to get into or out of the bath unaided should be hoisted using the particular model the bath was designed to accommodate.

A tilting bath may reduce the need for assistance and increase the independence of some people confined to a wheelchair.

A wheelchair user should check that he can transfer easily into and out of the tilting bath, using a transfer board if necessary.

If the user cannot close the door and operate the controls of the tilting bath a helper must be available to do so.

Check that the person is not likely to suffer dizziness when changing from horizontal to vertical.

## Baths with built-in seats

The small square bath is designed to fit into a bathroom with limited space. It can be used as a shower area by a seated person. This bath is made from cast acrylic sheet and has a slip-resistant finish. A seat is built-in and handgrips are fitted on each side.

## Bath inserts

A rigid insert may be more suitable than a bath board combined with bath seat if the person has great difficulty in getting out of an ordinary bath or lacks balance or co-ordination.

A bath board is useful for those with difficulty getting over the side of the bath, including those with lower limb disabilities, balance or co-ordination problems or stiff joints. The person sits on the board, feet outside the bath, slides backwards on the board, turns to swing the legs over into the bath and slides to the middle of the board.

A non-slip bath should always be used where available.

Those who lack limb strength or have poor balance may prefer to sit on the bath and use an over-bath shower. The curtain will need to hang outside the bath so suitable flooring is required with a drain gully in the floor.

A seat is useful for a person who is unable to sit in the bottom of a bath because of balance, mobility or lower limb problems; strong arms are needed to lower to the seat and onto the bottom of the bath. The seat can be used alone or in conjunction with a bath board. A bath rail may be necessary. The user can sit on the seat to bath or shower if he is unable to lower themselves into the bottom of the bath.

Some makes have mesh or slatted seats for water drainage. Only a seat which hangs from the bath rims or stands on the bottom of the bath is suitable in an acrylic bath.

## Bath lifts

Some bath lifts can be operated independently by the bather, others are assistant-operated.

Installing a lifting device may be more cost-effective than fitting a special bath or shower. Some are suitable for installing in small bathrooms and most can be re-sited if the person leaves the

house.

The disabled person or assisting helper must have sufficient arm movement and strength to operate a mechanical device effectively.

Some lifting devices are simple to use. They are portable and can be used by community nurses to bath patients at home. They are unsuitable for those with poor balance; devices with rigid seats are safer.

If the device is operated electrically, a suitable power point will be required outside the bathroom. Those involved in using the device must be made fully aware of the safety factors recommended by the manufacturer.

Before a floor-fixed device is installed the floor should be checked for suitability. Periodically, the user or helper should check the device for stability.

Portable patient lifters can be used in the bathroom provided adequate manoeuvring space is available and there is space under the bath for the legs of the hoist. Alternatively, a base plate can be floor-fixed at the side or end of the bath and hoist mast fitted into it.

An electrically-operated hoist can be used in the bathroom; the ceiling joists must be inspected and their structural strength confirmed to ensure that they are adequate to carry the tracking. Slings used must allow the water to drain and it is recommended that a spare set be supplied to allow for drying.

## Showering

Showers must be thermostatically controlled with maximum hot water outlet temperature of 35°C. Seek medical advice for each user's needs.

Discussion should be given to the choice between an over-bath shower and shower cubicle. Showering does not always overcome all problems of disabled bathers. Some, particularly the elderly disabled, dislike showers and prefer a strip-wash.

Grants may be available for part of the cost of installing a shower from Environmental Health Departments (for private housing) or the Local Authority (for council housing).

If new downstairs facilities are essential, consider the site of the shower with the WC and washbasin, allowing sufficient space for a wheelchair and a helper as necessary.

Heating, lighting and ventilation of the shower areas should be as detailed previously and the installation of an emergency call system is essential.

Shower trays designed for the disabled do not have a step-over ledge. Check the model and install a grabrail for safety by the entrance. A non-slip sloping floor area is much safer than a shower tray and it is essential for wheelchair use, though it is more expensive to install.

Sloping floors must be non-slip. Non-slip mats are dangerous in such areas. Adhesive safety treads can be used.

It may be difficult to install a sloping floor area in an upstairs bathroom.

The shower curtain or door should be easy for the disabled user to manage. Some magnetic door catches on cubicles require considerable dexterity. A shower curtain must hang inside the shower unit which reduces the area that can be used.

The shower mixing valve should have maximum temperature pre-set at 35°C and thermostatically controlled. This is especially important for those with sensory problems when the temperature must be pre-set lower to suit their medical needs. An anti-scald shut off device must be provided as an essential component.

An instantaneous electric heater must contain an anti-scald device to cope with variations in water pressure. There should be a visual method of checking the water temperature for those with sensory problems. The unit must be temperature pre-set to suit the user's medical needs. The temperature leaving the shower-head must not exceed 35°C.

The controls must be easy to operate and within safe reach of the user or helper. It is recommended that the shower be used for hairwashing and conveniently sited for this application.

A shower head fitted to a flexible tube with wall-mountings at alternative heights or a shower head with a sliding bracket on a wall-mounted tube are recommended in preference to a fixed spray position. The installaiton of these types of showers must be in compliance with the Water Regulations, with regard to backflow.

A tray for soap and sponges should be accessible to the user.

Floor drain gratings should be flush with the floor. The grating material should be nickel bronze or stainless steel.

## Bidets

A bidet is recommended for independent personal cleansing. The installation must conform to the Water Regulations.

The seat height of the bidet must be suitable for the disabled ambulant person; special models with a higher seat

are available. Grabrails will be necessary.

For a wheelchair user, the seat height must be the same as the wheelchair seat. The user can sit facing forwards or backwards on the bidet as convenient. The hot water requirements must be as for 'Showering' section previously.

## Urinals

Specially adapted wheelchairs, cushions or seat cushions may help those using urinals. Generally the wheelchair user will not be able to use wall hung or slab urinals.

## Grabrails

Grabrails are fitted in the bathroom to provide support to the disabled user when washing at the basin, getting into and out of the bath and on and off the WC. They should be positioned so that the washbasin, toilet roll holder or towel rail are never used for support through habit or emergency.

Rails should be positioned to suit the individual. Standard layouts and combination may not be satisfactory.

Walls and partition walls must be of sufficient structural strength to support the load exerted on the rail. Reinforcement may be necessary.

Installation should be carried out by a qualified person.

Grabrails fitted in a bathroom or WC must have an anti-slip finish.

Hinged grabrails should be checked regularly to ensure that the hinge is in good working order.

## Disposal of incontinence and sanitary towels

For reasons of hygiene and to prohibit the spread of disease by contamination, macerators or incinerators should be installed instead of bins. Maintenance personnel must be protected against contracting diseases; incinerators are therfore preferable. The use of macerators is only acceptable providing maintenance personnel are given training and protection against AIDS and other related diseases. Seek advice from Health and Safety at Work Commission.

## Drainage

If no disposal unit is made available, the incontinence and sanitary towels will be placed into the WC Pan for disposal as no other facility is provided. This is not good practice. The designer should

however design the drainage system to accommodate these items when the disposal units are not functioning.

All changes of direction must be designed with long radius easy bends and sufficient access points, readily available in practical positions for use by maintenance personnel.

Ensure that drainage gradients are not minimum but generous for self cleansing velocity of the solids from the drain. Before using dual water capacity flushing units, calculate the volume and discharge rates required to keep the drainage system from the toilet areas used by the disabled community clean of soiled items.

## Joints

Ensure all joints are sealed with non-setting ceramic sealants.

## Hot water and heating

### Scope

NHS Estates Guidance Note DN4 gives information for all health care and personal social services premises, Registered Homes Act 1984 and non-registered premises such as sheltered accommodation. All commercial activity to private or public homes and domestic facilities within requirements for all patients, residents and visitors.

### Requirement

All responsible persons including design staff, supervisors and contractors/ installers under the Health and Safety at Work (etc.) Act 1974 have a 'duty of care' and should be able to demonstrate that they are providing a safe environment. This requirement is equally applicable to new and existing premises.

Only where a resident or patient or user is under adequate continuous supervision may the use of low surface temperature radiators not be warranted. However what is adequate for one user may not be adequate for all. It is recommended for safety reasons that the whole installation works comply to the Guidance Note DN4.

### Safe hot water temperature

Hot water distribution temperature will be in excess of 50°C for the control of Legionella. See the appropriate section for details.

Safe hot water temperature must not exceed 35°C. All outlets must be thermostatically controlled and blended to temperatures below 35°C to accommodate the user's medical needs.

Recommended 'safe' hot water terminal tap, shower, bidet temperature is 35°C. All thermostatically controlled mixers must be fail safe to BS 1415 Part 2 and must not allow hot water to flow in the event of failure.

### Maintenance

It is essential to check the temperature settings and operation of all mixing devices at least half yearly. Other maintenance should be strictly in accordance with the manufacturers' instructions.

The local water quality, especially if the 'safe' water is not treated, will influence the maintenance frequency. Small pieces of debris can fail the operation of the temperature control.

### Space heating

Domestic hot water systems must not be used for space heating, towel rails, bed pan racks, etc.

# Advanced WC cubicle design for wheelchair disabled

This uses the recommended guidelines for the size of the WC compartment and facilities. The WC compartment is illuminated by an automatic light incorporating an infra red device which switches 'on' when a disabled person enters the room and only switches 'off' after the person has left the room.

The tap and hand dryer are operated by automatic sensors. The sanitary fittings are placed within easy reach of the disabled person whilst they are seated on the WC Pan.

Support rails of the standard size are placed in the positions shown in Figure 4. The whole cubicle has a fail safe mechanism.

Facilities should not be institutional looking. They should be well designed with good quality products and user friendly. The designer should use a wheelchair to gain experience for the user's needs. Everyone is unique and a person.

# Central heating for the disabled

Care must be exercised when designing and installing heating systems for the disabled to ensure that all components requiring adjustment or attention by the disabled user are accessible and safe to operate without risk to the disabled person or their attendants. All components must be selected and designed to ensure that no injury or harm can result to the disabled user during normal use or due to possible foreseeable accidents. The following represent the main criteria to consider.

## Living environment

Special consideration may be required with regard to the design internal temperature. This is particularly important for those users who do not move frequently and would therefore require a warmer environment. Each installation must be considered individually to determine the required temperature for the user. In some instances, higher than standard design ventilation rates will be required, these could be provided either by natural ventilation, ie openable windows or mechanical ventilation. In those instances, the additional heat load must be included within the design of the heating system.

The standard design heating flow and return temperatures of around 82°C and 71°C has to be used with convectors or low surface temperature radiators. If water temperatures are decreased it is imperative that heat output from the emitters are corrected. It will also be necessary to conceal or guard pipework to protect the user from the possibility of burns.

All bare radiators and pipework and controls within areas of use by disabled and elderly persons must be screen guarded to comply with Statutory requirements, low surface temperature radiators being the exception.

The system should be designed to ensure that all air and hydrogen dispels naturally through the open vent to avoid the necessity to vent radiators. Correct pipework gradients are therefore essential.

# Boilers

Boilers should be fully automatic in operation, requiring the minimum of adjustment by the user. They should be situated to ensure that all controls or components requiring adjustment or attention by the user are at such a height to facilitate easy access and that no obstructions, such as return edges of walls or kitchen cabinets, are placed close to the boiler to restrict or prevent the user gaining access to the controls. Doors or flaps concealing the controls must be provided with an adequate method to enable the user to open and close them easily. Control knobs and levers must be smooth in operation and of a design to enable the user to operate them easily. The controls must be so situated to ensure that the user could not be injured from the hot surfaces in the boiler. Boilers with sharp edges must be avoided.

## Solid fuel

It is recommended that where possible, solid fuel boilers should not be provided for disabled users. They must only be considered when the user would be capable of transferring fuel, removing ashes, lighting and stoking the fire. The associated dangers of this type of boiler must not be overlooked, particularly the necessity of the user coming into close contact with flames, heat and hot fuel and ashes. Where solid fuel boilers are used it is recommended that the fuel feed should be hopper fed requiring the minimum of attention. The bunker itself may require special consideration to ensure that the fuel can be readily racked to the outlet; it may be necessary to raise the bunker to provide adequate access. Consideration should be given to providing a method of ash removal direct to outside so that it is not necessary for the user to carry hot ashes through the premises.

## Gas/oil fired

These are generally more reliable, require less attention and are easier to operate than solid fuel boilers. The ignition system should be of the fully automatic self-igniting type to avoid the necessity of re-lighting the pilot in the event of failure. If this cannot be provided than a pilot having piezo or electronic ignition should be used. Pilots requiring manual ignition by flame should be avoided. The fuel can be oil, natural or liquid petroleum gas. If banks of liquid petroleum gas bottles are provided having standby or changeover provision , the valving arrangement must be readily accessible and easily operated by the user. The main isolating gas or oil cock must also be readily accessible for use in an emergency.

## Off-peak electric storage heaters

Off-peak electric heating is probably the safest and most easily operated method of heating for the severely disabled user. The cost of off-peak electricity may be more expensive than other fuels but the installation and maintenance costs are generally much lower for storage heaters than other forms of heating. All these factors must be taken into consideration to justify the installation if safety is not the prime consideration. The control of heat output from storage heaters is not as precise as other methods of heating and may cause overheating or underheating at times, particularly during autumn and spring when external temperatures vary considerably from day to day.

## Automatic controls

The automatic control system should be simple to operate and reliable in service. Room thermostats and thermostatic radiator valves should be selected with a method of adjustment that can be readily altered by the user. Special consideration may be necessary with regard to the mounting height and position of the thermostat. The temperature range of the thermostat must be adequate to ensure that a comfortable environment can be maintained. This is particularly important for those users who do not move frequently and therefore require a higher room temperature. The user would not normally adjust the domestic hot water cylinder thermostat and therefore no special provisions are required. The initial setting of the cylinder thermostat must receive special consideration to ensure that the stored water is maintained at a temperature to protect the user from legionella. The safe hot water temperature at the outlet of the fitting must be thermostatically controlled and blended not to exceed 35°C and incorporating an anti-scald device that will not cause harm to the user, particularly those who do not have complete sensitivity to heat. Consideration should be given to using digital time switches which many users would find easier to adjust than the electro-mechanical type.

## Heat emitters

Consideration must be given to selecting low surface temperature radiators and other suitable heat emitters without sharp edges or protrusions on which the user could be injured due to the accidental knock or fall. The protrusions could include radiator valves, air vent and plugged connections. Radiators and convectors are available with the facility to conceal angle valves or with bottom or side connections which could be used in conjunction with straight valves. Alternatively, some users would find top and bottom opposite end connections more desirable with the isolating valve or thermostatic valve at the top connection to prevent the necessity to bend down for adjustment. The radiator valves used should have an easy and smooth action to enable the user to isolate the radiator if required. The heat emitters used should be designed so that there are no surface hot spots together with no access holes which allow small hands to enter, that is they should be totally enclosed.

Where it is known that the occupant will require the aid of a wheelchair, it is essential to ensure that the heat emitters and pipework are installed in such a manner that damage is unlikely to result to the services in the event of an accidental collision. It may be necessary to provide a protective guard around the services.

Where possible, heat emitters should be positioned under windows to reduce cold down draughts and the cold radiant effect. Where this is not possible they should be installed adjacent to windows. Radiators should also be positioned adjacent to external doors to reduce the effect of cold draughts.

## Carbon Monoxide gas alarms

In all living areas where gas, oil, wood, solid fuel, appliances and electric storage heaters are used, Carbon Monoxide (CO) gas alarms should be installed. The CO Alarms must be manufactured in compliance with BS 7860:1996. The height of the alarm must be slightly higher than the disabled persons head height. This position allows for the audible alarm to sound and the disabled person to evacuate the premises before their breathing zone becomes contaminated with CO gas.

It should be remembered that the CO alarm does not wholly protect people who are at special risk due to age, pregnancy or medical condition. Also, a CO alarm is not a substitute for a smoke alarm or a combustible gas detector.

The installation location must not be in line with external fresh air, however it must be heard within the sleeping areas. Additional alarms should be installed near fuel burning appliances and electric storage heaters. Do not conceal the alarm behind curtains, pictures, false ceilings or other obstructions.

Carbon Monoxide gas is colourless, odourless, has the same buoyancy as air and can kill!

## References

The Building Regulations (Amendment) 1998 Part M (schedule 1) and the supporting Approved Document M: Access and facilities for disabled people: 1999 Edition.

BS 5588:Part 8:1988. Fire Precautions in the Design, Construction and Use of Buildings – Code of Practice for Means of Escape for Disabled People.

Spaces in the Home, Bathrooms and WCs. HMSO.

Existing buildings covered by: Disabled Discrimination Act of 1995 (gives suppliers until 2005 to remove all physical barriers).

Disabled Living Foundation, 380-384 Harrow Road, London W9 2HO. Tel: 020 8289 6111.

Equipment for the Disabled, Mary Marlborough Lodge, Nuffield Orthopaedic Centre, Headington, Oxford OX3 7LD. Tel: 01865 750103.

The Royal Association for Disability and Rehabilitation (RADAR), 25 Mortimer Street, London W1N 8AB. Tel: 020-7637 5400.

Access Committee for England, 35 Great Smith Street, London SW1P 3BJ. Tel: 020-7222 7980.

Centre for Accessible Environments, Nutmeg House, 60 Gainsford Street, London SE1 2NY. Tel: 010-7357 8182.

# Domestic swimming pools

# Introduction

Pools have been installed in this country for many years and although there are some dating back to the nineteenth century it has only been in the last fifty years that they have become really popular. There are now many companies that have been designing and installing swimming pools for a substantial number of years and it is a large industry with two to three thousand pools being put in the ground each year.

These range from the large leisure centre pool incorporating swimming areas and recreational areas to the smaller club and school pools and down to the domestic pool in the family home. The primary aim being to provide clear, warm, water that is pollutant free and safe to swim in and enjoy.

The installation of a swimming pool is not a particularly difficult operation but like most specialities if you don't know what you are doing things can go horribly wrong. It requires a great deal of specialist knowledge in the fields of construction, in some cases civil engineering, filtration, chemical treatment, and environmental control.

The Swimming Pool and Allied Trades Association (SPATA) publishes Standards as a guide to best practice in the whole field of 'Swimming Pools'. The Institute of Swimming Pool Engineers provides a home learning course for Technicians and organises four or five seminars per year on various topics. The Pool Water Treatment Advisory Group (PWTAG) is a research body mainly concerned with the pool water. The Institute of Sport and Recreation Managers (ISRM) deals with the day-to-day operation of commercial pools and also runs various course in that area. The Institute of Leisure Amenity Managers (ILAM) also concerns itself with the running of commercial pools as well as other matters. Information is widely available from these organisations. Additionally the Water Regulations give guidance and recommendations for the connection of main supplies to pools and the Electrical Regulations (BSi 7671) cover swimming pools in Special Locations Guidance Note 7.

The Health and Safety Commission has produced a booklet called *'Managing Health and Safety in Swimming Pools'*. In that publication is the now accepted demarcation definition between the private and public sectors. It states that all pools are commercial except certain medical and therapeutic pools, when used for the designed purpose, and pools in a private dwelling for the use of the home owner, the immediate family, and invited guests.

There are basically four areas, which are to be discussed

1. The pool shell construction and finishes
2. Filtration
3. Heating
4. Treatment.

Naturally enough it is not possible to cover everything in a short paper such as this.

# Pool shells

There are basically five types of pool shell; those erected above ground; the concrete, the liner, the fiberglass modular, and the stainless steel.

The *above ground pool* is designed, as its name implies, to sit on a flat surface above the ground. The word flat is included here, although it might sound superfluous, as water will always be in the horizontal plane regardless of the container in which it is put. In the above ground pool this could prove disastrous if the base is not flat, as the whole structure could topple over and collapse. There are two types of above ground shell. The first is a framework, which is erected on the ground comprising uprights and sheets of constant depth material fitted between them. The basic shape for this pool is round but with the addition of support 'buttress' frames the two halves of the circle can be elongated with the insertion of straight pieces. The walls are of a constant depth and the floor flat or with a shallow indentation to give a slightly deeper deep end. The floor is covered with soft sand placed directly on the flat cleared soil and a liner is the means of retaining the water. This is somewhat in the style of the liner pool described later.

The second type is a heavy-duty liner bag, which is tailored to a circular shape with the material forming the walls as well. A flotation collar is placed around the top of the walls and when water is introduced the collar floats upward and the pool fills. The result is a flexible wall bowing outwards. This means that the basic and only shape is circular although there is a range, which with air-inflated sides achieve a rectangular shape.

Both these designs have been extensively tested to show they can withstand the pressure of water pushing outwards. Videos show a demolition ball being dropped into a pool and the sides staying upright and another showed an elephant getting in and out of the full vinyl type. They are not designed to be installed in the ground.

As has been noted these pools have limitations in shape and depth and sit on the ground, consequently they are in great demand in the DIY market and are very much cheaper than the in ground shells. This is not intended to demean this type of pool, as with extensive and imaginative planning they can be very attractive.

First it is important to note that every in ground pool must be designed to suit the ground in which it is to be installed; the type of soil, the water table and the general surrounds. It is obvious to say but clay, chalk and sandy loam exhibit very different properties and it is vital that the contractor be aware of the conditions prevailing on the site before the pool is designed. Therefore if the ground conditions are unknown it is wise to have a trial hole dug and if necessary a soil analysis which should be passed to the structural engineer. It is also important to establish the use to which the pool is to be put and what is required of it. The bathing load will determine in part the size and vice versa and the type of swimming or leisure may also play a part.

*Concrete* shell can be designed to one of two different standards either BS 8007 which is for *'Water retaining structures'* or BS 8110 for *'Structures for retaining Aqueous Liquids'*. The former is used when absolute water tightness is required and demands that the concrete shell will hold water *before* the internal rendering is applied, in cases when it is to be installed over or immediately adjacent to habitable accommodation and in the commercial sector. The latter relies on the internal rendering to retain the water. Indeed SPATA Standards state that an acceptable water loss from any type of pool shell, excluding splash, evaporation and backwashing is 12mm in a seven-day period. This magnitude of loss is virtually and practically impossible to detect. However it is not unusual for new shells to be tested for water tightness where no water loss is accepted. This will depend on the specification.

A structural engineer should design concrete pool shells and according to SPATA Standards the calculations should be made available to the client if required. This shell is described as a monolithic structure in that it is an entity in its own right and should in theory be able to hold the volume of water whether in or out of the ground. In commercial and some domestic installations a void or undercroft is designed around the pool to house air heating ductwork and water pipes and in this case the strength of the pool shell is of paramount importance.

The method of constructing shells can also vary. In commercial installations one method is a poured floor and shuttered walls with both thickness and reinforcing according to the design. This is also suitable for smaller pools but the cost of the shuttering can be a high. Cavity block wall containing reinforced concrete tied to a poured floor is a method widely used in the domestic market and for smaller commercial pools. In this case the two block walls act as shuttering for the poured concrete in between once again both thickness and reinforcing according to the design. The blockwork is quicker and cheaper to construct but due to the block size is limited to gentle curves and therefore shape.

*Sprayed concrete*, either Shotcrete or Gunite depending on the aggregate size is applied by spraying it under pressure onto the pre-assembled reinforcement frame. The constituents of the concrete mixing at the nozzle of the spray gun. This method of application results in a much lighter shell but one with a greater degree of flexibility in shape.

*Stainless steel* pools are structurally designed to retain the weight of the water in the same manner as the concrete pool. Some products have supporting frames and others have reinforcing built into them. They are considerably lighter than the concrete type of shell and are usually restricted to the deck level type of pool as the surround channel adds to the strength. In some cases stainless steel can be the finish and in others vinyl. Angular shapes are favoured rather than free form.

*Liner pools* have a shell that is radically different. To start with the water tightness is achieved by a vinyl container (the liner). The structure is non-reinforced and the floor of the pool is porous. The porosity of the floor is to allow ground water to permeate through it should the ground water pressure become greater than the weight of the water in the pool at which time the flexibility of the liner allows movement to prevent collapse. The liner is supported by a structure, which is not meant to have any great strength in relation to the ground and water, but is there to give shape to the pool and to keep the liner in place. For this reason, this liner system is not generally used for large commercial installations however there are some products which are similar and due to their more robust design have structural strength.

The supporting structure can be constructed of a variety of materials. Years ago one would see liner walls made of wood or even steel as developments progressed galvanised metal and basic fibreglass were used but today there are many composite 'plastic' wall panels of high quality available. These are held in the vertical plane by braces usually known as 'A' frames. These frames are set in concrete for strength and support. Generally speaking this type of liner construction gives a constant panel depth of approximately 1 metre. The floor profile can then be graded from the bottom of the wall into either a hopper or wedge shape.

Blockwork can also be used for liner pool walls; depending on the depth of the wall either hollow agricultural type or ordinary blocks can be used. However this type of wall has to have sand and cement rendering to provide a smooth finish, which will not puncture the liner material. However the use of hollow blocks that can be reinforced can give greater wall and therefore water depths and this leads to gentle constant slope floors. The sand used on the walls and floor should be sharp sand as this gives a greater longevity. It is also good practice, with block walls without reinforcement, to have a ring beam of concrete at the top of the wall, which is reinforced and runs the length of the perimeter, to give added strength.

Again because of the construction of the walls liner pool have limitations in shape.

*Fibreglass pools* were usually small one-piece shells or if larger were in two pieces. The fibreglass was not particularly thick and the general principle on installation was to bed them soundly and then back fill between the shell and the dig with a lean-mix of concrete, which would give some strength to the structure. Additionally most, but not all, of these pools were of constant depth.

In the last few years there has been a resurgence of this type of pool but with better construction techniques used. The shells are made of good marine fibreglass, with timber incorporated to provide structural support, and are designed to hold water in or out of the ground. They are now usually factory fitted with flow control fittings and pipework to ease plant installation. They also come in quite a range of sizes. This in itself is one of the problems with this type of shell. The larger they are the heavier and more difficult they are to transport and to get into the site. They are moved with the use of low loader lorries, large cranes and even helicopters. Once the excavation is completed the pool is lowered onto the drainage bed on the floor of the hole, leveled and the backfilling carried out. Consequently despite the logistical

difficulties the shell should be installed very quickly. There is, once again, a size and shape limitation.

All the above comments apply to the freeboard pool whether commercial or domestic. The deck level pool with the water over flowing into a perimeter channel is usually built of reinforced concrete rather than a traditional liner. Once again there are products that are the exception to this but they are few in number. It would be technically possible to have a prefabricated fibreglass pool in this type but the practicality of it would be in doubt.

One common factor in relation to the proper installation of all pool shells is the question of ground water. If the ground water pressure builds up the shell of the pool will be at risk unless the pressure is relieved. Battleships were made of steel, weighed thousands of tons and floated. If the pressure is greater than the water and the weight of the concrete or fibreglass shell it could lift or float the shell. In concrete pools not only should a hydrostatic relief valve be fitted in the lowest point but also the drainage under and around the structure should be such that the water can easily gravitate to the deepest point and if necessary operate the relief valve. Liner pools with their porous base do not have hydrostatic relief valves because that water would permeate through the liner floor. Again the surround drainage should be designed to take water away from the structure as the liner will lift off the base and float and a floating liner is not conducive to swimming. This, in extreme cases, could mean the installation of a pumping chamber and float operated pump to take away the ground water. The fibreglass shell should be protected in the same way as the concrete pool. It is therefore important to assess the ground water situation, and consider the winter months, before the installation is started so that all necessary precautions can be included in the specification.

Although a discussion on the relative merits of the many pool finishes is not included here, the internal finish of the pool does have a bearing on the selection of pool shell construction method. The appearance and feel of the finished pool is important to the users, especially in the domestic market.

The different methods of construction described earlier indicate that there is an obvious cost difference between concrete pools and liner pools. Whether there is an appreciable difference between liner pools and fibreglass pools will depend on the problems on site related to access and general transportation. The actual costs will also depend on a number of factors, which vary from design to design

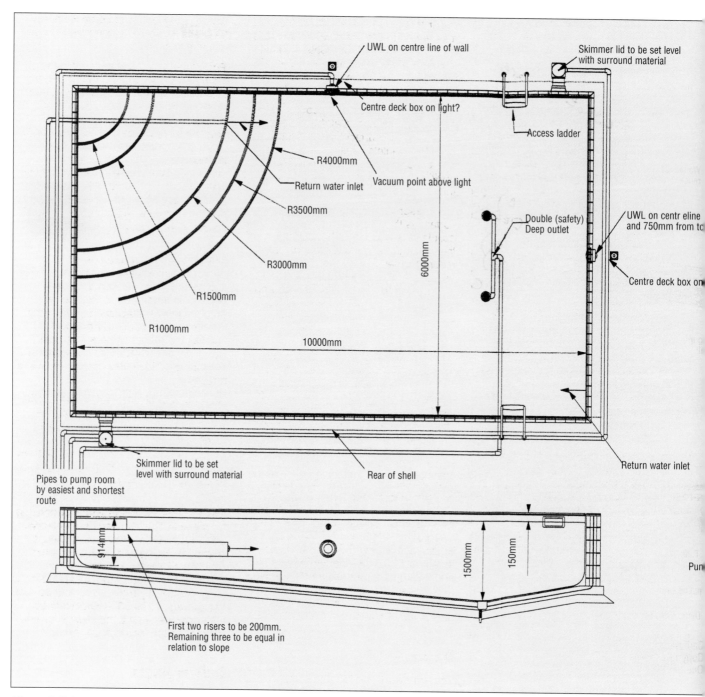

*Figure 1  Schematic domestic swimming pool layout of family pool with large step area for small toddlers*

and from project to project, consequently it is very difficult to be precise. One must bear in mind that the surround work, filtration, heating etc are going to be the same regardless of the shell construction and that there will be some variation in the cost of internal finish.

## Internal finishes

The liner and fiberglass pool have their finish as an integral part of the system. It is only the concrete structure that is tiled either with ceramic or vitreous glass mosaics. The large commercial pool is nearly always tiled with large ceramic tiles.

## Filtration

In a swimming pool the filtration system is there to remove, as far as possible the suspended inorganic matter from the water. This is done in all pools by a pump(s) sucking the water from the pool tank, blowing it through a filter medium and thereafter back into the pool tank. The filter medium can be a fine powder called diatomaceous earth or a material similar to cartridge paper but these days graded silica sand is mainly used. Sand provides a particulate removal down to 10 microns and although the other two

media produce a finer filtration the operational problems are such that they are rarely if ever used.

The water in the sand filter should pass uniformly through the surface area and it is the relation of the speed of the water and the surface area that give the filtration rate in $m^3/m^2/$per hour.

Low rate filtration up to $10m^3/m^2/$per hour is rarely if ever used these days. Medium rate from $11 - 30$ $m^3/m^2/$per hour is widely used in commercial pools and is recommended by PWTAG and SPATA. High rate from $31 - 50m^3/m^2/$per hour is the preferred rate for the domestic market although it is true to say that this

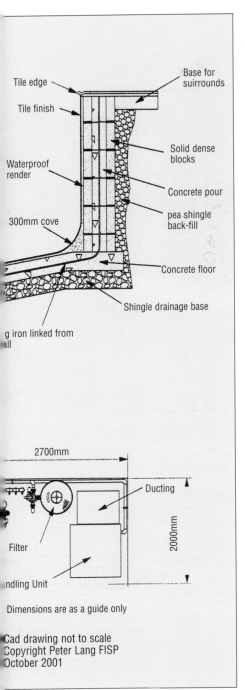

Tile edge
Tile finish
Waterproof render
300mm cove
g iron linked from ll

Base for suirrounds
Solid dense blocks
Concrete pour
pea shingle back-fill
Concrete floor
Shingle drainage base

2700mm
Ducting
2000mm
Filter
ndling Unit

Dimensions are as a guide only

Cad drawing not to scale
Copyright Peter Lang FISP
October 2001

rate can be used in the commercial pool providing the design work is to a high standard.

## Water circulation

In any pool, pollutants are going to enter the system via the water with the swimmers. In the outdoor pool the wind blown debris has also to be taken into consideration. It is therefore essential that the water, having been taken out of the pool, is returned and distributed in a manner to ensure maximum mixing and avoiding area where very little movement occurs. The filtration and heating of the

water takes place in the plant room and it is there that the chemical treatment is introduced into it. Dead spots within the pool tank mean that the pollution is neither treated nor removed and it will therefore proliferate.

Water is taken out of the pool by bottom outlets usually placed at the deepest point from the surface. It is returned into the pool by inlets usually placed in the wall but sometimes in the floor. The positioning of these points will depend on the shape and size of the pool tank.

The reason for taking water from the surface is that the vast majority of pollutants are found in the top 100mm of the water. In the commercial pool it is recommended that a 'level-deck' system be used. In this type of pool the water is at the same level as the surrounds and overflows the top of the pool wall into a perimeter channel. To keep the water level in the pool constant a 'balance tank' is built onto the pool outside the perimeter of the shell. The tank holds a quantity of water, which is added to the volume of the shell and is pumped around the system. As the capacity of the shell is less than the total water available the pool overflows. The overflow water gravitates back into the 'balance tank'. This creates a surface water outlet that is 100% of the perimeter.

Although this method can be used on any concrete pool it does add to the cost and consequently in the domestic pool water is taken off the surface over a weir set into the side of the pool wall. The water does not overflow and so there is a 'freeboard' between the top of the pool and the water of approximately 150mm. In this case, and when the number of bathers is very small, only one or two outlets may be used.

## Turnover

The turnover is the length of time the pump takes to move the total contents of the pool tank through the filter. However as the pump is sucking from the pool tank and immediately pumping the water back into the same tank the period over which it can be guaranteed that every drop of water has passed through the filter is much longer. However this theoretical figure is always used in designing the filtration system for any pool.

The turnover will vary from pool to pool depending on its use. A commercial spa with high temperature and high bather to water ratio will have a turn over of 5–15 minutes, a conventional 25m pool from 2.5 – 3 hours and a domestic low use pool up to 8 hours.

## Heating

Pool water can be heated using any of the fossil fuels and solar energy. There are some heaters, specifically designed for the pool industry where the pool water flows directly through the heater and is heated directly. It is also possible to utilise a standard commercial or domestic boiler and add to it a pool water calorifier, primary pipe connection with thermostat and motorised valve. Solar energy is low-grade heat and can be obtained either from a bank of panel collectors or by an air to water heat pump.

Solar panels will provide heat into an outdoor pool and are very rarely used on indoor pools. On outdoor pools they perform in proportion to the natural ambient temperature and therefore the heat input is erratic. They are best installed as a back-up to a fossil fuel heater. The installation can be expensive but the heat obtained in general terms is free.

Heat pumps will provide heat as required but the input is slow and cannot give bursts of high grade heat as can the fossil fuel heater. They are mainly used on outdoor pools in the domestic market and although the installation is slightly more expensive the running costs are lower.

The water temperature varies depending on the activity in the pool. A spa where bathers are static, and for therapeutic reasons is going to be in the region of 38-40°C. Similarly children and non-swimmers in a teaching pool are going to require a slightly higher temperature than the average of 28-30°C. Outdoor pools also vary and tend to be slightly lower on average in the region of 24-26°C.

## Indoor pools

Once a pool has been enclosed the air in the pool hall must be heated otherwise condensation can occur. This will not only damage the fabric of the building but can also be a hazard when visibility is reduced. Consequently it is necessary to heat the air as well, usually to 1°C above that of the water and to maintain that temperature in all parts of the pool hall. This is done by moving the air by blowing into the pool hall and sucking it out. Relying on natural movement has been proved not to be effective and the use of radiators is to be avoided at all times.

With the air temperature above that of the water the evaporation will be reduced but water will still find its way into the atmosphere. If the humidity rises the risk of condensation will again be increased and this must be eliminated. The air in the pool hall can be extracted and fresh air drawn in from the outside. This will also reduce the build up of odours but is costly, as the new air will have to be re-heated.

The incoming air can be heated by the out going air by means of modern plate heat exchangers but re-cycling the air and reducing the air changing to a minimum means that the heat losses are lower and the air handling unit can incorporate a de-humidifier to remove the humidity. Humidity is relative to the differential between the pool hall air temperatures and the ambient and the point at which condensation will happen, the dew point, will vary. In an average pool hall the dew point could be as high as 21°C.

Hot air is distributed around the pool hall either in underground or exposed ductwork or, in smaller halls by single inlet and outlet grilles. Either way consideration must be given to the positioning of the return air grilles so that short cycling is avoided.

The hot air must be contained within the pool hall otherwise it will migrate. Of particular concern in any pool hall is the construction and generally speaking it is wise to consider the inside of it as an external construction. Voids are to be avoided but if necessary a vapour barrier must be inserted. This can be in the vertical as well as the horizontal plane. There are vapour barrier materials widely available however great care must be taken when fixing them as ANY puncture hole, a nail, screw or tack MUST be sealed with a sealant.

Heater batteries fitted in the ductwork or in the air-handling unit heat the air. The usual method is by LPHW from a standard boiler with stats controlling motorised valves. In this case the pool water is heated in the same manner via a calorifier.

# Treatment

Pool water needs to be treated to remove the organic mater, bacteria etc, which enters the water on bathers and is generally blown or taken into it. There are several options but chlorine is the most widely used. However ozone and ultra-violet are also to be considered.

Not only should a 'disinfectant' be applied but also water balance has to take into account of the pH, the total alkalinity, the calcium hardness and the total dissolved solids.

The pH is in general terms the degree or level of concentration of acid or alkalis present in the water. Too alkaline and the effectiveness of chlorine is reduced, scale can be formed in small-bore waterways in calorifiers etc and there can be bather discomfort. To acidic and erosion and corrosion can occur and bathers will find discomfort. The Total Alkalinity is the quantitative analysis of the amount of alkali in the water. This has an effect on the movement of the pH and can also encourage scaling as can the calcium hardness. Total dissolved solids are, as the name implies the dissolved matter in the water, which can affect conductivity, and at levels water clarity.

It is recommended that in the commercial pool the water treatment is auto-mated so that the level of disinfectant and pH is measure electronically compared against the recommended levels and the appropriate chemicals pumped into the water. In order to prevent the build up of matter in the water it is also recommended that water be replaced at a rate of 30 litres per bather per day. This is partially achieved by backwashing/cleaning the filter medium.

# Electrical earthing and bonding of building services

# Introduction

The requirements for electrical earthing and bonding of building services are given in BS 7671: 2001 – *Requirements for electrical installations*; also known as the IEE Wiring Regulations.

The requirements for the different types of supply TN-C-S, TN-S and TT are all slightly different. The guidance given here is based on the requirements for a TN-C-S (or PME) supply. This is because new supplies are almost exclusively PME and the requirements for PME supplies are the most onerous. Compliance with the bonding requirements for a PME supply will result in compliance with requirements for TN-S and TT systems.

All incoming service pipes (gas, oil and water) and internal pipework (hot, cold, central heating) may now be of plastic. Guidance is given in this section on the requirements for the earthing and bonding of such installations as well as for metal services.

# General

Two types of equipotential bonding are recognised in the IEE Wiring Regulations as follows:

1. Main equipotential bonding

2. Supplementary equipotential bonding.

Main equipotential bonding is carried out at the origin of the electrical installation and supplementary bonding is carried out in areas of increased shock risk, such as bathrooms or swimming pools. This guidance is concerned only with the plumbing aspects of such bonding.

# Metal pipes and services

## Main equipotential bonding of metallic services

The IEE Wiring Regulations require that extraneous-conductive-parts including:

a. Metal water service pipes

b. Metal gas installation pipes

c. Other metal service pipes and ducting

d. Metal central heating and air conditioning systems

e. Exposed metal structural parts of the building

f. Lightning protective system.

be connected to the main earthing terminal of the installation (Regulation 413-02-02). 'Other metal service pipes and ducting' includes metallic waste pipes.

Figure 1 shows a typical main bonding installation.

The main bonding of the incoming metallic gas and metallic water services is required to be carried out as close as practicable to the point at which those services enter the premises (Regulation 547-02-02). Where there is an insulated

**Figure 1** *Main bonding and earthing of a typical domestic installation – metal service pipes and PME supply*

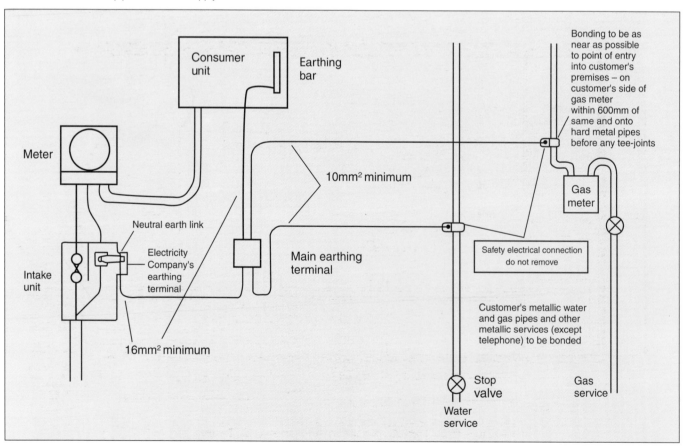

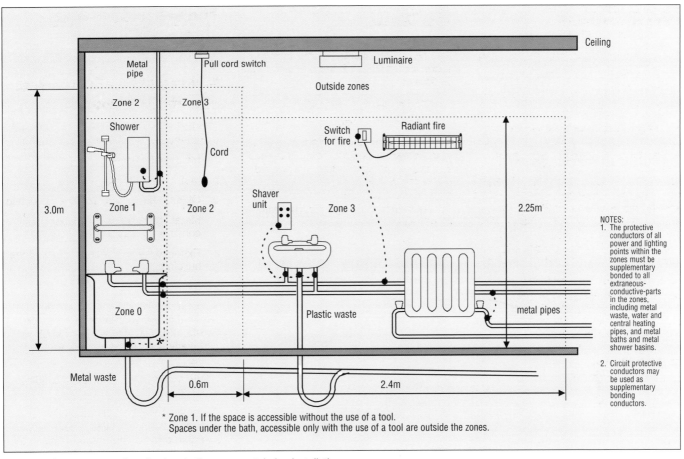

*Figure 2* Supplementary bonding in a bathroom – metal pipe installation

*Figure 3* Supplementary bonding in a bathroom – plastic pipe installation

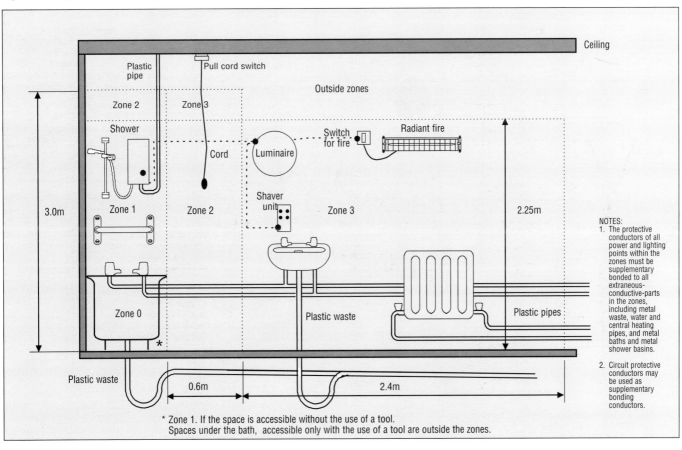

section or insert at that point or there is a meter, the connection must be made to the consumers' hard metal pipework and before any branch pipework. Where practicable the connection should be made within 600mm of the meter outlet union or at the point of entry to the building, if the meter is external.

## Supplementary equipotential bonding in locations of increased shock risk – metal pipework

Supplementary equipotential bonding is required only in locations of increased shock risk such as those as in Part 6 of the Wiring Regulations (471-08-01). In domestic premises the locations identified as having increased shock risks are rooms containing a bath or shower (bathrooms) and around swimming pools.

In a bathroom or shower room, local supplementary equipotential bonding is required to be provided, connecting together the terminals of protective conductors of each circuit supplying Class 1 and Class 2 equipment in zones 1, 2 or 3 and extraneous-conductive-parts in these zones including the following:

a. Metal pipes supplying services and metallic waste pipes (eg water, gas)

b. Metal central heating pipes and air conditioning systems

c. Accessible metal structural parts of the building (metallic door architraves, metal handrails, window frames and similar parts are not considered to be extraneous-conductive-parts unless they are connected to metallic structural parts of the building)

d. Metal baths and metallic shower basins.

The supplementary equipotential bonding may be provided in close proximity to the location.

A typical installation is shown in Figure 2.

## Supplementary bonding in other locations – metal pipework

There is no specific requirement in the Wiring Regulations to supplementary bond the following:

a. Kitchen pipes, sinks or draining boards

b. Metallic pipes and wash handbasins in domestic locations other than bathrooms.

*NOTE*
*Metal waste pipes in contact with earth should be main bonded back to the main earthing terminal.*

## Earthing and bonding clamps and labels

Earthing and bonding conductors must be connected to metal pipes with clamps to BS 951 (*Specification for clamps for earthing and bonding purposes*). A permanent label also to BS 951 with the words.

| SAFETY ELECTRICAL CONNECTION – DO NOT REMOVE |

shall be permanently fixed in a visible position at or near the point of connection of:

a. Every main and supplementary bonding conductor

c. Every earthing conductor to an earth electrode

d. At the main earthing terminal (where the terminal is not part of the main switchgear)

e. Plastic pipes and services.

*Table 1 Supplementary bonding in bathrooms*

| | Pipework material | | | | Supplementary bond required in zones 0, 1, 2 and 3 between: | Comments |
|---|---|---|---|---|---|---|
| | Waste pipes | Cold water | Hot water | CH | | |
| 1 | Metal | Metal | Metal | Metal | All metal pipes, earth terminals of Class I and Class 2 equipment, and exposed-conductive-parts of the building structure. | Metal pipes can be used as bonding conductors if joints are metal to metal and electrically continuous. |
| 2 | Plastic | Plastic | Plastic | Plastic | Earth terminals of Class I and Class 2 equipment and exposed-conductive-parts of the building structure. | Bonding of metal taps, metal radiators or metal baths is not required unless the bath is connected to the metallic building structure. |
| 3 | Plastic | Plastic | Metal | Metal | Hot water pipes, central heating pipes, earth terminals of Class I and Class 2 equipment and exposed-conductive-parts of the building structure. | A bond is not required to the taps either hot or cold, or to metal baths unless connected to the metallic building structure. |
| 4 | Plastic | Plastic | Plastic | Metal | Central heating pipes, the earth terminals of Class I and Class 2 equipment and exposed-conductive-parts of the building structure. | Bonding of metal water taps is not required, nor metal baths unless connected to the metallic building structure. |
| 5 | Plastic | Metal | Metal | Metal | All metal pipes, earth terminals of Class I and Class 2 equipment, and exposed-conductive-parts of the building structure. | Metal pipes themselves can be used as bonding conductors if joints are metal to metal and electrically continuous. |
| 6 | Plastic | Metal | Metal | Plastic | All metal pipes, earth terminals of Class I and Class 2 equipment, and exposed-conductive-parts of the building structure. | Metal central heating radiator does not require bonding. |

1. Supplementary bonding is carried out to the earth terminal of equipment within the bathroom with exposed-conductive-part. A supplementary bond is not run back to the main earth.
2. Metal window frames are not required to be supplementary bonded unless they are electrically connected to the metallic structure of the building.
3. Metal baths supplied by metal pipes do not require supplementary bonding if all the pipes are bonded and there is no other connection of the bath to earth.
4. All bonding connections must be accessible and labelled 'Safety Electrical Connection – Do Not Remove'.

# Plastic pipes and services

## Main equipotential bonding – plastic services

There is no requirement to main bond an incoming service where both the incoming service pipe and the pipework within the installation are both of plastic. Where there is a plastic incoming service and a metal installation within the premises, the main bonding must be carried out, the bonding being applied on the customer's side of meters, main stop cock or plastic inserts.

## Supplementary bonding of plastic pipe installations

Supplementary bonding is not required to metallic parts supplied by plastic pipes such as metal hot and cold water taps supplied from plastic pipes or a metal bath not connected to extraneous-conductive-parts such as structural steelwork and where the hot and cold water pipes and the waste are plastic. Supplementary bonding in a bathroom or shower room will still be required between the protective conductors of circuits supplying Class 1 and Class 2 equipment in the zones, eg heaters, showers and luminaires, see Figure 3.

## Plastic pipe central heating systems

Where metallic radiators are supplied by plastic pipes, there is no requirement to supplementary bond the metallic radiator including any radiator in the bathroom, unless the radiator incorporates an electric fan.

It is common practice to use plastic pipe works for the generality of a plumbing installation, and use copper pipe just for visible parts of the pipe runs. There is no need to supplementary bond such visible metal parts of pipework as are supplied by plastic pipes.

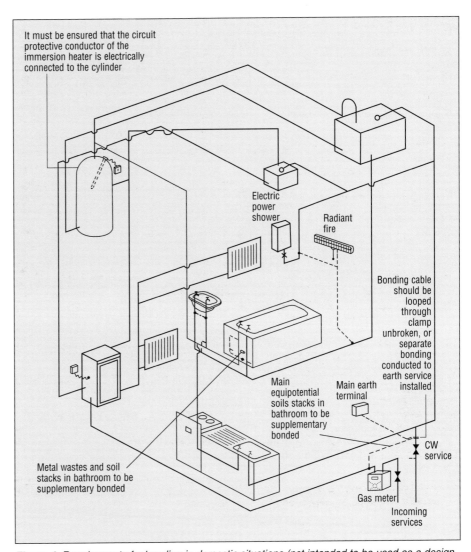

It must be ensured that the circuit protective conductor of the immersion heater is electrically connected to the cylinder

Electric power shower

Radiant fire

Bonding cable should be looped through clamp unbroken, or separate bonding conducted to earth service installed

Main equipotential soils stacks in bathroom to be supplementary bonded

Main earth terminal

CW service

Metal wastes and soil stacks in bathroom to be supplementary bonded

Gas meter

Incoming services

*Figure 4* Requirements for bonding in domestic situations (not intended to be used as a design for a plumbing installation).

# Size of bonding conductors

Where bonding is required, the minimum size of copper conductor is given below:

| | |
|---|---|
| Main bonding conductor | 10mm$^2$ PME supplies |
| Earthing conductor | 16mm$^2$ for PME supplies |
| Supplementary bonding conductor | 4mm$^2$ where mechanical protection is not provided. |

The size of main earthing, main equipotential and supplementary bonding conductors when insulated are given in Tables 2, 3 and 4.

*Table 2 Main earthing and main equipotential bonding conductor sizes (copper equivalent) for TN-S and TN-C-S supplies*

| Phase conductor or neutral conductor of PME supplies | (mm²) | 6 | 6 | 10 | 16 | 25 | 35 | 50 | 70 |
|---|---|---|---|---|---|---|---|---|---|
| Earthing conductor not buried or buried protected against corrosion and mechanical damage see notes | (mm²) | 6 | 6 | 10 | 16 | 16 | 16 | 25 | 25 |
| Main equipotential bonding conductor see notes | (mm²) | 6 | 6 | 6 | 10 | 10 | 10 | 16 | 16 |
| Main equipotential bonding conductor for PME supplies (TN-C-S) | (mm²) | 10 | 10 | 10 | 10 | 10 | 10 | 16 | 25 |

1. Protective conductors (including earthing and bonding conductors) of 10mm² cross-sectional area or less shall be copper.
2. Regional electricity companies may require a minimum of earthing conductor at the origin of the supply of 16mm² copper or greater for TN-S and TN-C-S supplies.
3. Buried earthing conductors must be at least:
   25mm² copper if not protected against mechanical damage or corrosion
   50mm² steel if not protected against mechanical damage or corrosion
   16mm² coated steel if not protected against mechanical damage but protected against corrosion.
4. Regional electricity companies should be consulted when in doubt.

*Table 3 Supplementary bonding conductors*

| Size of circuit protective conductor | Minimum cross-sectional area of supplementary bonding conductors | | | | | |
|---|---|---|---|---|---|---|
| | Exposed-conductive-part to extraneous-conductive-part | | Exposed-conductive-part to exposed-conductive-part | | Extraneous-conductive-part to extraneous-conductive-part (1) | |
| | Mechanically protected | Not mechanically protected | Mechanically protected | Not mechanically protected | Mechanically protected | Not mechanically protected |
| mm² | mm²   1 | mm²   2 | mm²   3 | mm²   4 | mm²   5 | mm²   6 |
| 1.0 | 1.0 | 4.0 | 1.0 | 4.0 | 2.5 | 4.0 |
| 1.5 | 1.0 | 4.0 | 1.5 | 4.0 | 2.5 | 4.0 |
| 2.5 | 1.5 | 4.0 | 2.5 | 4.0 | 2.5 | 4.0 |
| 4.0 | 2.5 | 4.0 | 2.5 | 4.0 | 2.5 | 4.0 |
| 6.0 | 4.0 | 4.0 | 6.0 | 6.0 | 2.5 | 4.0 |
| 10.0 | 6.0 | 6.0 | 10.0 | 10.0 | 2.5 | 4.0 |
| 16.0 | 10.0 | 10.0 | 10.0 | 16.0 | 2.5 | 4.0 |

1. If one of the extraneous-conductive-parts is connected to an exposed-conductive-part, the bond must be no smaller than that required for bonds between exposed-conductive-parts – columns 3 or 4.

*Table 4 Copper earthing conductor cross-sectional areas (csa) for TT supplies for earth fault loop impedances not less than 1 ohm (Ω)*

| Buried | | | Not Buried | | |
|---|---|---|---|---|---|
| Unprotected | Protected against corrosion | Protected against corrosion and mechanical damage | Unprotected | Protected against corrosion | Protected against corrosion and mechanical damage |
| (mm²) | (mm²) | (mm²) | (mm²) | (mm²) | (mm²) |
| 2.5 | 16 | 2.5 | 4 | 4 | 2.5 |

1. Protected against corrosion by a sheath.
2. For impedances less than 1 ohm determine as per Regulation 543-01-02.
3. The main equipotential bonding conductor shall have a cross-sectional area of not less than half that required of the earthing conductor and not less than 6mm².

# Standards, codes and miscellaneous data

# British & European Standards & Codes of Practice

Some of the BS ENs listed below were still to be published at the time of writing this guide. On publication these BS ENs will often completely or partially replace a British Standard, which will then be withdrawn or revised as appropriate. The exact title and possibly the number of parts may vary slightly when new BS ENs are actually published.

Users are advised to check the current status of these documents before using them. BSI have an excellent web site where on line checks can instantly be made. www.bsi-global.com

## Hot and cold water supplies

### Design

**BS EN 805** : Water supply - Requirements for systems and components outside buildings.

**BS EN 806** : Specification for installations inside buildings conveying water for human consumption.

**BS EN 806 - 1** : General.

**BS EN 806 - 2** : Design.

**BS EN 806 - 3** : Pipe sizing.

**BS EN 806 - 4** : Installation.

**BS EN 806 - 5** : Corrosion.

**BS 6700** : Specification for design, installation, testing and maintenance of services supplying water for domestic use within buildings and their curtilages.

### Materials

**BS 143 and 1256** : Specification for malleable cast iron and cast copper alloy threaded pipe fittings.

**BS EN 200** : Sanitary tapware – General technical specification for single taps & mixer taps (nominal size ½˝) PN10 – Minimum flow pressure of 0.05MPa (0.5 bar).

**BS EN 545** : Ductile iron pipes, fittings, accessories and their joints for water pipelines – Requirements and test methods.

**BS 699** : Specification for copper direct cylinders for domestic purposes.

**BS 853 - 1** : Calorifiers and storage vessels for central heating and hot water supply.

**BS 853 - 2** : Tubular heat exchangers and storage vessels for building and industrial services.

**BS EN 1057** : Copper & copper alloys - Seamless round copper tubes for water and gas in sanitary & heating applications.

**BS 1212** : Float operated valves.

**BS 1212 - 1** : Specification for piston type float operated valves (copper alloy body) (excluding floats).

**BS 1212 - 2** : Specification for diaphragm type float operated valves (copper alloy body) (excluding floats).

**BS 1212 - 3** : Specification for diaphragm type float operated valves (plastic bodied) for cold water services only (excluding floats).

**BS 1212 - 4** : Specification for compact type float operated valves for WC flushing cisterns (including floats).

**BS EN 1213** : Building valves - Copper alloy stop valves for potable water in buildings - General technical specifications.

**BS EN 1254** : Copper and copper alloys - Plumbing fittings.

**BS EN 1254 - 1** : Fittings with ends for capillary solder.

**BS EN 1254 - 2** : Fittings with compression ends for copper tube.

**BS EN 1254 - 3** : Fittings with compression ends for plastic pipes.

**BS EN 1254 - 4** : Fittings combining other end connections with capillary or compression ends.

**BS EN 1254 - 5** : Fittings with short ends for capillary brazing to copper tubes.

**BS EN 1452 -** Plastic piping systems for water supply - PVC-U.

**BS EN 1452 - 1** : General.

**BS EN 1452 - 2** : Pipes.

**BS EN 1452 - 3** : Fittings.

**BS EN 1452 - 4** : Valves and ancillary equipment.

**BS EN 1452 - 5** : Fitness for purpose of the system.

**BS EN 1452 - 6** : Recommended practice for installation.

**BS EN 1452 - 7** : Assessment of conformity.

**BS EN 1508** : Water supply - Requirements for systems & components for the storage of water.

**BS 1566** : Copper cylinders for domestic purposes.

**BS 1566 - 1** : Specification for double feed indirect cylinders.

**BS 1566 - 2** : Specification for single feed indirect cylinders.

**BS EN 1717** : Protection against pollution of potable water in drinking water installations & general requirements of devices to prevent pollution by backflow.

**BS 3198** : Specification for copper hot water storage combination units for domestic hot water.

**BS 4127** : Specification for light gauge stainless steel tubes, primarily for water applications.

**BS 5154** : Specification for copper alloy globe, globe stop and check, check and gate valves.

**BS 6282** : Devices with moving parts for the prevention of contamination of water by backflow.

**BS 6282 - 1** : Specification for check valves of nominal size up to and including DN54.

**BS 6282 - 2** : Specification for terminal anti-vacuum valves of nominal size up to and including DN54.

**BS 6282 - 3** : Specification for in-line anti-vacuum valves of nominal size up to and including DN42.

**BS 6282 - 4** : Specification for combined check and anti-vacuum valves of nominal size up to and including DN42.

**BS 6283** : Safety and control devices for use in hot water systems.

**BS 6283 - 2** : Specification for temperature relief valves for pressures from 1 bar to 10 bar.

**BS 6283 - 4** : Specification for drop-tight pressure reducing valves of nominal size up to and including DN 50 for supply pressures up to and including 12 bar.

**BS 6572** : Specification for blue polyethylene pipes up to nominal size 63mm for below ground use for potable water.

# Legionnaires disease

**BS 6068 – 4.12** : Water quality – Microbiological methods. Detection and enumeration of legionella.

**BS 7592** : Methods for sampling for legionella organisms in water and related materials.

**EN 13623** : Chemical disinfectants and antiseptics – Bactericidal activities of products against legionella pneumophila – Test methods and requirements (phase2/step1).

# Heating

**BS 853** : Specification for vessels for use in heating systems.

**BS EN 1264 – 1** : Floor heating – Systems and components – Definitions and symbols.

**BS EN 1264 – 2** : Floor heating – Systems and components – Determination of the thermal output.

**BS EN 1264 – 3** : Floor heating – Systems and components – Dimensioning.

**BS EN 1264 – 4** : Floor heating – Systems and components. Installation.

**BS 2767** : Specification for manually operated copper alloy valves for radiators.

**BS 2869** : Specification for fuel oils for agricultural, domestic and industrial engines and boilers.

**BS 4814** : Specification for expansion vessels using an internal diaphragm, for sealed hot water heating systems.

**BS 5250** : Code of practice for control of condensation in buildings.

**BS 5410 - 1** : Code of practice for oil firing – Installations up to 45kW output capacity for space heating and hot water supply purposes.

**BS 5410 – 2** : Code of practice for oil firing – Installations up to 45kW and above output capacity for space heating, hot water and steam supply services.

**BS 5440 – 1** : Installation and maintenance of flues and ventilation of gas appliances of rated input not exceeding 70kW net (1st, 2nd and 3rd family gases) – Specification for Installation and maintenance of flues.

**BS 5440 – 2** : Installation and maintenance of flues and ventilation of gas appliances of rated input not exceeding 70kW net (1st, 2nd and 3rd family gases) – Specification for Installation and maintenance of ventilation of gas appliances.

**BS 5449** : Specification for forced circulation hot water central heating systems for domestic premises.

**BS 5970** : Code of practice for thermal insulation of pipework and equipment in the temperature range of –100°C to +870°C.

**BS 6351 - 1** : Electric surface heating – Specification for electric surface heating devices.

**BS 6351 - 3** : Electric surface heating – Code of practice for the installation, testing and maintenance of electric surface heating systems.

**BS 6798** : Specification for installation of gas fired boilers of rated input not exceeding 70kW net.

**BS EN ISO 13370** : Thermal performance of buildings – Heat transfer via the ground – Calculation methods.

# Resource efficient design

**BS 5918** : Code of practice for solar heating systems for domestic hot water.

**BS 8207** : Code of practice for energy efficiency in buildings.

**BS 8211 – 1** : Energy efficiency in housing – Code of practice for energy efficient refurbishment of housing.

**BS EN 12975 – 1** : Thermal solar systems and components – Solar collectors – General requirements.

**BS EN 12976 – 1** : Thermal solar systems and components – Factory made systems – Test methods.

# Piped gas services

## Design

**BS 5482** : Domestic butane and propane gas installations.

**BS 5482 - 1** : Specification for installations at permanent dwellings.

**BS 5482 - 2** : Installations in caravans and non-permanent dwellings.

## Materials

**BS EN 26** : Gas fired instantaneous water heaters for the production of domestic hot water, fitted with atmospheric burners.

**BS EN 88** : Pressure governors for gas appliances for inlet pressures up to 200mbar.

**BS EN 89** : Gas fired storage water heaters for the production of domestic hot water.

**BS 143 and 1256** : Threaded pipe fittings in malleable cast iron and cast alloy.

**BS EN 297** : Gas fired central heating boilers – Type $B_{11}$ and $B_{11BS}$ boilers fitted with atmospheric burners of nominal heat input not exceeding 70kW.

**BS EN 483** : Gas fired central heating boilers – Type C boilers of nominal heat input not exceeding 70kW.

**BS EN 625** : Gas fired central heating boilers – Specific requirements for the domestic hot water operation of combination boilers of nominal heat input not exceeding 70kW.

**BS 669** : Flexible hoses, end fittings and sockets for gas burning appliances.

**BS 669 - 1** : Specification for strip-wound metallic flexible hoses, covers, end fittings and sockets for domestic appliances burning 1st and 2nd family gases.

**BS 669 - 2** : Specification for corrugated metallic flexible hoses, covers, end fittings and sockets for catering appliances burning 1st, 2nd and 3rd family gases.

**BS EN 677** : Gas fired central heating boilers – Specific requirements for condensing boilers of nominal heat input not exceeding 70kW.

**BS 746** : Specification for gas meter unions and adaptors.

**BS EN 1057** : Copper & copper alloys - Seamless round copper tubes for water and gas in sanitary & heating applications.

**BS EN 1254** : Copper and copper alloys - Plumbing fittings.

**BS EN 1254 - 1** : Fittings with ends for capillary solder.

**BS EN 1254 - 2** : Fittings with compression ends for copper tube.

**BS EN 1254 - 3** : Fittings with compression ends for plastic pipes.

**BS EN 1254 - 4 :** Fittings combining other end connections with capillary or compression ends.

**BS 1387** : Specification for screwed and socketed steel tubes and tubulars and for plain steel tubes suitable for welding or for screwing to BS 21 pipe threads.

**BS 1552** : Specification for open bottomed taper plug valves for 1st, 2nd and 3rd family gases up to 200mbar.

**BS 3016** : Specification for pressure regulators and automatic change-over devices for liquefied petroleum gases.

**BS 3212** : Specification for flexible rubber tubing, rubber hose and rubber hose assemblies for use in LPG vapour phase and LPG/air installations.

**BS 3554** : Specification for gas governors.

**BS 3554 - 1** : Independent governors for inlet pressures up to 25mbar.

**BS 3554 - 2** : Independent governors for inlet pressures up to 350mbar.

**BS 3601** : Specification for carbon steel pipes and tubes with specified room temperature properties for pressure purposes.

**BS 3604** : Steel pipes and tubes for pressure purposes – Ferritic alloy steel with specified elevated temperature properties.

**BS 3604 - 1** : Specification for seamless and electric resistance welded tubes.

**BS 3604 - 2** : Specification for longitudinally arc welded tubes.

**BS 3605** : Austenitic stainless steel pipes and tubes for pressure purposes.

**BS 3605 - 1** : Specification for seamless tubes.

**BS 3605 - 2** : Specification for longitudinally welded tube.

**BS 4089** : Specification for metallic hose assemblies for liquid petroleum gases and liquefied natural gas.

**BS 4161** : Gas meters.

**BS 4161 - 8** : Specification for electronic volume correctors.

**BS 4250** : Specification for commercial butane and commercial propane.

**BS 7281** : Specification for polyethylene pipes for the supply of gaseous fuels.

**BS 7336** : Specification for polyethylene fusion fittings with integral heating elements(s) for use with polyethylene pipes for the conveyance of gaseous fuels.

**BS 7838** : Specification for corrugated stainless steel semi-rigid pipe and associated fittings for low pressure gas pipework of up to 28mm.

# Sanitary plumbing and drainage

### Design

**BS EN 752** : Drain and sewer systems outside buildings.

**BS EN 752 - 1** : Generalities and definitions.

**BS EN 752 - 2** : Performance requirements.

**BS EN 752 - 3** : Planning.

**BS EN 752 - 4** : Hydraulic design and environmental considerations.

**BS EN 752 - 5** : Rehabilitation.

**BS EN 752 - 6**: Pumping installations.

**BS EN 752 - 7** : Maintenance and operations.

**BS EN 858** : Installations for separation of light liquids (oil & petrol).

**BS EN 858 - 1** : Principles of deign, performance, testing, marking and quality control.

**BS EN 1085** : Wastewater treatment - vocabulary.

**BS EN 1091** : Vacuum sewerage systems outside buildings.

**BS EN 12109** : Vacuum Drainage in Buildings.

**BS EN 1295** : Structural design of buried pipelines under various conditions of loadings – General requirements.

**BS EN 1610** : Construction and testing of drains and sewers.

**BS EN 1671** : Pressure sewer systems outside buildings.

**BS EN 1825 Part 2** : Installations for separation of grease.

**BS 6297** : Code of Practice for design and installation of small sewage treatment works.

**BS 6465** : Sanitary installations.

**BS 6465 - 1** : Code of practice for scale of provision, selection and installation of sanitary appliances.

**BS 6465 - 2** : Code of practice for space requirements for sanitary appliances.

**BS EN 12056** - Gravity drainage systems inside buildings.

**BS EN 12056 - 1** : General performance requirements.

**BS EN 12056 - 2** : Sanitary pipework, layout and calculation.

**BS EN 12056 - 3** : Roof drainage, layout and calculation.

**BS EN 12056 - 4** : Wastewater lifting plants, layout and calculation.

**BS EN 12056 - 5** : Installation and testing, instructions for operation and use.

**BS EN 12566** : Small wastewater treatment plants less than 50pt.

### Materials

**BS 65** : Specification for vitrified clay pipes, fittings and ducts, also flexible mechanical joints for use solely with surface water pipes and fittings.

**BS EN 124** : Gully tops and manhole tops for vehicular & pedestrian areas - Design requirements, type testing, marking, quality control.

**BS EN 274** : Sanitary tapware – Waste fittings for basins, bidets & baths. General technical specification.

**BS EN 295** : Specification for vitrified clay pipes and fittings and pipe joints for drains and sewers.

**BS EN 295 - 1** : Requirements.

**BS EN 295 - 2** : Quality control and sampling.

**BS EN 295 - 3** : Test methods.

**BS EN 295 - 4** : Requirements for special fittings, adaptors and compatible accessories.

**BS EN 295 - 5** : Requirements for perforated vitrified clay pipes and fittings.

**BS EN 295 - 6** : Requirements for vitrified clay manholes.

**BS EN 295 - 7** : Requirements for vitrified clay pipes and joints for pipe jacking.

**BS EN 329** : Sanitary tapware – Waste fittings for shower trays – General technical specifications.

**BS EN 411** : Sanitary tapware – Waste fittings for sinks – General technical specifications.

**BS 416 Part 1** : Discharge and ventilating pipes and fittings, sand-cast or spun in cast iron – Specification for spigot and socket systems.

**BS 437** : Specification for cast iron spigot and socket pipes and fittings.

**BS EN 476** : General requirements for the components used in discharge pipes, drains and sewers for gravity systems.

**BS EN 588** : Fibre cement pipes for drains and sewers.

**BS EN 588 - 1** : Pipes, joints & fittings for gravity systems.

**BS EN 588 - 2** : Manholes & inspection chambers.

**BS EN 598** : Ductile iron pipes, fittings, accessories and their joints for sewerage applications – Requirements and test methods.

**BS EN 607** : Eaves gutters and fittings made from PVC-U – Definitions, requirements and testing.

**BS EN 612** : Eaves gutters and rainwater down-pipes made from metal sheet – Definitions, classification, requirements and testing.

**BS EN 773** : General requirements for components used in hydraulically pressurised discharge pipes, drains and sewers.

**BS 882** : Specification for aggregates from natural sources for concrete.

**BS EN 877** : Cast iron pipes and fittings, their joints and accessories for the evacuation of water from buildings – Requirements, test methods and quality assurance.

**BS EN 1115** : Plastic piping systems for underground drainage & sewerage under pressure – Glass reinforced thermosetting plastics (GRP) based on unsaturated polyester (UP).

**BS EN 1115 - 1** : General.

**BS EN 1123** : Pipes and fittings of longitudinally welded hot-dip galvanised steel pipes with spigot and socket for wastewater systems.

**BS EN 1123 - 1** : Requirements, testing, quality control.

**BS EN 1123 - 2** : Dimensions.

**BS EN 1124** : Pipes and fittings of longitudinally welded stainless steel pipes with spigot and socket for wastewater systems.

**BS EN 1124 - 1** : Requirements, testing, quality control.

**BS EN 1124 - 2** : System S – Dimensions.

**BS EN 1124 - 3** : System X – Dimensions.

**BS 1247** : Manhole steps.

**BS 1247 Part 1** : Specification for galvanised ferrous or stainless steel manhole steps.

**BS 1247 Part 2** : Specification for plastic encapsulated manhole steps.

**BS 1247 Part 3** : Specification for aluminium manhole steps.

**BS EN 1253** : Gullies for buildings.

**BS EN 1253 - 1** : Requirements.

**BS EN 1253 - 2** : Test methods.

**BS EN 1253 - 3** : Quality control.

**BS EN 1253 - 4** : Access covers.

**BS EN 1254** : Copper and copper alloys – Plumbing fittings.

**BS EN 1254 - 1** : Fittings with ends for capillary soldering or capillary brazing to copper tubes.

**BS EN 1254 - 2** : Fittings with compression ends for use with copper tubes.

**BS EN 1254 - 4** : Fittings combining other end connections with capillary or compression ends.

**BS EN 1293** : General requirements for components used in pneumatically pressurised discharge pipes, drains and sewers.

**BS EN 1329** : Plastics piping systems for soil and waste discharge (low and high temperature) within the building structure – Unplastisized polyvinyl chloride (PVC-U).

**BS EN 1329 - 1** : Specification for pipes, fittings and the system.

**BS EN 1329 - 2** : Guidance for assessment of conformity.

**BS 1387** : Specification for screwed and socketed steel tubes and tubulars and for plain steel tubes suitable for welding or for screwing to BS 21 pipe threads.

**BS EN 1401** : Plastic piping systems for non-pressure underground drainage & sewerage – Unplastisized polyvinyl chloride (PVC-U).

**BS EN 1401 - 1** : Specification for pipes, fittings and the system.

**BS EN 1401 - 2** : Guidance for assessment of conformity.

**BS EN 1433** : Drainage channels for vehicular and pedestrian areas – Classification, design & testing requirements, marking and quality control.

**BS EN 1444** : Fibre-cement pipelines – Guide for laying and on site work practices.

**BS EN 1451** : Plastic piping for soil and waste discharge (low and high temperature) within the building structure – Polypropylene (PP).

**BS EN 1451 - 1** : Specification for pipes, fittings and the system.

**BS EN 1451 - 2** : Guidance for the assessment of conformity.

**BS EN 1453** : Plastic piping systems with structured wall pipes for soil and waste discharge (low and high temperature) within the building structure – Unplasticized polyvinyl chloride (PVC-U).

**BS EN 1453 - 1** : Specifications for pipes and the system.

**BS EN 1453 - 2** : Guidance for the assessment of conformity.

**BS EN 1455** : Plastic piping for soil and waste discharge (low and high temperature) within the building structure – Acrylonitrile-butadiene-styrene (ABS).

**BS EN 1455 - 1** : Specifications for pipes, fittings and the system.

**BS EN 1455 - 2** : Guidance for the assessment of conformity.

**BS EN 1456** : Plastic piping systems for buried and above ground drainage and sewerage under pressure – Unplasticized polyvinyl chloride (PVC-U).

**BS EN 1456 - 1** : Specification for piping components and the system.

**BS EN 1462** : Brackets for eaves gutters – Requirements and testing.

**BS EN 1519** : Plastic piping for soil and waste discharge (low and high temperature) within the building structure – Polyethylene (PE).

**BS EN 1519 - 1** : Specifications for pipes, fittings and the system.

**BS EN 1519 - 2** : Guidance for the assessment of conformity.

**BS EN 1565** : Plastic piping for soil and waste discharge (low and high temperature) within the building structure – Styrene copolymer blends (SAN + PVC).

**BS EN 1565 - 1** : Specifications for pipes, fittings and the system.

**BS EN 1565 - 2** : Guidance for the assessment of conformity.

**BS EN 1566** : Plastic piping for soil and waste discharge (low and high temperature) within the building structure – Chlorinated polyvinyl chloride (PVC-C).

**BS EN 1566 - 1** : Specifications for pipes, fittings and the system.

**BS EN 1566 - 2** : Guidance for the assessment of conformity.

**BS EN 1852** : Plastics piping systems for non-pressure underground drainage and sewerage – Polypropylene (PP).

**BS EN 1852 - 1** : Specifications for pipes, fittings and the system.

**BS EN 1852 - 2** : Guidance for the assessment of conformity.

**BS 2494** : Specification for elastomeric seals for joints in pipework and pipelines.

**BS 3868** : Specification for prefabricated drainage stack units in galvanised steel.

**BS 3943** : Specification for plastic waste traps.

**BS 4514** : Unplasticized PVC soil and ventilating pipes of 82.4mm minimum mean outside diameter, and fittings and accessories of 82.4mm and of other sizes – Specification.

**BS 4660** : Thermoplastics ancillary fittings of nominal sizes 110 and 160 for below ground gravity drainage and sewerage.

**BS 5911** : Precast concrete pipes, fittings and ancillary products.

**BS 5911 - 2** : Specification for inspection chambers.

**BS 5911 - 100** : Specification for unreinforced and reinforced pipes and fittings with flexible joints.

**BS 5911 - 103** : Specification for prestressed non-pressure pipes and fittings with flexible joints.

**BS 5911 - 110** : Specification for ogee pipes and fittings (including perforated).

**BS 5911 - 114** : Specification for porous pipes.

**BS 5911 - 120** : Specification for reinforced jacking pipes with flexible joints.

**BS 5911- 200** : Specification for unreinforced and reinforced manholes and soakaways of circular cross section.

**BS 5911 - 230** : Specification for road gullies and gully cover slabs.

**Sanitaryware**

**BS EN 31** : Pedestal wash basins - Connecting dimensions.

**BS EN 32** : Wall hung wash basins - Connecting dimensions.

**BS EN 33** : Pedestal WC pans with close coupled cistern - Connecting dimensions.

**BS EN 34** : Wall hung WC pans with close coupled cistern - Connecting dimensions.

**BS EN 35** : Pedestal bidets over rim supply only - Connecting dimensions.

**BS EN 36** : Wall hung bidets over rim supply only - Connecting dimensions.

**BS EN 37** : Pedestal WC pans with independent water supply - Connecting dimensions.

**BS EN 38** : Wall hung WC pans with independent water supply - Connecting dimensions.

**BS EN 80** : Wall hung urinals - Connecting dimensions.

**BS EN 111** : Specification for wall hung hand rinse basins - Connecting dimensions.

**BS EN 232** : Baths - Connecting dimensions.

**BS EN 251** : Shower trays - Connecting dimensions.

**BS EN 695** : Kitchen sinks - Connecting dimensions.

**BS EN 997** : WC pans with integral trap.

# Pumps and pumping

## Materials

**BS 5257** : Specification for horizontal and end suction centrifugal pumps (16 bar).

**BS EN 12050** : Wastewater lifting plants for buildings and sites – Principles of construction and testing.

**BS EN 12050 – 1** : Lifting plants for wastewater containing faecal matter.

**BS EN 12050 – 2** : Lifting plants for faecal-free wastewater.

**BS EN 12050 – 3** : Lifting plants for wastewater containing faecal matter for limited applications.

**BS EN 12050 – 4** : Non-return valves for faecal-free wastewater and wastewater containing faecal matter.

# Fire protection services

### Design

**BS 5306** : Fire extinguishing installations and equipment on premises.

**BS 5306 - 0** : Guide for the selection of installed systems and other fire equipment.

**BS 5306 - 1** : Hydrant systems, hose reels and foam inlets.

**BS 5306 - 2** : Specification for sprinkler systems.

**BS 5306 - 3** : Maintenance of portable fire extinguishers – Code of practice.

**BS 5306 - 4** : Specification for carbon dioxide systems.

**BS 5306 - 5.1** : Halon systems – Specification for halon 1301 total flooding systems.

**BS 5306 - 5.2** : Halon systems – Halon 1211 total flooding systems.

**BS 5306 - 6.1** : Foam systems – Specification for low expansion foam systems.

**BS 5306 - 6.2** : Foam systems – Specification for medium and high expansion foam systems.

**BS 5306 - 8** : Selection and installation of portable fire extinguishers – Code of practice.

**BS 5588** : Fire precautions in the design, construction and use of buildings.

**BS 5588 - 0** : Guide to fire safety codes of practice for particular premises/applications.

**BS 5588 - 1** : Code of practice for residential buildings.

**BS 5588 - 4** : Code of practice for smoke control using pressure differentials.

**BS 5588 - 5** : Code of practice for firefighting stairs and lifts.

**BS 5588 - 6** : Code of practice for places of assembly.

**BS 5588 - 7** : Code of practice for the incorporation of atria in buildings.

**BS 5588 - 8** : Code of practice for means of escape for disabled people.

**BS 5588 - 9** : Code of practice for ventilation and air conditioning of buildings.

**BS 5588 - 10** : Code of practice for shopping complexes.

**BS 5588 - 11** : Code of practice for shops, offices, industrial, storage and other similar buildings.

### Materials

**BS 336** : Specification for fire hose couplings and ancillary equipment.

**BS EN 1254** : Copper and copper alloys - Plumbing fittings.

**BS EN 1254 - 1** : Fittings with ends for capillary solder.

**BS EN 1254 - 2** : Fittings with compression ends for copper tube.

**BS EN 1254 - 4** : Fittings combining other end connections with capillary or compression ends.

**BS 1387** : Specification for screwed and socketed steel tubes and tubulars and for plain steel tubes suitable for welding or for screwing to BS 21 pipe threads.

**BS 3601** : Specification for carbon steel pipes and tubes with specified room temperature properties for pressure purposes.

**BS 3604** : Steel pipes and tubes for pressure purposes – Ferritic alloy steel with specified elevated temperature properties.

**BS 3604 - 1** : Specification for seamless and electric resistance welded tubes.

**BS 3604 - 2** : Specification for longitudinally arc welded tubes.

**BS 3605** : Austenitic stainless steel pipes and tubes for pressure purposes.

**BS 3605 - 1** : Specification for seamless tubes.

**BS 3605 - 2** : Specification for longitudinally welded tube.

**EN 671** : Fixed fire fighting systems – Hose systems.

**BS EN 671 - 1** : Hose reels with semi-rigid hose.

**BS EN 671 - 2** : Hose systems with lay-flat hose.

**BS EN 671 - 3** : Maintenance of hose reels with semi-rigid hose and hose systems with-lay flat hose.

**BS 750** : Specification for underground fire hydrants and surface box frames and covers.

**BS 1635** : Graphic symbols and abbreviations for fire protection drawings.

**BS 3169** : Specification for first aid reel hoses for fire brigade purposes.

**BS 3251** : Specification – Indicator plates for fire hydrants and emergency water supplies.

**BS 5041** : Fire hydrant systems equipment.

**BS 5041 - 1** : Specification for landing valves for wet risers.

**BS 5041 - 2** : Specification for landing valves for dry risers.

**BS 5041 - 3** : Specification for inlet breechings for dry riser inlets.

**BS 5041 - 4** : Specification for boxes for landing valves for dry risers.

**BS 5041 - 5** : Specification for boxes for foam inlets and dry riser inlets.

# Steam and condensate

**BS 845 – 1** : Methods for assessing thermal performance of boilers for steam, hot water and high temperature heat transfer fluids – Concise procedure.

**BS 845 – 2** : Methods for assessing thermal performance of boilers for steam, hot water and high temperature heat transfer fluids – Comprehensive procedure.

**BS 2486** : Recommendations for treatment of water for steam boilers and water heaters.

**BS 5122** : Specification for rubber hoses for low pressure and medium pressure saturated steam.

**BS 5292** : Specification for jointing materials for installations using water, low pressure steam or 1st, 2nd and 3rd family gases.

**BS 5342** : Specification for rubber hoses for high pressure saturated steam.

**BS 5410 – 2** : Code of practice for oil firing – Installation of 45kW and above output capacity for space heating, hot water and steam supply services.

**BS 6023** : Glossary of technical terms for automatic steam traps.

**BS 6068 – 6.7** : Water quality – Sampling – Guidance on sampling of water and steam in boiler plants.

**BS 6759 –1** : Safety valves – Specification for safety valves for steam and hot water.

**BS EN 26553** : Specification for marking of automatic steam traps.

**BS EN 56554** : Specification for face to face dimensions for flanged automatic steam traps.

**BS EN 26704** : Classification of automatic steam traps.

**BS EN 27841** : Methods for determination of steam loss of automatic steam traps.

**BS EN 27842** : Methods for determination of discharge capacity of automatic steam traps.

# Pipework Expansion

**BS 4618 – 3.1** : Recommendations for the presentation of plastic design data – Thermal properties – Linear thermal expansion.

**BS 6129 – 1** : Code of practice for the selection and application of bellows expansion joints for use in pressure systems – Metallic bellows expansion joints.

**BS EN 26801** : Rubber or plastic hoses – Determination of volumetric expansion.

# Mechanical Ventilation

**BS 5720** : Code of practice for mechanical ventilation and air conditioning in buildings.

**pr EN 13141 – 7** : Ventilation for buildings – Performance testing of components/products for residential ventilation – Part 7: Performance testing of a mechanical supply and exhaust ventilation units (including heat recovery) for mechanical ventilation systems intended for single family dwellings.

# Designing for the disabled

**BS 5588 - 8** : Fire precautions in the design, construction and use of buildings – Code of practice for means of escape for disabled people.

**PD 6523** : Information on access to and movement within and around buildings and on certain facilities for disabled people.

**BS 8300** : Design of buildings and their approaches to meet the needs of disabled people – Code of practice.

# Swimming pools

**BS 6785** : Code of practice for solar heating systems for swimming pools.

**BS 8007** : Code of practice for design of concrete structures for retaining aqueous liquids.

**BS 8110 – 1** : Structural use of concrete – Code of practice for design and construction.

# Electrical earthing and bonding

**BS 951** : Electrical earthing – Clamps for earthing and bonding. Specification.

**BS 7671** : Requirements for electrical installations – IEE Wiring Regulations – Sixteenth edition.

# Miscellaneous

**BS 1387** : Specification for screwed and socketed steel tube and tubulars and for plain end steel tubes suitable for welding or for screwing to BS 21 pipe threads.

**BS 1710** : Specification for identification of pipelines and services.

**BS 4800** : Schedule of paint colours for building purposes.

# Conversion factors and miscellaneous data

## Conversion factors

*Table 1*   *Imperial to SI metric/SI metric to imperial*

| | Imperial to Metric | | Metric to Imperial | |
|---|---|---|---|---|
| **Length** | 1 inch | 25.4mm | 1mm | 0.03937 in |
| | 1 foot | 0.3048m | 1m | 3.281 ft |
| | 1 yard | 0.9144m | 1m | 1.094 yds |
| | 1 mile | 1.609km | 1km | 0.6214 miles |
| | 1 thou | 25.4μm | 1μm | 0.03937 thou |
| **Area** | 1 in$^2$ | 645.2mm$^2$ | 1mm$^2$ | 0.00155 in$^2$ |
| | 1 ft$^2$ | 0.0929m$^2$ | 1m$^2$ | 10.76 ft$^2$ |
| | 1 yd$^2$ | 0.7646m$^2$ | 1m$^2$ | 1.196 yd$^2$ |
| | l acre | 0.4047 ha | 1 ha | 2.471 acres |
| **Volume** | 1 in$^3$ | 16390.0mm$^3$ | 1cm$^3$ | 0.006102 in$^3$ |
| | 1 in$^3$ | 16.39cm$^3$ | 1m$^3$ | 35.31 ft$^3$ |
| | 1 ft$^3$ | 0.02832m$^3$ | 1m$^3$ | 1.308 yd$^3$ |
| | 1 yd$^3$ | 0.7646m$^3$ | 1 litre | 0.22 gallons |
| | 1 gallon | 4.546 litres | 1 litre | 1.76 pints |
| | 1 pint | 0.5683 litres | 1 litre | 0.3531 ft$^3$ |
| | 1 ft$^3$ | 28.32 litres | 1 litres | 0.03531 ft$^3$ |
| **Velocity** | 1 ft/min | 0.00508 m/s | 1m/s | 196.9 ft/min |
| | 1 ft/sec | 0.3048 m/s | 1m/s | 3.281 ft/s |
| | 1 ft/sec | 1.097 kph | 1km/hr | 0.9113 ft/s |
| | 1 mile/hr | 0.4470 m/s | 1m/s | 2.237 mph |
| **Mass and density** | 1 oz | 28.35g | 1g | 0.03527 oz |
| | 1 oz | 0.02835kg | 1kg | 35.27 oz |
| | 1 lb | 0.4536kg | 1kg | 2.205 lb |
| | 1 cwt | 50.80kg | 1kg | 0.01968 cwt |
| | 1 ton | 1016.0kg | 1tonne | 0.9842 ton |
| | 1 ton | 1.016 tonne | 1kg/m | 0.672 lb/ft |
| | 1 lb/ft | 1.488kg/m | 1kg/m$^2$ | 0.2048 lb/ft$^2$ |
| | 1 lb/ft$^2$ | 4.883kg/m$^2$ | 1kg/m$^2$ | 0.001422 lb/in$^2$(psi) |
| | 1 lb/in$^2$(psi) | 703.1kg/m$^2$ | 1kg/m$^3$ | 0.06243 lb/ft$^3$ |
| | 1 lb/ft$^3$ | 16.02kg/m$^3$ | - | - |
| **Flow rate** | 1 gal/min | 0.07577 l/s | 1 l/s | 13.20 gal/min |
| | 1 gal/hr | 0.001263 l/s | 1 l/s | 791.9 gal/hr |
| | 1 ft$^3$/min | 0.4719 l/s | 1 l/s | 2119 ft$^3$/min |
| | 1 ft$^3$/min | 1.699 m$^3$/hr | 1 l$^3$/hr | 0.5886 ft$^3$/hr |
| | 1 ft$^3$/hr | 0.007866 l/s | 1 l/s | 127.1 ft$^3$/hr |
| | - | - | 1m$^3$/s | 2119.0 ft$^3$/min |
| **Force** (1 kgf = 9.807 N) | 1 lbf | 4.448 N | 1N | 0.2248 lb f |
| | 1 tonf | 9.964 kN | 1kN | 0.1004 ton f |
| **Pressure, stress** | *1m head H20 = 9.807 kN/m$^2$ (kPa)*    *1mb = 1002 N/m$^2$ (Pa)*    *1 bar = 100kmm$^2$ (kPa)* | | | |
| | 1 in WG | 249.1N/m$^2$ (Pa) | 1N/m$^2$ (Pa) | 0.004014 in WG |
| | 1 in WG | 2.491mBar | 1 m/Bar | 0.4014 in WG |
| | 1lb/in$^2$ (psi) | 6.895 kN/m$^2$ | 1 kN/m$^2$ | 0.145 lb/m$^2$ (psi) |
| | 1lb/in$^2$ (psi) | 68.95 mBar | 1 mBar | 0.01450 lb/in$^2$ (psi) |
| | 1 head ft H20 | 0.06895 kN/m$^2$ | 1 kN/m$^2$ | 0.3345 ft head H$_2$0 |
| | 1 head ft H20 | 0.02989 Bar | 1 Bar | 33.45 ft head H$_2$0 |
| | 1lb/in$^2$ (psi) | 0.06895 Bar | 1 Bar | 14.50 lb/in$^2$ (psi) |
| | 1 atmosphere (std) | 1.013 Bar | 1 Bar | 0.9872 atmos. (std) |

*Table 1 (continued)* *Imperial to SI metric/SI metric to imperial*

| | Imperial to Metric | | Metric to Imperial | |
|---|---|---|---|---|
| **Power heat flow** | 1 W = 1 J/s = 1 Nm/s | | 1 kW = 1kJ/s = 3.6MJ/s | |
| | 1 hp | 745.7 W | 1kW | 1.341 hp |
| | 1 btu/hr | 0.2931 W | 1W | 3.412 btu/hr |
| | 1 btu/hr ft$^2$ | 3.155W/m$^2$ | 1W/m$^2$ | 0.3170 btu/hr ft$^2$ |
| | 1 btu/ft$^3$ | 0.03726 mJ/m$^3$ | 1mJ/m$^3$ | 26.84 btu/ft$^3$ |
| | 1 btu in/ft$^2$h°F | 0.1442 W/m$^2$ °C | 1 W/m °C | 6.934 btu in/ft$^2$h°F |
| | (Thermal (Conductivity = k) | | 1 W/m$^2$ °C | 0.1761 btu/hr ft$^2$h°F |
| | 1 btu/hr ft$^2$h°F | 5.678 W/m$^2$°C | – | – |
| | (Thermal Transmittance = U) | | – | – |
| **Heat** | kWhr = 3.6mJ    1 Therm = 100,000 btu    1Cal = 4.1868J | | | |
| | 1 btu | 1055J | 1J | 0.0009478 btu |
| | 1 therm | 29.31kWhr | 1kWhr | 0.03412 therms |
| | 1 therm | 105.5MJ | 1MJ | 0.009479 therms |
| | 1 btu | 0.2520kCal | 1kCal | 3.968 btu |

# Head and pressure of water

*Table 2 Head and Pressure of Water*

| Head in metres | Pressure kN/m$^2$ or kPa | Pressure mbar & bar | Head in metres | Pressure kN/m$^2$ or kPa | Pressure mbar & bar |
|---|---|---|---|---|---|
| 1 | 9.81 | 98 mbar | 18.36 | 180 | 1.80 bar |
| 1.02 | 10 | 100 mbar | 19 | 186.33 | 1.86 bar |
| 2 | 19.61 | 196 mbar | 19.38 | 190 | 1.90 bar |
| 2.04 | 20 | 200 mbar | 20 | 196.13 | 1.96 bar |
| 3 | 29.42 | 294 mbar | 20.40 | 200 | 2.00 bar |
| 3.06 | 30 | 300 mbar | 25 | 245.17 | 2.45 bar |
| 4 | 39.23 | 392 mbar | 25.49 | 250 | 2.50 bar |
| 4.08 | 40 | 400 mbar | 30 | 294.20 | 2.94 bar |
| 5 | 49.03 | 490 mbar | 30.59 | 300 | 3.00 bar |
| 5.10 | 50 | 500 mbar | 35 | 343.23 | 3.43 bar |
| 6 | 58.84 | 588 mbar | 35.69 | 350 | 3.50 bar |
| 6.12 | 60 | 600 mbar | 40 | 392.27 | 3.92 bar |
| 7 | 68.65 | 686 mbar | 40.79 | 400 | 4.00 bar |
| 7.14 | 70 | 700 mbar | 45 | 441.30 | 4.41 bar |
| 8 | 78.45 | 785 mbar | 45.89 | 450 | 4.50 bar |
| 8.16 | 80 | 800 mbar | 50 | 490.33 | 4.90 bar |
| 9 | 88.26 | 883 mbar | 50.99 | 500 | 5.00 bar |
| 9.16 | 90 | 900 mbar | 60 | 588.40 | 5.88 bar |
| 10 | 98.07 | 981 mbar | 61.18 | 600 | 6.00 bar |
| 10.20 | 100 | 1.00 bar | 70 | 686.47 | 6.86 bar |
| 11 | 107.87 | 1.08 bar | 71.38 | 700 | 7.00 bar |
| 11.22 | 110 | 1.10 bar | 80 | 784.53 | 7.85 bar |
| 12 | 117.68 | 1.18 bar | 81.58 | 800 | 8.00 bar |
| 12.24 | 120 | 1.20 bar | 90 | 882.60 | 8.83 bar |
| 13 | 127.49 | 1.27 bar | 91.77 | 900 | 9.00 bar |
| 13.26 | 130 | 1.30 bar | 100 | 980.66 | 9.81 bar |
| 14 | 137.29 | 1.37 bar | 101.97 | 1 MN/m$^2$ | 10.00 bar |
| 14.28 | 140 | 1.42 bar | 200 | 1.96 MN/m$^2$ | 19.61 bar |
| 15 | 147.10 | 1.47 bar | 203.94 | 2MN/m$^2$ | 20.00 bar |
| 15.30 | 150 | 1.50 bar | 300 | 2.94 MN/m$^2$ | 29.42 bar |
| 16 | 156.91 | 1.57 bar | 305.92 | 3 MN/m$^2$ | 30.00 bar |
| 16.32 | 160 | 1.60 bar | 400 | 3.92 MN/m$^2$ | 39.23 bar |
| 17 | 166.71 | 1.67 bar | 407.89 | 4 MN/m$^2$ | 40.00 bar |
| 17.34 | 170 | 1.70 bar | 500 | 4.90 MN/m$^2$ | 49.03 bar |
| 18 | 176.52 | 1.77 bar | 509.86 | 5 MN/m$^2$ | 50.00 bar |

*The use of various units to describe pressure is creating some confusion and the increasing use of the Pascal (Pa) in lieu of the N/m$^2$ or the Bar may lead eventually to it becoming the most commonly used unit of pressure. This guide does not use the Pascal as a unit of pressure but generally refers to the SI unit for pressure, which is the N/m$^2$. However, as 1 Pa is equal to 1N/m$^2$ it presents no difficulty in relating Pa to N/m$^2$ and the symbol has been added to the table above to enable the user to more fully understand its function.*

# Hydrostatic tables

*Table 3* *Atmospheric pressure at sea level*

| SI Metric Units | Imperial Units |
|---|---|
| $100kN/m^2 = 101$ kPa | 14.7 $lbf/in^2$ |
| 10.33m Head of water | 34ft Head of water |
| 762mm Mercury | 30in Mercury |

*Table 4* *Hydrostatic table*

**SI Metric units**

| |
|---|
| 1 Litre of water weighs 1 kilogram |
| 1 Cubic meter of water equals 1000 litres |
| Head of water in meters $\times$ 9810 = pressure in $N/m^2$ |
| Head of water in meters $\times 9.81$ = pressure in $kN/m^2$ |
| Pressure in $kN/m^2 \times 0.120$ = Head of water in meters |
| 1 Bar equals 1000 mbar = $10^5 N/m^2$ = 10Pa |
| 1 millibar (mbar) = $100N/M^2$ =100Pa |

**Imperial units**

| |
|---|
| 1 Gallon of water weighs 10 pounds |
| 1 Gallon of water equals 0.16 Cubic feet |
| 6.25 Gallons of water equals 1 Cubic foot |
| Head of water in feet $\times$ 62.5 = pressure in $lbf/ft^2$ |
| Head of water in feet $\times$ 0.434 = pressure in $lbf/in^2$ |
| Pressure in $lbf/in^2 \times 2.3$ = Head of water in ft |

# Identification of pipelines

*For more detailed information see BS 1710 – Identification of Pipelines*

According to the complexity of an installation and to the variety of fluids conveyed, the pipes should be identified by either:

a.  Basic identification colours only for installations where the determination of merely the basic nature of the contents is sufficient

b.  Basic identification colours and code indications for installations where the precise determination of the contents is of importance.

## Basic identification of colours and colour references

The *Basic Identification Colour* may be applied:

i.   Over the whole length

ii.  As a band of about 150mm, depending on the diameter of the pipeline.

Where banding is adopted, any decorative or protective colour of the pipe shall not be any of the other *Basic Identification Colours*. The *Basic Identification Colour* shall be placed at all junctions, at both sides of the valves, bulkheads, wall penetrations and any other place where identification is necessary. Valves may be painted with the identification colour except where the pipeline has been coded with the safety colour for fire fighting, when the valves should be painted red.

*Table 5  Basic indication of colours*

| Pipe contents | Basic Identification Colour | BS Colour References BS4800 | Safety Colour References | |
|---|---|---|---|---|
| Water | Green | 12 AD 45 | Safety colours | BS colours References BS4800 |
| Steam | Silver-Grey | 10 A 03 | Red | 04 E 53 |
| Animal, vegetable, mineral oils & combustible liquids | Brown | 06 C 39 | Yellow | 08 E 51 |
| Gases in gaseous or liquified condition (except air) | Yellow Ochre | 08 C 35 | Auxiliary Blue | 18 E 53 |
| Acids and alkalis | Violet | 22 C 37 | Code indication colours *(if other than Safety Colours)* | |
| Air | Light blue | 20 E 51 | Crimson | 04 E 53 |
| Other fluids | Black | Black | Emerald green | 14 E 53 |
| Electrical services | Orange | 06 E 51 | Salmon pink | 04 C 33 |
| - | - | - | Yellow | 10 E 53 |

*Table 6  Optional colour code indications for general building services*

| Pipe contents | Basic colour (approx. 150mm) | Colour code indication (approx. 100mm) | | | Basic colour |
|---|---|---|---|---|---|
| **Water** | | | | | |
| Drinking | Green | | Blue | | Green |
| Cooling (Primary) | Green | | White | | Green |
| Boiler feed | Green | Crimson | White | Crimson | Green |
| Condensate | Green | Crimson | Em. Green | Crimson | Green |
| Chilled | Green | White | Em. Green | White | Green |
| Central htg < 100°C | Green | Blue | Crimson | Blue | Green |
| Central htg > 100°C | Green | Crimson | Blue | Crimson | Green |
| Cold down service | Green | White | Blue | White | Green |
| Hot water supply | Green | White | Crimson | White | Green |
| Hydraulic power | Green | | Salmon Pink | | Green |
| Sea, river, untreated | | | Green | | |
| Fire extinguishing | Green | | Safety Red | | Green |
| **Compressed air** | | | Light Blue | | |
| **Vacuum** | Light Blue | | White | | Light Blue |
| **Steam** | | | Silver Grey | | |
| **Drainage** | | | Black | | |
| **Electrical conduits and ducts** | | | Orange | | |
| **Town Gas** | | | | | |
| Manufactured gas | Yellow Ochre | | Em. Green | | Yellow Ochre |
| Natural gas | Yellow Ochre | | Yellow | | Yellow Ochre |
| **Oils** | | | | | |
| Diesel fuel | Brown | | White | | Brown |
| Furnace fuel | | | Brown | | |
| Lubricating | Brown | | Em. Green | | Brown |
| Hydraulic power | Brown | | Salmon Pink | | Brown |
| Transformer | Brown | | Crimson | | Brown |
| **Acids and alkalis** | | | Violet | | |

# Spacing of pipes

The accompanying table gives the allowable minimum distances between (a) two pipes, (b) pipe and wall and (c) pipe and furring for two pipes with standard malleable or cast iron screwed fittings.

The table has been developed on the basis of the following analysis: between two pipes of differing diameter there will be two values for the minimum distance which will allow free turning of an elbow or tee. The value used will depend upon which pipe is installed first.

In order that there will be no confusion as to which pipe should be installed first, the condition giving the greater distance between pipes will be considered. It is fairly obvious that turning the fitting on the larger pipe will require the large space between pipes for clearance, therefore less space will be required if the larger pipe is installed first.

It is evident that the minimum distance for the wall will be that distance which will allow turning of a fitting on the pipe. This will be the distance K shown in the first column of the table.

The minimum distance from furring (dimension F in the table) will not be less than 6mm larger than the radius of insulated pipe, because furring is constructed after pipes have been installed.

It should be noted that, for pipes smaller than 25mm, the distance for insulation is larger than that required for turning fittings. Therefore, on such small pipes, only the allowance for insulation has been considered in the table.

## Example

Find the minimum space required for 32mm and 100mm pipes of the smaller pipe is located near the wall.

### Solution

The table shows, under 32mm and opposite 100mm pipes, that 152mm is the minimum distance between 100mm and 32mm pipes.

To the left of 32mm in the second column of the table, find 54mm as the minimum distance from the wall of the smaller pipe.

The distance from the furring of the larger pipe is found (above 100mm) to be 95mm.

The total space is thus
152 + 54 + 95 = 301mm

In the same manner it can be shown that the total space if the pipes were reversed would be 152 + 124 + 51 = 327mm, so it would be advisable to locate the smaller pipe near the wall or column.

**Table 7** *Minimum Distance allowable between centre lines of screwed steel and copper pipes*

| Minimum distance from wall (K) (mm) | Nom. pipe size (mm) | Minimum distance between furring (F), (mm) | | | | | | | | | | | |
|---|---|---|---|---|---|---|---|---|---|---|---|---|---|
| | | 38 | 41 | 48 | 51 | 54 | 64 | 70 | 79 | 95 | 114 | 127 | 152 |
| | | Nominal pipe size (mm) | | | | | | | | | | | |
| | | 15 | 20 | 25 | 32 | 40 | 50 | 65 | 80 | 100 | 125 | 150 | 200 |
| | | Distance between pipes (mm) | | | | | | | | | | | |
| 216 | 200 | 323 | 238 | 241 | 248 | 251 | 257 | 267 | 276 | 289 | 305 | 321 | 356 |
| 168 | 150 | 187 | 191 | 194 | 200 | 203 | 210 | 219 | 229 | 241 | 260 | 273 | |
| 146 | 125 | 165 | 168 | 171 | 178 | 181 | 187 | 197 | 206 | 219 | 235 | | |
| 124 | 100 | 140 | 143 | 146 | 152 | 156 | 165 | 171 | 181 | 197 | | | |
| 98 | 90 | 117 | 120 | 124 | 130 | 133 | 140 | 149 | 159 | | | | |
| 86 | 65 | 101 | 108 | 111 | 117 | 120 | 127 | 133 | | | | | |
| 73 | 50 | 92 | 95 | 98 | 101 | 108 | 114 | | | | | | |
| 60 | 40 | 79 | 83 | 86 | 92 | 95 | | | | | | | |
| 54 | 32 | 76 | 79 | 83 | 89 | | | | | | | | |
| 48 | 25 | 73 | 76 | 79 | | | | | | | | | |
| 41 | 20 | 70 | 73 | | | | | | | | | | |
| 38 | 15 | 67 | | | | | | | | | | | |

# Maximum spacing of pipe supports

**Table 8** *Hot and cold water pipes and gas pipes*

| Type of Piping | Size of pipe (mm) | Spacing for Horizontal (m) | Spacing for Vertical (m) |
|---|---|---|---|
| Lead | All sizes | 0.6* | 0.9 |
| Copper (light gauge) and Stainless steel | 12 | 1.2 | 1.8 |
| | 15-28 | 1.8 | 2.4 |
| | 35-42 | 2.4 | 3.0 |
| | 54 | 2.7 | 3.0 |
| | 76-133 | 3.0 | 3.6 |
| | 159 | 3.6 | 4.2 |
| Steel to BS 1387 and Copper (heavy gauge) | 10-15 | 1.8 | 2.4 |
| | 20-25 | 2.4 | 3.0 |
| | 32 | 2.7 | 3.0 |
| | 40-50 | 3.0 | 3.6 |
| | 65-80 | 3.6 | 4.5 |
| | 100-125 | 4.0 | 4.5 |
| | 150 | 4.5 | 5.4 |
| Grey or ductile iron | 50 | 1.8 | 1.8 |
| | 75-100 | 2.7 | 2.7 |
| | 150 | 3.6 | 3.6 |

*For pipes conveying hot water and where it is essential to avoid air locks (e.g. primary circulation pipes), continuous support is recommended.

**Table 9** *Soil and waste pipes*     * At least one fixing must be provided for each unit length

| Type of piping | Size of pipe (mm) | Spacing for horizontal (m) | Spacing for vertical (m) |
|---|---|---|---|
| Cast iron* | All sizes | 2.0 | 3.0 |
| Copper | as for water pipes | | |
| Steel to BS 1387 | as for water pipes | | |
| Lead (single tacks) | Up to 50 | 0.6 | – |
| | 50 and over | 0.9 | – |
| Lead (double tacks) | All sizes | – | 1.2 |
| uPVC | 32-40 | 0.5 | 1.2 |
| | 50 | 0.6 | 1.2 |
| | 75-100 | 0.9 | 1.8 |
| | 150 | 1.2 | 1.8 |
| ABS | 32-40 | 0.5 | 1.2 |
| | 50 | 0.7 | 1.2 |
| Polypropylene | 32-40 | 0.5 | 1.2 |
| | 50 | 0.7 | 1.2 |

# Relation of services to each other

*Table 10  Relation to other services*

| Pipe or duct conveying | Cold water | Natural gas | Electricity | Telecom-munications | Hot water and steam | Ventilation and air conditioning | Drainage | Oil | Flammable gases and | Compressed air liquids |
|---|---|---|---|---|---|---|---|---|---|---|
| Hot water & steam | A | O | A | A | - | F | C | C | L | O |
| Ventilation & air Conditioning | F | L | A | A | F | - | C | C | L | O |
| Cold water | - | O | A | A | F | F | C | C | C | O |
| Electricity | C | F | - | M | B | B | C | C | L | O |
| Telecommunications | C | F | M | - | B | B | C | C | L | O |
| Natural Gas | C | - | F | F | C | L | AC | C | L | G |
| Drainage | D | D | A | A | D | D | - | D | L | D |
| Oil | C | J | A | A | B | B | C | - | O | O |
| Flammable gases & Liquid | C | L | L | L | L | L | L | O | - | L |
| Compressed air | O | G | O | A | O | O | C | O | L | - |

*It is on occasions necessary to run different services to the same position to operate equipment connected directly to a number of services, eg. Motor-driven pumps, thermostatic valves, electrically operated gas valves, etc. The above precautions should be taken in each instance as far as practicable.*

### Key to symbols in above table

| | |
|---|---|
| O. | *No precautions necessary.* |
| A. | *Not to be run adjacent to.* |
| B. | *Not to be exposed to temperature or leakage from.* |
| C. | *Not to be exposed to leakage from.* |
| D. | *Not to be exposed to effluent from.* |
| F. | *Shall not be prevented by spacing, insulation or other means from coming into contact with.* |

| | |
|---|---|
| G. | *Not to be run in such a position as would cause any escape of air to circulate a gas leakage, or to make the leakage become more dangerous.* |
| J. | *Not to be run where an escape of gas could cause risk of ignition in presence of oil.* |
| L. | *Not to be run in same duct.* |
| M. | *Not to be run adjacent to without further precautions.* |

# Miscellaneous data

*Table 11  Multiples and sub-multiples of units*

| x factor | Prefix | Symbol |
|---|---|---|
| 1,000,000,000,000 | $10^{12}$ Tera | T |
| 1,000,000,000 | $10^{9}$ Giga | G |
| 1,000,000 | $10^{6}$ Mega | M |
| 1,000 | $10^{3}$ Kilo | k |
| 100 | $10^{2}$ Hecto | h |
| 10 | $10^{1}$ Deca | da |
| 1 | $10^{0}$ Basic unit | |
| 0.1 | $10^{-1}$ Deci | d |
| 0.01 | $10^{-1}$ Centi | c |
| 0.001 | $10^{-3}$ Milli | m |
| 0.000 0001 | $10^{-6}$ Micro | $\mu$ |